PEARSON

Elayn Martin-Gay

Intermediate Algebra

Ninth Custom Edition for Community College of Philadelphia
FNMT 118

Taken from:
Intermediate Algebra, Seventh Edition
by Elayn Martin-Gay

Cover Art: Rainforest Leaves, by Alisa Harding Stein.

Taken from:

Intermediate Algebra, Seventh Edition
by Elayn Martin-Gay
Copyright © 2017, 2013, 2009 by Pearson Education, Inc.
New York, New York 10013

This special edition published in cooperation with Pearson Education, Inc.

Pearson Education, Inc., 330 Hudson Street, New York, New York 10013
A Pearson Education Company
www.pearsoned.com

Printed in the United States of America

4   18

000200010272102453

JK

PEARSON   ISBN 10: 1-323-74611-0
ISBN 13: 978-1-323-74611-0

Community
College
of Philadelphia

Welcome to Canvas

Community College of Philadelphia uses the Canvas online learning system. New Canvas users should create their Canvas password prior to the first day of the class. However, **you will not be able to access your courses in Canvas until the first day of the class**.

If you already have a Canvas account from a previous semester, you may continue to use your Canvas username and password.

If you are setting up your Canvas account for the first time, do the following:

1. Go to CCP's Canvas site: http://ccp.instructure.com There is also a link to Canvas on the MyCCP login page called "Canvas LMS".

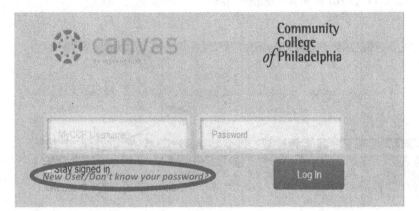

If you are a new Canvas user, do not enter any information in the boxes labeled "MyCCP Username" and "Password". Click on the "**New User/Don't know your password**" link (This is found under the "MyCCP Username" box, pictured left).

2. On the **next screen**, enter your CCP email address and click **Request Password**.

In a few minutes, you will get an email from Canvas in your CCP email account with a link to set your password. Click on that link and type your new password in both boxes.

2. Go to CCP's Canvas site: http://ccp.instructure.com (Please bookmark this link.)

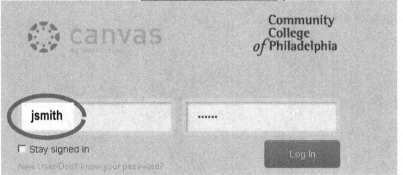

Enter your **MyCCP Username** (for example, **jsmith**) and the password you just set. Click on Log In.

NOTE: Your username is NOT your full email address! **Do not use @ccp.edu in the username box!**

If you have a problem with the sign in process, please contact the Office of Online Learning via email at onlinelearning@ccp.edu, or call the Help desk at 215-496-6000.

Community College of Philadelphia

Math 118 Students

To access your MyLabsPlus account:

1. Go to www.ccp.mylabsplus.com – You must use Internet Explorer as your browser (or a MyLabsPlus compatible browser).

2. In the Log In space, enter your J-number – you will need to use an upper case J.

3. In the Password space, enter "password".

4. Click on **Log In**.

5. At the Welcome Screen, find and click on **MyProfile** in the upper right:

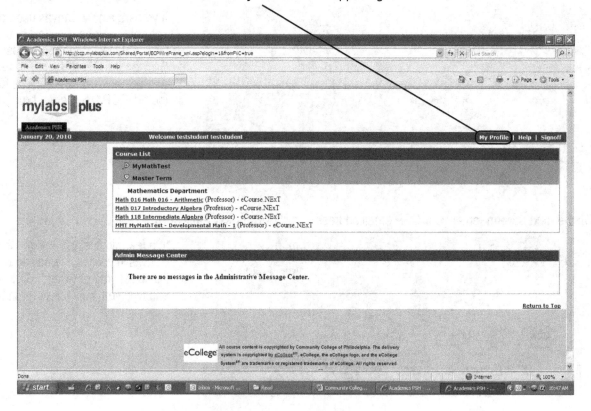

6. In the Old Password space, enter "password".

7. Create and Verify a New Password for your account.

Community College of Philadelphia

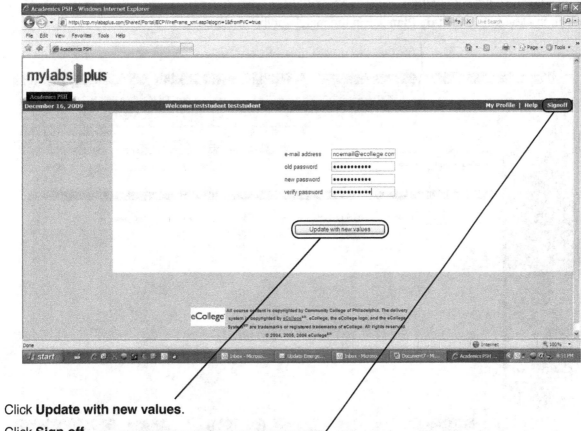

8. Click **Update with new values**.

9. Click **Sign off**.

10. Enter your Log In (CCP Student ID with the upper case J) and your NEW Password.

11. Click on **Log In**.

12. Click on **Math 118 Intermediate Algebra** (your appropriate section number will be listed as well).

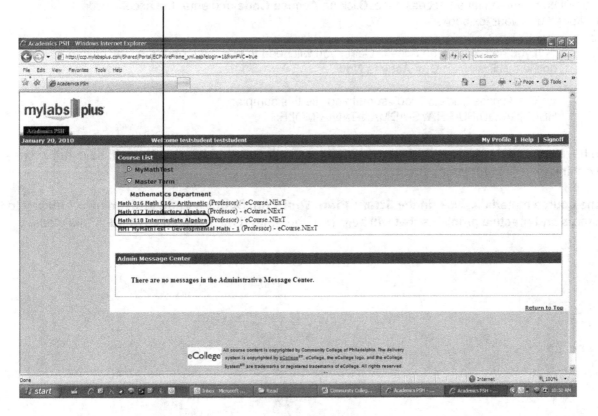

13. On the left side in the blue margin, click on **Study Plan**.

14. Click on the MyMathLab **Study Plan** link in the middle of the screen.

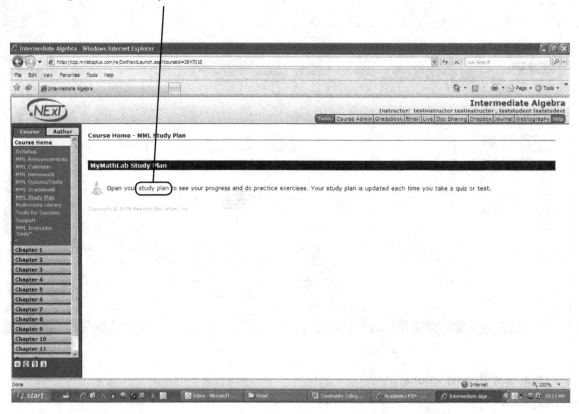

15. You will see the Licensing agreement. Scroll to the bottom and click on: **I Accept**.

16. You will be prompted for an access code. Click on **Access Code** and enter the access code packaged with your textbook.

  ● If you do not have an Access Code, you will need to purchase one. You may buy one online by clicking on **Buy Access Now**.

  ● The Access Code will look something like this sample:
  HSEMSA-QUIPU-PRAYS-ADMAN-TANIS-MOLES

Once you have entered the Access Code successfully, you will not need it again. You will have full access to all the on line materials for your course.

Once in the course materials, click on the Study Plan, Tools for Success and Multimedia Library to find tutorials, tools and practice problems that will help you understand the material covered in this class.

Contents

CHAPTER

QUADRATIC EQUATIONS AND FUNCTIONS   482

APPENDICES

Preface

Intermediate Algebra, **Seventh Edition** was written to provide a solid foundation in algebra for students who might not have previous experience in algebra. Specific care was taken to make sure students have the most up-to-date, relevant text preparation for their next mathematics course or for nonmathematical courses that require an understanding of algebraic fundamentals. I have tried to achieve this by writing a user-friendly text that is keyed to objectives and contains many worked-out examples. As suggested by AMATYC and the NCTM Standards (plus Addenda), real-life and real-data applications, data interpretation, conceptual understanding, problem solving, writing, cooperative learning, appropriate use of technology, number sense, estimation, critical thinking, and geometric concepts are emphasized and integrated throughout the book.

The many factors that contributed to the success of the previous editions have been retained. In preparing the Seventh Edition, I considered comments and suggestions of colleagues, students, and many users of the prior edition throughout the country.

What's New in the Seventh Edition?

- **New Getting Ready for the Test** can be found before each Chapter Test. These exercises help increase student success by helping students prepare for their chapter test. The purpose of these exercises is to check students' conceptual understanding of the topics in the chapter as well as common student errors. It is suggested that students complete and check these exercises before taking a practice Chapter Test. All Getting Ready for the Test exercises are either Multiple Choice or Matching, and all answers can be found in the answer section of this text.

  Video Solutions of all exercises can be found in MyMathLab and on the Interactive DVD Lecture Series. These video solutions contain brief explanations and reminders of material in the chapter. Where applicable, incorrect choices contain explanations.

  Getting Ready for the Test exercise numbers marked in blue indicate that the question is available in **Learning Catalytics**. [lc]

- **New Learning Catalytics** is an interactive student response tool that uses students' smartphones, tablets, or laptops to engage them in more sophisticated tasks and thinking. Generate class discussion, guide your lecture, and promote peer-to-peer learning with real-time analytics. Accessible through MyMathLab, instructors can use Learning Catalytics to:

  - Pose a variety of open-ended questions that help your students develop critical thinking skills.

  - Monitor responses to find out where students are struggling.

  - Use real-time data to adjust your instructional strategy and try other ways of engaging your students during class.

  - Manage student interactions by automatically grouping students for discussion, teamwork, and peer-to-peer learning.

  For *Intermediate Algebra,* Seventh Edition, new Getting Ready for the Test exercises marked in blue are available in Learning Catalytics. To find the questions in Learning Catalytics, search the question library for **MGIA7e Ch** and the chapter number. For example, search **MGIA7e Ch4** for questions from Chapter 4.

- **New Student Success Tips Videos** are 3- to 5-minute video segments designed to be daily reminders to students to continue practicing and maintaining good organizational and study habits. They are organized in three categories and are available in MyMathLab and the Interactive Lecture Series. The categories are:

1. Success Tips that apply to any course in college in general, such as Time Management.

2. Success Tips that apply to any mathematics course. One example is based on understanding that mathematics is a course that requires homework to be completed in a timely fashion.

3. Section- or Content-specific Success Tips to help students avoid common mistakes or to better understand concepts that often prove challenging. One example of this type of tip is how to apply the order of operations to simplify an expression.

- **New Key Concept Activity Lab Workbook** includes Extension Exercises, Exploration Activities, Conceptual Exercises, and Group Activities. These activities are a great way to engage students in conceptual projects and exploration as well as group work.

- **The Martin-Gay MyMathLab** course has been updated and revised to provide more exercise coverage, including assignable video check questions and an expanded video program. There are section lectures videos for every section, which students can also access at the specific objective level; new Getting Ready for the Test video solutions; new Student Success Tips videos; and an increased number of watch clips at the exercise level to help students while doing homework in MathXL.

  Vocabulary, Readiness & Video Check Questions continue to be available in the text and for assignment in MyMathLab. The **Readiness** exercises center on a student's understanding of a concept that is necessary in order to continue to the exercise set. The **video check questions** are included in every section for every learning objective. These exercises are a great way to assess whether students have viewed and understood the key concepts presented in the videos.

- **Exercise Sets Revised and Updated** The text exercise sets have been carefully examined and revised. Special focus was placed on making sure that even- and odd-numbered exercises are paired and that real-life applications are updated.

Key Continuing Resources and Pedagogical Features

- **Interactive DVD Lecture Series**, featuring your text author Elayn Martin-Gay, provides students with active learning at their own pace. The videos offer the following resources and more:

  A complete lecture for each section of the text highlights key examples and exercises from the text. Pop-ups reinforce key terms, definitions, and concepts.

  An interface with menu navigation features allows students to quickly find and focus on the examples and exercises they need to review.

  Interactive Concept Check exercises measure students' understanding of key concepts and common trouble spots.

  New Student Success Tips Videos.

- **The Interactive DVD Lecture Series** also includes the following resources for test prep:

  New Getting Ready for the Chapter Test Videos

  The Chapter Test Prep Videos help students during their most teachable moment—when they are preparing for a test. This innovation provides step-by-step solutions for the exercises found in each Chapter Test. For the Seventh Edition, the chapter test prep videos are also available on YouTube™. The videos are captioned in English and Spanish.

The Practice Final Exam Videos help students prepare for an end-of-course final. Students can watch full video solutions to each exercise in the Practice Final Exam at the end of this text.

● **The Video Organizer** is designed to help students take notes and work practice exercises while watching the Interactive Lecture Series videos (available in MyMathLab and on DVD). All content in the Video Organizer is presented in the same order as it is presented in the videos, making it easy for students to create a course notebook and build good study habits.

— Covers all of the video examples in order.

— Provides ample space for students to write down key definitions and properties.

— Includes Play and Pause button icons to prompt students to follow along with the author for some exercises while they try others on their own.

The Video Organizer is available in a loose-leaf, notebook-ready format. It is also available for download in MyMathLab. Answers to all video questions are available to instructors in MyMathLab and the Instructor's Resource Center.

Key Pedagogical Features

The following key features have been retained and/or updated for the Seventh Edition of the text:

Problem-Solving Process   This is formally introduced in Chapter 2 with a four-step process that is integrated throughout the text. The four steps are **Understand, Translate, Solve,** and **Interpret.** The repeated use of these steps in a variety of examples shows their wide applicability. Reinforcing the steps can increase students' comfort level and confidence in tackling problems.

Exercise Sets Revised and Updated   The exercise sets have been carefully examined and extensively revised. Special focus was placed on making sure that even- and odd-numbered exercises are paired.

Examples   Detailed, step-by-step examples were added, deleted, replaced, or updated as needed. Many examples reflect real life. Additional instructional support is provided in the annotated examples.

Practice Exercises   Throughout the text, each worked-out example has a parallel Practice Exercise. These invite students to be actively involved in the learning process. Students should try each Practice Exercise after finishing the corresponding example. Learning by doing will help students grasp ideas before moving on to other concepts. Answers to the Practice Exercises are provided in the back of the text.

Helpful Hints   Helpful Hints contain practical advice on applying mathematical concepts. Strategically placed where students are most likely to need immediate reinforcement, Helpful Hints help students avoid common trouble areas and mistakes.

Concept Checks   This feature allows students to gauge their grasp of an idea as it is being presented in the text. Concept Checks stress conceptual understanding at the point of use and help suppress misconceived notions before they start. Answers appear at the bottom of the page. Exercises related to Concept Checks are included in the exercise sets.

Mixed Practice Exercises   Found in the section exercise sets, these require students to determine the problem type and strategy needed to solve it just as they would need to do on a test.

Integrated Reviews   A unique, mid-chapter exercise set that helps students assimilate new skills and concepts that they have learned separately over several sections. These reviews provide yet another opportunity for students to work with mixed exercises as they master the topics.

Vocabulary Check   Provides an opportunity for students to become more familiar with the use of mathematical terms as they strengthen their verbal skills. These appear at the end of each chapter before the Chapter Highlights. Vocabulary, Readiness, and Video Check exercises provide practice at the section level.

Chapter Highlights   Found at the end of every chapter, these contain key definitions and concepts with examples to help students understand and retain what they have learned and help them organize their notes and study for tests.

Chapter Review   The end of every chapter contains a comprehensive review of topics introduced in the chapter. The Chapter Review offers exercises keyed to every section in the chapter, as well as Mixed Review exercises that are not keyed to sections.

Chapter Test and Chapter Test Prep Video   The Chapter Test is structured to include those problems that involve common student errors. The **Chapter Test Prep Videos** give students instant author access to a step-by-step video solution of each exercise in the Chapter Test.

Cumulative Review   Follows every chapter in the text (except Chapter 1). Each odd-numbered exercise contained in the Cumulative Review is an earlier worked example in the text that is referenced in the back of the book along with the answer.

Writing Exercises ⟍   These exercises occur in almost every exercise set and require students to provide a written response to explain concepts or justify their thinking.

Applications   Real-world and real-data applications have been thoroughly updated, and many new applications are included. These exercises occur in almost every exercise set, show the relevance of mathematics, and help students gradually and continuously develop their problem-solving skills.

Review Exercises   These exercises occur in each exercise set (except in Chapter 1) and are keyed to earlier sections. They review concepts learned earlier in the text that will be needed in the next section or chapter.

Exercise Set Resource Icons   Located at the opening of each exercise set, these icons remind students of the resources available for extra practice and support:

MyMathLab®

See Student Resource descriptions page xv for details on the individual resources available.

Exercise Icons   These icons facilitate the assignment of specialized exercises and let students know what resources can support them.

- ▶ Video icon: exercise worked on the Interactive DVD Lecture Series and in MyMathLab.
- △ Triangle icon: identifies exercises involving geometric concepts.
- ⟍ Pencil icon: indicates a written response is needed.
- ▦ Calculator icon: optional exercises intended to be solved using a scientific or graphing calculator.

Optional: Calculator Exploration Boxes and Calculator Exercises   The optional Calculator Explorations provide keystrokes and exercises at appropriate points to give an opportunity for students to become familiar with these tools. Section exercises that are best completed by using a calculator are identified by ▦ for ease of assignment.

Student and Instructor Resources

STUDENT RESOURCES

Interactive DVD Lecture Series Videos	Video Organizer	Student Solutions Manual
Provides students with active learning at their own pace. The videos offer: • A complete lecture for each text section. The interface allows easy navigation to examples and exercises students need to review. • Interactive Concept Check exercises • Student Success Tips Videos • Practice Final Exam • Getting Ready for the Chapter Test Videos • Chapter Test Prep Videos	Designed to help students take notes and work practice exercises while watching the Interactive Lecture Series videos. • Covers all of the video examples in order. • Provides ample space for students to write down key definitions and rules. • Includes Play and Pause button icons to prompt students to follow along with the author for some exercises while they try others on their own. Available in loose-leaf, notebook-ready format and in MyMathLab.	Provides completely worked-out solutions to the odd-numbered section exercises; all exercises in the Integrated Reviews, Chapter Reviews, Chapter Tests, and Cumulative Reviews. **Key Concept Activity Lab Workbook** includes Extension Exercises, Exploration Activities, Conceptual Exercises, and Group Activities.

INSTRUCTOR RESOURCES

Annotated Instructor's Edition	Instructor's Resource Manual with Tests and Mini-Lectures
Contains all the content found in the student edition, plus the following: • Classroom example paired to each example • Answers to exercises on the same text page • Teaching Tips throughout the text, placed at key points • Video Answer Section	• Mini-lectures for each text section • Additional Practice worksheets for each section • Several forms of test per chapter—free response and multiple choice • Answers to all items **Instructor's Solutions Manual** **TestGen**® (Available for download from the IRC)
Instructor-to-Instructor Videos—available in the Instructor Resources section of the MyMathLab course.	**Online Resources** **MyMathLab**® (access code required) **MathXL**® (access code required)

Get the most out of
MyMathLab®

MyMathLab is the world's leading online resource for teaching and learning mathematics. MyMathLab helps students and instructors improve results and provides engaging experiences and personalized learning for each student so learning can happen in any environment. Plus, it offers flexible and time-saving course-management features to allow instructors to easily manage their classes while remaining in complete control, regardless of course format.

Personalized Support for Students

- MyMathLab comes with many learning resources–eText, animations, videos, and more–all designed to support your students as they progress through their course.

- The Adaptive Study Plan acts as a personal tutor, updating in real time based on student performance to provide personalized recommendations on what to work on next. With the new Companion Study Plan assignments, instructors can now assign the Study Plan as a prerequisite to a test or quiz, helping to guide students through concepts they need to master.

- Personalized Homework allows instructors to create homework assignments tailored to each student's specific needs by focusing on just the topics they have not yet mastered.

Used by nearly 4 million students each year, the MyMathLab and MyStatLab family of products delivers consistent, measurable gains in student learning outcomes, retention, and subsequent course success.

Acknowledgments

Many people helped me develop this text, and I will attempt to thank some of them here. Cindy Trimble was *invaluable* for contributing to the overall accuracy of the text. Dawn Nuttall, Emily Keaton, and Suellen Robinson were *invaluable* for their many suggestions and contributions during the development and writing of this Seventh Edition. Chakira Lane, Patty Bergin, and Lauren Morse provided guidance throughout the production process.

A very special thank you goes to my editor, Mary Beckwith, for being there 24/7/365, as my students say. Last, my thanks to the staff at Pearson for all their support: Michael Hirsch, Rachel Ross, Heather Scott, Michelle Renda, Chris Hoag, and Paul Corey.

I would like to thank the following reviewers for their input and suggestions:

Rosalie Abraham, *Florida Community College—Jacksonville*
Ana Bacica, *Brazosport College*
Nelson Collins, *Joliet Junior College*
Nancy Desilet, *Carroll Community College*
Elizabeth Eagle, *University of North Carolina—Charlotte*
Dorothy French, *Community College of Philadelphia*
Sharda Gudehithla, *Wilbur Wright College*
Pauline Hall, *Iowa State University*
Debra R. Hill, *University of North Carolina—Charlotte*
Glenn Jablonski, *Triton College*
Sue Kellicut, *Seminole State College*
Jean McArthur, *Joliet Junior College*
Mary T. McMahon, *North Central College*
Owen Mertens, *Missouri State University*
Jeri Rogers, *Seminole State College*
William Stammerman, *Des Moines Area Community College*
Patrick Stevens, *Joliet Junior College*
Arnavaz Taraporevala, *New York City College of Technology*

I would also like to thank the following dedicated group of instructors who participated in our focus groups, Martin-Gay Summits, and our design review for the series. Their feedback and insights have helped to strengthen this edition of the text. These instructors include:

Billie Anderson, *Tyler Junior College*
Cedric Atkins, *Mott Community College*
Lois Beardon, *Schoolcraft College*
Laurel Berry, *Bryant & Stratton College*
John Beyers, *University of Maryland*
Bob Brown, *Community College of Baltimore County–Essex*
Lisa Brown, *Community College of Baltimore County–Essex*
NeKeith Brown, *Richland College*
Gail Burkett, *Palm Beach State College*
Cheryl Cantwell, *Seminole State College*
Ivette Chuca, *El Paso Community College*
Jackie Cohen, *Augusta State College*
Julie Dewan, *Mohawk Valley Community College*
Monette Elizalde, *Palo Alto College*
Kiel Ellis, *Delgado Community College*
Janice Ervin, *Central Piedmont Community College*
Richard Fielding, *Southwestern College*
Dena Frickey, *Delgado Community College*
Cindy Gaddis, *Tyler Junior College*
Gary Garland, *Tarrant County Community College*
Kim Ghiselin, *State College of Florida*
Nita Graham, *St. Louis Community College*

Kim Granger, *St. Louis Community College*
Pauline Hall, *Iowa State University*
Pat Hussey, *Triton College*
Dorothy Johnson, *Lorain County Community College*
Sonya Johnson, *Central Piedmont Community College*
Ann Jones, *Spartanburg Community College*
Irene Jones, *Fullerton College*
Paul Jones, *University of Cincinnati*
Mike Kirby, *Tidewater Community College*
Kathy Kopelousous, *Lewis and Clark Community College*
Tara LaFrance, *Delgado Community College*
John LaMaster, *Indiana Purdue University Fort Wayne*
Nancy Lange, *Inver Hills Community College*
Judy Langer, *Westchester Community College*
Lisa Lindloff, *McLennan Community College*
Sandy Lofstock, *St. Petersburg College*
Kathy Lavelle, *Westchester Community College*
Nicole Mabine, *North Lake College*
Jean McArthur, *Joliet Junior College*
Kevin McCandless, *Evergreen Valley College*
Ena Michael, *State College of Florida*
Armando Perez, *Laredo Community College*
Davidson Pierre, *State College of Florida*
Marilyn Platt, *Gaston College*
Chris Riola, *Moraine Valley Community College*
Carole Shapero, *Oakton Community College*
Janet Sibol, *Hillsborough Community College*
Anne Smallen, *Mohawk Valley Community College*
Barbara Stoner, *Reading Area Community College*
Jennifer Strehler, *Oakton Community College*
Ellen Stutes, *Louisiana State University Eunice*
Tanomo Taguchi, *Fullerton College*
Robyn Toman, *Anne Arundel Community College*
MaryAnn Tuerk, *Elgin Community College*
Walter Wang, *Baruch College*
Leigh Ann Wheeler, *Greenville Technical Community College*
Darlene Williams, *Delgado Community College*
Valerie Wright, *Central Piedmont Community College*

A special thank you to those students who participated in our design review:
Katherine Browne, Mike Bulfin, Nancy Canipe, Ashley Carpenter, Jeff Chojnachi,
Roxanne Davis, Mike Dieter, Amy Dombrowski, Kay Herring, Todd Jaycox, Kaleena
Levan, Matt Montgomery, Tony Plese, Abigail Polkinghorn, Harley Price, Eli Robinson,
Avery Rosen, Robyn Schott, Cynthia Thomas, and Sherry Ward.

Elayn Martin-Gay

About the Author

Elayn Martin-Gay has taught mathematics at the University of New Orleans for more than 25 years. Her numerous teaching awards include the local University Alumni Association's Award for Excellence in Teaching, and Outstanding Developmental Educator at University of New Orleans, presented by the Louisiana Association of Developmental Educators.

Prior to writing textbooks, Elayn Martin-Gay developed an acclaimed series of lecture videos to support developmental mathematics students in their quest for success. These highly successful videos originally served as the foundation material for her texts. Today, the videos are specific to each book in the Martin-Gay series. The author has also created Chapter Test Prep videos to help students during their most "teachable moment"—as they prepare for a test—along with Instructor-to-Instructor videos that provide teaching tips, hints, and suggestions for each developmental mathematics course, including basic mathematics, prealgebra, beginning algebra, and intermediate algebra. Her most recent innovations are the Algebra Prep Apps for the iPhone and iPod Touch. These Apps embrace the different learning styles, schedules, and paces of students and provide them with quality math tutoring.

Elayn is the author of 12 published textbooks as well as multimedia interactive mathematics, all specializing in developmental mathematics courses. She has participated as an author across the broadest range of educational materials: textbooks, videos, tutorial software, and courseware. This offers an opportunity of various combinations for an integrated teaching and learning package offering great consistency for the student.

Applications Index

CHAPTER 1

Real Numbers and Algebraic Expressions

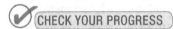

✓ CHECK YOUR PROGRESS

In arithmetic, we add, subtract, multiply, divide, raise to powers, and take roots of numbers. In algebra, we add, subtract, multiply, divide, raise to powers, and take roots of variables. Letters, such as *x*, that represent numbers are called **variables.** Understanding these algebraic expressions depends on your understanding of arithmetic expressions. This chapter reviews the arithmetic operations on real numbers and the corresponding algebraic expressions.

A Selection of Resources for Success in this Mathematics Course

Textbook

Instructor

MyMathLab and MathXL

Video Organizer

Interactive Lecture Series

For more information about the resources illustrated above, read Section 1.1.

1.1 Study Skill Tips for Success in Mathematics

Before reading Section 1.1, you might want to ask yourself a few questions.

1. When you took your last math course, were you organized? Were your notes and materials from that course easy to find, or were they disorganized and hard to find—if you saved them at all?

2. Were you satisfied—really satisfied—with your performance in that course? In other words, do you feel that your outcome represented your best effort?

If the answer is "no" to these questions, then it is time to make a change. Changing to or resuming good study skill habits is not a process you can start and stop as you please. It is something that you must remember and practice each and every day. To begin, continue reading this section.

OBJECTIVE
1 Getting Ready for This Course

Now that you have decided to take this course, remember that a *positive attitude* will make all the difference in the world. Your belief that you can succeed is just as important as your commitment to this course. Make sure you are ready for this course by having the time and positive attitude that it takes to succeed.

Make sure that you are familiar with the way that this course is being taught. Is it a traditional course, in which you have a printed textbook and meet with an instructor? Is it taught totally online, and your textbook is electronic and you e-mail your instructor? Or is your course structured somewhere in between these two methods? (Not all of the tips that follow will apply to all forms of instruction.)

Also make sure that you have scheduled your math course for a time that will give you the best chance for success. For example, if you are also working, you may want to check with your employer to make sure that your work hours will not conflict with your course schedule.

On the day of your first class period, double-check your schedule and allow yourself extra time to arrive on time in case of traffic problems or difficulty locating your classroom. Make sure that you are aware of and bring all necessary class materials.

OBJECTIVE
2 General Tips for Success

Below are some general tips that will increase your chance for success in a mathematics class. Many of these tips will also help you in other courses you may be taking.

Most important! Organize your class materials. In the next couple pages, many ideas will be presented to help you organize your class materials—notes, any handouts, completed homework, previous tests, etc. In general, you MUST have these materials organized. All of them will be valuable references throughout your course and when studying for upcoming tests and the final exam. One way to make sure you can locate these materials when you need them is to use a three-ring binder. This binder should be used solely for your mathematics class and should be brought to each and every class or lab. This way, any material can be immediately inserted in a section of this binder and will be there when you need it.

Form study groups and/or exchange names and e-mail addresses. Depending on how your course is taught, you may want to keep in contact with your fellow students. Some ways of doing this are to form a study group—whether in person or through the Internet. Also, you may want to ask if anyone is interested in exchanging e-mail addresses or any other form of contact.

Choose to attend all class periods. If possible, sit near the front of the classroom. This way, you will see and hear the presentation better. It may also be easier for you to participate in classroom activities.

> **Helpful Hint**
>
> **MyMathLab® and MathXL®**
> When assignments are turned in online, keep a hard copy of your complete written work. You will need to refer to your written work to be able to ask questions and to study for tests later.

Do your homework. You've probably heard the phrase "practice makes perfect" in relation to music and sports. It also applies to mathematics. You will find that the more time you spend solving mathematics exercises, the easier the process becomes. Be sure to schedule enough time to complete your assignments before the due date assigned by your instructor.

Check your work. Review the steps you took while working a problem. Learn to check your answers in the original exercises. You may also compare your answers with the "Answers to Selected Exercises" section in the back of the book. If you have made a mistake, try to figure out what went wrong. Then correct your mistake. If you can't find what went wrong, **don't** erase your work or throw it away. Show your work to your instructor, a tutor in a math lab, or a classmate. It is easier for someone to find where you had trouble if he or she looks at your original work.

Learn from your mistakes and be patient with yourself. Everyone, even your in-structor, makes mistakes. (That definitely includes me—Elayn Martin-Gay.) Use your errors to learn and to become a better math student. The key is finding and under-standing your errors.

Was your mistake a careless one, or did you make it because you can't read your own math writing? If so, try to work more slowly or write more neatly and make a con-scious effort to carefully check your work.

Did you make a mistake because you don't understand a concept? Take the time to review the concept or ask questions to better understand it.

Did you skip too many steps? Skipping steps or trying to do too many steps men-tally may lead to preventable mistakes.

Know how to get help if you need it. It's all right to ask for help. In fact, it's a good idea to ask for help whenever there is something that you don't understand. Make sure you know when your instructor has office hours and how to find his or her office. Find out whether math tutoring services are available on your campus. Check on the hours, location, and requirements of the tutoring service.

Don't be afraid to ask questions. You are not the only person in class with ques-tions. Other students are normally grateful that someone has spoken up.

Turn in assignments on time. This way, you can be sure that you will not lose points for being late. Show every step of a problem and be neat and organized. Also be sure that you understand which problems are assigned for homework. If allowed, you can always double-check the assignment with another student in your class.

OBJECTIVE

3 Knowing and Using Your Text

Flip through the pages of this text or view the e-text pages on a computer screen. Start noticing examples, exercise sets, end-of-chapter material, and so on. Every text is organized in some manner. Learn the way this text is organized by reading about and then finding an example in your text of each type of resource listed below. Finding and using these resources throughout your course will increase your chance of success.

- *Practice Exercises.* Each example in every section has a parallel Practice exercise. As you read a section, try each Practice exercise after you've finished the corre-sponding example. This "learn-by-doing" approach will help you grasp ideas be-fore you move on to other concepts. Answers are at the back of the text.
- *Symbols at the Beginning of an Exercise Set.* If you need help with a particular sec-tion, the symbols listed at the beginning of each exercise set will remind you of the numerous resources available.
- *Objectives.* The main section of exercises in each exercise set is referenced by an an example(s). There is also often a section of exercises entitled "Mixed Practice," which may be referenced by two or more examples or sections. These are mixed exercises written to prepare you for your next exam. Use all of this referencing if you have trouble completing an assignment from the exercise set.

- *Icons (Symbols).* Make sure that you understand the meaning of the icons that are beside many exercises. ▶ tells you that the corresponding exercise may be viewed on the video segment that corresponds to that section. ⬧ tells you that this exercise is a writing exercise in which you should answer in complete sentences. △ tells you that the exercise involves geometry. ▦ tells you that this exercise is worked more efficiently with the aid of a calculator. Also, a feature called Graphing Calculator Explorations may be found before select exercise sets.
- *Integrated Reviews.* Found in the middle of each chapter, these reviews offer you a chance to practice—in one place—the many concepts that you have learned separately over several sections.
- *End-of-Chapter Opportunities.* There are many opportunities at the end of each chapter to help you understand the concepts of the chapter.

  Vocabulary Checks contain key vocabulary terms introduced in the chapter.

  Chapter Highlights contain chapter summaries and examples.

  Chapter Reviews contain review exercises. The first part is organized section by section and the second part contains a set of mixed exercises.

  Getting Ready for the Tests contain conceptual exercises written to prepare students for chapter test directions as well as mixed sections of exercises.

  Chapter Tests are sample tests to help you prepare for an exam. The Chapter Test Prep Videos found in the Interactive Lecture Series, MyMathLab, and YouTube provide the video solution to each question on each Chapter Test.

  Cumulative Reviews start at Chapter 2 and are reviews consisting of material from the beginning of the book to the end of that particular chapter.
- *Student Resources in Your Textbook.* You will find a **Student Resources** section at the back of this textbook. It contains the following to help you study and prepare for tests:

  Study Skill Builders contain study skills advice. To increase your chance for success in the course, read these study tips, and answer the questions.

  Bigger Picture—Study Guide Outline provides you with a study guide outline of the course, with examples.

  Practice Final provides you with a Practice Final Exam to help you prepare for a final. The video solutions to each question are provided in the Interactive DVD Lecture Series and within MyMathLab®.
- *Resources to Check Your Work.* The **Answers to Selected Exercises** section provides answers to all odd-numbered section exercises and all integrated review and chapter test exercises.

OBJECTIVE

4 Knowing and Using Video and Notebook Organizer Resources

Video Resources

Below is a list of video resources that are all made by me—the author of your text, Elayn Martin-Gay. By making these videos, I can be sure that the methods presented are consistent with those in the text.

> **Helpful Hint**
>
> **MyMathLab®**
> In MyMathLab, you have access to the following video resources:
> - Lecture Videos for each section
> - Chapter Test Prep Videos
>
> Use these videos provided by the author to prepare for class, review, and study for tests.

- *Interactive DVD Lecture Series.* Exercises marked with a ▶ are fully worked out by the author on the DVDs and within MyMathLab. The lecture series provides approximately 20 minutes of instruction per section and is organized by Objective.
- *Chapter Test Prep Videos.* These videos provide solutions to all of the Chapter Test exercises worked out by the author. They can be found in MyMathLab, the Interactive Lecture series, and YouTube. This supplement is very helpful before a test or exam.
- *Student Success Tips.* These video segments are about 3 minutes long and are daily reminders to help you continue practicing and maintaining good organizational and study habits.
- *Final Exam Videos.* These video segments provide solutions to each question. These videos can be found within MyMathLab and the Interactive Lecture Series.

Notebook Organizer Resource

This resource is in three-ring notebook ready form. It is to be inserted in a three-ring binder and completed. This resource is numbered according to the sections in your text to which they refer.

- *Video Organizer.* This organizer is closely tied to the Interactive Lecture (Video) Series. Each section should be completed while watching the lecture video on the same section. Once completed, you will have a set of notes to accompany the Lecture (Video) Series section by section.

> **Helpful Hint**
>
> **MyMathLab® and MathXL®**
>
> - Use the **Help Me Solve This** button to get step-by-step help for the exercise you are working. You will need to work an additional exercise of the same type before you can get credit for having worked it correctly.
> - Use the **Video** button to view a video clip of the author working a similar exercise.

OBJECTIVE

5 Getting Help

If you have trouble completing assignments or understanding the mathematics, get help as soon as you need it! This tip is presented as an objective on its own because it is so important. In mathematics, usually the material presented in one section builds on your understanding of the previous section. This means that if you don't understand the concepts covered during a class period, there is a good chance that you will not understand the concepts covered during the next class period. If this happens to you, get help as soon as you can.

Where can you get help? Many suggestions have been made in this section on where to get help, and now it is up to you to get it. Try your instructor, a tutoring center, or a math lab, or you may want to form a study group with fellow classmates. If you do decide to see your instructor or go to a tutoring center, make sure that you have a neat notebook and are ready with your questions.

OBJECTIVE

6 Preparing for and Taking an Exam

Make sure that you allow yourself plenty of time to prepare for a test. If you think that you are a little "math anxious," it may be that you are not preparing for a test in a way that will ensure success. The way that you prepare for a test in mathematics is important. To prepare for a test:

> **Helpful Hint**
>
> **MyMathLab® and MathXL®**
>
> Review your written work for previous assignments. Then, go back and re-work previous assignments. Open a previous assignment, and click **Similar Exercise** to generate new exercises. Re-work the exercises until you fully understand them and can work them without help features.

1. Review your previous homework assignments.

2. Review any notes from class and section-level quizzes you have taken. (If this is a final exam, also review chapter tests you have taken.)

3. Review concepts and definitions by reading the Chapter Highlights at the end of each chapter.

4. Practice working out exercises by completing the Chapter Review found at the end of each chapter. (If this is a final exam, go through a Cumulative Review. There is one found at the end of each chapter except Chapter 1. Choose the review found at the end of the latest chapter that you have covered in your course.) *Don't stop here!*

5. It is important that you place yourself in conditions similar to test conditions to find out how you will perform. In other words, as soon as you feel that you know the material, get a few blank sheets of paper and take a sample test. There is a Chapter Test available at the end of each chapter, or you can work selected problems from the Chapter Review. Your instructor may also provide you with a review sheet. During this sample test, do not use your notes or your textbook. Then check your sample test. If your sample test is the Chapter Test in the text, don't forget that the video solutions are in MyMathLab, the Interactive Lecture Series, and YouTube. If you are not satisfied with the results, study the areas that you are weak in and try again.

6. On the day of the test, allow yourself plenty of time to arrive at where you will be taking your exam.

When taking your test:

1. Read the directions on the test carefully.
2. Read each problem carefully as you take the test. Make sure that you answer the question asked.
3. Watch your time and pace yourself so that you can attempt each problem on your test.
4. If you have time, check your work and answers.
5. Do not turn your test in early. If you have extra time, spend it double-checking your work.

OBJECTIVE

7 Managing Your Time

As a college student, you know the demands that classes, homework, work, and family place on your time. Some days you probably wonder how you'll ever get everything done. One key to managing your time is developing a schedule. Here are some hints for making a schedule:

1. Make a list of all of your weekly commitments for the term. Include classes, work, regular meetings, extracurricular activities, etc. You may also find it helpful to list such things as laundry, regular workouts, grocery shopping, etc.
2. Next, estimate the time needed for each item on the list. Also make a note of how often you will need to do each item. Don't forget to include time estimates for the reading, studying, and homework you do outside of your classes. You may want to ask your instructor for help estimating the time needed.
3. In the exercise set that follows, you are asked to block out a typical week on the schedule grid given. Start with items with fixed time slots like classes and work.
4. Next, include the items on your list with flexible time slots. Think carefully about how best to schedule items such as study time.
5. Don't fill up every time slot on the schedule. Remember that you need to allow time for eating, sleeping, and relaxing! You should also allow a little extra time in case some items take longer than planned.
6. If you find that your weekly schedule is too full for you to handle, you may need to make some changes in your workload, classload, or other areas of your life. You may want to talk to your advisor, manager or supervisor at work, or someone in your college's academic counseling center for help with such decisions.

1.1 Exercise Set MyMathLab®

1. What is your instructor's name?
2. What are your instructor's office location and office hours?
3. What is the best way to contact your instructor?
4. Do you have the name and contact information of at least one other student in class?
5. Will your instructor allow you to use a calculator in this class?
6. Why is it important that you write step-by-step solutions to homework exercises and keep a hard copy of all work submitted?
7. Is there a tutoring service available on campus? If so, what are its hours? What services are available?

8. Have you attempted this course before? If so, write down ways that you might improve your chances of success during this next attempt.
9. List some steps that you can take if you begin having trouble understanding the material or completing an assignment. If you are completing your homework in MyMathLab® and MathXL®, list the resources you can use for help.
10. How many hours of studying does your instructor advise for each hour of instruction?
11. What does the ＼ icon in this text mean?
12. What does the △ icon in this text mean?
13. What does the ▶ icon in this text mean?

14. What are Practice exercises?

15. When might be the best time to work a Practice exercise?

16. Where are the answers to Practice exercises?

17. What answers are contained in this text and where are they?

18. What are Study Skills Builders and where are they?

19. What and where are Integrated Reviews?

20. How many times is it suggested that you work through the homework exercises in MathXL® before the submission deadline?

21. How far in advance of the assigned due date is it suggested that homework be submitted online? Why?

22. Chapter Highlights are found at the end of each chapter. Find the Chapter 1 Highlights and explain how you might use it and how it might be helpful.

23. Chapter Reviews are found at the end of each chapter. Find the Chapter 1 Review and explain how you might use it and how it might be helpful.

24. Chapter Tests are found at the end of each chapter. Find the Chapter 1 Test and explain how you might use it and how it might be helpful when preparing for an exam on Chapter 1. Include how the Chapter Test Prep Videos may help. If you are working in MyMathLab® and MathXL®, how can you use previous homework assignments to study?

25. What is the Video Organizer? Explain the contents and how it might be used.

26. Explain how the Video Organizer can help you when watching a lecture video.

27. Read or reread objective **7** and fill out the following schedule grid.

	Monday	*Tuesday*	*Wednesday*	*Thursday*	*Friday*	*Saturday*	*Sunday*
1:00 a.m.							
2:00 a.m.							
3:00 a.m.							
4:00 a.m.							
5:00 a.m.							
6:00 a.m.							
7:00 a.m.							
8:00 a.m.							
9:00 a.m.							
10:00 a.m.							
11:00 a.m.							
Noon							
1:00 p.m.							
2:00 p.m.							
3:00 p.m.							
4:00 p.m.							
5:00 p.m.							
6:00 p.m.							
7:00 p.m.							
8:00 p.m.							
9:00 p.m.							
10:00 p.m.							
11:00 p.m.							
Midnight							

1.2 Algebraic Expressions and Sets of Numbers

OBJECTIVES

1 Identify and Evaluate Algebraic Expressions.

2 Identify Natural Numbers, Whole Numbers, Integers, and Rational and Irrational Real Numbers.

3 Find the Absolute Value of a Number.

4 Find the Opposite of a Number.

5 Write Phrases as Algebraic Expressions.

OBJECTIVE

1 Evaluating Algebraic Expressions

Recall that letters that represent numbers are called **variables.** An **algebraic expression** (or simply **expression**) is formed by numbers and variables connected by the operations of addition, subtraction, multiplication, division, raising to powers, or taking roots. For example,

$$2x, \quad \frac{x+5}{6}, \quad \sqrt{y} - 1.6, \quad \text{and} \quad z^3$$

are algebraic expressions or, more simply, expressions. (Recall that the expression $2x$ means $2 \cdot x$.)

Algebraic expressions occur often during problem solving. For example, the average cost to own and operate a sedan in the United States for 2014 was $0.592 per mile. The expression $0.592m$ gives the total cost to operate a car (sedan) annually for m miles. (*Source:* AAA)

Driving Costs

Driving 15,000 Miles per Year	Sedan Average	SUV HWD	Minivan
Cost per Mile	$0.592	$0.736	$0.65
Cost per Year	?	$11,040	$9750

To find the cost of driving a car for 15,000 miles, for example, we replace the variable m with 15,000 and perform the indicated operation. This process is called **evaluating** an expression, and the result is called the **value** of the expression for the given replacement value.

In our example, when $m = 15,000$,

$$0.592m = 0.592(15,000) = 8880$$

Helpful Hint

Recall that $0.592m$ means $0.592 \times m$

Thus, it costs $8880 to own and operate a sedan for 15,000 miles of driving.

EXAMPLE 1   Finding the Area of a Tile

The research department of a flooring company is considering a new flooring design that contains parallelograms. The area of a parallelogram with base b and height h is bh. Find the area of a parallelogram with base 10 centimeters and height 8.2 centimeters.

Solution We replace b with 10 and h with 8.2 in the algebraic expression bh.

$$bh = 10 \cdot 8.2 = 82$$

The area is 82 square centimeters

PRACTICE

1   The tile edging for a bathroom is in the shape of a triangle. The area of a triangle with base b and height h is $A = \frac{1}{2}bh$. Find the area of the tile if the base measures 3.5 cm and the height measures 8 cm.

Algebraic expressions simplify to different values depending on replacement values. (Order of operations is needed for simplifying many expressions. We fully review this in Section 1.3.)

EXAMPLE 2   Evaluate $3x - y$ when $x = 15$ and $y = 4$.

Solution   We replace x with 15 and y with 4 in the expression.

$$3x - y = 3 \cdot 15 - 4 = 45 - 4 = 41$$

PRACTICE

2   Evaluate $2p - q$ when $p = 17$ and $q = 3$.

When evaluating an expression to solve a problem, we often need to think about the kind of number that is appropriate for the solution. For example, if we are asked to determine the maximum number of parking spaces for a parking lot to be constructed, an answer of $98\frac{1}{10}$ is not appropriate because $\frac{1}{10}$ of a parking space is not realistic.

OBJECTIVE

2   Identifying Common Sets of Numbers

Let's review some common sets of numbers and their graphs on a number line. To construct a number line, we draw a line and label a point 0 with which we associate the number 0. This point is called the **origin.** Choose a point to the right of 0 and label it 1. The distance from 0 to 1 is called the **unit distance** and can be used to locate more points. The **positive numbers** lie to the right of the origin, and the **negative numbers** lie to the left of the origin. The number 0 is neither positive nor negative.

A number is **graphed** on a number line by shading the point on the number line that corresponds to the number. Some common sets of numbers and their graphs include:

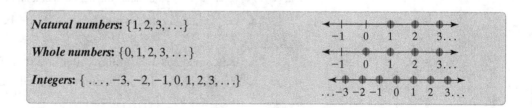

Natural numbers: $\{1, 2, 3, \ldots\}$

Whole numbers: $\{0, 1, 2, 3, \ldots\}$

Integers: $\{\ldots, -3, -2, -1, 0, 1, 2, 3, \ldots\}$

Each listing of three dots, $\ldots$, is called an **ellipsis** and means to continue in the same pattern.

A **set** is a collection of objects. The objects of a set are called its **members** or **elements.** When the elements of a set are listed, such as those displayed in the box above, the set is written in **roster** form.

A set can also be written in **set builder notation,** which describes the members of a set but does not list them. The following set is written in set builder notation.

$$\{x \mid x \text{ is a natural number less than } 3\}$$

The set of all x such that x is a natural number less than 3

Helpful Hint

Use { } or ∅ to write the empty set. {∅} is **not** the empty set because it has one element: ∅.

This same set written in roster form is $\{1, 2\}$.

A set that contains *no* elements is called the **empty set** (or **null set**), symbolized by { } or ∅. The set

$$\{x \mid x \text{ is a month with 32 days}\} \text{ is } \emptyset \text{ or } \{ \ \}$$

because no month has 32 days. The set has no elements.

EXAMPLE 3   Write each set in roster form. (List the elements of each set.)

   a. $\{x \mid x \text{ is a natural number greater than } 100\}$

   b. $\{x \mid x \text{ is a whole number between 1 and 6}\}$

Solution

   a. $\{101, 102, 103, \ldots\}$ **b.** $\{2, 3, 4, 5\}$ □

PRACTICE
3   Write each set in roster form. (List the elements of each set.)

   a. $\{x \mid x \text{ is a whole number between 5 and 10}\}$

   b. $\{x \mid x \text{ is a natural number greater than } 40\}$ ▪

The symbol $\in$ denotes that an element is in a particular set. The symbol $\in$ is read as "is an element of." For example, the true statement

$$3 \text{ is an element of } \{1, 2, 3, 4, 5\}$$

can be written in symbols as

$$3 \in \{1, 2, 3, 4, 5\}$$

The symbol $\notin$ is read as "is not an element of." In symbols, we write the true statement "p is not an element of $\{a, 5, g, j, q\}$" as

$$p \notin \{a, 5, g, j, q\}$$

EXAMPLE 4   Determine whether each statement is true or false.

   a. $3 \in \{x \mid x \text{ is a natural number}\}$ **b.** $7 \notin \{1, 2, 3\}$

Solution

   a. True, since 3 is a natural number and therefore an element of the set.

   b. True, since 7 is not an element of the set $\{1, 2, 3\}$.   □

PRACTICE
4   Determine whether each statement is true or false.

   a. $7 \in \{x \mid x \text{ is a natural number}\}$ **b.** $6 \notin \{1, 3, 5, 7\}$ ▪

We can use set builder notation to describe three other common sets of numbers.

Identifying Numbers

Real numbers: $\{x \mid x \text{ corresponds to a point on a number line}\}$

0

Rational numbers: $\left\{\dfrac{a}{b} \,\middle|\, a \text{ and } b \text{ are integers and } b \neq 0\right\}$

Irrational numbers: $\{x \mid x \text{ is a real number and } x \text{ is not a rational number}\}$

Helpful Hint

Notice from the definition that all real numbers are either rational or irrational.

Every rational number can be written as a decimal that either repeats in a pattern or terminates. For example,

Rational Numbers

$$\frac{1}{2} = 0.5 \qquad\qquad\qquad \frac{5}{4} = 1.25$$

$$\frac{2}{3} = 0.6666666\ldots = 0.\overline{6} \quad \frac{1}{11} = 0.090909\ldots = 0.\overline{09}$$

An irrational number written as a decimal neither terminates nor repeats. For example, π and $\sqrt{2}$ are irrational numbers. Their decimal form neither terminates nor repeats. Decimal approximations of each are below:

Irrational Numbers

$$\pi \approx 3.141592\ldots \quad \sqrt{2} \approx 1.414213\ldots$$

Notice that every integer is also a rational number since each integer can be written as the quotient of itself and 1:

$$3 = \frac{3}{1}, \quad 0 = \frac{0}{1}, \quad -8 = \frac{-8}{1}$$

Not every rational number, however, is an integer. The rational number $\frac{2}{3}$, for example, is not an integer. Some square roots are rational numbers and some are irrational numbers. For example, $\sqrt{2}$, $\sqrt{3}$, and $\sqrt{7}$ are irrational numbers while $\sqrt{25}$ is a rational number because $\sqrt{25} = 5 = \frac{5}{1}$. The set of rational numbers together with the set of irrational numbers make up the set of real numbers. To help you make the distinction between rational and irrational numbers, here are a few examples of each.

Real Numbers			
	Rational Numbers		**Irrational Numbers**
Examples	**Equivalent Quotient of Integers, $\dfrac{a}{b}$**		**Examples**
$-\dfrac{2}{3}$	$=$	$\dfrac{-2}{3}$ or $\dfrac{2}{-3}$	$\sqrt{5}$
$\sqrt{36}$	$=$	$\dfrac{6}{1}$	$\dfrac{\sqrt{6}}{7}$
5	$=$	$\dfrac{5}{1}$	$-\sqrt{3}$
0	$=$	$\dfrac{0}{1}$	π
1.2	$=$	$\dfrac{12}{10}$	$\dfrac{2}{\sqrt{3}}$
$3\dfrac{7}{8}$	$=$	$\dfrac{31}{8}$	

Some rational and irrational numbers are graphed below.

Earlier, we mentioned that every integer is also a rational number. In other words, all the elements of the set of integers are also elements of the set of rational numbers. When this happens, we say that the set of integers, set Z, is a subset of the set of rational numbers, set Q. In symbols,

$$Z \subseteq Q$$

$\underbrace{}_{\text{is a subset of}}$

The natural numbers, whole numbers, integers, rational numbers, and irrational numbers are each a subset of the set of real numbers. The relationships among these sets of numbers are shown in the following diagram.

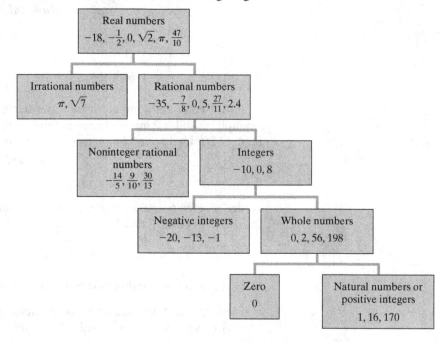

EXAMPLE 5 Determine whether the following statements are true or false.

a. 3 is a real number.

b. $\dfrac{1}{5}$ is an irrational number.

c. Every rational number is an integer.

d. $\{1, 5\} \subseteq \{2, 3, 4, 5\}$

Solution

a. True. Every whole number is a real number.

b. False. The number $\dfrac{1}{5}$ is a rational number since it is in the form $\dfrac{a}{b}$ with a and b integers and $b \neq 0$.

c. False. The number $\dfrac{2}{3}$, for example, is a rational number, but it is not an integer.

d. False. The element 1 in the first set is not an element of the second set. □

PRACTICE
5 Determine whether the following statements are true or false.

a. −5 is a real number.

b. $\sqrt{8}$ is a rational number.

c. Every whole number is a rational number.

d. $\{2, 4\} \subseteq \{1, 3, 4, 7\}$

OBJECTIVE

3 Finding the Absolute Value of a Number

A number line can also be used to visualize distance, which leads to the concept of absolute value. The **absolute value** of a real number a, written as $|a|$, is the distance between a and 0 on a number line. Since distance is always positive or zero, $|a|$ is always positive or zero.

Using the number line, we see that

$$|4| = 4 \quad \text{and also} \quad |-4| = 4$$

Why? Because both 4 and -4 are a distance of 4 units from 0.

An equivalent definition of the absolute value of a real number a is given next.

Absolute Value

The absolute value of a, written as $|a|$, is

$$|a| = \begin{cases} a \text{ if } a \text{ is 0 or a positive number} \\ -a \text{ if } a \text{ is a negative number} \end{cases}$$

$\underbrace{}_{\text{the opposite of}}$

EXAMPLE 6 Find each absolute value.

a. $|3|$ **b.** $\left|-\dfrac{1}{7}\right|$ **c.** $-|2.7|$ **d.** $-|-8|$ **e.** $|0|$

Solution

a. $|3| = 3$ since 3 is located 3 units from 0 on a number line.

b. $\left|-\dfrac{1}{7}\right| = \dfrac{1}{7}$ since $-\dfrac{1}{7}$ is $\dfrac{1}{7}$ units from 0 on a number line.

c. $-|2.7| = -2.7$. The negative sign outside the absolute value bars means to take the opposite of the absolute value of 2.7.

d. $-|-8| = -8$. Since $|-8|$ is 8, $-|-8| = -8$.

e. $|0| = 0$ since 0 is located 0 units from 0 on a number line. □

PRACTICE

6 Find each absolute value.

a. $|4|$ **b.** $\left|-\dfrac{1}{2}\right|$ **c.** $|1|$ **d.** $-|6.8|$ **e.** $-|-4|$ ■

✔ **CONCEPT CHECK**

Explain how you know that $|14| = -14$ is a false statement.

OBJECTIVE

4 Finding the Opposite of a Number

A number line can also help us visualize opposites. Two numbers that are the same distance from 0 on a number line but are on opposite sides of 0 are called **opposites.**

See the definition illustrated on the number lines below.

The opposite of 6.5 is −6.5

The opposite of $\frac{2}{3}$ is $-\frac{2}{3}$.

The opposite of −4 is 4.

> **Opposite**
>
> The opposite of a number a is the number $-a$.

Above, we state that the opposite of a number a is $-a$. This means that the opposite of −4 is $-(-4)$. But from the number line above, the opposite of −4 is 4. This means that $-(-4) = 4$, and in general, we have the following property.

> **Double Negative Property**
>
> For every real number a, $-(-a) = a$.

EXAMPLE 7   Write the opposite of each number.

    a. 8   **b.** $\frac{1}{5}$ **c.** −9.6

Solution

    a. The opposite of 8 is −8.

    b. The opposite of $\frac{1}{5}$ is $-\frac{1}{5}$.

    c. The opposite of −9.6 is $-(-9.6) = 9.6$.   □

PRACTICE
7   Write the opposite of each number.

    a. 5.4   **b.** $-\frac{3}{5}$ **c.** 18   ■

OBJECTIVE
5 Writing Phrases as Algebraic Expressions

Often, solving problems involves translating a phrase to an algebraic expression. The following is a partial list of key words and phrases and their usual direct translations.

Selected Key Words/Phrases and Their Translations			
Addition	**Subtraction**	**Multiplication**	**Division**
sum	difference of	product	quotient
plus	minus	times	divide
added to	subtracted from	multiply	into
more than	less than	twice	ratio
increased by	decreased by	of	
total	less		

EXAMPLE 8   Translate each phrase to an algebraic expression. Use the variable x to represent each unknown number.

    a. Eight times a number

    b. Three more than eight times a number

    c. The quotient of a number and -7

    d. One and six-tenths subtracted from twice a number

    e. Six less than a number

    f. Twice the sum of four and a number

Solution

    a. $8 \cdot x$ or $8x$

    b. $8x + 3$

    c. $x \div -7$ or $\dfrac{x}{-7}$

    d. $2x - 1.6$ or $2x - 1\dfrac{6}{10}$

    e. $x - 6$

    f. $2(4 + x)$

PRACTICE
8   Translate each phrase to an algebraic expression. Use the variable x to represent each unknown number.

    a. The product of 3 and a number

    b. Five less than twice a number

    c. Three and five-eighths more than a number

    d. The quotient of a number and 2

    e. Fourteen subtracted from a number

    f. Five times the sum of a number and ten

✔ Vocabulary, Readiness & Video Check

Use the choices below to fill in each blank. Not all choices will be used.

whole numbers	integers	rational number	a
natural numbers	value	irrational number	$-a$
absolute value	expression	variables	

1. Letters that represent numbers are called _____.

2. Finding the _____ of an expression means evaluating the expression.

3. The _____ of a number is that number's distance from 0 on a number line.

4. A(n) _____ is formed by numbers and variables connected by operations such as addition, subtraction, multiplication, division, raising to powers, and/or taking roots.

5. The _____ are $\{1, 2, 3, \ldots\}$.

6. The _____ are $\{0, 1, 2, 3, \ldots\}$.

7. The _____ are $\{\ldots -3, -2, -1, 0, 1, 2, 3, \ldots\}$.

8. The number $\sqrt{5}$ is a(n) _____.

9. The number $\dfrac{5}{7}$ is a(n) _____.

10. The opposite of a is _____.

Martin-Gay Interactive Videos

See Video 1.2

Watch the section lecture video and answer the following questions.

OBJECTIVE 1
11. When the algebraic expression in Example 2 is evaluated for the variable, why is 10,612.8 not the final answer for this application?

OBJECTIVE 2
12. Based on the lecture before Example 3, what is the relationship among real numbers, rational numbers, and irrational numbers?

OBJECTIVE 3
13. Based on the lecture before Example 7, complete the following statements. The absolute value of a number is that number's _____ from zero on a number line. Or, more formally, $|a| = a$ if a is _____ or a _____ number. Also, $|a| = -a$ if a is a _____ number.

OBJECTIVE 4
14. Based on the lecture before Example 10, the description of opposite using a number line is given. Explain the difference between the absolute value of a number and the opposite of a number using the number line descriptions.

OBJECTIVE 5
15. From Example 12, why must we be careful when translating phrases dealing with subtraction?

1.2 Exercise Set MyMathLab®

Find the value of each algebraic expression at the given replacement values. See Examples 1 and 2.

1. $5x$ when $x = 7$

2. $3y$ when $y = 45$

3. $9.8z$ when $z = 3.1$

4. $7.1a$ when $a = 1.5$

5. ab when $a = \dfrac{1}{2}$ and $b = \dfrac{3}{4}$

6. yz when $y = \dfrac{2}{3}$ and $z = \dfrac{1}{5}$

7. $3x + y$ when $x = 6$ and $y = 4$

8. $2a - b$ when $a = 12$ and $b = 7$

9. The B737-400 aircraft flies an average speed of 400 miles per hour.

The expression $400t$ gives the distance traveled by the aircraft in t hours. Find the distance traveled by the B737-400 in 5 hours.

10. The algebraic expression $1.5x$ gives the total length of shelf space needed in inches for x encyclopedias. Find the length of shelf space needed for a set of 30 encyclopedias.

△ **11.** Employees at Walmart constantly reorganize and reshelve merchandise. In doing so, they calculate floor space needed for displays. The algebraic expression $l \cdot w$ gives the floor space needed in square units for a display that measures length l units and width w units. Calculate the floor space needed for a display whose length is 5.1 feet and whose width is 4 feet.

12. The algebraic expression $\dfrac{x}{5}$ can be used to calculate the distance in miles that you are from a flash of lightning, where x is the number of seconds between the time you see a flash of lightning and the time you hear the thunder. Calculate the distance that you are from the flash of lightning if you hear the thunder 2 seconds after you see the lightning.

13. The B737-400 aircraft costs $2948 dollars per hour to operate. The algebraic expression $2948t$ gives the total cost to operate the aircraft for t hours. Find the total cost to operate the B737-400 for 3.6 hours.

14. On November 16, 2004, the NASA X-43A scramjet achieved the designation of fastest airplane in the world, reaching a speed of 7500 miles per hour. At this speed, the algebraic expression $7500t$ gives the total distance flown in t hours. Find the distance flown by the X-43A scramjet in 1.6 hours.

Write each set in roster form. (List the elements of each set.) See Example 3.

15. $\{x \,|\, x \text{ is a natural number less than } 6\}$

16. $\{x \,|\, x \text{ is a natural number greater than } 6\}$

17. $\{x \,|\, x \text{ is a natural number between } 10 \text{ and } 17\}$

18. $\{x \,|\, x \text{ is an odd natural number}\}$

19. $\{x \,|\, x \text{ is a whole number that is not a natural number}\}$

20. $\{x \,|\, x \text{ is a natural number less than } 1\}$

21. $\{x \,|\, x \text{ is an even whole number less than } 9\}$

22. $\{x \,|\, x \text{ is an odd whole number less than } 9\}$

Graph each set on a number line.

23. $\{0, 2, 4, 6\}$

24. $\{1, 3, 5, 7\}$

25. $\left\{\dfrac{1}{2}, \dfrac{2}{3}\right\}$

26. $\left\{\dfrac{1}{4}, \dfrac{1}{3}\right\}$

27. $\{-2, -6, -10\}$

28. $\{-1, -2, -3\}$

29. $\left\{-\dfrac{1}{3}, -1\dfrac{1}{3}\right\}$

30. $\left\{-\dfrac{1}{2}, -1\dfrac{1}{2}\right\}$

List the elements of the set $\left\{3, 0, \sqrt{7}, \sqrt{36}, \dfrac{2}{5}, -134\right\}$ *that are also elements of the given set. See Example 4.*

31. Whole numbers

32. Integers

33. Natural numbers

34. Rational numbers

35. Irrational numbers

36. Real numbers

Place $\in$ or $\notin$ in the space provided to make each statement true. See Example 4.

37. -11 $\{x \mid x \text{ is an integer}\}$

38. 0 $\{x \mid x \text{ is a positive integer}\}$

39. -6 $\{2, 4, 6, \ldots\}$ **40.** 12 $\{1, 2, 3, \ldots\}$

41. 12 $\{1, 3, 5, \ldots\}$ **42.** 0 $\{1, 2, 3, \ldots\}$

43. $\dfrac{1}{2}$ $\{x \mid x \text{ is an irrational number}\}$

44. 0 $\{x \mid x \text{ is a natural number}\}$

Determine whether each statement is true or false. See Examples 4 and 5. Use the following sets of numbers.

$$N = \text{set of natural numbers}$$
$$Z = \text{set of integers}$$
$$I = \text{set of irrational numbers}$$
$$Q = \text{set of rational numbers}$$
$$\mathbb{R} = \text{set of real numbers}$$

45. $Z \subseteq \mathbb{R}$ **46.** $\mathbb{R} \subseteq N$

47. $-1 \in Z$ **48.** $\dfrac{1}{2} \in Q$

49. $0 \in N$ **50.** $Z \subseteq Q$

51. $\sqrt{5} \notin I$ **52.** $\pi \notin \mathbb{R}$

53. $N \subseteq Z$ **54.** $I \subseteq N$

55. $\mathbb{R} \subseteq Q$ **56.** $N \subseteq Q$

Find each absolute value. See Example 6.

57. $-|2|$ **58.** $|8|$

59. $|-4|$ **60.** $|-6|$

61. $|0|$ **62.** $|-1|$

63. $-|-3|$ **64.** $-|-11|$

Write the opposite of each number. See Example 7.

65. -6.2 **66.** -7.8

67. $\dfrac{4}{7}$ **68.** $\dfrac{9}{5}$

69. $-\dfrac{2}{3}$ **70.** $-\dfrac{14}{3}$

71. 0 **72.** 10.3

Translating *Write each phrase as an algebraic expression. Use the variable x to represent each unknown number. See Example 8.*

73. Twice a number.   **74.** Six times a number.

75. Five more than twice a number.

76. One more than six times a number.

77. Ten less than a number.

78. A number minus seven.

79. The sum of a number and two.

80. The difference of twenty-five and a number.

81. A number divided by eleven.

82. The quotient of a number and thirteen.

83. Twelve, minus three times a number.

84. Four, subtracted from three times a number.

85. A number plus two and three-tenths.

86. Fifteen and seven-tenths plus a number

87. One and one-third less a number.

88. A number less two and three-fourths.

89. The quotient of five and the difference of four and a number.

90. The quotient of four and the sum of a number and one.

91. Twice the sum of a number and three.

92. Eight times the difference of a number and nine.

CONCEPT EXTENSIONS

Use the bar graph below to complete the given table by estimating the millions of tourists predicted for each region. (Use whole numbers.)

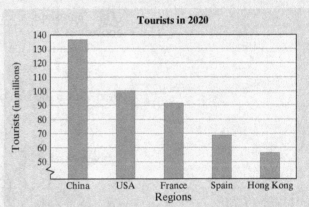

Source: Dan Smith, *The State of the World Atlas.*

93. China	
94. France	
95. Spain	
96. Hong Kong	

97. Explain why $-(-2)$ and $-|-2|$ simplify to different numbers.

98. The boxed definition of absolute value states that $|a| = -a$ if a is a negative number. Explain why $|a|$ is always non-negative, even though $|a| = -a$ for negative values of a.

99. In your own words, explain why every natural number is also a rational number but not every rational number is a natural number.

100. In your own words, explain why every irrational number is a real number but not every real number is an irrational number.

101. In your own words, explain why the empty set is a subset of every set.

102. In your own words, explain why every set is a subset of itself.

1.3 Operations on Real Numbers and Order of Operations

OBJECTIVE

1 Adding and Subtracting Real Numbers

When solving problems, we often have to add real numbers. For example, if the New Orleans Saints lose 5 yards in one play, then lose another 7 yards in the next play, their total loss may be described by $-5 + (-7)$.

The addition of two real numbers may be summarized by the following.

> **Adding Real Numbers**
>
> **1.** To add two numbers with the *same sign*, add their absolute values and attach their common sign.
>
> **2.** To add two numbers with *different signs*, subtract the smaller absolute value from the larger absolute value and attach the sign of the number with the larger absolute value.

For example, to add $-5 + (-7)$, first add their absolute values.

$$|-5| = 5, \quad |-7| = 7, \quad \text{and} \quad 5 + 7 = 12$$

Next, attach their common negative sign.

$$-5 + (-7) = -12$$

(This represents a total loss of 12 yards for the New Orleans Saints in the example above.)

To find $(-4) + 3$, first subtract their absolute values.

$$|-4| = 4, \quad |3| = 3, \quad \text{and} \quad 4 - 3 = 1$$

Next, attach the sign of the number with the larger absolute value.

$$(-4) + 3 = -1$$

EXAMPLE 1 Add.

a. $-3 + (-11)$ **b.** $3 + (-7)$ **c.** $-10 + 15$

d. $-8.3 + (-1.9)$ **e.** $-\dfrac{1}{4} + \dfrac{1}{2}$ **f.** $-\dfrac{2}{3} + \dfrac{3}{7}$

Solution

a. $-3 + (-11) = -(3 + 11) = -14$

b. $3 + (-7) = -4$

c. $-10 + 15 = 5$

d. $-8.3 + (-1.9) = -10.2$

e. $-\dfrac{1}{4} + \dfrac{1}{2} = -\dfrac{1}{4} + \dfrac{1 \cdot 2}{2 \cdot 2} = -\dfrac{1}{4} + \dfrac{2}{4} = \dfrac{1}{4}$

f. $-\dfrac{2}{3} + \dfrac{3}{7} = -\dfrac{14}{21} + \dfrac{9}{21} = -\dfrac{5}{21}$

PRACTICE

1 Add.

a. $-6 + (-2)$ **b.** $5 + (-8)$ **c.** $-4 + 9$

d. $-3.2 + (-4.9)$ **e.** $-\dfrac{3}{5} + \dfrac{2}{3}$ **f.** $-\dfrac{5}{11} + \dfrac{3}{22}$

Subtraction of two real numbers may be defined in terms of addition.

> **Subtracting Real Numbers**
>
> If a and b are real numbers,
>
> $$a - b = a + (-b)$$

In other words, to subtract a real number, we add its opposite.

EXAMPLE 2   Subtract.

   a. $2 - 8$ **b.** $-8 - (-1)$ **c.** $-11 - 5$ **d.** $10.7 - (-9.8)$

   e. $-\dfrac{2}{3} - \dfrac{1}{2}$ **f.** $1 - 0.06$ **g.** Subtract 7 from 4.

Solution   Add the opposite   Add the opposite

   a. $2 - 8 = 2 + (-8) = -6$ **b.** $-8 - (-1) = -8 + (1) = -7$

   c. $-11 - 5 = -11 + (-5) = -16$ **d.** $10.7 - (-9.8) = 10.7 + 9.8 = 20.5$

   e. $-\dfrac{2}{3} - \dfrac{1}{2} = -\dfrac{2 \cdot 2}{3 \cdot 2} - \dfrac{1 \cdot 3}{2 \cdot 3} = -\dfrac{4}{6} + \left(-\dfrac{3}{6}\right) = -\dfrac{7}{6}$

   f. $1 - 0.06 = 1 + (-0.06) = 0.94$ **g.** $4 - 7 = 4 + (-7) = -3$ □

PRACTICE
2   Subtract.

   a. $3 - 11$ **b.** $-6 - (-3)$ **c.** $-7 - 5$ **d.** $4.2 - (-3.5)$

   e. $-\dfrac{5}{7} - \dfrac{1}{3}$ **f.** $3 - 1.2$ **g.** Subtract 9 from 2.   ■

To add or subtract three or more real numbers, add or subtract from left to right.

EXAMPLE 3   Simplify the following expressions.

   a. $11 + 2 - 7$ **b.** $-5 - 4 + 2$

Solution

   a. $11 + 2 - 7 = 13 - 7 = 6$ **b.** $-5 - 4 + 2 = -9 + 2 = -7$ □

PRACTICE
3   Simplify the following expressions.

   a. $13 + 5 - 6$ **b.** $-6 - 2 + 4$ ■

OBJECTIVE
2   Multiplying and Dividing Real Numbers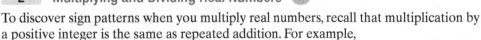

To discover sign patterns when you multiply real numbers, recall that multiplication by a positive integer is the same as repeated addition. For example,

$$3(2) = 2 + 2 + 2 = 6$$
$$3(-2) = (-2) + (-2) + (-2) = -6$$

Notice here that $3(-2) = -6$. This illustrates that the product of two numbers with different signs is negative. We summarize sign patterns for multiplying any two real numbers as follows.

> **Multiplying Two Real Numbers**
>
> The product of two numbers with the *same* sign is positive.
> The product of two numbers with *different* signs is negative.

Also recall that the product of zero and any real number is zero.

$$0 \cdot a = 0$$

> **Product Property of 0**
> $0 \cdot a = 0$ Also $a \cdot 0 = 0$

EXAMPLE 4   Multiply.

a. $(-8)(-1)$ b. $-2\left(\dfrac{1}{6}\right)$ c. $-1.2(0.3)$ d. $0(-11)$

e. $\dfrac{1}{5}\left(-\dfrac{10}{11}\right)$ f. $(7)(1)(-2)(-3)$ g. $8(-2)(0)$

Solution

a. Since the signs of the two numbers are the same, the product is positive. Thus $(-8)(-1) = +8$, or 8.

b. Since the signs of the two numbers are different or unlike, the product is negative. Thus $-2\left(\dfrac{1}{6}\right) = -\dfrac{2}{6} = -\dfrac{1}{3}$.

c. $-1.2(0.3) = -0.36$

d. $0(-11) = 0$

e. $\dfrac{1}{5}\left(-\dfrac{10}{11}\right) = -\dfrac{10}{55} = -\dfrac{2}{11}$

f. To multiply three or more real numbers, you may multiply from left to right.

$$(7)(1)(-2)(-3) = 7(-2)(-3)$$
$$= -14(-3)$$
$$= 42$$

g. Since zero is a factor, the product is zero.

$$(8)(-2)(0) = 0$$

PRACTICE
4   Multiply.

a. $(-5)(3)$ b. $(-7)\left(-\dfrac{1}{14}\right)$ c. $5.1(-2)$ d. $14(0)$

e. $\left(-\dfrac{1}{4}\right)\left(\dfrac{8}{13}\right)$ f. $6(-1)(-2)(3)$ g. $5(-2.3)$

> Helpful Hint
> The following sign patterns may be helpful when we are multiplying.
> **1.** An odd number of negative factors gives a negative product.
> **2.** An even number of negative factors gives a positive product.

Recall that $\dfrac{8}{4} = 2$ because $2 \cdot 4 = 8$. Likewise, $\dfrac{8}{-4} = -2$ because $(-2)(-4) = 8$.

Also, $\dfrac{-8}{4} = -2$ because $(-2)4 = -8$, and $\dfrac{-8}{-4} = 2$ because $2(-4) = -8$. From these examples, we can see that the sign patterns for division are the same as for multiplication.

> **Dividing Two Real Numbers**
>
> The quotient of two numbers with the *same* sign is positive.
>
> The quotient of two numbers with *different* signs is negative.

Recall from your knowledge of fractions that division by a nonzero real number b is the same as multiplication by $\dfrac{1}{b}$. In other words,

$$\frac{a}{b} = a \div b = a \cdot \frac{1}{b}$$

This means that to simplify $\dfrac{a}{b}$, we can divide by b or multiply by $\dfrac{1}{b}$. The nonzero numbers b and $\dfrac{1}{b}$ are called **reciprocals.**

Notice that b *must* be a nonzero number. We do not define division by 0. For example, $5 \div 0$, or $\dfrac{5}{0}$, is undefined. To see why, recall that if $5 \div 0 = n$, a number, then $n \cdot 0 = 5$. This is not possible since $n \cdot 0 = 0$ for any number n and is never 5. Thus far, we have learned that we cannot divide 5 or any other nonzero number by 0.

Can we divide 0 by 0? By the same reasoning, if $0 \div 0 = n$, a number, then $n \cdot 0 = 0$. This is true for any number n so that the quotient $0 \div 0$ would not be a single number. To avoid this, we say that

> Division by 0 is undefined.

EXAMPLE 5   Divide.

a. $\dfrac{20}{-4}$ **b.** $\dfrac{-9}{-3}$ **c.** $-\dfrac{3}{8} \div 3$ **d.** $\dfrac{-40}{10}$ **e.** $\dfrac{-1}{10} \div \dfrac{-2}{5}$ **f.** $\dfrac{8}{0}$

Solution

a. Since the signs are different or unlike, the quotient is negative and $\dfrac{20}{-4} = -5$.

b. Since the signs are the same, the quotient is positive and $\dfrac{-9}{-3} = 3$.

c. $-\dfrac{3}{8} \div 3 = -\dfrac{3}{8} \cdot \dfrac{1}{3} = -\dfrac{1}{8}$ **d.** $\dfrac{-40}{10} = -4$

e. $\dfrac{-1}{10} \div \dfrac{-2}{5} = -\dfrac{1}{10} \cdot -\dfrac{5}{2} = \dfrac{1}{4}$ **f.** $\dfrac{8}{0}$ is undefined.   □

PRACTICE
5   Divide.

a. $\dfrac{-16}{8}$ **b.** $\dfrac{-15}{-3}$ **c.** $-\dfrac{2}{3} \div 4$

d. $\dfrac{54}{-9}$ **e.** $-\dfrac{1}{12} \div \left(-\dfrac{3}{4}\right)$ **f.** $\dfrac{0}{-7}$ ■

With sign rules for division, we can understand why the positioning of the negative sign in a fraction does not change the value of the fraction. For example,

$$\frac{-12}{3} = -4, \quad \frac{12}{-3} = -4, \quad \text{and} \quad -\frac{12}{3} = -4$$

Since all the fractions equal -4, we can say that

$$\frac{-12}{3} = \frac{12}{-3} = -\frac{12}{3}$$

In general, the following holds true.

If a and b are real numbers and $b \neq 0$, then $\dfrac{a}{-b} = \dfrac{-a}{b} = -\dfrac{a}{b}$.

OBJECTIVE

3 Evaluating Expressions Containing Exponents

Recall that when two numbers are multiplied, they are called **factors.** For example, in $3 \cdot 5 = 15$, the 3 and 5 are called factors.

A natural number *exponent* is a shorthand notation for repeated multiplication of the same factor. This repeated factor is called the **base,** and the number of times it is used as a factor is indicated by the **exponent.** For example,

$$\underset{\text{base}}{4}\overset{\text{exponent}}{^3} = \underset{\text{4 is a factor 3 times.}}{4 \cdot 4 \cdot 4} = 64$$

Exponents

If a is a real number and n is a natural number, then the ***n*th power of *a*,** or ***a* raised to the *n*th power,** written as a^n, is the product of n factors, each of which is a.

$$\underset{\text{base}}{a}\overset{\text{exponent}}{^n} = \underset{a \text{ is a factor } n \text{ times.}}{a \cdot a \cdot a \cdot a \cdot \cdots \cdot a}$$

It is not necessary to write an exponent of 1. For Example, 3 is assumed to be 3^1.

EXAMPLE 6 Evaluate each expression.

a. 3^2 b. $\left(\dfrac{1}{2}\right)^4$ c. -5^2

d. $(-5)^2$ e. -5^3 f. $(-5)^3$

Solution

a. $3^2 = 3 \cdot 3 = 9$ b. $\left(\dfrac{1}{2}\right)^4 = \left(\dfrac{1}{2}\right)\left(\dfrac{1}{2}\right)\left(\dfrac{1}{2}\right)\left(\dfrac{1}{2}\right) = \dfrac{1}{16}$

c. $-5^2 = -(5 \cdot 5) = -25$ d. $(-5)^2 = (-5)(-5) = 25$

e. $-5^3 = -(5 \cdot 5 \cdot 5) = -125$ f. $(-5)^3 = (-5)(-5)(-5) = -125$ □

PRACTICE

6 Evaluate each expression.

a. 2^3 b. $\left(\dfrac{1}{3}\right)^2$ c. -12^2

d. $(-12)^2$ e. -4^3 f. $(-4)^3$ ■

✔ **CONCEPT CHECK**

When $(-8.2)^7$ is evaluated, will the value be positive or negative? How can you tell without making any calculations?

Answer to Concept Check:

negative; the exponent is an odd number

> **Helpful Hint**
>
> Be very careful when simplifying expressions such as -5^2 and $(-5)^2$.
>
> $$-5^2 = -(5 \cdot 5) = -25 \quad \text{and} \quad (-5)^2 = (-5)(-5) = 25$$
>
> Without parentheses, the base to square is 5, not −5.

OBJECTIVE

4 Finding Roots of Numbers

The opposite of squaring a number is taking the **square root** of a number. For example, since the square of 4, or 4^2, is 16, we say that a square root of 16 is 4. The notation $\sqrt{a}$ denotes the **positive, or principal, square root** of a nonnegative number a. We then have in symbols that $\sqrt{16} = 4$. The negative square root of 16 is written $-\sqrt{16} = -4$. The square root of a negative number such as $\sqrt{-16}$ is not a real number. Why? There is no real number that, when squared, gives a negative number.

EXAMPLE 7   Find the square roots.

a. $\sqrt{9}$ **b.** $\sqrt{25}$ **c.** $\sqrt{\dfrac{1}{4}}$ **d.** $-\sqrt{36}$ **e.** $\sqrt{-36}$

Solution

a. $\sqrt{9} = 3$ since 3 is positive and $3^2 = 9.$ **b.** $\sqrt{25} = 5$ since $5^2 = 25.$

c. $\sqrt{\dfrac{1}{4}} = \dfrac{1}{2}$ since $\left(\dfrac{1}{2}\right)^2 = \dfrac{1}{4}.$ **d.** $-\overset{\downarrow}{\sqrt{36}} = -6$

e. $\sqrt{-36}$ is not a real number.

PRACTICE

7 Find the square roots.

a. $\sqrt{49}$ **b.** $\sqrt{\dfrac{1}{16}}$ **c.** $-\sqrt{64}$ **d.** $\sqrt{-64}$ **e.** $\sqrt{100}$

We can find roots other than square roots. Since $(-2)^3$ is −8, we say that the **cube root** of −8 is −2. This is written as

$$\sqrt[3]{-8} = -2.$$

Also, since $3^4 = 81$ and 3 is positive,

$$\sqrt[4]{81} = 3.$$

EXAMPLE 8   Find the roots.

a. $\sqrt[3]{-27}$ **b.** $\sqrt[5]{1}$ **c.** $\sqrt[4]{16}$

Solution

a. $\sqrt[3]{-27} = -3$ since $(-3)^3 = -27.$

b. $\sqrt[5]{1} = 1$ since $1^5 = 1.$

c. $\sqrt[4]{16} = 2$ since 2 is positive and $2^4 = 16.$

PRACTICE

8 Find the roots.

a. $\sqrt[3]{64}$ **b.** $\sqrt[5]{-1}$ **c.** $\sqrt[4]{10,000}$

Of course, as mentioned in Section 1.2, not all roots simplify to rational numbers. We study radicals further in Chapter 7.

OBJECTIVE

5 Using the Order of Operations

Expressions containing more than one operation are written to follow a particular agreed-upon **order of operations.** For example, when we write $3 + 2 \cdot 10$, we mean to multiply first and then add.

Order of Operations

Simplify expressions using the order that follows.

If grouping symbols such as parentheses are present, simplify expressions within those first, starting with the innermost set. If fraction bars are present, simplify the numerator and denominator separately.

1. Evaluate exponential expressions, roots, or absolute values in order from left to right.
2. Multiply or divide in order from left to right.
3. Add or subtract in order from left to right.

Helpful Hint

Fraction bars, radical signs, and absolute value bars can sometimes be used as grouping symbols. For example,

	Fraction Bar	*Radical Sign*	*Absolute Value Bars*
Grouping Symbol	$\dfrac{-1-7}{6-11}$	$\sqrt{15+1}$	$\lvert -7.2 - \sqrt{4} \rvert$
Not Grouping Symbol	$-\dfrac{8}{9}$	$\sqrt{9}$	$\lvert -3.2 \rvert$

EXAMPLE 9 Simplify.

a. $20 \div 2 \cdot 10$ 　　　　**b.** $1 + 2(1-4)^2$ 　　　　**c.** $\dfrac{\lvert -2 \rvert^3 + 1}{-7 - \sqrt{4}}$

Solution

a. Be careful! Here, we multiply or divide in order from left to right. Thus, divide, then multiply.

$$20 \div 2 \cdot 10 = 10 \cdot 10 = 100$$

b. Remember the order of operations so that you are *not* tempted to add 1 and 2 first.

$$
\begin{aligned}
1 + 2(1-4)^2 &= 1 + 2(-3)^2 &&\text{Simplify inside grouping symbols first.}\\
&= 1 + 2(9) &&\text{Write } (-3)^2 \text{ as 9.}\\
&= 1 + 18 &&\text{Multiply.}\\
&= 19 &&\text{Add.}
\end{aligned}
$$

c. Simplify the numerator and the denominator separately; then divide.

$$
\begin{aligned}
\frac{\lvert -2 \rvert^3 + 1}{-7 - \sqrt{4}} &= \frac{2^3 + 1}{-7 - 2} &&\text{Write } \lvert -2 \rvert \text{ as 2 and } \sqrt{4} \text{ as 2.}\\[6pt]
&= \frac{8 + 1}{-9} &&\text{Write } 2^3 \text{ as 8.}\\[6pt]
&= \frac{9}{-9} = -1 &&\text{Simplify the numerator, then divide.} \quad \square
\end{aligned}
$$

PRACTICE

9   Simplify.

a. $14 - 3 \cdot 4$ b. $3(5 - 8)^2$ c. $\dfrac{|-5|^2 + 4}{\sqrt{4} - 3}$

Besides parentheses, other symbols used for grouping expressions are brackets [ ] and braces { }. These other grouping symbols are commonly used when we group expressions that already contain parentheses.

EXAMPLE 10   Simplify: $3 - [(4 - 6) + 2(5 - 9)]$

Solution $3 - [(4 - 6) + 2(5 - 9)] = 3 - [-2 + 2(-4)]$ Simplify within the innermost sets of parentheses.

$$= 3 - [-2 + (-8)]$$
$$= 3 - [-10]$$
$$= 13$$

> **Helpful Hint**
> When grouping symbols occur within grouping symbols, remember to perform operations on the innermost set first.

PRACTICE

10   Simplify: $5 - [(3 - 5) + 6(2 - 4)]$

EXAMPLE 11   Simplify: $\dfrac{-5\sqrt{30 - 5} + (-2)^2}{4^2 + |7 - 10|}$

Solution   Here, the fraction bar, radical sign, and absolute value bars serve as grouping symbols. Thus, we simplify within the radical sign and absolute value bars first, remembering to calculate above and below the fraction bar separately.

$$\frac{-5\sqrt{30 - 5} + (-2)^2}{4^2 + |7 - 10|} = \frac{-5\sqrt{25} + (-2)^2}{4^2 + |-3|} = \frac{-5 \cdot 5 + 4}{16 + 3} = \frac{-25 + 4}{16 + 3}$$

$$= \frac{-21}{19} \text{ or } -\frac{21}{19}$$

PRACTICE

11   Simplify: $\dfrac{-2\sqrt{12 + 4} - (-3)^2}{6^2 + |1 - 9|}$

✔ **CONCEPT CHECK**

True or false? If two people use the order of operations to simplify a numerical expression and neither makes a calculation error, it is not possible that they each obtain a different result. Explain.

OBJECTIVE

6   Evaluating Algebraic Expressions

Recall from Section 1.2 that an algebraic expression is formed by numbers and variables connected by the operations of addition, subtraction, multiplication, division, raising to powers, and/or taking roots. Also, if numbers are substituted for the variables in an algebraic expression and the operations performed, the result is called **the value of the expression** for the given replacement values. This entire process is called **evaluating an expression.**

EXAMPLE 12 Evaluate each expression when $x = 4$ and $y = -3$.

a. $3x - 7y$ **b.** $-2y^2$ **c.** $\dfrac{\sqrt{x}}{y} - \dfrac{y}{x}$

Solution For each expression, replace x with 4 and y with -3.

a. $3x - 7y = 3 \cdot 4 - 7(-3)$ Let $x = 4$ and $y = -3$.

$\qquad\qquad = 12 - (-21)$ Multiply.

$\qquad\qquad = 12 + 21$ Write as an addition.

$\qquad\qquad = 33$ Add.

b. $-2y^2 = \underbrace{-2(-3)^2}$ Let $y = -3$.

> **Helpful Hint**
> In $-2(-3)^2$, the exponent 2 goes with the base of -3 only.

$\qquad\quad = -2(9)$ Write $(-3)^2$ as 9.

$\qquad\quad = -18$ Multiply.

c. $\dfrac{\sqrt{x}}{y} - \dfrac{y}{x} = \dfrac{\sqrt{4}}{-3} - \dfrac{-3}{4}$

$\qquad\qquad = -\dfrac{2}{3} + \dfrac{3}{4}$ Write $\sqrt{4}$ as 2.

$\qquad\qquad = -\dfrac{2}{3} \cdot \dfrac{4}{4} + \dfrac{3}{4} \cdot \dfrac{3}{3}$ The LCD is 12.

$\qquad\qquad = -\dfrac{8}{12} + \dfrac{9}{12}$ Write each fraction with a denominator of 12.

$\qquad\qquad = \dfrac{1}{12}$ Add.

PRACTICE
12 Evaluate each expression when $x = 16$ and $y = -5$

a. $2x - 7y$ **b.** $-4y^2$ **c.** $\dfrac{\sqrt{x}}{y} - \dfrac{y}{x}$

Sometimes variables such as x_1 and x_2 will be used in this book. The small 1 and 2 are called **subscripts.** The variable x_1 can be read as "x sub 1," and the variable x_2 can be read as "x sub 2." The important thing to remember is that they are two different variables. For example, if $x_1 = -5$ and $x_2 = 7$, then

$$x_1 - x_2 = -5 - 7 = -12.$$

EXAMPLE 13 The algebraic expression $\dfrac{5(x - 32)}{9}$ represents the equivalent temperature in degrees Celsius when x is the temperature in degrees Fahrenheit. Complete the following table by evaluating this expression at the given values of x.

Degrees Fahrenheit	x	-4	10	32
Degrees Celsius	$\dfrac{5(x - 32)}{9}$			

Solution To complete the table, evaluate $\dfrac{5(x-32)}{9}$ at each given replacement value.

When $x = -4$,

$$\frac{5(x-32)}{9} = \frac{5(-4-32)}{9} = \frac{5(-36)}{9} = -20$$

When $x = 10$,

$$\frac{5(x-32)}{9} = \frac{5(10-32)}{9} = \frac{5(-22)}{9} = -\frac{110}{9} \text{ or } -12\frac{2}{9}$$

When $x = 32$,

$$\frac{5(x-32)}{9} = \frac{5(32-32)}{9} = \frac{5 \cdot 0}{9} = 0$$

The completed table is

Degrees Fahrenheit	x	-4	10	32
Degrees Celsius	$\dfrac{5(x-32)}{9}$	-20	$-\dfrac{110}{9}$ or $-12\dfrac{2}{9}$	0

Degrees
Fahrenheit

Degrees
Celsius

Thus, $-4°$F is equivalent to $-20°$C, $10°$F is equivalent to $-\dfrac{110°}{9}$ C, and $32°$F is equivalent to $0°$C.   ☐

PRACTICE
13   The algebraic expression $\dfrac{9}{5}x + 32$ represents the equivalent temperature in degrees Fahrenheit when x is the temperature in degrees Celsius. Complete the following table by evaluating this expression at the given values of x.

Degrees Celsius	x	-5	10	25
Degrees Fahrenheit	$\dfrac{9}{5}x + 32$			

✓ Vocabulary, Readiness & Video Check

Use the choices below to fill in each blank. Some choices may be used more than once and some used not at all.

exponent	undefined	base	1	$\dfrac{-a}{-b}$	$\dfrac{a}{b}$
square root	reciprocal	0	9	$\dfrac{-a}{b}$	$\dfrac{a}{-b}$

1. $0 \cdot a = $ _____ .

2. $\dfrac{0}{4}$ simplifies to _____ while $\dfrac{4}{0}$ is _____ .

3. The _____ of the nonzero number b is $\dfrac{1}{b}$.

4. The fraction $-\dfrac{a}{b} = $ _____ $= $ _____ .

5. A(n) _____ is a shorthand notation for repeated multiplication of the same number.

6. In $(-5)^2$, the 2 is the _____ and the -5 is the _____ .

7. The opposite of squaring a number is taking the _____ of a number.

8. Using order of operations, $9 \div 3 \cdot 3 = $ _____ .

Martin-Gay Interactive Videos

See Video 1.3

Watch the section lecture video and answer the following questions.

OBJECTIVE
1

9. From Example 2, we learn that subtraction of two real numbers may be defined in terms of what operation?

OBJECTIVE
2

10. From Examples 3 and 4, explain the significance of the signs of numbers when multiplying and dividing two real numbers.

OBJECTIVE
3

11. Explain the significance of the use of parentheses when comparing Examples 7 and 8.

OBJECTIVE
4

12. From Example 9, what does the $\sqrt{}$ notation mean?

OBJECTIVE
5

13. In the lecture before Example 12, what reason is given for needing the order of operations?

OBJECTIVE
6

14. In Example 15, why can you not first add the 3 and 2 in the numerator?

1.3 Exercise Set MyMathLab®

Add or subtract as indicated. See Examples 1 through 3

1. $-3 + 8$

2. $12 + (-7)$

3. $-14 + (-10)$

4. $-5 + (-9)$

5. $-4.3 - 6.7$

6. $-8.2 - (-6.6)$

7. $13 - 17$

8. $15 - (-1)$

9. $\frac{11}{15} - \left(-\frac{3}{5}\right)$

10. $\frac{7}{10} - \frac{4}{5}$

11. $19 - 10 - 11$

12. $-13 - 4 + 9$

13. $-\frac{4}{5} - \left(-\frac{3}{10}\right)$

14. $-\frac{5}{2} - \left(-\frac{2}{3}\right)$

15. Subtract 14 from 8.

16. Subtract 9 from -3.

Multiply or divide as indicated. See Examples 4 and 5.

17. $-5 \cdot 12$

18. $-3 \cdot 8$

19. $-17 \cdot 0$

20. $-5 \cdot 0$

21. $\frac{0}{-2}$

22. $\frac{-2}{0}$

23. $\frac{-9}{3}$

24. $\frac{-20}{5}$

25. $\frac{-12}{-4}$

26. $\frac{-36}{-6}$

27. $3\left(-\frac{1}{18}\right)$

28. $5\left(-\frac{1}{50}\right)$

29. $(-0.7)(-0.8)$

30. $(-0.9)(-0.5)$

31. $9.1 \div (-1.3)$

32. $22.5 \div (-2.5)$

33. $-4(-2)(-1)$

34. $-5(-3)(-2)$

Evaluate each expression. See Example 6.

35. -7^2

36. $(-7)^2$

37. $(-6)^2$

38. -6^2

39. $(-2)^3$

40. -2^3

41. $\left(-\frac{1}{3}\right)^3$

42. $\left(-\frac{1}{2}\right)^4$

Find the following roots. See Examples 7 and 8.

43. $\sqrt{49}$

44. $\sqrt{81}$

45. $-\sqrt{\frac{4}{9}}$

46. $-\sqrt{\frac{4}{25}}$

47. $\sqrt[3]{64}$

48. $\sqrt[5]{32}$

49. $\sqrt[4]{81}$

50. $\sqrt[3]{1}$

51. $\sqrt{-100}$

52. $\sqrt{-25}$

MIXED PRACTICE

Simplify each expression. See Examples 1 through 11.

53. $3(5 - 7)^4$

54. $7(3 - 8)^2$

55. $-3^2 + 2^3$

56. $-5^2 - 2^4$

57. $\frac{3.1 - (-1.4)}{-0.5}$

58. $\frac{4.2 - (-8.2)}{-0.4}$

59. $(-3)^2 + 2^3$

60. $(-15)^2 - 2^4$

61. $-8 \div 4 \cdot 2$

62. $-20 \div 5 \cdot 4$

63. $-8\left(-\frac{3}{4}\right) - 8$

64. $-10\left(-\frac{2}{5}\right) - 10$

65. $2 - [(7-6) + (9-19)]$

66. $8 - [(4-7) + (8-1)]$

67. $\frac{(-9 + 6)(-1^2)}{-2 - 2}$

68. $\frac{(-1 - 2)(-3^2)}{-6 - 3}$

69. $\left(\sqrt[3]{8}\right)(-4) - \left(\sqrt{9}\right)(-5)$

70. $\left(\sqrt[3]{27}\right)(-5) - \left(\sqrt{25}\right)(-3)$

71. $25 - [(3 - 5) + (14 - 18)]^2$

72. $10 - [(4 - 5)^2 + (12 - 14)]^4$

73. $\dfrac{(3 - \sqrt{9}) - (-5 - 1.3)}{-3}$

74. $\dfrac{-\sqrt{16} - (6 - 2.4)}{-2}$

75. $\dfrac{|3 - 9| - |-5|}{-3}$

76. $\dfrac{|-14| - |2 - 7|}{-15}$

77. $\dfrac{3(-2 + 1)}{5} - \dfrac{-7(2 - 4)}{1 - (-2)}$

78. $\dfrac{-1 - 2}{2(-3) + 10} - \dfrac{2(-5)}{-1(8) + 1}$

79. $\dfrac{\frac{1}{3} \cdot 9 - 7}{3 + \frac{1}{2} \cdot 4}$

80. $\dfrac{\frac{1}{5} \cdot 20 - 6}{10 + \frac{1}{4} \cdot 12}$

81. $3\{-2 + 5[1 - 2(-2 + 5)]\}$ **82.** $2\{-1 + 3[7 - 4(-10 + 12)]\}$

83. $\dfrac{-4\sqrt{80 + 1} + (-4)^2}{3^3 + |-2(3)|}$

84. $\dfrac{(-2)^4 + 3\sqrt{120 - 20}}{4^3 + |5(-1)|}$

Evaluate each expression when $x = 9$ and $y = -2$. See Example 12.

85. $9x - 6y$

86. $4x - 10y$

87. $-3y^2$

88. $-7y^2$

89. $\dfrac{\sqrt{x}}{y} - \dfrac{y}{x}$

90. $\dfrac{y}{2x} - \dfrac{\sqrt{x}}{3y}$

91. $\dfrac{3 + 2|x - y|}{x + 2y}$

92. $\dfrac{5 + 2|y - x|}{x + 6y}$

93. $\dfrac{y^3 + \sqrt{x} - 5}{|4x - y|}$

94. $\dfrac{y^2 + \sqrt{x} + 7}{|3x - y|}$

See Example 13.

95. The algebraic expression $8 + 2y$ represents the perimeter of a rectangle with width 4 and length y.

a. Complete the table that follows by evaluating this expression at the given values of y.

Length	y	5	7	10	100
Perimeter	$8 + 2y$				

b. Use the results of the table in part **a** to answer the following question. As the width of a rectangle remains the same and the length increases, does the perimeter increase or decrease? Explain how you arrived at your answer.

96. The algebraic expression πr^2 represents the area of a circle with radius r.

a. Complete the table below by evaluating this expression at given values of r. (Use 3.14 for π.)

Radius	r	2	3	7	10
Area	πr^2				

b. As the radius of a circle increases (see the table), does its area increase or decrease? Explain your answer.

97. The algebraic expression $\dfrac{100x + 5000}{x}$ represents the cost per bookshelf (in dollars) of producing x bookshelves.

a. Complete the table below.

Number of Bookshelves	x	10	100	1000
Cost per Bookshelf	$\dfrac{100x + 5000}{x}$			

b. As the number of bookshelves manufactured increases (see the table), does the cost per bookshelf increase or decrease? Why do you think that this is so?

98. If c is degrees Celsius, the algebraic expression $1.8c + 32$ represents the equivalent temperature in degrees Fahrenheit.

a. Complete the table below.

Degrees Celsius	c	−10	0	50
Degrees Fahrenheit	$1.8c + 32$			

b. As degrees Celsius increase (see the table), do degrees Fahrenheit increase or decrease?

CONCEPT EXTENSIONS

Choose the fraction(s) equivalent to the given fraction. (There may be more than one correct choice.)

99. $-\dfrac{1}{7}$ **a.** $\dfrac{-1}{-7}$ **b.** $\dfrac{-1}{7}$ **c.** $\dfrac{1}{-7}$ **d.** $\dfrac{1}{7}$

100. $\dfrac{-x}{y}$ **a.** $\dfrac{x}{-y}$ **b.** $-\dfrac{x}{y}$ **c.** $\dfrac{x}{y}$ **d.** $\dfrac{-x}{-y}$

101. $\dfrac{5}{-(x + y)}$ **a.** $\dfrac{5}{(x + y)}$ **b.** $\dfrac{-5}{(x + y)}$ **c.** $\dfrac{-5}{-(x + y)}$ **d.** $-\dfrac{5}{(x + y)}$

102. $-\dfrac{(y + z)}{3y}$ **a.** $\dfrac{-(y + z)}{3y}$ **b.** $\dfrac{-(y + z)}{-3y}$ **c.** $\dfrac{(y + z)}{3y}$ **d.** $\dfrac{(y + z)}{-3y}$

103. $\dfrac{-9x}{-2y}$ **a.** $\dfrac{-9x}{2y}$ **b.** $\dfrac{9x}{2y}$ **c.** $\dfrac{9x}{-2y}$ **d.** $-\dfrac{9x}{2y}$

104. $\dfrac{-a}{-b}$ **a.** $\dfrac{a}{b}$ **b.** $\dfrac{a}{-b}$ **c.** $\dfrac{-a}{b}$ **d.** $-\dfrac{a}{b}$

Find the value of the expression when $x_1 = 2$, $x_2 = 4$, $y_1 = -3$, and $y_2 = 2$.

105. $\dfrac{y_2 - y_1}{x_2 - x_1}$ **106.** $\sqrt{(x_2 - x_1)^2 + (y_2 - y_1)^2}$

Each circle below represents a whole, or 1. Determine the unknown fractional part of each circle.

107.

108.

109. Most of Mauna Kea, a volcano on Hawaii, lies below sea level. If this volcano begins at 5998 meters below sea level and then rises 10,203 meters, find the height of the volcano above sea level.

110. The highest point on land on Earth is the top of Mt. Everest in the Himalayas, at an elevation of 29,028 feet above sea level. The lowest point on land is the Dead Sea, between Israel and Jordan, at 1319 feet below sea level. Find the difference in elevations.

Insert parentheses so that each expression simplifies to the given number.

111. $2 + 7 \cdot 1 + 3$; 36

112. $6 - 5 \cdot 2 + 2$; -6

The following graph is called a broken-line graph, or simply a line graph. This particular graph shows the past, present, and future predicted U.S. population over 65. Just as with a bar graph, to find the population over 65 for a particular year, read the height of the corresponding point. To read the height, follow the point horizontally to the left until you reach the vertical axis. Use this graph to answer Exercises 113 through 118.

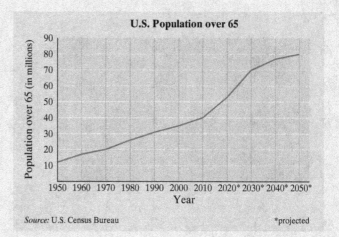

U.S. Population over 65

Source: U.S. Census Bureau   *projected

113. Estimate the population over 65 in the year 1970.

114. Estimate the predicted population over 65 in the year 2050.

115. Estimate the predicted population over 65 in the year 2030.

116. Estimate the population over 65 in the year 2000.

117. Is the population over 65 increasing as time passes or decreasing? Explain how you arrived at your answer.

118. The percent of Americans over 65 in 1950 was 8.1%. The percent of Americans over 65 in 2050 is expected to be 2.5 times the percent over 65 in 1950. Estimate the percent of Americans expected to be over age 65 in 2050.

119. Explain why -3^2 and $(-3)^2$ simplify to different numbers.

120. Explain why -3^3 and $(-3)^3$ simplify to the same number.

Use a calculator to approximate each square root. For Exercises 125 and 126, simplify the expression. Round answers to four decimal places.

121. $\sqrt{10}$

122. $\sqrt{273}$

123. $\sqrt{7.9}$

124. $\sqrt{19.6}$

125. $\dfrac{-1.682 - 17.895}{(-7.102)(-4.691)}$

126. $\dfrac{(-5.161)(3.222)}{7.955 - 19.676}$

Integrated Review Algebraic Expressions and Operations on Whole Numbers

Sections 1.2–1.3

Find the value of each expression when $x = -1$, $y = 3$, and $z = -4$.

1. z^2

2. $-z^2$

3. $\dfrac{4x - z}{2y}$

4. $x(y - 2z)$

Perform the indicated operations.

5. $-7 - (-2)$

6. $\dfrac{9}{10} - \dfrac{11}{12}$

7. $\dfrac{-13}{2 - 2}$

8. $(1.2)^2 - (2.1)^2$

9. $\sqrt{64} - \sqrt[3]{64}$

10. $-5^2 - (-5)^2$

11. $9 + 2[(8 - 10)^2 + (-3)^2]$

12. $8 - 6[\sqrt[3]{8}\,(-2) + \sqrt{4}(-5)]$

Translating *For Exercises 13 and 14, write each phrase as an algebraic expression. Use x to represent each unknown number.*

13. Subtract twice a number from -15.

14. Five more than three times a number.

15. Name the whole number that is not a natural number.

16. True or false: A real number is either a rational number or an irrational number but never both.

1.4 Properties of Real Numbers and Algebraic Expressions

OBJECTIVES

1 Use Operation and Order Symbols to Write Mathematical Sentences.

2 Identify Identity Numbers and Inverses.

3 Identify and Use the Commutative, Associative, and Distributive Properties.

4 Write Algebraic Expressions.

5 Simplify Algebraic Expressions.

OBJECTIVE

1 Using Symbols to Write Mathematical Sentences

In Section 1.2, we used the symbol $=$ to mean "is equal to." All of the following key words and phrases also imply equality.

Equality

equals	is/was	represents	is the same as
gives	yields	amounts to	is equal to

EXAMPLES   Write each sentence as an equation.

1. The sum of x and 5 is 20.

$$x + 5 \quad = 20$$

2. Two times the sum of 3 and y amounts to 4.

$$2 \quad (3 + y) \quad = \quad 4$$

3. The difference of 8 and x is the same as the product of 2 and x.

$$8 - x \quad = \quad 2 \cdot x$$

4. The quotient of z and 9 amounts to 9 plus z.

$$z \div 9 \quad = \quad 9 + z$$

or $$\frac{z}{9} \quad = \quad 9 + z$$

PRACTICE

1–4   Write each sentence using mathematical symbols.

1. The product of -4 and x is 20.

2. Three times the difference of z and 3 equals 9.

3. The sum of x and 5 is the same as 3 less than twice x.

4. The sum of y and 2 is 4 more than the quotient of z and 8.

If we want to write in symbols that two numbers are not equal, we can use the symbol $\neq$, which means "**is not equal to.**" For example,

$$3 \neq 2$$

Graphing two numbers on a number line gives us a way to compare two numbers. For two real numbers a and b, we say a **is less than** b if on the number line a lies to the left of b. Also, if b is to the right of a on the number line, then b **is greater than** a. The symbol $<$ means "**is less than.**" Since a is less than b, we write

$$a < b$$

Helpful Hint

Notice that if $a < b$, then $b > a$. For example, since $-1 < 7$, then $7 > -1$.

The symbol $>$ means "**is greater than.**" Since b is greater than a, we write

$$b > a$$

EXAMPLE 5 Insert $<$, $>$, or $=$ between each pair of numbers to form a true statement.

a. -1 -2 **b.** $\dfrac{12}{4}$ 3 **c.** -5 0 **d.** -3.5 -3.05

e. $\dfrac{5}{8}$ $\dfrac{3}{8}$ **f.** $\dfrac{2}{3}$ $\dfrac{3}{4}$

Solution

a. $-1 > -2$ since -1 lies to the right of -2 on the number line.

b. $\dfrac{12}{4} = 3$.

c. $-5 < 0$ since -5 lies to the left of 0 on the number line.

d. $-3.5 < -3.05$ since -3.5 lies to the left of -3.05 on the number line.

e. $\dfrac{5}{8} > \dfrac{3}{8}$ The denominators are the same, so $\dfrac{5}{8} > \dfrac{3}{8}$ since $5 > 3$.

f. $\dfrac{2}{3} < \dfrac{3}{4}$ By dividing, we see that $\dfrac{3}{4} = 0.75$ and $\dfrac{2}{3} = 0.666\ldots$.

Thus $\dfrac{2}{3} < \dfrac{3}{4}$ since $0.666\ldots < 0.75$.

PRACTICE
5 Insert $<$, $>$, or $=$ between each pair of numbers to form a true statement.

a. -6 -5 **b.** $\dfrac{24}{3}$ 8 **c.** 0 -7 **d.** -2.76 -2.67

e. $\dfrac{9}{10}$ $\dfrac{7}{10}$ **f.** $\dfrac{2}{3}$ $\dfrac{7}{9}$

> **Helpful Hint**
> When inserting the $>$ or $<$ symbol, think of the symbols as arrowheads that point toward the smaller number when the statement is true.

In addition to $<$ and $>$, there are the inequality symbols $\leq$ and $\geq$. The symbol

$\leq$ means "**is less than or equal to**" and the symbol

$\geq$ means "**is greater than or equal to.**"

For example, the following are true statements.

$$10 \leq 10 \quad \text{since} \quad 10 = 10$$
$$-8 \leq 13 \quad \text{since} \quad -8 < 13$$
$$-5 \geq -5 \quad \text{since} \quad -5 = -5$$
$$-7 \geq -9 \quad \text{since} \quad -7 > -9$$

EXAMPLE 6 Write each sentence using mathematical symbols.

a. The sum of 5 and y is greater than or equal to 7.

b. 11 is not equal to z.

c. 20 is less than the difference of 5 and twice x.

Solution

    a. $5 + y \geq 7$ **b.** $11 \neq z$ **c.** $20 < 5 - 2x$ ☐

PRACTICE
6   Write each sentence using mathematical symbols.

    a. The difference of x and 3 is less than or equal to 5.

    b. y is not equal to -4.

    c. Two is less than the sum of 4 and one-half z.   ■

OBJECTIVE
2 Identifying Identities and Inverses

Of all the real numbers, two of them stand out as extraordinary: 0 and 1. **Zero** is the only number that, when *added* to any real number, results in the same real number. Zero is thus called the **additive identity.** Also, **one** is the only number that, when *multiplied* by any real number, results in the same real number. One is thus called the **multiplicative identity.**

	Addition	*Multiplication*
Identity Properties	The additive identity is 0. $a + 0 = 0 + a = a$	The multiplicative identity is 1. $a \cdot 1 = 1 \cdot a = a$

In Section 1.2, we learned that a and $-a$ are opposites.

    Another name for opposite is **additive inverse.** For example, the additive inverse of 3 is -3. Notice that the sum of a number and its opposite is always 0.

    In Section 1.3, we learned that, for a nonzero number, b and $\frac{1}{b}$ are reciprocals.

Another name for reciprocal is **multiplicative inverse.** For example, the multiplicative inverse of $-\frac{2}{3}$ is $-\frac{3}{2}$. Notice that the product of a number and its reciprocal is always 1.

	Opposite or Additive Inverse	*Reciprocal or Multiplicative Inverse*
Inverse Properties	For each number a, there is a unique number $-a$ called the **additive inverse** or **opposite** of a such that $a + (-a) = (-a) + a = 0$	For each nonzero a, there is a unique number $\frac{1}{a}$ called the **multiplicative inverse** or **reciprocal** of a such that $a \cdot \frac{1}{a} = \frac{1}{a} \cdot a = 1$

EXAMPLE 7   Write the additive inverse, or opposite, of each.

    a. 4   **b.** $\frac{3}{7}$ **c.** -11.2

Solution

    a. The opposite of 4 is -4.

    b. The opposite of $\frac{3}{7}$ is $-\frac{3}{7}$.

    c. The opposite of -11.2 is $-(-11.2) = 11.2$.   ☐

PRACTICE
7   Write the additive inverse, or opposite, of each.

    a. -7 **b.** 4.7   **c.** $-\frac{3}{8}$ ■

EXAMPLE 8 Write the multiplicative inverse, or reciprocal, of each.

a. 11 **b.** −9 **c.** $\dfrac{7}{4}$

Solution

a. The reciprocal of 11 is $\dfrac{1}{11}$.

b. The reciprocal of −9 is $-\dfrac{1}{9}$.

c. The reciprocal of $\dfrac{7}{4}$ is $\dfrac{4}{7}$ because $\dfrac{7}{4} \cdot \dfrac{4}{7} = 1$.

PRACTICE
8 Write the multiplicative inverse, or reciprocal, of each.

a. $-\dfrac{5}{3}$ **b.** 14 **c.** −2

> **Helpful Hint**
> The number 0 has no reciprocal. Why? There is no number that when multiplied by 0 gives a product of 1.

 CONCEPT CHECK
Can a number's additive inverse and multiplicative inverse ever be the same? Explain.

OBJECTIVE

3 Using the Commutative, Associative, and Distributive Properties

In addition to these special real numbers, all real numbers have certain properties that allow us to write equivalent expressions—that is, expressions that have the same value. These properties will be especially useful in Chapter 2 when we solve equations.

The **commutative properties** state that the order in which two real numbers are added or multiplied does not affect their sum or product.

> **Commutative Properties**
> For real numbers a and b,
>
> $$\text{Addition: } \quad a + b = b + a$$
> $$\text{Multiplication: } \quad a \cdot b = b \cdot a$$

The **associative properties** state that regrouping numbers that are added or multiplied does not affect their sum or product.

> **Associative Properties**
> For real numbers a, b, and c,
>
> $$\text{Addition: } \quad (a + b) + c = a + (b + c)$$
> $$\text{Multiplication: } \quad (a \cdot b) \cdot c = a \cdot (b \cdot c)$$

Answer to Concept Check:
no; answers may vary

EXAMPLE 9   Use the commutative property of addition to write an expression equivalent to $7x + 5$.

Solution $7x + 5 = 5 + 7x$ □

PRACTICE
9   Use the commutative property of addition to write an expression equivalent to $8 + 13x$.   ■

EXAMPLE 10   Use the associative property of multiplication to write an expression equivalent to $4 \cdot (9y)$. Then simplify this equivalent expression.

Solution $4 \cdot (9y) = (4 \cdot 9)y = 36y$ □

PRACTICE
10   Use the associative property of multiplication to write an expression equivalent to $3 \cdot (11b)$. Then simplify the equivalent expression.   ■

The **distributive property** states that multiplication distributes over addition.

Distributive Property

For real numbers a, b, and c,

$$a(b + c) = ab + ac$$

Also,

$$a(b - c) = ab - ac$$

EXAMPLE 11   Use the distributive property to multiply.

   a. $3(2x + y)$ **b.** $-(3x - 1)$ **c.** $0.7a(b - 2)$

Solution

   a. $3(2x + y) = 3 \cdot 2x + 3 \cdot y$ Apply the distributive property.

            $= 6x + 3y$ Apply the associative property of multiplication.

   b. Recall that $-(3x - 1)$ means $-1(3x - 1)$.

                    $-1(3x - 1) = -1(3x) + (-1)(-1)$
                              $= -3x + 1$

   c. $0.7a(b - 2) = 0.7a \cdot b - 0.7a \cdot 2 = 0.7ab - 1.4a$ □

PRACTICE
11   Use the distributive property to multiply.
   a. $4(x + 5y)$ **b.** $-(3 - 2z)$ **c.** $0.3x(y - 3)$ ■

✔ **CONCEPT CHECK**
Is the statement below true? Why or why not?

$$6(2a)(3b) = 6(2a) \cdot 6(3b)$$

Answer to Concept Check:
no; $6(2a)(3b) = 12a(3b) = 36ab$

OBJECTIVE

4 Writing Algebraic Expressions

As mentioned earlier, an important step in problem solving is to be able to write algebraic expressions from word phrases. Sometimes this involves a direct translation, but often an indicated operation is not directly stated but rather implied.

EXAMPLE 12 Write each as an algebraic expression.

    a. A vending machine contains x quarters. Write an expression for the *value* of the quarters.

    b. The number of grams of fat in x pieces of bread if each piece of bread contains 2 grams of fat.

    c. The cost of x desks if each desk costs $156.

    d. Sales tax on a purchase of x dollars if the tax rate is 9%.

Solution

Each of these examples implies finding a product.

    a. The value of the quarters is found by multiplying the value of a quarter (0.25 dollar) by the number of quarters.

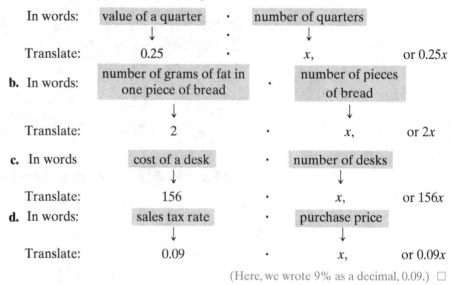

(Here, we wrote 9% as a decimal, 0.09.) ☐

PRACTICE

12 Write each as an algebraic expression.

    a. A parking meter contains x dimes. Write an expression for the value of the dimes.

    b. The grams of carbohydrates in y cookies if each cookie has 26 g of carbohydrates.

    c. The cost of z birthday cards if each birthday card costs $1.75.

    d. The amount of money you save on a new cell phone costing t dollars if it has a 15% discount. ∎

Let's continue writing phrases as algebraic expressions. Two or more unknown numbers in a problem may sometimes be related. If so, try letting a variable represent one unknown number and then represent the other unknown number or numbers as expressions containing the same variable.

EXAMPLE 13 Write each as an algebraic expression.

    a. Two numbers have a sum of 20. If one number is x, represent the other number as an expression in x.

    b. The older sister is 8 years older than her younger sister. If the age of the younger sister is x, represent the age of the older sister as an expression in x.

△ **c.** Two angles are complementary if the sum of their measures is 90°. If the measure of one angle is x degrees, represent the measure of the other angle as an expression in x.

d. If x is the first of two consecutive integers, represent the second integer as an expression in x.

Solution

a. If two numbers have a sum of 20 and one number is x, the other number is "the rest of 20."

In words: twenty   minus x
                ↓   ↓   ↓
Translate: 20   − x

b. The older sister's age is

In words: eight years   added to   younger sister's age
                  ↓   ↓   ↓
Translate: 8   + x

c. In words: ninety   minus x
                        ↓   ↓   ↓
Translate: 90   − x

d. The next consecutive integer is always one more than the previous integer.

In words: the first integer   plus   one
                    ↓   ↓   ↓
Translate: x +   1   □

PRACTICE
13   Write each as an algebraic expression.

a. Two numbers have a sum of 16. If one number is x, represent the other number as an expression in x.

b. Two angles are supplementary if the sum of their measures is 180°. If the measure of one angle is x degrees, represent the measure of the other angle as an expression in x.

c. If x is the first of two consecutive even integers, represent the next even integer as an expression in x.

d. One brother is 9 years younger than another brother. If the age of the younger brother is x, represent the age of the older brother as an expression in x. ■

OBJECTIVE
5   Simplifying Algebraic Expressions

Often, an expression may be **simplified** by removing grouping symbols and combining any like terms. The **terms** of an expression are the addends of the expression. For example, in the expression $3x^2 + 4x$, the terms are $3x^2$ and $4x$.

Expression	*Terms*
$-2x + y$	$-2x, y$
$3x^2 - \dfrac{y}{5} + 7$	$3x^2, -\dfrac{y}{5}, 7$

Terms with the same variable(s) raised to the same power are called **like terms**. We can add or subtract like terms by using the distributive property. This process is called **combining like terms.**

EXAMPLE 14 Use the distributive property to simplify each expression.

    a. $3x - 5x + 4$ **b.** $7yz + yz$ **c.** $4z + 6.1$

Solution

    a. $3x - 5x + 4 = (3 - 5)x + 4$ Apply the distributive property.

                     $= -2x + 4$

    b. $7yz + yz = (7 + 1)yz = 8yz$

    c. $4z + 6.1$ cannot be simplified further since $4z$ and 6.1 are not like terms.   ☐

PRACTICE
14   Use the distributive property to simplify.

    a. $6ab - ab$ **b.** $4x - 5 + 6x$ **c.** $17p - 9$ ■

Let's continue to use properties of real numbers to simplify expressions. Recall that the distributive property can also be used to multiply. For example,

$$-2(x + 3) = -2(x) + (-2)(3) = -2x - 6$$

The associative and commutative properties may sometimes be needed to re-arrange and group like terms when we simplify expressions.

$$-7x^2 + 5 + 3x^2 - 2 = -7x^2 + 3x^2 + 5 - 2$$
$$= (-7 + 3)x^2 + (5 - 2)$$
$$= -4x^2 + 3$$

EXAMPLE 15 Simplify each expression.

    a. $3xy - 2xy + 5 - 7 + xy$ **b.** $7x^2 + 3 - 5(x^2 - 4)$

    c. $(2.1x - 5.6) - (-x - 5.3)$ **d.** $\dfrac{1}{2}(4a - 6b) - \dfrac{1}{3}(9a + 12b - 1) + \dfrac{1}{4}$

Solution

    a. $3xy - 2xy + 5 - 7 + xy = 3xy - 2xy + xy + 5 - 7$ Apply the commu-tative property.

                           $= (3 - 2 + 1)xy + (5 - 7)$ Apply the distribu-tive property.

                           $= 2xy - 2$ Simplify.

    b. $7x^2 + 3 - 5(x^2 - 4) = 7x^2 + 3 - 5x^2 + 20$ Apply the distributive property.

                      $= 2x^2 + 23$ Simplify.

    c. Think of $-(-x - 5.3)$ as $-1(-x - 5.3)$ and use the distributive property.

      $(2.1x - 5.6) - 1(-x - 5.3) = 2.1x - 5.6 + 1x + 5.3$

                            $= 3.1x - 0.3.$ Combine like terms

    d. $\dfrac{1}{2}\left(4a - 6b\right) - \dfrac{1}{3}\left(9a + 12b - 1\right) + \dfrac{1}{4}$

      $= 2a - 3b - 3a - 4b + \dfrac{1}{3} + \dfrac{1}{4}$ Use the distributive property.

      $= -a - 7b + \dfrac{7}{12}$ Combine like terms.   ☐

PRACTICE
15   Simplify each expression.

    a. $5pq - 2pq - 11 - 4pq + 18$

    b. $3x^2 + 7 - 2(x^2 - 6)$

c. $(3.7x + 2.5) - (-2.1x - 1.3)$

d. $\frac{1}{5}(15c - 25d) - \frac{1}{2}(8c + 6d + 1) + \frac{3}{4}$

 CONCEPT CHECK

Find and correct the error in the following.

$$x - 4(x - 5) = x - 4x - 20$$
$$= -3x - 20$$

Answer to Concept Check:
$x - 4(x - 5) = x - 4x + 20$
$= -3x + 20$

✔ Vocabulary, Readiness & Video Check

Complete the table by filling in the symbols.

	Symbol	Meaning
1.		is less than
3.		is not equal to
5.		is greater than or equal to

	Symbol	Meaning
2.		is greater than
4.		is equal to
6.		is less than or equal to

Use the choices below to fill in each blank. Not all choices will be used.

like	terms	distributive	$-a$	commutative
unlike	combining	associative	$\frac{1}{a}$	

7. The opposite of nonzero number a is _____.

8. The reciprocal of nonzero number a is _____.

9. The _____ property has to do with "order."

10. The _____ property has to do with "grouping."

11. $a(b + c) = ab + ac$ illustrates the _____ property.

12. The _____ of an expression are the addends of the expression.

Martin-Gay Interactive Videos

See Video 1.4 🔵

Watch the section lecture video and answer the following questions.

OBJECTIVE 1

13. In the lecture before ▦ Example 1, what six symbols are discussed that can be used to compare two numbers?

OBJECTIVE 2

14. Complete these statements based on the lecture given before ▦ Example 4. *Reciprocal* is the same as _____ inverse and *opposite* is the same as _____ inverse.

OBJECTIVE 3

15. The commutative and associative properties are discussed in ▦ Examples 7 and 8 and the lecture before. What's the one word used again and again to describe the commutative property? The associative property?

OBJECTIVE 4

16. In ▦ Example 10, what important point are you told to keep in mind when working with applications that have to do with money?

OBJECTIVE 5

17. From ▦ Examples 12–14, how do we simplify algebraic expressions? If the expression contains parentheses, what property might we apply first?

1.4 Exercise Set MyMathLab®

MIXED PRACTICE

Translating. *Write each sentence using mathematical symbols. See Examples 1 through 4 and 6 through 8.*

1. The sum of 10 and x is -12.

2. The difference of y and 3 amounts to 12.

3. Twice x, plus 5, is the same as -14.

4. Three more than the product of 4 and c is 7.

5. The quotient of n and 5 is 4 times n.

6. The quotient of 8 and y is 3 more than y.

7. The difference of z and one-half is the same as the product of z and one-half.

8. Five added to one-fourth q is the same as 4 more than q.

9. The product of 7 and x is less than or equal to -21.

10. 10 subtracted from the reciprocal of x is greater than 0.

11. Twice the difference of x and 6 is greater than the reciprocal of 11.

12. Four times the sum of 5 and x is not equal to the opposite of 15.

13. Twice the difference of x and 6 is -27.

14. 5 times the sum of 6 and y is -35.

Insert $<$, $>$, or $=$ between each pair of numbers to form a true statement. See Example 5.

15. -16 -17

16. -14 -24

17. 7.4 7.40

18. $\dfrac{7}{2}$ $\dfrac{35}{10}$

19. $\dfrac{7}{11}$ $\dfrac{9}{11}$

20. $\dfrac{9}{20}$ $\dfrac{3}{20}$

21. $\dfrac{1}{2}$ $\dfrac{5}{8}$

22. $\dfrac{3}{4}$ $\dfrac{7}{8}$

23. -7.9 -7.09

24. -13.07 -13.7

Fill in the chart. See Examples 7 and 8.

	Number	**Opposite**	**Reciprocal**
25.	5		
26.	7		
27.		8	
28.			$-\dfrac{1}{4}$
29.	$-\dfrac{1}{7}$		
30.	$\dfrac{1}{11}$		
31.	0		
32.	1		
33.			$\dfrac{8}{7}$
34.		$\dfrac{23}{5}$	

Use a commutative property to write an equivalent expression. See Example 9.

35. $7x + y$

36. $3a + 2b$

37. $z \cdot w$

38. $r \cdot s$

39. $\dfrac{1}{3} \cdot \dfrac{x}{5}$

40. $\dfrac{x}{2} \cdot \dfrac{9}{10}$

Use an associative property to write an equivalent expression. See Example 10.

41. $5 \cdot (7x)$

42. $3 \cdot (10z)$

43. $(x + 1.2) + y$

44. $5q + (2r + s)$

45. $(14z) \cdot y$

46. $(9.2x) \cdot y$

Use the distributive property to find the product. See Example 11.

47. $3(x + 5)$

48. $7(y + 2)$

49. $-(2a + b)$

50. $-(c + 7d)$

51. $2(6x + 5y + 2z)$

52. $5(3a + b + 9c)$

53. $-4(x - 2y + 7)$

54. $-10(2a - 3b - 4)$

55. $0.5x(6y - 3)$

56. $1.2m(9n - 4)$

Complete the statement to illustrate the given property.

57. $3x + 6 = $ _____ Commutative property of addition

58. $8 + 0 = $ __ Additive identity property

59. $\dfrac{2}{3} + \left(-\dfrac{2}{3}\right) = $ __ Additive inverse property

60. $4(x + 3) = $ _____ Distributive property

61. $7 \cdot 1 = $ __ Multiplicative identity property

62. $0 \cdot (-5.4) = $ __ Multiplication property of zero

63. $10(2y) = $ _____ Associative property

64. $9y + (x + 3z) = $ _____ Associative property

Translating *Write each of the following as an algebraic expression. See Examples 12 and 13.*

65. Write an expression for the amount of money (in dollars) in d dimes.

66. Write an expression for the amount of money (in dollars) in n nickels.

67. Two numbers have a sum of 112. If one number is x, represent the other number as an expression in x.

68. Two numbers have a sum of 25. If one number is x, represent the other number as an expression in x.

△**69.** Two angles are supplementary if the sum of their measures is $180°$. If the measure of one angle is x degrees, represent the measure of the other angle as an expression in x.

△**70.** Two angles are complementary if the sum of their measures is $90°$. If the measure of an angle is $5x$ degrees, represent the measure of its complement as an expression in x.

71. The cost of x compact discs if each compact disc costs $\$6.49$.

72. The cost of y books if each book costs $35.61.

73. If x is an odd integer, represent the next odd integer as an expression in x.

74. If $2x$ is an even integer, represent the next even integer as an expression in x.

MIXED PRACTICE

Simplify each expression. See Examples 11, 14, and 15.

▶ **75.** $-9 + 4x + 18 - 10x$

76. $5y - 14 + 7y - 20y$

77. $5k - (3k - 10)$

78. $-11c - (4 - 2c)$

79. $(3x + 4) - (6x - 1)$

80. $(8 - 5y) - (4 + 3y)$

▶ **81.** $3(xy - 2) + xy + 15 - x^2$

82. $-4(yz + 3) - 7yz + 1 + y^2$

83. $-(n + 5) + (5n - 3)$

84. $-(8 - t) + (2t - 6)$

85. $4(6n^2 - 3) - 3(8n^2 + 4)$

86. $5(2z^3 - 6) + 10(3 - z^3)$

87. $3x - 2(x - 5) + x$

88. $7n + 3(2n - 6) - 2$

89. $1.5x + 2.3 - 0.7x - 5.9$

90. $6.3y - 9.7 + 2.2y - 11.1$

91. $\dfrac{3}{4}b - \dfrac{1}{2} + \dfrac{1}{6}b - \dfrac{2}{3}$

92. $\dfrac{7}{8}a - \dfrac{11}{12} - \dfrac{1}{2}a + \dfrac{5}{6}$

93. $2(3x + 7)$

94. $4(5y + 12)$

▶ **95.** $\dfrac{1}{2}(10x - 2) - \dfrac{1}{6}(60x - 5y)$

96. $\dfrac{1}{4}(8x - 4) - \dfrac{1}{5}(20x - 6y)$

97. $\dfrac{1}{6}(24a - 18b) - \dfrac{1}{7}(7a - 21b - 2) - \dfrac{1}{5}$

98. $\dfrac{1}{3}(6x - 33y) - \dfrac{1}{8}(24x - 40y + 1) - \dfrac{1}{3}$

CONCEPT EXTENSIONS

In each statement, a property of real numbers has been incorrectly applied. Correct the right-hand side of each statement. See the second Concept Check in this section.

99. $3(x + 4) = 3x + 4$

100. $4 + 8y = 4y + 8$

101. $5(7y) = (5 \cdot 7)(5 \cdot y)$

102. $5(3a)(7b) = 5(3a) \cdot 5(7b)$

To demonstrate the distributive property geometrically, represent the area of the larger rectangle in two ways: first as width times length and second as the sum of the areas of the smaller rectangles.

Example:

Area of larger rectangle: $x(y + z)$
Area of larger rectangle: $xy + xz$
Thus: $x(y + z) = xy + xz$

103.

104.

105. Name the only real number that is its own opposite, and explain why this is so.

106. Name the only real number that has no reciprocal, and explain why this is so.

107. Is division commutative? Explain why or why not.

108. Is subtraction commutative? Explain why or why not.

109. Evaluate $24 \div (6 \div 3)$ and $(24 \div 6) \div 3$. Use these two expressions and discuss whether division is associative.

110. Evaluate $12 - (5 - 3)$ and $(12 - 5) - 3$. Use these two expressions and discuss whether subtraction is associative.

Simplify each expression.

111. $8.1z + 7.3(z + 5.2) - 6.85$

112. $6.5y - 4.4(1.8x - 3.3) + 10.95$

Chapter 1 Vocabulary Check

Fill in each blank with one of the words or phrases listed below.

distributive	real	reciprocals	absolute value	opposite	associative
inequality	commutative	whole	algebraic expression	exponent	variable

1. A(n) _____ is formed by numbers and variables connected by the operations of addition, subtraction, multiplication, division, raising to powers, and/or taking roots.

2. The _____ of a number a is $-a$.

3. $3(x - 6) = 3x - 18$ by the _____ property.

4. The _____ of a number is the distance between that number and 0 on a number line.

5. A(n) _____ is a shorthand notation for repeated multiplication of the same factor.

6. A letter that represents a number is called a(n) _____.

7. The symbols $<$ and $>$ are called _____ symbols.

8. If a is not 0, then a and $\dfrac{1}{a}$ are called _____.

9. $A + B = B + A$ by the _____ property.

10. $(A + B) + C = A + (B + C)$ by the _____ property.

11. The numbers $0, 1, 2, 3, \ldots$ are called _____ numbers.

12. If a number corresponds to a point on a number line, we know that number is a _____ number.

Chapter 1 Highlights

DEFINITIONS AND CONCEPTS	EXAMPLES

Section 1.2   Algebraic Expressions and Sets of Numbers

Letters that represent numbers are called **variables.**

Examples of variables are
$$x, a, m, y$$

An **algebraic expression** is formed by numbers and variables connected by the operations of addition, subtraction, multiplication, division, raising to powers, and/or taking roots.

Examples of algebraic expressions are
$$7y, \quad -3, \quad \frac{x^2 - 9}{-2} + 14x, \quad \sqrt{3} + \sqrt{m}$$

To **evaluate** an algebraic expression containing variables, substitute the given numbers for the variables and simplify. The result is called the **value** of the expression.

Evaluate $2.7x$ if $x = 3$.
$$2.7x = 2.7(3)$$
$$= 8.1$$

Natural numbers: $\{1, 2, 3, \ldots\}$

Whole numbers: $\{0, 1, 2, 3, \ldots\}$

Integers: $\{\ldots, -3, -2, -1, 0, 1, 2, 3, \ldots\}$

Given the set $\left\{-9.6, -5, -\sqrt{2}, 0, \dfrac{2}{5}, 101\right\}$ list the elements that belong to the set of

Each listing of three dots above is called an **ellipsis,** which means the pattern continues.

The members of a set are called its **elements.**

Natural numbers: 101
Whole numbers: 0, 101
Integers: $-5, 0, 101$

Set builder notation describes the elements of a set but does not list them.

List the elements in the set $\{x \mid x$ is an integer between -2 and $5\}$.
$$\{-1, 0, 1, 2, 3, 4\}$$

Real numbers: $\{x \mid x$ corresponds to a point on a number line$\}$.

Real numbers: $-9.6, -5, -\sqrt{2}, 0, \dfrac{2}{5}, 101$

Rational numbers: $\left\{\dfrac{a}{b} \,\middle|\, a \text{ and } b \text{ are integers and } b \neq 0\right\}$.

Rational numbers: $-9.6, -5, 0, \dfrac{2}{5}, 101$

DEFINITIONS AND CONCEPTS	EXAMPLES

Section 1.2 Algebraic Expressions and Sets of Numbers (continued)

Irrational numbers: $\{x \mid x \text{ is a real number and } x \text{ is not a rational number}\}$.

If 3 is an element of set A, we write $3 \in A$.

If all the elements of set A are also in set B, we say that set A is a **subset** of set B, and we write $A \subseteq B$.

Absolute value:

$$|a| = \begin{cases} a \text{ if } a \text{ is 0 or a positive number} \\ -a \text{ if } a \text{ is a negative number} \end{cases}$$

The opposite of a number a is the number $-a$.

Irrational numbers: $-\sqrt{2}$

$$\{1, 2, 4\} \subseteq \{1, 2, 3, 4\}.$$

$$|3| = 3, \; |0| = 0, \; |-7.2| = 7.2$$

The opposite of 5 is -5. The opposite of -11 is 11.

Section 1.3 Operations on Real Numbers and Order of Operations

Adding Real Numbers

1. To add two numbers with the same sign, add their absolute values and attach their common sign.

2. To add two numbers with different signs, subtract the smaller absolute value from the larger absolute value and attach the sign of the number with the larger absolute value.

Subtracting real numbers:

$$a - b = a + (-b)$$

Multiplying and dividing real numbers:

The product or quotient of two numbers with the same sign is positive.

The product or quotient of two numbers with different signs is negative.

A natural number **exponent** is a shorthand notation for repeated multiplication of the same factor.

The notation $\sqrt{a}$ denotes the **positive,** or **principal, square root** of a nonnegative number a.

$$\sqrt{a} = b \text{ if } b^2 = a \text{ and } b \text{ is positive.}$$

Also,

$$\sqrt[3]{a} = b \text{ if } b^3 = a$$
$$\sqrt[4]{a} = b \text{ if } b^4 = a \text{ and } b \text{ is positive}$$

Order of Operations

Simplify expressions using the order that follows. If grouping symbols such as parentheses are present, simplify expressions within those first, starting with the innermost set. If fraction bars are present, simplify the numerator and denominator separately.

1. Raise to powers or take roots in order from left to right.
2. Multiply or divide in order from left to right.
3. Add or subtract in order from left to right.

$$\frac{2}{7} + \frac{1}{7} = \frac{3}{7}$$

$$-5 + (-2.6) = -7.6$$
$$-18 + 6 = -12$$
$$20.8 + (-10.2) = 10.6$$
$$18 - 21 = 18 + (-21) = -3$$

$$(-8)(-4) = 32 \qquad \frac{-8}{-4} = 2$$
$$8 \cdot 4 = 32 \qquad \frac{8}{4} = 2$$

$$-17 \cdot 2 = -34 \qquad \frac{-14}{2} = -7$$
$$4(-1.6) = -6.4 \qquad \frac{22}{-2} = -11$$
$$3^4 = 3 \cdot 3 \cdot 3 \cdot 3 = 81$$

$$\sqrt{49} = 7$$

$$\sqrt[3]{64} = 4$$
$$\sqrt[4]{16} = 2$$

Simplify $\dfrac{42 - 2(3^2 - \sqrt{16})}{-8}$.

$$\frac{42 - 2(3^2 - \sqrt{16})}{-8} = \frac{42 - 2(9 - 4)}{-8}$$

$$= \frac{42 - 2(5)}{-8}$$

$$= \frac{42 - 10}{-8}$$

$$= \frac{32}{-8} = -4$$

DEFINITIONS AND CONCEPTS	EXAMPLES

Section 1.4   Properties of Real Numbers and Algebraic Expressions

Symbols: $=$ is equal to

$\neq$ is not equal to

$>$ is greater than

$<$ is less than

$\geq$ is greater than or equal to

$\leq$ is less than or equal to

$-5 = -5$

$-5 \neq -3$

$1.7 > 1.2$

$-1.7 < -1.2$

$\dfrac{5}{3} \geq \dfrac{5}{3}$

$-\dfrac{1}{2} \leq \dfrac{1}{2}$

Identity:

$$a + 0 = a \qquad 0 + a = a$$
$$a \cdot 1 = a \qquad 1 \cdot a = a$$

$$3 + 0 = 3 \qquad 0 + 3 = 3$$
$$-1.8 \cdot 1 = -1.8 \qquad 1 \cdot -1.8 = -1.8$$

Inverse:

$$a + (-a) = 0 \qquad -a + a = 0$$
$$a \cdot \dfrac{1}{a} = 1 \qquad \dfrac{1}{a} \cdot a = 1, a \neq 0$$

$$7 + (-7) = 0 \qquad -7 + 7 = 0$$
$$5 \cdot \dfrac{1}{5} = 1 \qquad \dfrac{1}{5} \cdot 5 = 1$$

Commutative:

$$a + b = b + a$$
$$a \cdot b = b \cdot a$$

$$x + 7 = 7 + x$$
$$9 \cdot y = y \cdot 9$$

Associative:

$$(a + b) + c = a + (b + c)$$
$$(a \cdot b) \cdot c = a \cdot (b \cdot c)$$

$$(3 + 1) + 10 = 3 + (1 + 10)$$
$$(3 \cdot 1) \cdot 10 = 3 \cdot (1 \cdot 10)$$

Distributive:

$$a(b + c) = ab + ac$$

$$6(x + 5) = 6 \cdot x + 6 \cdot 5$$
$$= 6x + 30$$

Chapter 1   Review

(1.2) Find the value of each algebraic expression at the given replacement values.

1. $7x$ when $x = 3$

2. st when $s = 1.6$ and $t = 5$

The hummingbird has an average wing speed of 70 beats per second. The expression 70t gives the number of wingbeats in t seconds.

3. Calculate the number of wingbeats in 1 *minute*. (*Hint:* How many seconds are in 1 minute?)

4. Calculate the number of wingbeats in 1 *hour* for the hummingbird. (See the Hint for Exercise 3.)

List the elements in each set.

5. $\{x \mid x \text{ is an odd integer between } -2 \text{ and } 4\}$

6. $\{x \mid x \text{ is an even integer between } -3 \text{ and } 7\}$

7. $\{x \mid x \text{ is a negative whole number}\}$

8. $\{x \mid x \text{ is a natural number that is not a rational number}\}$

9. $\{x \mid x \text{ is a whole number greater than } 5\}$

10. $\{x \mid x \text{ is an integer less than } 3\}$

Determine whether each statement is true or false if
$A = \{6, 10, 12\}, B = \{5, 9, 11\},$
$C = \{\ldots, -3, -2, -1, 0, 1, 2, 3, \ldots\}, D = \{2, 4, 6, \ldots, 16\}$
$E = \{x \mid x \text{ is a rational number}\}, F = \{\ \},$
$G = \{x \mid x \text{ is an irrational number}\}, \text{ and } H = \{x \mid x \text{ is a real number}\}.$

11. $10 \in D$

12. $59 \in B$

13. $\sqrt{169} \notin G$

14. $0 \notin F$

15. $\pi \in E$

16. $\pi \in H$

17. $\sqrt{4} \in G$

18. $-9 \in E$

19. $A \subseteq D$

20. $C \nsubseteq B$

21. $C \nsubseteq E$

22. $F \subseteq H$

List the elements of the set $\left\{5, -\dfrac{2}{3}, \dfrac{8}{2}, \sqrt{9}, 0.3, \sqrt{7}, 1\dfrac{5}{8}, -1, \pi\right\}$
that are also elements of each given set.

23. Whole numbers

24. Natural numbers

25. Rational numbers

26. Irrational numbers

27. Real numbers

28. Integers

Find the opposite.

29. $-\dfrac{3}{4}$

30. 0.6

31. 0

32. 1

(1.3) *Find the reciprocal.*

33. $-\dfrac{3}{4}$

34. 0.6

35. 0

36. 1

Simplify.

37. $-7 + 3$

38. $-10 + (-25)$

39. $5(-0.4)$

40. $(-3.1)(-0.1)$

41. $-7 - (-15)$

42. $9 - (-4.3)$

43. $(-6)(-4)(0)(-3)$

44. $(-12)(0)(-1)(-5)$

45. $-24 \div 0$

46. $0 \div (-45)$

47. $-36 \div (-9)$

48. $60 \div (-12)$

49. $-\dfrac{4}{5} - \left(-\dfrac{2}{3}\right)$

50. $\dfrac{5}{4} - \left(-2\dfrac{3}{4}\right)$

51. Determine the unknown fractional part.

52. The Bertha Rogers gas well in Washita County, Oklahoma, is the deepest well in the United States. From the surface, this now-capped well extends 31,441 feet into the earth. The elevation of the nearby Cordell Municipal Airport is 1589 feet above sea level. Assuming that the surface elevation of the well is the same as at the Cordell Municipal Airport, find the elevation relative to sea level of the *bottom* of the Bertha Rogers gas well. (*Sources:* U.S. Geological Survey, Oklahoma Department of Transportation)

Simplify.

53. $-5 + 7 - 3 - (-10)$

54. $8 - (-3) + (-4) + 6$

55. $3(4 - 5)^4$

56. $6(7 - 10)^2$

57. $\left(-\dfrac{8}{15}\right) \cdot \left(-\dfrac{2}{3}\right)^2$

58. $\left(-\dfrac{3}{4}\right)^2 \cdot \left(-\dfrac{10}{21}\right)$

59. $-\dfrac{6}{15} \div \dfrac{8}{25}$

60. $\dfrac{4}{9} \div -\dfrac{8}{45}$

61. $-\dfrac{3}{8} + 3(2) \div 6$

62. $5(-2) - (-3) - \dfrac{1}{6} + \dfrac{2}{3}$

63. $|2^3 - 3^2| - |5 - 7|$

64. $|5^2 - 2^2| + |9 \div (-3)|$

65. $(2^3 - 3^2) - (5 - 7)$

66. $(5^2 - 2^4) + [9 \div (-3)]$

67. $\dfrac{(8 - 10)^3 - (-4)^2}{2 + 8(2) \div 4}$

68. $\dfrac{(2 + 4)^2 + (-1)^5}{12 \div 2 \cdot 3 - 3}$

69. $\dfrac{(4 - 9) + 4 - 9}{10 - 12 \div 4 \cdot 8}$

70. $\dfrac{3 - 7 - (7 - 3)}{15 + 30 \div 6 \cdot 2}$

71. $\dfrac{\sqrt{25}}{4 + 3 \cdot 7}$

72. $\dfrac{\sqrt{64}}{24 - 8 \cdot 2}$

Find the value of each expression when $x = 0$, $y = 3$, and $z = -2$.

73. $x^2 - y^2 + z^2$

74. $\dfrac{5x + z}{2y}$

75. $\dfrac{-7y - 3z}{-3}$

76. $(x - y + z)^2$

The algebraic expression $2\pi r$ represents the circumference of (distance around) a circle of radius r.

77. Complete the table below by evaluating the expression at the given values of r. (Use 3.14 for π.)

Radius	r	1	10	100
Circumference	$2\pi r$			

78. As the radius of a circle increases, does the circumference of the circle increase or decrease?

(1.4) *Simplify each expression.*

79. $5xy - 7xy + 3 - 2 + xy$

80. $4x + 10x - 19x + 10 - 19$

81. $6x^2 + 2 - 4(x^2 + 1)$

82. $-7(2x^2 - 1) - x^2 - 1$

83. $(3.2x - 1.5) - (4.3x - 1.2)$

84. $(7.6x + 4.7) - (1.9x + 3.6)$

Translating *Write each statement using mathematical symbols.*

85. Twelve is the product of x and negative 4.

86. The sum of n and twice n is negative fifteen.

87. Four times the sum of y and three is -1.

88. The difference of t and five, multiplied by six, is four.

89. Seven subtracted from z is six.

90. Ten less than the product of x and nine is five.

91. The difference of x and 5 is at least 12.

92. The opposite of four is less than the product of y and seven.

93. Two-thirds is not equal to twice the sum of n and one-fourth.

94. The sum of t and six is not more than negative twelve.

Name the property illustrated.

95. $(M + 5) + P = M + (5 + P)$

96. $5(3x - 4) = 15x - 20$

97. $(-4) + 4 = 0$

98. $(3 + x) + 7 = 7 + (3 + x)$

99. $(XY)Z = (YZ)X$

100. $\left(-\dfrac{3}{5}\right) \cdot \left(-\dfrac{5}{3}\right) = 1$

101. $T \cdot 0 = 0$

102. $(ab)c = a(bc)$

103. $A + 0 = A$

104. $8 \cdot 1 = 8$

Complete the equation using the given property.

105. $5x - 15z = $ _____ Distributive property

106. $(7 + y) + (3 + x) = $ _____ Commutative property

107. $0 = $ _____ Additive inverse property

108. $1 = $ _____ Multiplicative inverse property

109. $[(3.4)(0.7)]5 = $ _____ Associative property

110. $7 = $ _____ Additive identity property

Insert $<$, $>$, or $=$ to make each statement true.

111. -9 _____ -12

112. 0 _____ -6

113. -3 _____ -1

114. 7 _____ $|-7|$

115. -5 _____ $-(-5)$

116. $-(-2)$ _____ -2

MIXED REVIEW

Complete the table.

	Number	Opposite of Number	Reciprocal of Number
117.	$-\dfrac{3}{4}$		
118.		-5	

Simplify each expression.

119. $-2\left(5x + \dfrac{1}{2}\right) + 7.1$

120. $\sqrt{36} \div 2 \cdot 3$

121. $-\dfrac{7}{11} - \left(-\dfrac{1}{11}\right)$

122. $10 - (-1) + (-2) + 6$

123. $\left(-\dfrac{2}{3}\right)^3 \div \dfrac{10}{9}$

124. $\dfrac{(3 - 5)^2 + (-1)^3}{1 + 2(3 - (-1))^2}$

125. $\dfrac{1}{3}(9x - 3y) - (4x - 1) + 4y$

126. The average price for an ounce of gold in the United States during a month in 2014 was \$1266.40. The algebraic expression $1266.4z$ gives the average cost of z ounces of gold during this period. Find the average cost if 7.5 ounces of gold was purchased during this time. (*Source:* Kitco Metals)

The bar graph shows the U.S. life expectancy at birth for females born in the years shown. Use the graph to calculate the increase in life expectancy over each ten-year period shown. (The first row has been completed for you.)

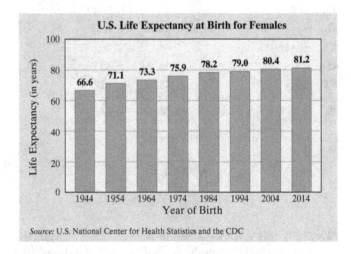

U.S. Life Expectancy at Birth for Females

Source: U.S. National Center for Health Statistics and the CDC

Year	Increase in Life Expectancy (in years) from 10 Years Earlier
1954	4.5
127. 1964	
128. 1974	
129. 1984	
130. 1994	
131. 2004	
132. 2014	

Chapter 1   Getting Ready for the Test

1c

MULTIPLE CHOICE *The exercise statement and the correct answer are given. Select the correct directions.*

   A. Find the opposite.   **B.** Find the reciprocal.   **C.** Evaluate or simplify.

1. $\dfrac{2}{5}$ Answer: $-\dfrac{2}{5}$

2. $|7 - 10| + (4 - 6)^3$ Answer: -5

3. $\dfrac{2}{5}$ Answer: $\dfrac{5}{2}$

4. 0   Answer: 0

MATCHING *Match each number in the first column with the set of numbers that it is an element of in the second column. Not every letter will be used.*

5. $\sqrt{5}$

6. $\dfrac{7}{8}$

7. 0

8. -12

   A. Negative Integer

   B. Rational Number

   C. Irrational Number

   D. Whole Number

   E. Natural Number

MATCHING *Match each equation in the first column with the property it illustrates it in the second column. Letters may be used more than once.*

9. $7 + (x + y) = (7 + x) + y$

10. $-2(x - 7) = -2x + 14$

11. $20 + y^3 = y^3 + 20$

12. $z \cdot 1 = z$

13. $a(xy) = (ax)y$

14. $0 + x^2 = x^2$

   A. Commutative Property

   B. Associative Property

   C. Distributive Property

   D. Additive Identity Property

   E. Multiplicative Identity Property

MULTIPLE CHOICE *Choose the correct answer.*

15. $-5(2x^2 - 3) - (2 - x^2) + 1$ simplifies to

   A. $-11x^2 + 14$ **B.** $-9x^2 + 14$ **C.** $-9x^2 + 13$ **D.** $-11x^2 + 13$

16. The sentence "Nine times the difference of x and 7 is -14" translates to:

   A. $9(x - 7) - 14$ **B.** $9x - 7 = -14$ **C.** $9(x - 7) = -14$ **D.** $9(7 - x) = -14$

Chapter 1 Test   MyMathLab® YouTube

Determine whether each statement is true or false.

1. $-2.3 > -2.33$

2. $-6^2 = (-6)^2$

3. $-5 - 8 = -(5 - 8)$

4. $(-2)(-3)(0) = \dfrac{-4}{0}$

5. All natural numbers are integers.

6. All rational numbers are integers.

Simplify.

7. $5 - 12 \div 3(2)$

8. $5^2 - 3^4$

9. $(4 - 9)^3 - |-4 - 6|^2$

10. $12 + \{6 - [5 - 2(-5)]\}$

11. $\dfrac{6(7 - 9)^3 + (-2)}{(-2)(-5)(-5)}$

12. $\dfrac{(4 - \sqrt{16}) - (-7 - 20)}{-2(1 - 4)^2}$

Evaluate each expression when $q = 4$, $r = -2$, and $t = 1$.

13. $q^2 - r^2$

14. $\dfrac{5t - 3q}{3r - 1}$

15. The algebraic expression $8.75x$ represents the total cost for x adults to attend the theater.

a. Complete the table that follows.

Adults	x	1	3	10	20
Total Cost	$8.75x$				

b. As the number of adults increases, does the total cost increase or decrease?

Write each statement using mathematical symbols.

16. Twice the sum of x and five is 30.

17. The square of the difference of six and y, divided by seven, is less than -2.

18. The product of nine and z, divided by the absolute value of -12, is not equal to 10.

19. Three times the quotient of n and five is the opposite of n.

20. Twenty is equal to 6 subtracted from twice x.

21. Negative two is equal to x divided by the sum of x and five.

Name each property illustrated.

22. $6(x - 4) = 6x - 24$

23. $(4 + x) + z = 4 + (x + z)$

24. $(-7) + 7 = 0$

25. $(-18)(0) = 0$

Solve.

26. Write an expression for the total amount of money (in dollars) in n nickels and d dimes.

27. Find the reciprocal and opposite of $-\dfrac{7}{11}$.

Simplify each expression.

28. $\dfrac{1}{3}a - \dfrac{3}{8} + \dfrac{1}{6}a - \dfrac{3}{4}$

29. $4y + 10 - 2(y + 10)$

30. $(8.3x - 2.9) - (9.6x - 4.8)$

2

Equations, Inequalities, and Problem Solving

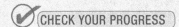

CHECK YOUR PROGRESS

Mathematics is a tool for solving problems in such diverse fields as transportation, engineering, economics, medicine, business, and biology. We solve problems using mathematics by modeling real-world phenomena with mathematical equations or inequalities. Our ability to solve problems using mathematics, then, depends in part on our ability to solve equations and inequalities. In this chapter, we solve linear equations and inequalities in one variable and graph their solutions on number lines.

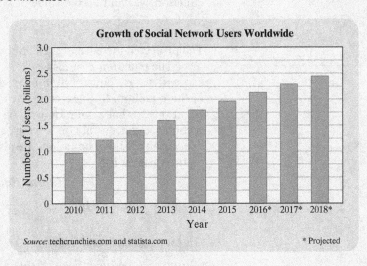

Growth of Social Network Users

Whatever your interests, there are many social media choices that fit your preferences. For example, we may check on family in Facebook, tweet latest activities, look for new ideas in Pinterest, or go to Instagram or WhatsApp or Tumblr. In a recent year, U.S. users spent more than 121.8 billion minutes monthly on social media. This is consistent over much of the world. The following graph demonstrates the current and projected growth in social network users worldwide.

In Section 2.1, Objective 1, and Section 2.2, Exercises 35 and 36, we will find the projected growth in the number of social network users worldwide as well as the percent of increase.

2.1 Linear Equations in One Variable

OBJECTIVES

1 Solve Linear Equations Using Properties of Equality.

2 Solve Linear Equations That Can Be Simplified by Combining Like Terms.

3 Solve Linear Equations Containing Fractions or Decimals.

4 Recognize Identities and Equations with No Solution.

OBJECTIVE

1 Solving Linear Equations Using Properties of Equality

Linear equations model many real-life problems. For example, we can use a linear equation to calculate the increase in the number, in billions, of worldwide users of social network sites.

Social network sites allow us to connect with more people, and many sites allow us to project our own image to the world. The number of social network sites is constantly in flux, and today's hot spot is tomorrow's has-been. Current and predicted users of social network sites are shown below.

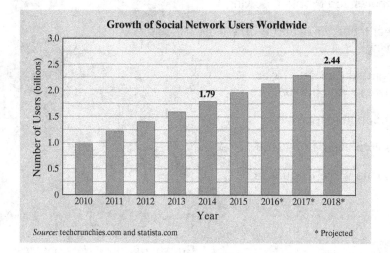

Growth of Social Network Users Worldwide

Source: techcrunchies.com and statista.com   * Projected

To find the projected increase in the number of social network users worldwide from 2014 to 2018, for example, we can use the equation below.

In words:	Increase in social network users	is	users in 2018	minus	users in 2014
Translate:	x	$=$	2.44	$-$	1.79

Since our variable x (increase in social network users) is by itself on one side of the equation, we can find the value of x by simplifying the right side.

$$x = 0.65$$

The projected increase in social network users worldwide is 0.65 billion people.

The **equation** $x = 2.44 - 1.79$, like every other equation, is a statement that two expressions are equal. Oftentimes, the unknown variable is not by itself on one side of the equation. In these cases, we will use properties of equality to write equivalent equations so that a solution may be found. This is called **solving the equation.** In this section, we concentrate on solving equations such as this one, called **linear equations** in one variable. Linear equations are also called **first-degree equations** since the exponent on the variable is 1.

Linear Equations in One Variable

$$3x = -15 \qquad 7 - y = 3y \qquad 4n - 9n + 6 = 0 \qquad z = -2$$

> **Linear Equation in One Variable**
>
> A linear equation in one variable is an equation that can be written in the form
>
> $$ax + b = c$$
>
> where $a, b,$ and c are real numbers and $a \neq 0$.

When a variable in an equation is replaced by a number and the resulting equation is true, then that number is called a **solution** of the equation. For example, 1 is a solution of the equation $3x + 4 = 7$, since $3(1) + 4 = 7$ is a true statement. But 2 is not a solution of this equation, since $3(2) + 4 = 7$ is not a true statement. The **solution set** of an equation is the set of solutions of the equation. For example, the solution set of $3x + 4 = 7$ is $\{1\}$.

To **solve an equation** is to find the solution set of the equation. Equations with the same solution set are called **equivalent equations.** For example,

$$3x + 4 = 7 \qquad 3x = 3 \qquad x = 1$$

are equivalent equations because they all have the same solution set, namely $\{1\}$. To solve an equation in x, we start with the given equation and write a series of simpler equivalent equations until we obtain an equation of the form

$$x = \textbf{number}$$

Two important properties are used to write equivalent equations.

The Addition and Multiplication Properties of Equality

If a, b, and c, are real numbers, then

$$a = b \quad \text{and} \quad a + c = b + c \text{ are equivalent equations.}$$

Also, $a = b$ and $\quad ac = bc$ are equivalent equations as long as $c \neq 0$.

The **addition property of equality** guarantees that the same number may be added to both sides of an equation, and the result is an equivalent equation. The **multiplication property of equality** guarantees that both sides of an equation may be multiplied by the same nonzero number, and the result is an equivalent equation. Because we define subtraction in terms of addition $(a - b = a + (-b))$, and division in terms of multiplication $\left(\dfrac{a}{b} = a \cdot \dfrac{1}{b} \right)$, these properties also guarantee that we may *subtract* the same number from both sides of an equation, or *divide* both sides of an equation by the same nonzero number and the result is an equivalent equation.

For example, to solve $2x + 5 = 9$, use the addition and multiplication properties of equality to isolate x—that is, to write an equivalent equation of the form

$$x = \textbf{number}$$

We will do this in the next example.

EXAMPLE 1   Solve for x: $2x + 5 = 9$

<u>Solution</u>   First, use the addition property of equality and subtract 5 from both sides. We do this so that our only variable term, $2x$, is by itself on one side of the equation.

$$2x + 5 = 9$$
$$2x + 5 - 5 = 9 - 5 \quad \text{Subtract 5 from both sides.}$$
$$2x = 4 \qquad \text{Simplify.}$$

Now that the variable term is isolated, we can finish solving for x by using the multiplication property of equality and dividing both sides by 2.

$$\frac{2x}{2} = \frac{4}{2} \quad \text{Divide both sides by 2.}$$

$$x = 2 \quad \text{Simplify.}$$

(Continued on next page)

Check: To see that 2 is the solution, replace x with 2 in the original equation.

$$2x + 5 = 9 \quad \text{Original equation}$$
$$2(2) + 5 \stackrel{?}{=} 9 \quad \text{Let } x = 2.$$
$$4 + 5 \stackrel{?}{=} 9$$
$$9 = 9 \quad \text{True}$$

Since we arrive at a true statement, 2 is the solution or the solution set is $\{2\}$. □

PRACTICE

1 Solve for x: $3x + 7 = 22$

EXAMPLE 2 Solve: $0.6 = 2 - 3.5c$

Solution We use both the addition property and the multiplication property of equality.

$$0.6 = 2 - 3.5c$$
$$0.6 - 2 = 2 - 3.5c - 2 \quad \text{Subtract 2 from both sides.}$$
$$-1.4 = -3.5c \quad \text{Simplify. The variable term is now isolated.}$$
$$\frac{-1.4}{-3.5} = \frac{-3.5c}{-3.5} \quad \text{Divide both sides by } -3.5.$$
$$0.4 = c \quad \text{Simplify } \frac{-1.4}{-3.5}.$$

> **Helpful Hint**
>
> Don't forget that
>
> $0.4 = c$ and $c = 0.4$ are equivalent equations.
>
> We may solve an equation so that the variable is alone on either side of the equation.

Check:

$$0.6 = 2 - 3.5c$$
$$0.6 \stackrel{?}{=} 2 - 3.5(0.4) \quad \text{Replace } c \text{ with } 0.4.$$
$$0.6 \stackrel{?}{=} 2 - 1.4 \quad \text{Multiply.}$$
$$0.6 = 0.6 \quad \text{True}$$

The solution is 0.4, or the solution set is $\{0.4\}$. □

PRACTICE

2 Solve: $2.5 = 3 - 2.5t$

OBJECTIVE

2 Solving Linear Equations That Can Be Simplified by Combining Like Terms ▶

Often, an equation can be simplified by removing any grouping symbols and combining any like terms.

EXAMPLE 3 Solve: $-4x - 1 + 5x = 9x + 3 - 7x$

Solution First we simplify both sides of this equation by combining like terms. Then, let's get variable terms on the same side of the equation by using the addition property of equality to subtract $2x$ from both sides. Next, we use this same property to add 1 to both sides of the equation.

$$-4x - 1 + 5x = 9x + 3 - 7x$$
$$x - 1 = 2x + 3 \quad \text{Combine like terms.}$$
$$x - 1 - 2x = 2x + 3 - 2x \quad \text{Subtract } 2x \text{ from both sides.}$$
$$-x - 1 = 3 \quad \text{Simplify.}$$
$$-x - 1 + 1 = 3 + 1 \quad \text{Add 1 to both sides.}$$
$$-x = 4 \quad \text{Simplify.}$$

Notice that this equation is not solved for x since we have $-x$ or $-1x$, not x. To solve for x, we divide both sides by -1.

$$\frac{-x}{-1} = \frac{4}{-1} \quad \text{Divide both sides by } -1.$$
$$x = -4 \quad \text{Simplify.}$$

Check to see that the solution is -4, or the solution set is $\{-4\}$.   □

PRACTICE
3   Solve: $-8x - 4 + 6x = 5x + 11 - 4x$ ■

If an equation contains parentheses, use the distributive property to remove them.

EXAMPLE 4   Solve: $2(x - 3) = 5x - 9$

Solution   First, use the distributive property.

$$2(x - 3) = 5x - 9$$
$$2x - 6 = 5x - 9 \quad \text{Use the distributive property.}$$

Next, get variable terms on the same side of the equation by subtracting $5x$ from both sides.

$$2x - 6 - 5x = 5x - 9 - 5x \quad \text{Subtract } 5x \text{ from both sides.}$$
$$-3x - 6 = -9 \quad \text{Simplify.}$$
$$-3x - 6 + 6 = -9 + 6 \quad \text{Add 6 to both sides.}$$
$$-3x = -3 \quad \text{Simplify.}$$
$$\frac{-3x}{-3} = \frac{-3}{-3} \quad \text{Divide both sides by } -3.$$
$$x = 1$$

Let $x = 1$ in the original equation to see that 1 is the solution.   □

PRACTICE
4   Solve: $3(x - 5) = 6x - 3$ ■

OBJECTIVE
3   Solving Linear Equations Containing Fractions or Decimals ▶

If an equation contains fractions, we first clear the equation of fractions by multiplying both sides of the equation by the *least common denominator* (LCD) of all fractions in the equation.

EXAMPLE 5   Solve for y: $\dfrac{y}{3} - \dfrac{y}{4} = \dfrac{1}{6}$

Solution   First, clear the equation of fractions by multiplying both sides of the equation by 12, the LCD of denominators 3, 4, and 6.

$$\frac{y}{3} - \frac{y}{4} = \frac{1}{6}$$

$$12\left(\frac{y}{3} - \frac{y}{4}\right) = 12\left(\frac{1}{6}\right) \quad \text{Multiply both sides by the LCD, 12.}$$

$$12\left(\frac{y}{3}\right) - 12\left(\frac{y}{4}\right) = 2 \quad \text{Apply the distributive property.}$$

$$4y - 3y = 2 \quad \text{Simplify.}$$
$$y = 2 \quad \text{Simplify.}$$

Check: To check, let $y = 2$ in the original equation.

$$\frac{y}{3} - \frac{y}{4} = \frac{1}{6} \quad \text{Original equation.}$$

$$\frac{2}{3} - \frac{2}{4} \stackrel{?}{=} \frac{1}{6} \quad \text{Let } y = 2.$$

(Continued on next page)

$$\frac{8}{12} - \frac{6}{12} \stackrel{?}{=} \frac{1}{6} \quad \text{Write fractions with the LCD.}$$

$$\frac{2}{12} \stackrel{?}{=} \frac{1}{6} \quad \text{Subtract.}$$

$$\frac{1}{6} = \frac{1}{6} \quad \text{Simplify.}$$

This is a true statement, so the solution is 2.

PRACTICE
5 Solve for y: $\dfrac{y}{2} - \dfrac{y}{5} = \dfrac{1}{4}$

As a general guideline, the following steps may be used to solve a linear equation in one variable.

Solving a Linear Equation in One Variable

Step 1. Clear the equation of fractions by multiplying both sides of the equation by the least common denominator (LCD) of all denominators in the equation.

Step 2. Use the distributive property to remove grouping symbols such as parentheses.

Step 3. Combine like terms on each side of the equation.

Step 4. Use the addition property of equality to rewrite the equation as an equivalent equation with variable terms on one side and numbers on the other side.

Step 5. Use the multiplication property of equality to isolate the variable.

Step 6. Check the proposed solution in the original equation.

EXAMPLE 6 Solve for x: $\dfrac{x+5}{2} + \dfrac{1}{2} = 2x - \dfrac{x-3}{8}$

Solution Multiply both sides of the equation by 8, the LCD of 2 and 8.

$$8\left(\frac{x+5}{2} + \frac{1}{2}\right) = 8\left(2x - \frac{x-3}{8}\right) \quad \text{Multiply both sides by 8.}$$

$$8\left(\frac{x+5}{2}\right) + 8\cdot\frac{1}{2} = 8\cdot 2x - 8\left(\frac{x-3}{8}\right) \quad \text{Apply the distributive property.}$$

$$4(x+5) + 4 = 16x - (x-3) \quad \text{Simplify.}$$

$$4x + 20 + 4 = 16x - x + 3 \quad \text{Use the distributive property to remove parentheses.}$$

$$4x + 24 = 15x + 3 \quad \text{Combine like terms.}$$

$$-11x + 24 = 3 \quad \text{Subtract } 15x \text{ from both sides.}$$

$$-11x = -21 \quad \text{Subtract 24 from both sides.}$$

$$\frac{-11x}{-11} = \frac{-21}{-11} \quad \text{Divide both sides by } -11.$$

$$x = \frac{21}{11} \quad \text{Simplify.}$$

Helpful Hint
When we multiply both sides of an equation by a number, the distributive property tells us that each term of the equation is multiplied by the number.

Check: To check, verify that replacing x with $\dfrac{21}{11}$ makes the original equation true. The solution is $\dfrac{21}{11}$.

PRACTICE
6 Solve for x: $x - \dfrac{x-2}{12} = \dfrac{x+3}{4} + \dfrac{1}{4}$

If an equation contains decimals, you may want to first clear the equation of decimals.

EXAMPLE 7 Solve: $0.3x + 0.1 = 0.27x - 0.02$

Solution To clear this equation of decimals, we multiply both sides of the equation by 100. Recall that multiplying a number by 100 moves its decimal point two places to the right.

$$100(0.3x + 0.1) = 100(0.27x - 0.02)$$

$$100(0.3x) + 100(0.1) = 100(0.27x) - 100(0.02) \quad \text{Use the distributive property.}$$

$$30x + 10 = 27x - 2 \qquad\qquad \text{Multiply.}$$

$$30x - 27x = -2 - 10 \qquad\qquad \text{Subtract } 27x \text{ and } 10 \text{ from both sides.}$$

$$3x = -12 \qquad\qquad\qquad \text{Simplify.}$$

$$\frac{3x}{3} = \frac{-12}{3} \qquad\qquad\qquad \text{Divide both sides by 3.}$$

$$x = -4 \qquad\qquad\qquad \text{Simplify.}$$

Check to see that the solution is -4. ☐

PRACTICE

7 Solve: $0.15x - 0.03 = 0.2x + 0.12$ ∎

✔ **CONCEPT CHECK**

Explain what is wrong with the following:

$$3x - 5 = 16$$
$$3x = 11$$
$$\frac{3x}{3} = \frac{11}{3}$$
$$x = \frac{11}{3}$$

OBJECTIVE

4 Recognizing Identities and Equations with No Solution

So far, each linear equation that we have solved has had a single solution. A linear equation in one variable that has exactly one solution is called a **conditional equation.** We will now look at two other types of equations: contradictions and identities.

An equation in one variable that has no solution is called a **contradiction,** and an equation in one variable that has every number (for which the equation is defined) as a solution is called an **identity.** For review: A linear equation in one variable with

No solution	is a	Contradiction
Every real number as a solution (as long as the equation is defined)	is an	Identity

The next examples show how to recognize contradictions and identities.

EXAMPLE 8 Solve for x: $3x + 5 = 3(x + 2)$

Solution First, use the distributive property and remove parentheses.

$$3x + 5 = 3(\overset{\frown}{x + 2})$$

$$3x + 5 = 3x + 6 \qquad \text{Apply the distributive property.}$$

$$3x + 5 - 3x = 3x + 6 - 3x \quad \text{Subtract } 3x \text{ from both sides.}$$

$$5 = 6$$

Helpful Hint

A solution set of $\{0\}$ and a solution set of $\{\ \}$ are not the same. The solution set $\{0\}$ means 1 solution, 0. The solution set $\{\ \}$ means *no* solution.

The equation $5 = 6$ is a false statement no matter what value the variable x might have. Thus, the original equation has no solution. Its solution set is written either as $\{\ \}$ or $\varnothing$. This equation is a contradiction. ☐

PRACTICE

8 Solve for x: $4x - 3 = 4(x + 5)$ ■

EXAMPLE 9 Solve for x: $6x - 4 = 2 + 6(x - 1)$

Solution First, use the distributive property and remove parentheses.

$$6x - 4 = 2 + 6(x - 1)$$
$$6x - 4 = 2 + 6x - 6 \qquad \text{Apply the distributive property.}$$
$$6x - 4 = 6x - 4 \qquad \text{Combine like terms.}$$

At this point, we might notice that both sides of the equation are the same, so replacing x by any real number gives a true statement. Thus the solution set of this equation is the set of real numbers, and the equation is an identity. Continuing to "solve" $6x - 4 = 6x - 4$, we eventually arrive at the same conclusion.

$$6x - 4 + 4 = 6x - 4 + 4 \qquad \text{Add 4 to both sides.}$$
$$6x = 6x \qquad \text{Simplify.}$$
$$6x - 6x = 6x - 6x \qquad \text{Subtract } 6x \text{ from both sides.}$$
$$0 = 0 \qquad \text{Simplify.}$$

Since $0 = 0$ is a true statement for every value of x, all real numbers are solutions. The solution set is the set of all real numbers or $\mathbb{R}$, $\{x \mid x \text{ is a real number}\}$, and the equation is called an identity. ☐

PRACTICE

9 Solve for x: $5x - 2 = 3 + 5(x - 1)$ all real numbers or $\{x \mid x \text{ is a real number}\}$ ■

Helpful Hint

For linear equations, *any* false statement such as $5 = 6, 0 = 1$, or $-2 = 2$ informs us that the original equation has no solution. Also, *any* true statement such as $0 = 0, 2 = 2$, or $-5 = -5$ informs us that the original equation is an identity.

✔ **Vocabulary, Readiness & Video Check**

Use the choices below to fill in the blanks. Not all choices will be used.

multiplication   value   like

addition   solution   equivalent

1. Equations with the same solution set are called _____ equations.

2. A value for the variable in an equation that makes the equation a true statement is called a(n) _____ of the equation.

3. By the _____ property of equality, $y = -3$ and $y - 7 = -3 - 7$ are equivalent equations.

4. By the _____ property of equality, $2y = -3$ and $\dfrac{2y}{2} = \dfrac{-3}{2}$ are equivalent equations.

Identify each as an equation or an expression.

5. $\dfrac{1}{3}x - 5$ _____

6. $2(x - 3) = 7$ _____

7. $\dfrac{5}{9}x + \dfrac{1}{3} = \dfrac{2}{9} - x$ _____

8. $\dfrac{5}{9}x + \dfrac{1}{3} - \dfrac{2}{9} - x$ _____

Martin-Gay Interactive Videos

See Video 2.1

Watch the section lecture video and answer the following questions.

OBJECTIVE 1

9. Complete these statements based on the lecture given before ▣ Example 1. The addition property of equality allows us to add the same number to (or subtract the same number from) _____ of an equation and have an equivalent equation. The multiplication property of equality allows us to multiply (or divide) both sides of an equation by the _____ nonzero number and have an equivalent equation.

OBJECTIVE 2

10. From ▣ Example 2, if an equation is simplified by removing parentheses before the properties of equality are applied, what property is used?

OBJECTIVE 3

11. In ▣ Example 3, what is the main reason given for first removing fractions from the equation?

OBJECTIVE 4

12. Complete this statement based on ▣ Example 4. When solving a linear equation and all variable terms subtract out and:
a. you have a _____ statement, then the equation has all real numbers for which the equation is defined as solutions.
b. you have a _____ statement, then the equation has no solution.

2.1   Exercise Set   MyMathLab®

Solve each equation and check. See Examples 1 and 2.

1. $-5x = -30$

2. $-2x = 18$

3. $-10 = x + 12$

4. $-25 = y + 30$

5. $x - 2.8 = 1.9$

6. $y - 8.6 = -6.3$

7. $5x - 4 = 26 + 2x$

8. $5y - 3 = 11 + 3y$

9. $-4.1 - 7z = 3.6$

10. $10.3 - 6x = -2.3$

11. $5y + 12 = 2y - 3$

12. $4x + 14 = 6x + 8$

Solve each equation and check. See Examples 3 and 4.

13. $3x - 4 - 5x = x + 4 + x$

14. $13x - 15x + 8 = 4x + 2 - 24$

15. $8x - 5x + 3 = x - 7 + 10$

16. $6 + 3x + x = -x + 8 - 26 + 24$

17. $5x + 12 = 2(2x + 7)$

18. $2(4x + 3) = 7x + 5$

19. $3(x - 6) = 5x$

20. $6x = 4(x - 5)$

21. $-2(5y - 1) - y = -4(y - 3)$

22. $-4(3n - 2) - n = -11(n - 1)$

Solve each equation and check. See Examples 5 through 7.

23. $\dfrac{x}{2} + \dfrac{x}{3} = \dfrac{3}{4}$

24. $\dfrac{x}{2} + \dfrac{x}{5} = \dfrac{5}{4}$

25. $\dfrac{3t}{4} - \dfrac{t}{2} = 1$

26. $\dfrac{4r}{5} - \dfrac{r}{10} = 7$

27. $\dfrac{n - 3}{4} + \dfrac{n + 5}{7} = \dfrac{5}{14}$

28. $\dfrac{2 + h}{9} + \dfrac{h - 1}{3} = \dfrac{1}{3}$

29. $0.6x - 10 = 1.4x - 14$

30. $0.3x + 2.4 = 0.1x + 4$

31. $\dfrac{3x - 1}{9} + x = \dfrac{3x + 1}{3} + 4$

32. $\dfrac{2z + 7}{8} - 2 = z + \dfrac{z - 1}{2}$

33. $1.5(4 - x) = 1.3(2 - x)$

34. $2.4(2x + 3) = -0.1(2x + 3)$

Solve each equation. See Examples 8 and 9.

35. $4(n + 3) = 2(6 + 2n)$

36. $6(4n + 4) = 8(3 + 3n)$

37. $3(x + 1) + 5 = 3x + 2$

38. $4(x + 2) + 4 = 4x - 8$

39. $2(x - 8) + x = 3(x - 6) + 2$

40. $5(x - 4) + x = 6(x - 2) - 8$

41. $4(x + 5) = 3(x - 4) + x$

42. $9(x - 2) = 8(x - 3) + x$

MIXED PRACTICE

Solve each equation. See Examples 1 through 9.

43. $\dfrac{3}{8} + \dfrac{b}{3} = \dfrac{5}{12}$

44. $\dfrac{a}{2} + \dfrac{7}{4} = 5$

45. $x - 10 = -6x - 10$

46. $4x - 7 = 2x - 7$

47. $5(x - 2) + 2x = 7(x + 4) - 38$

48. $3x + 2(x + 4) = 5(x + 1) + 3$

49. $y + 0.2 = 0.6(y + 3)$

50. $-(w + 0.2) = 0.3(4 - w)$

51. $\dfrac{1}{4}(a + 2) = \dfrac{1}{6}(5 - a)$

52. $\dfrac{1}{3}(8 + 2c) = \dfrac{1}{5}(3c - 5)$

53. $2y + 5(y - 4) = 4y - 2(y - 10)$

54. $9c - 3(6 - 5c) = c - 2(3c + 9)$

55. $6x - 2(x - 3) = 4(x + 1) + 4$

56. $10x - 2(x + 4) = 8(x - 2) + 6$

▶ **57.** $\dfrac{m - 4}{3} - \dfrac{3m - 1}{5} = 1$ **58.** $\dfrac{n + 1}{8} - \dfrac{2 - n}{3} = \dfrac{5}{6}$

59. $8x - 12 - 3x = 9x - 7$

60. $10y - 18 - 4y = 12y - 13$

61. $-(3x - 5) - (2x - 6) + 1 = -5(x - 1) - (3x + 2) + 3$

62. $-4(2x - 3) - (10x + 7) - 2 = -(12x - 5) - (4x + 9) - 1$

63. $\dfrac{1}{3}(y + 4) + 6 = \dfrac{1}{4}(3y - 1) - 2$

64. $\dfrac{1}{5}(2y - 1) - 2 = \dfrac{1}{2}(3y - 5) + 3$

65. $2[7 - 5(1 - n)] + 8n = -16 + 3[6(n + 1) - 3n]$

66. $3[8 - 4(n - 2)] + 5n = -20 + 2[5(1 - n) - 6n]$

REVIEW AND PREVIEW

Translating. Translate each phrase into an expression. Use the variable x to represent each unknown number. See Section 1.2.

67. The quotient of 8 and a number

68. The sum of 8 and a number

69. The product of 8 and a number

70. The difference of 8 and a number

71. Five subtracted from twice a number

72. Two more than three times a number

CONCEPT EXTENSIONS

Find the error for each proposed solution. Then correct the proposed solution. See the Concept Check in this section.

73. $2x + 19 = 13$
$2x = 32$
$\dfrac{2x}{2} = \dfrac{32}{2}$
$x = 16$

74. $-3(x - 4) = 10$
$-3x - 12 = 10$
$-3x = 22$
$\dfrac{-3x}{-3} = \dfrac{22}{-3}$
$x = -\dfrac{22}{3}$

75. $9x + 1.6 = 4x + 0.4$
$5x = 1.2$
$\dfrac{5x}{5} = \dfrac{1.2}{5}$
$x = 0.24$

76. $\dfrac{x}{3} + 7 = \dfrac{5x}{3}$
$x + 7 = 5x$
$7 = 4x$
$\dfrac{7}{4} = \dfrac{4x}{4}$
$\dfrac{7}{4} = x$

By inspection, decide which equations have no solution and which equations have all real numbers as solutions.

77. $2x + 3 = 2x + 3$

78. $5x - 3 = 5x - 3$

79. $2x + 1 = 2x + 3$

80. $5x - 2 = 5x - 7$

81. a. Simplify the expression $4(x + 1) + 1$.

    b. Solve the equation $4(x + 1) + 1 = -7$.

    c. Explain the difference between solving an equation for a variable and simplifying an expression.

82. Explain why the multiplication property of equality does not include multiplying both sides of an equation by 0. (*Hint:* Write down a false statement and then multiply both sides by 0. Is the result true or false? What does this mean?)

83. In your own words, explain why the equation $x + 7 = x + 6$ has no solution, while the solution set of the equation $x + 7 = x + 7$ contains all real numbers.

84. In your own words, explain why the equation $x = -x$ has one solution—namely, 0—while the solution set of the equation $x = x$ is all real numbers.

Find the value of K such that the equations are equivalent.

85. $3.2x + 4 = 5.4x - 7$
$3.2x = 5.4x + K$

86. $-7.6y - 10 = -1.1y + 12$
$-7.6y = -1.1y + K$

87. $\dfrac{7}{11}x + 9 = \dfrac{3}{11}x - 14$
$\dfrac{7}{11}x = \dfrac{3}{11}x + K$

88. $\dfrac{x}{6} + 4 = \dfrac{x}{3}$
$x + K = 2x$

89. Write a linear equation in x whose only solution is 5.

90. Write an equation in x that has no solution.

Solve the following.

91. $x(x - 6) + 7 = x(x + 1)$

92. $7x^2 + 2x - 3 = 6x(x + 4) + x^2$

93. $3x(x + 5) - 12 = 3x^2 + 10x + 3$

94. $x(x + 1) + 16 = x(x + 5)$

Solve and check.

95. $2.569x = -12.48534$

96. $-9.112y = -47.537304$

97. $2.86z - 8.1258 = -3.75$

98. $1.25x - 20.175 = -8.15$

2.2 | An Introduction to Problem Solving

OBJECTIVES

1 Write Algebraic Expressions That Can Be Simplified.

2 Apply the Steps for Problem Solving.

OBJECTIVE

1 Writing and Simplifying Algebraic Expressions

To prepare for problem solving, we practice writing algebraic expressions that can be simplified.

Our first example involves consecutive integers and perimeter. Recall that *consecutive integers* are integers that follow one another in order. Study the examples of consecutive, even, and odd integers and their representations.

Consecutive Integers:

$$+1 \quad +2$$

6   7   8
x $x+1$ $x+2$

Consecutive Even Integers:

$$+2 \quad +4$$

10 11 12 13 14
x $x+2$ $x+4$

Consecutive Odd Integers:

$$+2 \quad +4$$

7   8   9   10   11
x $x+2$ $x+4$

Helpful Hint

You may want to begin this section by studying key words and phrases and their translations in Section 1.2 Objective 5.

EXAMPLE 1 Write the following as algebraic expressions. Then simplify.

a. The sum of three consecutive integers if x is the first consecutive integer.

△ b. The perimeter of a triangle with sides of length x, $5x$, and $6x - 3$.

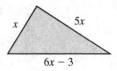

Solution

a. Recall that if x is the first integer, then the next consecutive integer is 1 more, or $x + 1$ and the next consecutive integer is 1 more than $x + 1$, or $x + 2$.

In words:	first integer	plus	next consecutive integer	plus	next consecutive integer
	↓	↓	↓	↓	↓
Translate:	x	$+$	$(x + 1)$	$+$	$(x + 2)$

Then $x + (x + 1) + (x + 2) = x + x + 1 + x + 2$

$= 3x + 3$ Simplify by combining like terms.

b. The perimeter of a triangle is the sum of the lengths of the sides.

In words:	side	plus	side	plus	side
	↓	↓	↓	↓	↓
Translate:	x	$+$	$5x$	$+$	$(6x - 3)$

Then $x + 5x + (6x - 3) = x + 5x + 6x - 3$

$= 12x - 3$ Simplify.   □

PRACTICE

1 Write the following algebraic expressions. Then simplify.

a. The sum of three consecutive odd integers if x is the first consecutive odd integer

b. The perimeter of a trapezoid with bases x and $2x$ and sides of $x + 2$ and $2x - 3$

> **EXAMPLE 2**   Writing Algebraic Expressions Representing Urban Areas

The United Nations defines a world urban area as a continuously built-up land mass of urban development that is within a labor market. World urban areas often transcend political boundaries. The most populous urban area in the United States is New York, although it is only the ninth most populous in the world. Tokyo-Yokohama is the most populous urban area. Delhi, India, is third in size. Delhi's urban area population is 4.6 million more than that of New York, and Tokyo-Yokohama's population is twice that of New York, decreased by 3.4 million. Write the sum of the population of these three urban areas as an algebraic expression. Let x be the population of New York (in millions). (*Source:* Demographia World Urban Areas, 2015.01)

Solution:

$$\text{If } x = \text{the population of New York (in millions), then}$$
$$x + 4.6 = \text{the population of Delhi (in millions) and}$$
$$2x - 3.4 = \text{the population of Tokyo-Yokohama (in millions).}$$

In words:	population of New York	plus	population of Delhi	plus	population of Tokyo-Yokohama
Translate:	x	$+$	$(x + 4.6)$	$+$	$(2x - 3.4)$

$$\text{Then } x + (x + 4.6) + (2x - 3.4) = x + x + 2x + 4.6 - 3.4$$
$$= 4x + 1.2 \quad \text{Combine like terms.}$$

In Exercise 57 we will find the actual populations of these cities. □

Populous Urban Areas

PRACTICE
2   The three busiest airports by number of passengers in the United States are in Atlanta, Chicago, and Los Angeles. Chicago's O'Hare airport had 3.1 million more passengers than Los Angeles International Airport. Atlanta's Hartsfield-Jackson had double the number of passengers as Los Angeles International Airport less 31.9 million. Write the sum of the passengers from these three airports as a simplified algebraic expression. Let x be the number of passengers (in millions) at Los Angeles International. (*Source:* Airport Council International)

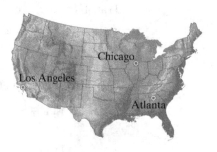

OBJECTIVE
2   Applying Steps for Problem Solving ▶

Our main purpose for studying algebra is to solve problems. The following problem-solving strategy will be used throughout this text and may also be used to solve real-life problems that occur outside the mathematics classroom.

General Strategy for Problem Solving

1. UNDERSTAND the problem. During this step, become comfortable with the problem. Some ways of doing this are to:

   Read and reread the problem.

   Propose a solution and check. Pay careful attention to how you check your proposed solution. This will help when writing an equation to model the problem.

   Construct a drawing.

   Choose a variable to represent the unknown. (Very important part)

2. TRANSLATE the problem into an equation.

3. SOLVE the equation.

4. INTERPRET the results: *Check* the proposed solution in the stated problem and *state* your conclusion.

Let's review this strategy by solving a problem involving unknown numbers.

EXAMPLE 3   Finding Unknown Numbers

Find three numbers such that the second number is 3 more than twice the first number, and the third number is four times the first number. The sum of the three numbers is 164.

Solution

1. UNDERSTAND the problem. First let's read and reread the problem and then propose a solution. For example, if the first number is 25, then the second number is 3 more than twice 25, or 53. The third number is four times 25, or 100. The sum of 25, 53, and 100 is 178, not the required sum, but we have gained some valuable information about the problem. First, we know that the first number is less than 25 since our guess led to a sum greater than the required sum. Also, we have gained some information as to how to model the problem.

   Next let's assign a variable and use this variable to represent any other unknown quantities. If we let

$$x = \text{the first number, then}$$

$$2x + 3 = \text{the second number}$$

3 more than
twice the second number

$$4x = \text{the third number}$$

> **Helpful Hint**
>
> The purpose of guessing a solution is not to guess correctly but to gain confidence and to help understand the problem and how to model it.

2. TRANSLATE the problem into an equation. To do so, we use the fact that the sum of the numbers is 164. First let's write this relationship in words and then translate to an equation.

In words:	first number	added to	second number	added to	third number	is	164
Translate:	x	$+$	$(2x + 3)$	$+$	$4x$	$=$	164

3. SOLVE the equation.

$$x + (2x + 3) + 4x = 164$$

$$x + 2x + 4x + 3 = 164 \quad \text{Remove parentheses.}$$

$$7x + 3 = 164 \quad \text{Combine like terms.}$$

$$7x = 161 \quad \text{Subtract 3 from both sides.}$$

$$x = 23 \quad \text{Divide both sides by 7.}$$

4. INTERPRET. Here, we *check* our work and *state* the solution. Recall that if the first number $x = 23$, then the second number $2x + 3 = 2 \cdot 23 + 3 = 49$ and the third number $4x = 4 \cdot 23 = 92$.

(Continued on next page)

Check: Is the second number 3 more than twice the first number? Yes, since 3 more than twice 23 is 46 + 3, or 49. Also, their sum, 23 + 49 + 92 = 164, is the required sum.

State: The three numbers are 23, 49, and 92.

PRACTICE
3 Find three numbers such that the second number is 8 less than triple the first number, the third number is five times the first number, and the sum of the three numbers is 118.

Many of today's rates and statistics are given as percents. Interest rates, tax rates, nutrition labeling, and percent of households in a given category are just a few examples. Before we practice solving problems containing percents, let's briefly review the meaning of percent and how to find a percent of a number.

The word *percent* means "per hundred," and the symbol % denotes percent.

This means that 23% is 23 per hundred, or $\frac{23}{100}$. Also,

$$41\% = \frac{41}{100} = 0.41$$

To find a percent of a number, we multiply.

$$16\% \text{ of } 25 = 16\% \cdot 25 = 0.16 \cdot 25 = 4$$

Thus, 16% of 25 is 4.

Study the table below. It will help you become more familiar with finding percents.

Percent	Meaning/Shortcut	Example
50%	$\frac{1}{2}$ or half of a number	50% of 60 is 30.
25%	$\frac{1}{4}$ or a quarter of a number	25% of 60 is 15.
10%	0.1 or $\frac{1}{10}$ of a number (move the decimal point 1 place to the left)	10% of 60 is 6.0 or 6.
1%	0.01 or $\frac{1}{100}$ of a number (move the decimal point 2 places to the left)	1% of 60 is 0.60 or 0.6.
100%	1 or all of a number	100% of 60 is 60.
200%	2 or double a number	200% of 60 is 120.

✔ CONCEPT CHECK

Suppose you are finding 112% of a number x. Which of the following is a correct description of the result? Explain.

a. The result is less than x.   **b.** The result is equal to x.   **c.** The result is greater than x.

Next, we solve a problem containing a percent.

 EXAMPLE 4   **Finding the Original Price of a Computer**

Suppose that a computer store just announced an 8% decrease in the price of a particular computer model. If this computer sells for $2162 after the decrease, find the original price of this computer.

Solution

1. UNDERSTAND. Read and reread the problem. Recall that a percent decrease means a percent of the original price. Let's guess that the original price of the computer was $2500. The amount of decrease is then 8% of $2500, or (0.08)($2500) = $200. This means that the new price of the computer is the original price minus the decrease, or $2500 − $200 = $2300. Our guess is incorrect, but we now have an idea of how to model this problem. In our model, we will let x = the original price of the computer.

2. TRANSLATE.

In words:	the original price of computer	minus	8% of the original price	is	the new price
	↓	↓	↓	↓	↓
Translate:	x	−	$0.08x$	=	2162

3. SOLVE the equation.

$$x - 0.08x = 2162$$
$$0.92x = 2162 \qquad \text{Combine like terms.}$$
$$x = \frac{2162}{0.92} = 2350 \quad \text{Divide both sides by 0.92.}$$

4. INTERPRET.

Check: If the original price of the computer was $2350, the new price is

$$\$2350 - (0.08)(\$2350) = \$2350 - \$188$$
$$= \$2162 \qquad \text{The given new price}$$

State: The original price of the computer was $2350.   □

PRACTICE
4   At the end of the season, the cost of a snowboard was reduced by 40%. If the snowboard sells for $270 after the decrease, find the original price of the board.

△   **EXAMPLE 5**   Finding the Lengths of a Triangle's Sides

A pennant in the shape of an isosceles triangle is to be constructed for the Slidell High School Athletic Club and sold at a fund-raiser. The company manufacturing the pennant charges according to perimeter, and the athletic club has determined that a perimeter of 149 centimeters should make a nice profit. If each equal side of the triangle is twice the length of the third side, increased by 12 centimeters, find the lengths of the sides of the triangular pennant.

Solution

1. UNDERSTAND. Read and reread the problem. Recall that the perimeter of a triangle is the distance around. Let's guess that the third side of the triangular pennant is 20 centimeters. This means that each equal side is twice 20 centimeters, increased by 12 centimeters, or $2(20) + 12 = 52$ centimeters.

This gives a perimeter of $20 + 52 + 52 = 124$ centimeters. Our guess is incorrect, but we now have a better understanding of how to model this problem.

Now we let the third side of the triangle = x.

the first side =	twice	the third side	increased by	12
	↓	↓	↓	↓
=	2	x	+	12

or $2x + 12$

the second side = $2x + 12$

(Continued on next page)

2. TRANSLATE.

In words:

| first side | + | second side | + | third side | = | 149 |

Translate: $(2x + 12) + (2x + 12) + x = 149$

3. SOLVE the equation.

$$
\begin{aligned}
(2x + 12) + (2x + 12) + x &= 149 \\
2x + 12 + 2x + 12 + x &= 149 \quad \text{Remove parentheses.} \\
5x + 24 &= 149 \quad \text{Combine like terms.} \\
5x &= 125 \quad \text{Subtract 24 from both sides.} \\
x &= 25 \quad \text{Divide both sides by 5.}
\end{aligned}
$$

4. INTERPRET. If the third side is 25 centimeters, then the first side is $2(25) + 12 = 62$ centimeters, and the second side is 62 centimeters.

Check: The first and second sides are each twice 25 centimeters increased by 12 centimeters or 62 centimeters. Also, the perimeter is $25 + 62 + 62 = 149$ centimeters, the required perimeter.

State: The lengths of the sides of the triangle are 25 centimeters, 62 centimeters, and 62 centimeters. □

PRACTICE

5 For its 40th anniversary, North Campus Community College is placing rectangular banners on all the light poles on campus. The perimeter of these banners is 160 inches. If the longer side of each banner is 16 inches less than double the width, find the dimensions of the banners. ■

EXAMPLE 6 **Finding Consecutive Integers**

Kelsey Ohleger was helping her friend Benji Burnstine study for an algebra exam. Kelsey told Benji that her three latest art history quiz scores are three consecutive even integers whose sum is 264. Help Benji find the scores.

Solution

1. UNDERSTAND. Read and reread the problem. Since we are looking for consecutive even integers, let

$$
\begin{aligned}
x &= \text{the first integer. Then} \\
x + 2 &= \text{the second consecutive even integer and} \\
x + 4 &= \text{the third consecutive even integer.}
\end{aligned}
$$

2. TRANSLATE.

In words:

| first integer | + | second even integer | + | third even integer | = | 264 |

Translate: $x + (x + 2) + (x + 4) = 264$

3. SOLVE.

$$
\begin{aligned}
x + (x + 2) + (x + 4) &= 264 \\
3x + 6 &= 264 \quad \text{Combine like terms.} \\
3x &= 258 \quad \text{Subtract 6 from both sides.} \\
x &= 86 \quad \text{Divide both sides by 3.}
\end{aligned}
$$

4. INTERPRET. If $x = 86$, then $x + 2 = 86 + 2$ or 88, and $x + 4 = 86 + 4$ or 90.

Check: The numbers 86, 88, and 90 are three consecutive even integers. Their sum is 264, the required sum.

State: Kelsey's art history quiz scores are 86, 88, and 90.   □

PRACTICE
6   Find three consecutive odd integers whose sum is 81.   ■

✔ Vocabulary, Readiness & Video Check

Fill in each blank with $<$, $>$, *or* $=$. *(Assume that the unknown number is a positive number.)*

1. 130% of a number ____ the number.

2. 70% of a number ____ the number.

3. 100% of a number ____ the number.

4. 200% of a number ____ the number.

Complete the table. The first row has been completed for you.

	First Integer	All Described Integers
Three consecutive integers	18	18, 19, 20
5. Four consecutive integers	31	
6. Three consecutive odd integers	31	
7. Three consecutive even integers	18	
8. Four consecutive even integers	92	
9. Three consecutive integers	y	
10. Three consecutive even integers	z (z is even)	
11. Four consecutive integers	p	
12. Three consecutive odd integers	s (s is odd)	

Martin-Gay Interactive Videos

See Video 2.2 ●

Watch the section lecture video and answer the following questions.

OBJECTIVE
1   **13.** In Example 2, once the phrase is translated, what property is used to remove parentheses?

OBJECTIVE
2   **14.** The equation for ▦ Example 3 is solved and the result is $x = 45$. Why is 45 not the complete solution to the application?

2.2   **Exercise Set**   MyMathLab® ●

Write the following as algebraic expressions. Then simplify. See Examples 1 and 2.

△ **1.** The perimeter of a square with side length y.

△ **2.** The perimeter of a rectangle with length x and width $x - 5$.

● **3.** The sum of three consecutive integers if the first is z.

4. The sum of three consecutive odd integers if the first odd integer is x.

● **5.** The total amount of money (in cents) in x nickels, $(x + 3)$ dimes, and $2x$ quarters. (*Hint:* The value of a nickel is 5 cents, the value of a dime is 10 cents, and the value of a quarter is 25 cents.)

6. The total amount of money (in cents) in y quarters, $7y$ dimes, and $(2y - 1)$ nickels. (Use the hint for Exercise 5.)

△ **7.** A piece of land along Bayou Liberty is to be fenced and subdivided as shown so that each rectangle has the same dimensions. Express the total amount of fencing needed as an algebraic expression in *x*.

8. A flooded piece of land near the Mississippi River in New Orleans is to be surveyed and divided into 4 rectangles of equal dimension. Express the total amount of fencing needed as an algebraic expression in *x*.

△ 9. Write the perimeter of the floor plan shown as an algebraic expression in *x*.

10. Write the perimeter of the floor plan shown as an algebraic expression in *x*.

Solve. For Exercises 11 and 12, the solutions have been started for you. See Example 3.

11. Four times the difference of a number and 2 is the same as 2, increased by four times the number, plus twice the number. Find the number.

Start the solution:

1. UNDERSTAND the problem. Reread it as many times as needed.
2. TRANSLATE into an equation. (Fill in the blanks below.)

Four times	the difference of a number and 2	is the same as	2	increased by	four times the number	plus	twice the number
↓	↓	↓	↓	↓	↓	↓	↓
4 ·	$(x - 2)$	=	2	___	___	___	___

Finish with:

3. SOLVE and 4. INTERPRET

12. Twice the sum of a number and 3 is the same as five times the number, minus 1, minus four times the number. Find the number.

Start the solution:

1. UNDERSTAND the problem. Reread it as many times as needed.
2. TRANSLATE into an equation. (Fill in the blanks below.)

Twice	the sum of a number and 3	is the same as	five times the number	minus	1	minus	four times the number
↓	↓	↓	↓	↓	↓	↓	↓
2	$(x + 3)$	=	___	___	1	___	___

Finish with:

3. SOLVE and 4. INTERPRET

13. A second number is five times a first number. A third number is 100 more than the first number. If the sum of the three numbers is 415, find the numbers.

14. A second number is 6 less than a first number. A third number is twice the first number. If the sum of the three numbers is 306, find the numbers.

Solve. See Example 4.

15. The United States consists of 2271 million acres of land. Approximately 29% of this land is federally owned. Find the number of acres that are not federally owned. (*Source: U.S. General Services Administration*)

16. The state of Nevada contains the most federally owned acres of land in the United States. If 90% of the state's 70 million acres of land is federally owned, find the number of acres that are not federally owned. (*Source: U.S. General Services Administration*)

17. In 2014, 16,674 earthquakes occurred world wide. Of these, 89.6% were minor tremors with magnitudes of 4.9 or less on the Richter scale. How many minor earthquakes occurred in the world in 2014? Round to the nearest whole. (*Source: U.S. Geological Survey National Earthquake Information Center*)

18. Of the 881 tornadoes that occurred in the United States during 2014, 32.2% occurred during the month of June. How many tornadoes occurred in the United States during June, 2014? Round to the nearest whole. (*Source:* National Climatic Data Center, National Oceanic and Atmospheric Administration)

19. In a recent survey, 15% of online shoppers in the United States say that they prefer to do business only with large, well-known retailers. In a group of 1500 online shoppers, how many are willing to do business with any size retailers? (*Source:* Inc.com)

20. In 2014, the restaurant industry employed 10% of the U.S. workforce. If there are estimated to be 147 million Americans in the workforce, how many people are employed by the restaurant industry? (*Source:* National Restaurant Association, U.S. Bureau of Labor Statistics)

The following graph is called a circle graph or pie chart. The circle represents a whole, or in this case, 100%. This particular graph shows the average percent of the workday that is spent on various tasks. Use this graph to answer Exercises 21 through 24.

Time Spent on Tasks at Work

Role-Specific Tasks 39%

Email 2x%

Collaborating Internally x%

Searching and Gathering Info 19%

Source: Mckinsey Global Institute

21. What percent of an average worker's time is spent on tasks other than role-specific tasks?

22. According to a Gallup Poll, the average work week in the United States is now 47 hours. How many hours per week would an average worker spend on role-specific tasks? Round to the nearest tenth of an hour.

23. What percent of an average worker's time is spent on communicating and collaborating internally?

24. What percent of an average worker's time at work is spent on e-mail?

Use the diagrams to find the unknown measures of angles or lengths of sides. Recall that the sum of the angle measures of a triangle is 180°. See Example 5.

25.

$4x°$

$(x + 6)°$

$x°$

26.

$3x°$

$(x + 10)°$

$x°$

27.

$(4x)$ m

$(5x + 1)$ m

$(5x + 3)$ m

Perimeter is 102 meters.

28.

$(2x)$ cm

$(3.5x)$ cm

$(3x + 7)$ cm

Perimeter is 75 centimeters.

29.

$(2.5x − 9)$ in.

x in. Isoceles Trapezoid x in.

$1.5x$ in.

Perimeter is 99 inches.

30.

$(9.2x − 3)$ ft

$7.3x$ ft   Parallelogram $7.3x$ ft

$(9.2x − 3)$ ft

Perimeter is 324 feet.

Solve. See Example 6.

31. The sum of three consecutive integers is 228. Find the integers.

32. The sum of three consecutive odd integers is 327. Find the integers.

33. The ZIP codes of three Nevada locations—Fallon, Fernley, and Gardnerville Ranchos—are three consecutive even integers. If twice the first integer added to the third is 268,222, find each ZIP code.

34. During a recent year, the average SAT scores in math for the states of Alabama, Louisiana, and Michigan were 3 consecutive integers. If the sum of the first integer, second integer, and three times the third integer is 2637, find each score.

MIXED PRACTICE

Solve. See Examples 1 through 6.

Many companies predict the growth or decline of various social network use. The following data is from Techcrunchies, a technical information site. Notice that the first table is the predicted increase in the number of people using social network sites worldwide (in billions) and the second is the predicted percent increase in the number of social network site users worldwide.

35. Use the middle column in the table to find the predicted number of social network site users for each year.

Year	Increase in Social Network Users	Predicted Number
2015	$2x$	
2016	$2x + 170$	
2017	$3x - 650$	
Total	6380 million	

36. Use the middle column in the table to find the predicted percent of increase in the number of social network site users for each year.

Year	Percent of Increase in Social Network Users	Predicted Percent of Increase
2015	x	
2016	$3x - 11$	
2017	$2x + 11$	
Total	66%	

37. The occupations of registered nurse, food service employee, and customer service representative are among the 10 with the largest predicted growth from 2012 to 2022. The number of registered nurses is predicted to grow 317 thousand less than twice the number of food service jobs. The number of customer service jobs is predicted to grow 88 thousand more than half the number of food service jobs. If the total growth of these three jobs is predicted to be 1248 thousand, find the predicted growth of each job. (*Source:* U.S. Department of Labor, Bureau of Labor Statistics)

38. The occupations of reporter, travel agent, and flight attendant are among the 10 jobs with the largest predicted decline from 2012 to 2022. The number of reporter or correspondent jobs is predicted to decline 17 hundred less than the number of travel agent jobs. The number of flight attendant jobs is predicted to decline 21 hundred less than twice the number of travel agent jobs. If the total decline of these three jobs is predicted to be 318 hundred, find the predicted decline of each job. (*Source:* U.S. Department of Labor, Bureau of Labor Statistics)

39. The B767-300ER aircraft has 88 more seats than the B737-200 aircraft. The F-100 has 32 fewer seats than the B737-200 aircraft. If their total number of seats is 413, find the number of seats for each aircraft. (*Source:* Air Transport Association of America)

40. AT&T Stadium, home of the Dallas Cowboys of the NFL, seats approximately 11,200 more fans than does Gillette Stadium, home of the New England Patriots. CenturyLink Field, home of the Seattle Seahawks, seats 3800 fewer than Gillette Stadium. If the total seats in these three stadiums is 213,800, how many seats are in each of the three stadiums?

41. A new fax machine was recently purchased for an office in Hopedale for $464.40 including tax. If the tax rate in Hopedale is 8%, find the price of the fax machine before tax.

42. A premedical student at a local university was complaining that she had just paid $158.60 for her human anatomy book, including tax. Find the price of the book before taxes if the tax rate at this university is 9%.

43. The median compensation for a U.S. university president was $479,000 for the 2013–2014 academic year. Suppose a U.S. university president had a salary of $479,000 for that year. Calculate her salary if she received a 3.6% raise.

44. In 2014, the population of Germany was 80.9 million. This represented a decrease in population of 1.96% from 2004. What was the population of Germany in 2004? Round to the nearest tenth of a million. (*Source:* Population Reference Bureau)

45. In 2014, the population of Angola was 22,400,000 people. From 2014 to 2050, Angola's population is expected to increase by 272%. Find the expected population of Angola in 2050. (*Source:* Population Reference Bureau)

46. Dana, an auto parts supplier headquartered in Toledo, Ohio, recently announced it would be cutting 11,000 jobs worldwide. This is equivalent to 15% of Dana's workforce. Find the size of Dana's workforce prior to this round of job layoffs. Round to the nearest whole. (*Source:* Dana Corporation)

Recall that two angles are complements of each other if their sum is 90°. Two angles are supplements of each other if their sum is 180°. Find the measure of each angle.

47. One angle is three times its supplement increased by 20°. Find the measures of the two supplementary angles.

48. One angle is twice its complement increased by 30°. Find the measure of the two complementary angles.

Recall that the sum of the angle measures of a triangle is 180°.

△ **49.** Find the measures of the angles of a triangle if the measure of one angle is twice the measure of a second angle and the third angle measures 3 times the second angle decreased by 12.

△ **50.** Find the angles of an isoceles triangle whose two base angles are equal and whose third angle is 10° less than three times a base angle.

51. Two frames are needed with the same perimeter: one frame in the shape of a square and one in the shape of an equilateral triangle. Each side of the triangle is 6 centimeters longer than each side of the square. Find the side lengths of each frame. (An equilateral triangle has sides that are the same length.)

52. Two frames are needed with the same perimeter: one frame in the shape of a square and one in the shape of a regular pentagon. Each side of the square is 7 inches longer than each side of the pentagon. Find the side lengths of each frame. (A regular polygon has sides that are the same length.)

53. The sum of the first and third of three consecutive even integers is 156. Find the three even integers.

54. The sum of the second and fourth of four consecutive integers is 110. Find the four integers.

55. Daytona International Speedway in Florida has 37,000 more grandstand seats than twice the number of grandstand seats at Darlington Motor Raceway in South Carolina. Together, these two race tracks seat 220,000 NASCAR fans. How many seats does each race track have? (*Source:* NASCAR)

56. For the 2014–2015 National Hockey League season, the payroll for the San Jose Sharks was $5,049,585 less than that of the Montreal Canadiens. The total payroll for these two teams was $129,215,719. What were the payrolls for these two teams for the 2014–2015 NHL season?

57. The sum of the populations of the urban areas of New York, Delhi, and Tokyo-Yokohama is 83.6 million. Use this information and Example 2 in this section to find the population of each urban area. Round to the nearest tenth of a million. (*Source:* Demographia World Urban Areas, 2015.01)

58. The airports in Atlanta, Chicago, and Los Angeles have a total of 226 million annual passengers. Use this information and Practice 2 in this section to find the number of passengers at each airport.

△ **59.** Suppose the perimeter of the triangle in Example 1(b) in this section is 483 feet. Find the length of each side.

△ **60.** Suppose the perimeter of the trapezoid in Practice 1(b) in this section is 110 meters. Find the lengths of its sides and bases.

61. Incandescent, fluorescent, and halogen bulbs are lasting longer today than ever before. On average, the number of bulb hours for a fluorescent bulb is 25 times the number of bulb hours for a halogen bulb. The number of bulb hours for an incandescent bulb is 2500 less than the halogen bulb. If the total number of bulb hours for the three types of bulbs is 105,500, find the number of bulb hours for each type. (*Source: Popular Science* magazine)

62. LED (light-emitting diode) bulbs and lamps are gaining popularity because of their low energy cost and production of very little heat. Over a 20-year span, the energy cost of a CFL bulb is $26 more than an LED bulb. Also, the energy cost of an incandescent bulb is $18 more than 6 times an LED bulb. If the total energy cost of these three bulb types is $476, find the energy cost of each. (Based on 13cents/kWh; *Source*: Wikipedia)

63. During the 2014 Major League Baseball season, the number of wins for the Toronto Blue Jays, the New York Yankees, and the Milwaukee Brewers were three consecutive integers. Of these three teams, the Yankees had the most wins and the Brewers had the least wins. The total number of wins by these three teams was 249. How many wins did each team have in the 2014 season?

64. In the 2014 Winter Olympics, Norway won more medals than Canada, which won more medals than the Netherlands. If the numbers of medals won by these three countries are consecutive integers whose sum is 75, find the number of medals won by each. (*Source:* Sochi 2014)

65. The three tallest hospitals in the world are Guy's Tower in London, Queen Mary Hospital in Hong Kong, and Galter Pavilion in Chicago. These buildings have a total height of 1320 feet. Guy's Tower is 67 feet taller than Galter Pavilion, and the Queen Mary Hospital is 47 feet taller than Galter Pavilion. Find the heights of the three hospitals.

△ 66. The official manual for traffic signs is the *Manual on Uniform Traffic Control Devices* published by the Government Printing Office. The rectangular sign below has a length 12 inches more than twice its height. If the perimeter of the sign is 312 inches, find its dimensions.

REVIEW AND PREVIEW

Find the value of each expression for the given values. See Section 1.3.

67. $4ab - 3bc$; $a = -5$, $b = -8$, and $c = 2$

68. $ab + 6bc$; $a = 0$, $b = -1$, and $c = 9$

69. $n^2 - m^2$; $n = -3$ and $m = -8$

70. $2n^2 + 3m^2$; $n = -2$ and $m = 7$

71. $P + PRT$; $P = 3000$, $R = 0.0325$, and $T = 2$

72. $\frac{1}{3} lwh$; $l = 37.8$, $w = 5.6$, and $h = 7.9$

CONCEPT EXTENSIONS

73. For Exercise 36, the percents have a sum of 66% not 100%. Is this possible? Why or why not?

74. In your own words, explain the differences in the tables for Exercises 35 and 36.

75. Find an angle such that its supplement is equal to 10 times its complement.

76. Find an angle such that its supplement is equal to twice its complement increased by 50°.

The average annual number of cigarettes smoked by an American adult continues to decline. For the years 2000–2012, the equation $y = -80.6x + 2054$ approximates this data. Here, x is the number of years after 2000 and y is the average annual number of cigarettes smoked. (Source: Centers for Disease Control)

77. If this trend continues, find the year in which the average annual number of cigarettes smoked is zero. To do this, let $y = 0$ and solve for x.

78. Predict the average annual number of cigarettes smoked by an American adult in 2017. To do so, let $x = 17$ (since $2017 - 2000 = 17$) and find y.

79. Predict the average annual number of cigarettes smoked by an American adult in 2020. To do so, let $x = 20$ (since $2020 - 2000 = 20$) and find y.

80. Use the result of Exercise 78 to predict the average *daily* number of cigarettes smoked by an American adult in 2017. Round to the nearest whole. Do you think this number represents the average daily number of cigarettes smoked by an adult? Why or why not?

81. Determine whether there are three consecutive integers such that their sum is three times the second integer.

82. Determine whether there are two consecutive odd integers such that 7 times the first exceeds 5 times the second by 54.

To break even in a manufacturing business, income or revenue R must equal the cost of production C. Use this information to answer Exercises 83 through 86.

83. The cost C to produce x skateboards is $C = 100 + 20x$. The skateboards are sold wholesale for $24 each, so revenue R is given by $R = 24x$. Find how many skateboards the manufacturer needs to produce and sell to break even. (*Hint:* Set the cost expression equal to the revenue expression and solve for x.)

84. The revenue R from selling x computer boards is given by $R = 60x$, and the cost C of producing them is given by $C = 50x + 5000$. Find how many boards must be sold to break even. Find how much money is needed to produce the break-even number of boards.

85. In your own words, explain what happens if a company makes and sells fewer products than the break-even number.

86. In your own words, explain what happens if more products than the break-even number are made and sold.

2.3 | Formulas and Problem Solving

OBJECTIVES

1 Solve a Formula for a Specified Variable.

2 Use Formulas to Solve Problems.

OBJECTIVE

1 Solving a Formula for a Specified Variable

Solving problems that we encounter in the real world sometimes requires us to express relationships among measured quantities. An equation that describes a known relationship among quantities such as distance, time, volume, weight, money, and gravity is called a **formula.** Some examples of formulas are

Formula	Meaning
$I = PRT$	Interest = principal · rate · time
$A = lw$	Area of a rectangle = length · width
$d = rt$	Distance = rate · time
$C = 2\pi r$	Circumference of a circle = $2 \cdot \pi \cdot$ radius
$V = lwh$	Volume of a rectangular solid = length · width · height

Other formulas are listed in this text. Notice that the formula for the volume of a rectangular solid $V = lwh$ is solved for V since V is by itself on one side of the equation with no V's on the other side of the equation. Suppose that the volume of a rectangular solid is known as well as its width and its length, and we wish to find its height. One way to find its height is to begin by solving the **formula** $V = lwh$ for h.

 EXAMPLE 1   Solve: $V = lwh$ for h

Solution To solve $V = lwh$ for h, isolate h on one side of the equation. To do so, divide both sides of the equation by lw.

$$V = lwh$$
$$\frac{V}{lw} = \frac{lw\,h}{lw} \qquad \text{Divide both sides by } lw.$$
$$\frac{V}{lw} = h \text{ or } h = \frac{V}{lw} \qquad \text{Simplify.}$$

Thus we see that to find the height of a rectangular solid, we divide its volume by the product of its length and its width.   □

PRACTICE

1   Solve: $I = PRT$ for T ∎

The following steps may be used to solve formulas and equations in general for a specified variable.

Solving Equations for a Specified Variable

Step 1. Clear the equation of fractions by multiplying each side of the equation by the least common denominator.

Step 2. Use the distributive property to remove grouping symbols such as parentheses.

Step 3. Combine like terms on each side of the equation.

Step 4. Use the addition property of equality to rewrite the equation as an equivalent equation with terms containing the specified variable on one side and all other terms on the other side.

Step 5. Use the distributive property and the multiplication property of equality to isolate the specified variable.

EXAMPLE 2 Solve: $3y - 2x = 7$ for y

Solution This is a linear equation in two variables. Often an equation such as this is solved for y to reveal some properties about the graph of this equation, which we will learn more about in Chapter 3. Since there are no fractions or grouping symbols, we begin with Step 4 and isolate the term containing the specified variable y by adding $2x$ to both sides of the equation.

$$3y - 2x = 7$$
$$3y - 2x + 2x = 7 + 2x \quad \text{Add } 2x \text{ to both sides.}$$
$$3y = 7 + 2x$$

To solve for y, divide both sides by 3.

$$\frac{3y}{3} = \frac{7 + 2x}{3} \quad \text{Divide both sides by 3.}$$

$$y = \frac{2x + 7}{3} \quad \text{or} \quad y = \frac{2x}{3} + \frac{7}{3}$$

PRACTICE
2 Solve: $7x - 2y = 5$ for y

△ **EXAMPLE 3** Solve: $A = \frac{1}{2}(B + b)h$ for b

Solution Since this formula for finding the area of a trapezoid contains fractions, we begin by multiplying both sides of the equation by the LCD, 2.

$$A = \frac{1}{2}(B + b)h$$

$$2 \cdot A = 2 \cdot \frac{1}{2}(B + b)h \quad \text{Multiply both sides by 2.}$$

$$2A = (B + b)h \quad \text{Simplify.}$$

Next, use the distributive property and remove parentheses.

$$2A = (B + b)h$$
$$2A = Bh + bh \qquad \text{Apply the distributive property.}$$
$$2A - Bh = bh \qquad \text{Isolate the term containing } b \text{ by subtracting } Bh \text{ from both sides.}$$
$$\frac{2A - Bh}{h} = \frac{bh}{h} \qquad \text{Divide both sides by } h.$$
$$\frac{2A - Bh}{h} = b \quad \text{or} \quad b = \frac{2A - Bh}{h}$$

Helpful Hint

Remember that we may get the specified variable alone on either side of the equation.

PRACTICE
3 Solve: $A = P + Prt$ for r

OBJECTIVE

2 Using Formulas to Solve Problems

In this section, we also solve problems that can be modeled by known formulas. We use the same problem-solving steps that were introduced in the previous section.

Formulas are very useful in problem solving. For example, the compound interest formula

$$A = P\left(1 + \frac{r}{n}\right)^{nt}$$

is used by banks to compute the amount A in an account that pays compound interest. The variable P represents the principal or amount invested in the account, r is the annual rate of interest, t is the time in years, and n is the number of times compounded per year.

EXAMPLE 4   Finding the Amount in a Savings Account

Karen Estes just received an inheritance of $10,000 and plans to place all the money in a savings account that pays 5% compounded quarterly to help her son go to college in 3 years. How much money will be in the account in 3 years?

Solution

1. UNDERSTAND. Read and reread the problem. The appropriate formula to solve this problem is the compound interest formula

$$A = P\left(1 + \frac{r}{n}\right)^{nt}.$$

   Make sure that you understand the meaning of all the variables in this formula.

   A = amount in the account after t years
   P = principal or amount invested
   t = time in years
   r = annual rate of interest
   n = number of times compounded per year

2. TRANSLATE. Use the compound interest formula and let P = $10,000, r = 5% = 0.05, t = 3 years, and n = 4 since the account is compounded quarterly, or 4 times a year.

   Formula: $A = P\left(1 + \dfrac{r}{n}\right)^{nt}$

   Substitute: $A = 10,000\left(1 + \dfrac{0.05}{4}\right)^{4\cdot3}$

3. SOLVE. We simplify the right side of the equation.

   $$A = 10,000\left(1 + \frac{0.05}{4}\right)^{4\cdot3}$$

   $A = 10,000(1.0125)^{12}$ Simplify $1 + \dfrac{0.05}{4}$ and write $4\cdot3$ as 12.

   $A \approx 10,000(1.160754518)$ Approximate $(1.0125)^{12}$.

   $A \approx 11,607.55$ Multiply and round to two decimal places.

4. INTERPRET.

   Check: Repeat your calculations to make sure that no error was made. Notice that $11,607.55 is a reasonable amount to have in the account after 3 years.

   State: In 3 years, the account will contain $11,607.55.   □

PRACTICE
4   Russ placed $8000 into his credit union account paying 6% compounded semiannually (twice a year). How much will be in Russ's account in 4 years?   ■

Graphing Calculator Explorations

To solve Example 4, we approximated the expression

$$10{,}000\left(1 + \frac{0.05}{4}\right)^{4 \cdot 3}.$$

Use the keystrokes shown in the accompanying calculator screen to evaluate this expression using a graphing calculator. Notice the use of parentheses.

EXAMPLE 5 **Finding Cycling Time**

The fastest average speed by a cyclist across the continental United States is 15.4 mph, by Pete Penseyres. If he traveled a total distance of about 3107.5 miles at this speed, find his time cycling. Write the time in days, hours, and minutes. *(Source: The Guinness Book of World Records)*

Solution

1. UNDERSTAND. Read and reread the problem. The appropriate formula is the distance formula

$$d = rt \quad \text{where}$$
$$d = \text{distance traveled} \quad r = \text{rate} \quad \text{and} \quad t = \text{time}$$

2. TRANSLATE. Use the distance formula and let $d = 3107.5$ miles and $r = 15.4$ mph.

$$d = rt$$
$$3107.5 = 15.4t$$

3. SOLVE.

$$\frac{3107.5}{15.4} = \frac{15.4t}{15.4} \quad \text{Divide both sides by 15.4.}$$
$$201.79 \approx t$$

The time is approximately 201.79 hours. Since there are 24 hours in a day, we divide 201.79 by 24 and find that the time is approximately 8.41 days. Now, let's convert the decimal part of 8.41 days back to hours. To do this, multiply 0.41 by 24 and the result is 9.84 hours. Next, we convert the decimal part of 9.84 hours to minutes by multiplying by 60 since there are 60 minutes in an hour. We have $0.84 \cdot 60 \approx 50$ minutes rounded to the nearest whole. The time is then approximately

8 days, 9 hours, 50 minutes.

4. INTERPRET.

Check: Repeat your calculations to make sure that an error was not made.

State: Pete Penseyres's cycling time was approximately 8 days, 9 hours, 50 minutes. □

PRACTICE
5 Nearly 5500 cyclists from 34 U.S. states and 9 countries rode in the Pan Massachusetts challenge in 2014 to raise money for cancer research and treatment. If the riders on a certain team traveled their 190-mile route at an average speed of 7.5 miles per hour, find the time they spent cycling. Write the answer in hours. Then write the answer in hours and minutes. ■

✓ Vocabulary, Readiness & Video Check

Solve each equation for the specified variable. See Examples 1 through 3.

1. $2x + y = 5$ for y

2. $7x - y = 3$ for y

3. $a - 5b = 8$ for a

4. $7r + s = 10$ for s

5. $5j + k - h = 6$ for k

6. $w - 4y + z = 0$ for z

Martin-Gay Interactive Videos

See Video 2.3 🔵

Watch the section lecture video and answer the following questions.

OBJECTIVE 1

7. Based on the lecture before Example 1, what two things does solving an equation for a specified variable mean?

OBJECTIVE 2

8. As the solution is checked at the end of ▦ Example 3, why do you think it is mentioned to be especially careful that you use the correct formula when solving problems?

2.3 Exercise Set MyMathLab® ▶

Solve each equation for the specified variable. See Examples 1–3.

1. $d = rt$; for t

2. $W = gh$; for g

3. $I = PRT$; for R

△ **4.** $V = lwh$; for l

▶ **5.** $9x - 4y = 16$; for y

6. $2x + 3y = 17$; for y

△ **7.** $P = 2L + 2W$; for W

8. $A = 3M - 2N$; for N

9. $J = AC - 3$; for A

10. $y = mx + b$; for x

11. $W = gh - 3gt^2$; for g

12. $A = Prt + P$; for P

13. $T = C(2 + AB)$; for B

14. $A = 5H(b + B)$; for b

△ **15.** $C = 2\pi r$; for r

△ **16.** $S = 2\pi r^2 + 2\pi rh$; for h

17. $E = I(r + R)$; for r

18. $A = P(1 + rt)$; for t

▶ **19.** $s = \dfrac{n}{2}(a + L)$; for L

20. $C = \dfrac{5}{9}(F - 32)$; for F

21. $N = 3st^4 - 5sv$; for v

22. $L = a + (n - 1)d$; for d

△ **23.** $S = 2LW + 2LH + 2WH$; for H

24. $T = 3vs - 4ws + 5vw$; for v

In this exercise set, round all dollar amounts to two decimal places. Solve. See Example 4.

25. Complete the table and find the balance A if $3500 is invested at an annual percentage rate of 3% for 10 years and compounded n times a year.

n	1	2	4	12	365
A					

26. Complete the table and find the balance A if $5000 is invested at an annual percentage rate of 6% for 15 years and compounded n times a year.

n	1	2	4	12	365
A					

27. A principal of $6000 is invested in an account paying an annual percentage rate of 4%. Find the amount in the account after 5 years if the account is compounded
  a. semiannually   **b.** quarterly   **c.** monthly

28. A principal of $25,000 is invested in an account paying an annual percentage rate of 5%. Find the amount in the account after 2 years if the account is compounded
  a. semiannually   **b.** quarterly   **c.** monthly

MIXED PRACTICE

Solve. For Exercises 29 and 30, the solutions have been started for you. Round all dollar amounts to two decimal places. See Examples 4 and 5.

29. Omaha, Nebraska, is about 90 miles from Lincoln, Nebraska. Irania Schmidt must go to the law library in Lincoln to get a document for the law firm she works for. Find how long it takes her to drive *round-trip* if she averages 50 mph.

Start the solution:

1. **UNDERSTAND** the problem. Reread it as many times as needed.

2. **TRANSLATE** into an equation. (Fill in the blanks below.) Here, we simply use the formula $d = r \cdot t$.

Finish with:

3. **SOLVE** and 4. **INTERPRET**

30. It took the Selby family $5\frac{1}{2}$ hours round-trip to drive from their house to their beach house 154 miles away. Find their average speed.

Start the solution:

1. **UNDERSTAND** the problem. Reread it as many times as needed.

2. **TRANSLATE** into an equation. (Fill in the blanks below.) Here, we simply use the formula $d = r \cdot t$.

Finish with:

3. **SOLVE** and 4. **INTERPRET**

31. The day's high temperature in Phoenix, Arizona, was recorded as 104°F. Write 104°F as degrees Celsius. [Use the formula $C = \frac{5}{9}(F - 32)$.]

32. The average low temperature in Nome, Alaska, was recorded as −15°C. Write −15°C as degrees Fahrenheit. [Use the formula $F = \frac{9}{5}C + 32$.]

△ **33.** A package of floor tiles contains 24 one-foot-square tiles. Find how many packages should be bought to cover a square ballroom floor whose side measures 64 feet.

△ **34.** One-foot-square ceiling tiles are sold in packages of 50. Find how many packages must be bought for a rectangular ceiling 18 feet by 12 feet.

△ **35.** If the area of a triangular kite is 18 square feet and its base is 4 feet, find the height of the kite.

36. Bailey, Ethan, Avery, Mia, and Madison would like to go to Disneyland in 3 years. Their total cost should be $4500. If each invests $800 in a savings account paying 5.5% interest compounded semiannually, will they have enough in 3 years?

△ **37.** A gallon of latex paint can cover 500 square feet. Find how many gallon containers of paint should be bought to paint two coats on each wall of a rectangular room whose dimensions are 14 feet by 16 feet (assume 8-foot ceilings).

△ **38.** A gallon of enamel paint can cover 300 square feet. Find how many gallon containers of paint should be bought to paint three coats on a wall measuring 21 feet by 8 feet.

To prepare for Exercises 43 and 44, use the volume formulas below to solve Exercises 39–42. Remember, volume is measured in cubic units.

$$\text{Cylinder: } V = \pi r^2 h \qquad \text{Sphere: } V = \frac{4}{3}\pi r^3$$

39. The cylinder below has an exact volume of 980π cubic meters. Find its height.

40. The battery below is in the shape of a cylinder and has an exact volume of 825π cubic millimeters. Find its height.

41. The steel ball below is in the shape of a sphere and has a diameter of 12 millimeters.

a. Find the exact volume of the sphere.

b. Find a 2-decimal-place approximation for the volume.

42. The spherical ball below has a diameter of 18 centimeters.

$d = 18$ cm

   a. Find the exact volume of the ball.

   b. Find a 2-decimal-place approximation of the volume.

△ **43.** A portion of the external tank of the Space Shuttle *Endeavour* was a liquid hydrogen tank. If the ends of the tank are hemispheres, find the volume of the tank. To do so, answer parts **a** through **c**. (*Note: Endeavour* completed its last mission in 2011.)

4.2 m

21.2 m

4.2 m   Cylinder

Sphere

   a. Find the volume of the cylinder shown. Round to 2 decimal places.

   b. Find the volume of the sphere shown. Round to 2 decimal places.

   c. Add the results of parts **a** and **b**. This sum is the approximate volume of the tank.

44. A vitamin is in the shape of a cylinder with a hemisphere at each end, as shown. Use the art in Exercise 43 to help find the volume of the vitamin.

4 mm

15 mm

   a. Find the volume of the cylinder part. Round to two decimal places.

   b. Find the volume of the sphere formed by joining the two hemispherical ends. Round to two decimal places.

   c. Add the results of parts **a** and **b** to find the approximate volume of the vitamin.

45. Amelia Earhart was the first woman to fly solo nonstop coast to coast, setting the women's nonstop transcontinental speed record. She traveled 2447.8 miles in 19 hours 5 minutes. Find the average speed of her flight in miles per hour. (Change 19 hours 5 minutes into hours and use the formula $d = rt$.) Round to the nearest tenth of a mile per hour.

△ **46.** In 1945, Arthur C. Clarke, a scientist and science-fiction writer, predicted that an artificial satellite placed at a height of 22,248 miles directly above the equator would orbit the globe at the same speed with which the Earth was rotating. This belt along the equator is known as the Clarke belt. Use the formula for circumference of a circle and find the "length" of the Clarke belt. (*Hint:* Recall that the radius of the Earth is approximately 4000 miles. Round to the nearest whole mile.)

22,248 mi

△ **47.** The deepest hole in the ocean floor is beneath the Pacific Ocean and is called Hole 504B. It is located off the coast of Ecuador. Scientists are drilling it to learn more about the Earth's history. Currently, the hole is in the shape of a cylinder whose volume is approximately 3800 cubic feet and whose length is 1.3 miles. Find the radius of the hole to the nearest hundredth of a foot. (*Hint:* Make sure the same units of measurement are used.)

48. The deepest man-made hole is called the Kola Superdeep Borehole. It is approximately 8 miles deep and is located near a small Russian town in the Arctic Circle. If it takes 7.5 hours to remove the drill from the bottom of the hole, find the rate that the drill can be retrieved in feet per second. Round to the nearest tenth. (*Hint:* Write 8 miles as feet, 7.5 hours as seconds, then use the formula $d = rt$.)

△ **49.** Eartha is the world's largest globe. It is located at the headquarters of DeLorme, a mapmaking company in Yarmouth, Maine. Eartha is 41.125 feet in diameter. Find its exact circumference (distance around) and then approximate its circumference rounding to three decimal places. (*Source:* DeLorme)

△ **50.** Eartha is in the shape of a sphere. Its radius is about 20.6 feet. Approximate its volume to the nearest cubic foot. (*Source:* DeLorme)

51. Find *how much interest* $10,000 earns in 2 years in a certificate of deposit paying 8.5% interest compounded quarterly.

52. Find how long it takes Mark to drive 135 miles on I-10 if he merges onto I-10 at 10 a.m. and drives nonstop with his cruise control set on 60 mph.

The calorie count of a serving of food can be computed based on its composition of carbohydrate, fat, and protein. The calorie count C for a serving of food can be computed using the formula $C = 4h + 9f + 4p$, where h is the number of grams of carbohydrate contained in the serving, f is the number of grams of fat contained in the serving, and p is the number of grams of protein contained in the serving.

53. Solve this formula for f, the number of grams of fat contained in a serving of food.

54. Solve this formula for h, the number of grams of carbohydrate contained in a serving of food.

55. A serving of cashews contains 14 grams of fat, 7 grams of carbohydrate, and 6 grams of protein. How many calories are in this serving of cashews?

56. A serving of chocolate candies contains 9 grams of fat, 30 grams of carbohydrate, and 2 grams of protein. How many calories are in this serving of chocolate candies?

57. A serving of raisins contains 130 calories and 31 grams of carbohydrate. If raisins are a fat-free food, how much protein is provided by this serving of raisins?

58. A serving of yogurt contains 120 calories, 21 grams of carbohydrate, and 5 grams of protein. How much fat is provided by this serving of yogurt? Round to the nearest tenth of a gram.

REVIEW AND PREVIEW

Determine which numbers in the set $\{-3, -2, -1, 0, 1, 2, 3\}$ are solutions of each inequality. See Sections 1.4 and 2.1.

59. $x < 0$ **60.** $x > 1$

61. $x + 5 \leq 6$

62. $x - 3 \geq -7$

63. In your own words, explain what real numbers are solutions of $x < 0$.

64. In your own words, explain what real numbers are solutions of $x > 1$.

CONCEPT EXTENSIONS

Solar system distances are so great that units other than miles or kilometers are often used. For example, the astronomical unit (AU) is the average distance between Earth and the Sun, or 92,900,000 miles. Use this information to convert each planet's distance in miles from the Sun to astronomical units. Round to three decimal places. The planet Mercury's AU from the Sun has been completed for you. (Source: National Space Science Data Center)

	Planet	Miles from the Sun	AU from the Sun
	Mercury	36 million	0.388
65.	Venus	67.2 million	
66.	Earth	92.9 million	
67.	Mars	141.5 million	
68.	Jupiter	483.3 million	
69.	Saturn	886.1 million	

	Planet	Miles from the Sun	AU from the Sun
70.	Uranus	1783 million	
71.	Neptune	2793 million	
72.	Pluto (dwarf planet)	3670 million	

73. To borrow money at a rate of r, which loan plan should you choose—one compounding 4 times a year or 12 times a year? Explain your choice.

74. If you are investing money in a savings account paying a rate of r, which account should you choose—an account compounded 4 times a year or 12 times a year? Explain your choice.

75. To solve the formula $W = gh - 3gt^2$ for g, explain why it is a good idea to factor g first from the terms on the right side of the equation. Then perform this step and solve for g.

76. An orbit such as Clarke's belt in Exercise 46 is called a geostationary orbit. In your own words, why do you think that communications satellites are placed in geostationary orbits?

*The measure of the chance or likelihood of an event occurring is its **probability**. A formula basic to the study of probability is the formula for the probability of an event when all the outcomes are equally likely. This formula is*

$$\text{Probability of an event} = \frac{\text{number of ways that the event can occur}}{\text{number of possible outcomes}}$$

For example, to find the probability that a single spin on the spinner below will result in red, notice first that the spinner is divided into 8 parts, so there are 8 possible outcomes. Next, notice that there is only one sector of the spinner colored red, so the number of ways that the spinner can land on red is 1. Then this probability denoted by P(red) is

$$P(\text{red}) = \tfrac{1}{8}$$

Find each probability in simplest form.

77. $P(\text{green})$ **78.** $P(\text{yellow})$

79. $P(\text{black})$ **80.** $P(\text{blue})$

81. $P(\text{green or blue})$ **82.** $P(\text{black or yellow})$

83. $P(\text{red, green, or black})$

84. $P(\text{yellow, blue, or black})$

85. $P(\text{white})$

86. $P(\text{red, yellow, green, blue, or black})$

87. From the previous probability formula, what do you think is always the probability of an event that is impossible to occur?

88. What do you think is always the probability of an event that is sure to occur?

2.4   Linear Inequalities and Problem Solving

OBJECTIVES

1 Use Interval Notation.

2 Solve Linear Inequalities Using the Addition Property of Inequality.

3 Solve Linear Inequalities Using the Multiplication and the Addition Properties of Inequality.

4 Solve Problems That Can Be Modeled by Linear Inequalities.

Relationships among measurable quantities are not always described by equations. For example, suppose that a salesperson earns a base of $600 per month plus a commission of 20% of sales. Suppose we want to find the minimum amount of sales needed to receive a total income of *at least* $1500 per month. Here, the phrase "at least" implies that an income of $1500 *or more* is acceptable. In symbols, we can write

$$\text{income} \geq 1500$$

This is an example of an inequality, and we will solve this problem in Example 8.

A **linear inequality** is similar to a linear equation except that the equality symbol is replaced with an inequality symbol, such as $<$, $>$, $\leq$, or $\geq$.

Linear Inequalities in One Variable

$3x + 5 \geq 4$	$2y < 0$	$3(x - 4) > 5x$	$\dfrac{x}{3} \leq 5$
↑	↑	↑	↑
is greater than or equal to	is less than	is greater than	is less than or equal to

---

Linear Inequality in One Variable

A linear inequality in one variable is an inequality that can be written in the form

$$ax + b < c$$

where a, b, and c are real numbers and $a \neq 0$.

In this section, when we make definitions, state properties, or list steps about an inequality containing the symbol $<$, we mean that the definition, property, or steps also apply to inequalities containing the symbols $>$, $\leq$, and $\geq$.

OBJECTIVE

1 Using Interval Notation

A **solution** of an inequality is a value of the variable that makes the inequality a true statement. The **solution set** of an inequality is the set of all solutions. Notice that the solution set of the inequality $x > 2$, for example, contains all numbers greater than 2. Its graph is an interval on the number line since an infinite number of values satisfy the variable. If we use open/closed-circle notation, the graph of $\{x \mid x > 2\}$ looks like the following.

In this text **interval notation** will be used to write solution sets of inequalities. To help us understand this notation, a different graphing notation will be used. Instead of an open circle, we use a parenthesis. With this new notation, the graph of $\{x \mid x > 2\}$ now looks like

and can be represented in interval notation as $(2, \infty)$. The symbol ∞ is read "infinity" and indicates that the interval includes *all* numbers greater than 2. The left parenthesis indicates that 2 *is not* included in the interval.

When 2 *is* included in the interval, we use a bracket. The graph of $\{x \mid x \geq 2\}$ is below

and can be represented as $[2, \infty)$.

The following table shows three equivalent ways to describe an interval: in set notation, as a graph, and in interval notation.

Set Notation	Graph	Interval Notation
$\{x \mid x < a\}$		$(-\infty, a)$
$\{x \mid x > a\}$		(a, ∞)
$\{x \mid x \leq a\}$		$(-\infty, a]$
$\{x \mid x \geq a\}$		$[a, \infty)$
$\{x \mid a < x < b\}$		(a, b)
$\{x \mid a \leq x \leq b\}$		$[a, b]$
$\{x \mid a < x \leq b\}$		$(a, b]$
$\{x \mid a \leq x < b\}$		$[a, b)$

Helpful Hint

Notice that a parenthesis is always used to enclose ∞ and $-\infty$.

✔ **CONCEPT CHECK**

Explain what is wrong with writing the interval $(5, \infty]$.

EXAMPLE 1 Graph each set on a number line and then write in interval notation.

a. $\{x \mid x \geq 2\}$ **b.** $\{x \mid x < -1\}$ **c.** $\{x \mid 0.5 < x \leq 3\}$

Solution

a. $[2, \infty)$

b. $(-\infty, -1)$

c. $(0.5, 3]$

PRACTICE

1 Graph each set on a number line and then write in interval notation.

a. $\{x \mid x < 3.5\}$

b. $\{x \mid x \geq -3\}$

c. $\{x \mid -1 \leq x < 4\}$

OBJECTIVE

2 Solving Linear Inequalities Using the Addition Property

Answer to Concept Check:
should be $(5, \infty)$ since a parenthesis is
always used to enclose ∞

We will use interval notation to write solutions of linear inequalities. To solve a linear inequality, we use a process similar to the one used to solve a linear equation. We use properties of inequalities to write equivalent inequalities until the variable is isolated.

> **Addition Property of Inequality**
>
> If a, b, and c are real numbers, then
>
> $$a < b \quad \text{and} \quad a + c < b + c$$
>
> are equivalent inequalities.

In other words, we may add the same real number to both sides of an inequality, and the resulting inequality will have the same solution set. This property also allows us to subtract the same real number from both sides.

EXAMPLE 2   Solve $x - 2 < 5$. Graph the solution set and write it in interval notation.

Solution

$$x - 2 < 5$$
$$x - 2 + 2 < 5 + 2 \quad \text{Add 2 to both sides.}$$
$$x < 7 \quad \text{Simplify.}$$

The solution set is $\{x \mid x < 7\}$, which in interval notation is $(-\infty, 7)$. The graph of the solution set is

PRACTICE

2   Solve $x + 5 > 9$. Graph the solution set and write it in interval notation.

> **Helpful Hint**
>
> In Example 2, the solution set is $\{x \mid x < 7\}$. This means that *all* numbers less than 7 are solutions. For example, 6.9, 0, $-\pi$, 1, and -56.7 are solutions, just to name a few. To see this, replace x in $x - 2 < 5$ with each of these numbers and see that the result is a true inequality.

EXAMPLE 3   Solve $3x + 4 \geq 2x - 6$. Graph the solution set and write it in interval notation.

Solution

$$3x + 4 \geq 2x - 6$$
$$3x + 4 - 2x \geq 2x - 6 - 2x \quad \text{Subtract } 2x \text{ from both sides.}$$
$$x + 4 \geq -6 \quad \text{Combine like terms.}$$
$$x + 4 - 4 \geq -6 - 4 \quad \text{Subtract 4 from both sides.}$$
$$x \geq -10 \quad \text{Simplify.}$$

The solution set is $\{x \mid x \geq -10\}$, which in interval notation is $[-10, \infty)$. The graph of the solution set is

PRACTICE

3   Solve $3x + 1 \leq 2x - 3$. Graph the solution set and write it in interval notation.

OBJECTIVE

3   Solving Linear Inequalities Using the Multiplication and Addition Properties ▶

Next, we introduce and use the multiplication property of inequality to solve linear inequalities. To understand this property, let's start with the true statement $-3 < 7$ and multiply both sides by 2.

$$-3 < 7$$
$$-3(2) < 7(2) \quad \text{Multiply by 2.}$$
$$-6 < 14 \quad \text{True}$$

The statement remains true.

Notice what happens if both sides of $-3 < 7$ are multiplied by -2.

$$-3 < 7$$
$$-3(-2) < 7(-2) \quad \text{Multiply by } -2.$$
$$6 < -14 \quad \text{False}$$

The inequality $6 < -14$ is a false statement. However, **if the direction of the inequality sign is reversed,** the result is true.

$$6 > -14 \quad \text{True}$$

These examples suggest the following property.

Multiplication Property of Inequality

If a, b, and c are real numbers and c is **positive**, then

$$a < b \text{ and } ac < bc$$

are equivalent inequalities.

If a, b, and c are real numbers and c is **negative**, then

$$a < b \text{ and } ac > bc$$

are equivalent inequalities.

In other words, we may multiply both sides of an inequality by the same positive real number and the result is an equivalent inequality.

We may also multiply both sides of an inequality by the same **negative number** and **reverse the direction of the inequality symbol,** and the result is an equivalent inequality. The multiplication property holds for division also, since division is defined in terms of multiplication.

> **Helpful Hint**
> Whenever both sides of an inequality are multiplied or divided by a negative number, the direction of the inequality symbol **must be** reversed to form an equivalent inequality.

EXAMPLE 4 Solve and graph the solution set. Write the solution set in interval notation.

a. $\dfrac{1}{4}x \le \dfrac{3}{8}$ **b.** $-2.3x < 6.9$

Solution

> **Helpful Hint**
> The inequality symbol is the same since we are multiplying by a *positive* number.

a.
$$\frac{1}{4}x \le \frac{3}{8}$$

$$4 \cdot \frac{1}{4}x \le 4 \cdot \frac{3}{8} \quad \text{Multiply both sides by 4.}$$

$$x \le \frac{3}{2} \quad \text{Simplify.}$$

The solution set is $\left\{ x \,\middle|\, x \le \dfrac{3}{2} \right\}$, which in interval notation is $\left(-\infty, \dfrac{3}{2} \right]$. The graph of the solution set is

The inequality symbol is *reversed* since we divided by a *negative* number.

b.
$$-2.3x < 6.9$$

$$\frac{-2.3x}{-2.3} > \frac{6.9}{-2.3}$$ Divide both sides by -2.3 and reverse the inequality symbol.

$$x > -3$$ Simplify.

The solution set is $\{x \mid x > -3\}$, which is $(-3, \infty)$ in interval notation. The graph of the solution set is

□

PRACTICE

4   Solve and graph the solution set. Write the solution set in interval notation.

a. $\dfrac{2}{5}x \geq \dfrac{4}{15}$

b. $-2.4x < 9.6$ ■

✔ **CONCEPT CHECK**

In which of the following inequalities must the inequality symbol be reversed during the solution process?

a. $-2x > 7$ **b.** $2x - 3 > 10$

c. $-x + 4 + 3x < 7$ **d.** $-x + 4 < 5$

To solve linear inequalities in general, we follow steps similar to those for solving linear equations.

Solving a Linear Inequality in One Variable

Step 1.   Clear the inequality of fractions by multiplying both sides of the inequality by the least common denominator (LCD) of all fractions in the inequality.

Step 2.   Use the distributive property to remove grouping symbols such as parentheses.

Step 3.   Combine like terms on each side of the inequality.

Step 4.   Use the addition property of inequality to write the inequality as an equivalent inequality with variable terms on one side and numbers on the other side.

Step 5.   Use the multiplication property of inequality to isolate the variable.

EXAMPLE 5   Solve $-(x - 3) + 2 \leq 3(2x - 5) + x$. Graph the solution set and write it in interval notation.

Solution
$$-(x - 3) + 2 \leq 3(2x - 5) + x$$

$$-x + 3 + 2 \leq 6x - 15 + x$$ Apply the distributive property.

$$5 - x \leq 7x - 15$$ Combine like terms.

$$5 - x + x \leq 7x - 15 + x$$ Add x to both sides.

$$5 \leq 8x - 15$$ Combine like terms.

$$5 + 15 \leq 8x - 15 + 15$$ Add 15 to both sides.

$$20 \leq 8x$$ Combine like terms.

$$\frac{20}{8} \leq \frac{8x}{8}$$ Divide both sides by 8.

$$\frac{5}{2} \leq x, \text{ or } x \geq \frac{5}{2}$$ Simplify.

Don't forget that $\dfrac{5}{2} \leq x$ means the same as $x \geq \dfrac{5}{2}$.

Answer to Concept Check: **a, d**

(Continued on next page)

The solution set written in interval notation is $\left[\dfrac{5}{2}, \infty\right)$ and its graph is

PRACTICE
5 Solve $-(4x + 6) \leq 2(5x + 9) + 2x$. Graph the solution set and write it in interval notation.

EXAMPLE 6 Solve $\dfrac{2}{5}(x - 6) \geq x - 1$. Graph the solution set and write it in interval notation.

Solution

$$\dfrac{2}{5}(x - 6) \geq x - 1$$

$$5\left[\dfrac{2}{5}(x - 6)\right] \geq 5(x - 1) \qquad \text{Multiply both sides by 5 to eliminate fractions.}$$

$$2(x - 6) \geq 5(x - 1)$$

$$2x - 12 \geq 5x - 5 \qquad \text{Apply the distributive property.}$$

$$-3x - 12 \geq -5 \qquad \text{Subtract } 5x \text{ from both sides.}$$

$$-3x \geq 7 \qquad \text{Add 12 to both sides.}$$

$$\dfrac{-3x}{-3} \leq \dfrac{7}{-3} \qquad \text{Divide both sides by } -3 \text{ and reverse the inequality symbol.}$$

$$x \leq -\dfrac{7}{3} \qquad \text{Simplify.}$$

The solution set written in interval notation is $\left(-\infty, -\dfrac{7}{3}\right]$ and its graph is

PRACTICE
6 Solve $\dfrac{3}{5}(x - 3) \geq x - 7$. Graph and write the solution set in interval notation.

EXAMPLE 7 Solve $2(x + 3) > 2x + 1$. Graph the solution set and write it in interval notation.

Solution

$$2(x + 3) > 2x + 1$$

$$2x + 6 > 2x + 1 \qquad \text{Distribute on the left side.}$$

$$2x + 6 - 2x > 2x + 1 - 2x \qquad \text{Subtract } 2x \text{ from both sides.}$$

$$6 > 1 \qquad \text{Simplify.}$$

$6 > 1$ is a true statement for all values of x, so this inequality and the original inequality are true for all numbers. The solution set is $\{x \mid x \text{ is a real number}\}$, or $(-\infty, \infty)$ in interval notation, and its graph is

PRACTICE
7 Solve $4(x - 2) < 4x + 5$. Graph the solution set and write it in interval notation.

OBJECTIVE

4 Solving Problems Modeled by Linear Inequalities

Application problems containing words such as "at least," "at most," "between," "no more than," and "no less than" usually indicate that an inequality is to be solved instead of an equation. In solving applications involving linear inequalities, we use the same procedure as when we solved applications involving linear equations.

EXAMPLE 8 Calculating Income with Commission

A salesperson earns $600 per month plus a commission of 20% of sales. Find the minimum amount of sales needed to receive a total income of at least $1500 per month.

Solution

1. UNDERSTAND. Read and reread the problem. Let x = amount of sales.

2. TRANSLATE. As stated in the beginning of this section, we want the income to be greater than or equal to $1500. To write an inequality, notice that the salesperson's income consists of $600 plus a commission (20% of sales).

In words:	600	+	commission (20% of sales)	≥	1500
	↓		↓		↓
Translate:	600	+	0.20x	≥	1500

3. SOLVE the inequality for x.

$$600 + 0.20x \geq 1500$$
$$600 + 0.20x - 600 \geq 1500 - 600$$
$$0.20x \geq 900$$
$$x \geq 4500$$

4. INTERPRET.

Check: The income for sales of $4500 is

$$600 + 0.20(4500), \text{ or } 1500.$$

Thus, if sales are greater than or equal to $4500, income is greater than or equal to $1500.

State: The minimum amount of sales needed for the salesperson to earn at least $1500 per month is $4500 per month. □

PRACTICE

8 A salesperson earns $900 a month plus a commission of 15% of sales. Find the minimum amount of sales needed to receive a total income of at least $2400 per month. ■

EXAMPLE 9 Finding the Annual Consumption

In the United States, the annual consumption of cigarettes is declining. The consumption c in billions of cigarettes per year since the year 2004 can be approximated by the formula

$$c = -11.8t + 390$$

where t is the number of years after 2004. Use this formula to predict the years that the consumption of cigarettes will be less than 200 billion per year.

Solution

1. UNDERSTAND. Read and reread the problem. To become familiar with the given formula, let's find the cigarette consumption after 15 years, which would be the year 2004 + 15, or 2019. To do so, we substitute 15 for t in the given formula.

$$c = -11.8(15) + 390 = 213$$

(Continued on next page)

Thus, in 2019, we predict cigarette consumption to be about 213 billion.

Variables have already been assigned in the given formula. For review, they are

c = the annual consumption of cigarettes in the
United States in billions of cigarettes and

t = the number of years after 2004

2. **TRANSLATE.** We are looking for the years that the consumption of cigarettes c is less than 200. Since we are finding years t, we substitute the expression in the formula given for c, or

$$-11.8t + 390 < 200$$

3. **SOLVE** the inequality.

$$-11.8t + 390 < 200$$
$$-11.8t < -190$$
$$\frac{-11.8}{-11.8}t > \frac{-190}{-11.8}$$
$$t > \text{approximately } 16.1$$

4. **INTERPRET.**

Check: Substitute a number greater than 16.1 and see that c is less than 200.

State: The annual consumption of cigarettes will be less than 200 billion more than 16.1 years after 2004, or approximately for 2004 + 16 = 2020 and all years after.   □

PRACTICE
9   Use the formula given in Example 9 to predict when the consumption of cigarettes will be less than 175 billion per year.   ■

Vocabulary, Readiness & Video Check

Choose the interval notation that describes each graph. Not all choices will be used.

1.

-7 -6 -5 -4 -3 -2 -1 0

a. $(-5, \infty)$ b. $(-5, -\infty)$
c. $(\infty, -5)$ d. $(-\infty, -5)$

2.

-13 -12 -11 -10 -9 -8

a. $(-\infty, -11]$ b. $(-11, \infty)$
c. $[-11, \infty)$ d. $(-\infty, -11)$

3.

-2.5 $\frac{7}{4}$

-3 -2 -1 0 1 2 3 4

a. $\left[\frac{7}{4}, -2.5\right)$ b. $\left(-2.5, \frac{7}{4}\right]$
c. $\left[-2.5, \frac{7}{4}\right)$ d. $\left(\frac{7}{4}, -2.5\right]$

4.

$-\frac{10}{3}$ 0.2

-4 -3 -2 -1 0 1 2 3

a. $\left[-\frac{10}{3}, 0.2\right)$ b. $\left(0.2, -\frac{10}{3}\right]$
c. $\left(-\frac{10}{3}, 0.2\right]$ d. $\left[0.2, -\frac{10}{3}\right)$

Use the choices below to fill in each blank. Not all choices will be used.

$(-\infty, -0.4)$ $(-\infty, -0.4]$ $[-0.4, \infty)$ $(-0.4, \infty)$ $(\infty, -0.4]$

5. The set $\{x \mid x \geq -0.4\}$ written in interval notation is _____.

6. The set $\{x \mid x < -0.4\}$ written in interval notation is _____.

7. The set $\{x \mid x \leq -0.4\}$ written in interval notation is _____.

8. The set $\{x \mid x > -0.4\}$ written in interval notation is _____.

Martin-Gay Interactive Videos

See Video 2.4

Watch the section lecture video and answer the following questions.

OBJECTIVE 1

9. Using Example 1 as a reference, explain how the graph of the solution set of an inequality can help you write the solution set in interval notation.

OBJECTIVE 2

10. From the lecture before Example 3, explain the addition property of inequality in your own words. What equality property does it closely resemble?

OBJECTIVE 3

11. Based on the lecture before Example 4, complete the following statement. If you multiply or divide both sides of an inequality by the _____ nonzero negative number, you must _____ the direction of the inequality symbol.

OBJECTIVE 4

12. What words or phrases in the Example 7 statement tell you this is an inequality application (besides the last line telling you to use an inequality)?

2.4 Exercise Set MyMathLab®

Graph the solution set of each inequality and write it in interval notation. See Example 1.

1. $\{x \mid x < -3\}$
2. $\{x \mid x > 5\}$
3. $\{x \mid x \geq 0.3\}$
4. $\{x \mid x < -0.2\}$
5. $\{x \mid -7 \leq x\}$
6. $\{x \mid -7 \geq x\}$
7. $\{x \mid -2 < x < 5\}$
8. $\{x \mid -5 \leq x \leq -1\}$
9. $\{x \mid 5 \geq x > -1\}$
10. $\{x \mid -3 > x \geq -7\}$

Solve. Graph the solution set and write it in interval notation. See Examples 2 through 4.

11. $x - 7 \geq -9$
12. $x + 2 \leq -1$
13. $7x < 6x + 1$
14. $11x < 10x + 5$
15. $8x - 7 \leq 7x - 5$
16. $7x - 1 \geq 6x - 1$
17. $\frac{3}{4}x \geq 6$
18. $\frac{5}{6}x \geq 5$
19. $5x < -23.5$
20. $4x > -11.2$
21. $-3x \geq 9$
22. $-4x \geq 8$

Solve. Write the solution set using interval notation. See Examples 5 through 7.

23. $-2x + 7 \geq 9$

24. $8 - 5x \leq 23$

25. $15 + 2x \geq 4x - 7$

26. $20 + x < 6x - 15$

27. $4(2x + 1) > 4$

28. $6(2 - 3x) \geq 12$

29. $3(x - 5) < 2(2x - 1)$

30. $5(x + 4) \leq 4(2x + 3)$

31. $\frac{5x + 1}{7} - \frac{2x - 6}{4} \geq -4$

32. $\frac{1 - 2x}{3} + \frac{3x + 7}{7} > 1$

33. $-3(2x - 1) < -4[2 + 3(x + 2)]$

34. $-2(4x + 2) > -5[1 + 2(x - 1)]$

MIXED PRACTICE

Solve. Write the solution set using interval notation. See Examples 1 through 7.

35. $x + 9 < 3$

36. $x - 9 < -12$

37. $-x < -4$

38. $-x > -2$

39. $-7x \leq 3.5$

40. $-6x \leq 4.2$

41. $\frac{1}{2} + \frac{2}{3} \geq \frac{x}{6}$

42. $\frac{3}{4} - \frac{2}{3} \geq \frac{x}{6}$

43. $-5x + 4 \leq -4(x - 1)$

44. $-6x + 2 < -3(x + 4)$

45. $\frac{3}{4}(x - 7) \geq x + 2$

46. $\frac{4}{5}(x + 1) \leq x + 1$

47. $0.8x + 0.6x \geq 4.2$

48. $0.7x - x > 0.45$

49. $4(x - 6) + 2x - 4 \geq 3(x - 7) + 10x$

50. $7(2x + 3) + 4x \leq 7 + 5(3x - 4) + x$

51. $14 - (5x - 6) \geq -6(x + 1) - 5$

52. $13y - (9y + 2) \leq 5(y - 6) + 10$

53. $4(x - 1) \geq 4x - 8$

54. $8(x + 3) \leq 7(x + 5) + x$

55. $3x + 1 < 3(x - 2)$

56. $7x < 7(x - 2)$

57. $0.4(4x - 3) < 1.2(x + 2)$

58. $0.2(8x - 2) < 1.2(x - 3)$

59. $\frac{2}{5}x - \frac{1}{4} \leq \frac{3}{10}x - \frac{4}{5}$

60. $\frac{7}{12}x - \frac{1}{3} \leq \frac{3}{8}x - \frac{5}{6}$

61. $\frac{1}{2}(3x - 4) \leq \frac{3}{4}(x - 6) + 1$

62. $\frac{2}{3}(x + 3) < \frac{1}{6}(2x - 8) + 2$

63. $\frac{-x + 2}{2} - \frac{1 - 5x}{8} < -1$

64. $\frac{3 - 4x}{6} - \frac{1 - 2x}{12} \leq -2$

65. $\frac{x + 5}{5} - \frac{3 + x}{8} \geq -\frac{3}{10}$

66. $\frac{x - 4}{2} - \frac{x - 2}{3} > \frac{5}{6}$

67. $\frac{x + 3}{12} + \frac{x - 5}{15} < \frac{2}{3}$

68. $\frac{3x + 2}{18} - \frac{1 + 2x}{6} \leq -\frac{1}{2}$

Solve. See Examples 8 and 9. For Exercises 69 through 76,
***a.** answer with an inequality and **b.**, in your own words, explain the meaning of your answer to part **a**.*

Exercises 69 and 70 are written to help you get started. Exercises 71 and 72 are written to help you write and solve the inequality.

69. Justin Moore has scores of 72, 67, 82, and 79 on his algebra tests.

   a. Use an inequality to find the scores he must make on the final exam to pass the course with an average of 77 or higher, given that the final exam counts as two tests.

   b. In your own words, explain the meaning of your answer to part **a**.

70. In a Winter Olympics 5000-meter speed-skating event, Hans Holden scored times of 6.85, 7.04, and 6.92 minutes on his first three trials.

   a. Use an inequality to find the times he can score on his last trial so that his average time is under 7.0 minutes.

   b. In your own words, explain the meaning of your answer to part **a**.

71. A clerk must use an elevator to move boxes of paper. The elevator's maximum weight limit is 1500 pounds. If each box of paper weighs 66 pounds and the clerk weighs 147 pounds, use an inequality to find the number of whole boxes she can move on the elevator at one time.

Start the solution:

   1. UNDERSTAND the problem. Reread it as many times as needed.

   2. TRANSLATE into an inequality. (Fill in the blanks below.)

   Let x = number of boxes

Clerk's weight	+	number of boxes	times	weight of each box	≤	elevator maximum weight
↓	↓	↓	↓	↓	↓	↓
___	+	x	·	___	≤	___

Finish with:

3. SOLVE and

4. INTERPRET

72. To mail a large envelope first class, the U.S. Post Office charges 98 cents for the first ounce and 21 cents per ounce for each additional ounce. Use an inequality to find the number of whole ounces that can be mailed for no more than $3.00.

Start the solution:

   1. UNDERSTAND the problem. Reread it as many times as needed.

   2. TRANSLATE into an inequality. (Fill in the blanks below.)

   Let x = number of additional ounces (after first ounce)

Price of first ounce	+	number of additional ounces	times	price per additional ounce	≤	300 maximum cents
↓	↓	↓	↓	↓	↓	↓
___	+	x	·	___	≤	___

Finish with:

3. SOLVE and

4. INTERPRET

73. A small plane's maximum takeoff weight is 2000 pounds or less. Four passengers and the two-person crew weigh an average of 160 pounds each. Use an inequality to find the weight of luggage and cargo the plane can carry.

74. A shopping mall parking garage charges $1 for the first hour and 60 cents for each additional half-hour. Use an inequality to find how long you can park if you have only $4.00 in cash.

75. A car rental company offers two subcompact rental plans.

   Plan A: $36 per day and unlimited mileage

   Plan B: $24 per day plus $0.15 per mile

   Use an inequality to find the number of daily miles for which plan A is more economical than plan B.

76. Northeast Telephone Company offers two billing plans for local calls.

Plan 1: $25 per month for unlimited calls

Plan 2: $13 per month plus $0.06 per call

Use an inequality to find the number of monthly calls for which plan 1 is more economical than plan 2.

77. At room temperature, glass used in windows actually has some properties of a liquid. It has a very slow, viscous flow. (Viscosity is the property of a fluid that resists internal flow. For example, lemonade flows more easily than fudge syrup. Fudge syrup has a higher viscosity than lemonade.) Glass does not become a true liquid until temperatures are greater than or equal to 500°C. Find the Fahrenheit temperatures for which glass is a liquid. (Use the formula $F = \frac{9}{5}C + 32$.)

78. Stibnite is a silvery white mineral with a metallic luster. It is one of the few minerals that melts easily in a match flame or at temperatures of approximately 977°F or greater. Find the Celsius temperatures at which stibnite melts. [Use the formula $C = \frac{5}{9}(F - 32)$.]

79. Although beginning salaries vary greatly according to your field of study, the equation

$$s = 2464t + 40{,}067$$

can be used to approximate and to predict average beginning salaries for candidates with bachelor degrees. The variable s is the starting salary and t is the number of years after 2011. (*Source: Statistical Abstract of the U.S.*)

a. Approximate the year in which beginning salaries for candidates will be greater than $70,000. (Round your answer up and use it to calculate the year.)

b. Determine the year you plan to graduate from college. Use this year to find the corresponding value of t and approximate a beginning salary for a bachelor degree candidate.

80. a. Use the formula in Example 9 to estimate the years that the consumption of cigarettes will be less than 50 billion per year.

b. Use your answer to part **a** to describe the limitations of your answer.

The average consumption per person per year of whole milk w can be approximated by the equation

$$w = -1.9t + 59$$

where t is the number of years after 2004 and w is measured in pounds. The average consumption of skim milk s per person per year can be approximated by the equation

$$s = -0.22t + 27.4$$

where t is the number of years after 2004 and s is measured in pounds. The consumption of whole milk is shown on the graph in blue and the consumption of skim milk is shown on the graph in red. Use this information to answer Exercises 81 through 90.

Source: Based on data from U.S. Department of Agriculture, Economic Research Service

81. Is the consumption of whole milk increasing or decreasing over time? Explain how you arrived at your answer.

82. Is the consumption of skim milk increasing or decreasing over time? Explain how you arrived at your answer.

83. Predict the consumption of whole milk in 2024. (*Hint:* Find the value of t that corresponds to 2024.)

84. Predict the consumption of skim milk in 2024. (*Hint:* Find the value of t that corresponds to 2024.)

85. Determine when the consumption of whole milk will be less than 35 pounds per person per year.

86. For 2004 through 2014, the consumption of whole milk was greater than the consumption of skim milk. Explain how this can be determined from the graph.

87. Both lines have a negative slope, that is, the amount of each type of milk consumed per person per year is decreasing as time goes on. However, the amount of whole milk being consumed is decreasing faster than the amount of skim milk being consumed. Explain how this could be.

88. Do you think it is possible that the consumption of whole milk will eventually be the same as the consumption of skim milk? Explain your answer.

89. The consumption of skim milk will be greater than the consumption of whole milk when $s > w$.

a. Find when this will occur by substituting the given equivalent expression for w and the given equivalent expression for s and solving for t.

b. Estimate to the nearest whole the first year when this will occur.

90. How will the two lines in the graph appear if the consumption of whole milk is the same as the consumption of skim milk?

REVIEW AND PREVIEW

List or describe the integers that make both inequalities true. See Section 1.4.

91. $x < 5$ and $x > 1$

92. $x \geq 0$ and $x \leq 7$

93. $x \geq -2$ and $x \geq 2$

94. $x < 6$ and $x < -5$

Solve each equation for x. See Section 2.1.

95. $2x - 6 = 4$

96. $3x - 12 = 3$

97. $-x + 7 = 5x - 6$

98. $-5x - 4 = -x - 4$

CONCEPT EXTENSIONS

Each row of the table shows three equivalent ways of describing an interval. Complete this table by filling in the equivalent descriptions. The first row has been completed for you.

	Set Notation	Graph	Interval Notation
	$\{x \mid x < -3\}$	(graph with open circle at −3, arrow left) -3	$(-\infty, -3)$
99.		(graph at 2) 2	
100.		(graph at −4) -4	
101.	$\{x \mid x < 0\}$		
102.	$\{x \mid x \leq 5\}$		
103.			$(-2, 1.5]$
104.			$[-3.7, 4)$

Each inequality below (Exercises 105–108) is solved by dividing both sides by the coefficient of x. Determine whether the inequality symbol will be reversed during this solution process.

105. $-3x \leq 14$

106. $3x > -14$

107. $-x \geq -23$

108. $-x \leq 9$

109. Solve: $2x - 3 = 5$

110. Solve: $2x - 3 > 5$

111. Solve: $2x - 3 < 5$

112. Read the equations and inequalities for Exercises 109, 110, and 111 and their solutions. In your own words, write down your thoughts.

113. When graphing the solution set of an inequality, explain how you know whether to use a parenthesis or a bracket.

114. Explain what is wrong with the interval notation $(-6, -\infty)$.

115. Explain how solving a linear inequality is similar to solving a linear equation.

116. Explain how solving a linear inequality is different from solving a linear equation.

Integrated Review   Linear Equations and Inequalities

Sections 2.1–2.4

Solve each equation or inequality. For inequalities, write the solution set in interval notation.

1. $-4x = 20$

2. $-4x < 20$

3. $\dfrac{3x}{4} \geq 2$

4. $5x + 3 \geq 2 + 4x$

5. $6(y - 4) = 3(y - 8)$

6. $-4x \leq \dfrac{2}{5}$

7. $-3x \geq \dfrac{1}{2}$

8. $5(y + 4) = 4(y + 5)$

9. $7x < 7(x - 2)$

10. $\dfrac{-5x + 11}{2} \leq 7$

11. $-5x + 1.5 = -19.5$

12. $-5x + 4 = -26$

13. $5 + 2x - x = -x + 3 - 14$

14. $12x + 14 < 11x - 2$

15. $\dfrac{x}{5} - \dfrac{x}{4} = \dfrac{x - 2}{2}$

16. $12x - 12 = 8(x - 1)$

17. $2(x - 3) > 70$

18. $-3x - 4.7 = 11.8$

19. $-2(b - 4) - (3b - 1) = 5b + 3$

20. $8(x + 3) < 7(x + 5) + x$

21. $\dfrac{3t + 1}{8} = \dfrac{5 + 2t}{7} + 2$

22. $4(x - 6) - x = 8(x - 3) - 5x$

23. $\dfrac{x}{6} + \dfrac{3x - 2}{2} < \dfrac{2}{3}$

24. $\dfrac{y}{3} + \dfrac{y}{5} = \dfrac{y + 3}{10}$

25. $5(x - 6) + 2x > 3(2x - 1) - 4$

26. $14(x - 1) - 7x \leq 2(3x - 6) + 4$

27. $\dfrac{1}{4}(3x + 2) - x \geq \dfrac{3}{8}(x - 5) + 2$

28. $\dfrac{1}{3}(x - 10) - 4x > \dfrac{5}{6}(2x + 1) - 1$

2.5 | Compound Inequalities

Two inequalities joined by the words **and** or **or** are called **compound inequalities**.

Compound Inequalities

$$x + 3 < 8 \quad \text{and} \quad x > 2$$

$$\frac{2x}{3} \geq 5 \quad \text{or} \quad -x + 10 < 7$$

OBJECTIVE

1 Finding the Intersection of Two Sets ▷

The solution set of a compound inequality formed by the word **and** is the **intersection** of the solution sets of the two inequalities. We use the symbol ∩ to represent "intersection."

> **Intersection of Two Sets**
>
> The intersection of two sets, A and B, is the set of all elements common to both sets. A intersect B is denoted by $A \cap B$.
>
> $A \cap B$
>
> A B

EXAMPLE 1   If $A = \{x \mid x$ is an even number greater than 0 and less than 10$\}$ and $B = \{3, 4, 5, 6\}$, find $A \cap B$.

Solution   Let's list the elements in set A.

$$A = \{2, 4, 6, 8\}$$

The numbers 4 and 6 are in sets A and B. The intersection is $\{4, 6\}$.   ☐

PRACTICE

1   If $A = \{x \mid x$ is an odd number greater than 0 and less than 10$\}$ and $B = \{1, 2, 3, 4\}$, find $A \cap B$.   ◼

OBJECTIVE

2 Solving Compound Inequalities Containing "and"

A value is a solution of a compound inequality formed by the word **and** if it is a solution of _both_ inequalities. For example, the solution set of the compound inequality $x \leq 5$ and $x \geq 3$ contains all values of x that make the inequality $x \leq 5$ a true statement **and** the inequality $x \geq 3$ a true statement. The first graph shown below is the graph of $x \leq 5$, the second graph is the graph of $x \geq 3$, and the third graph shows the intersection of the two graphs. The third graph is the graph of $x \leq 5$ **and** $x \geq 3$.

$\{x \mid x \leq 5\}$	(graph: -1 0 1 2 3 4 5 6)	$(-\infty, 5]$
$\{x \mid x \geq 3\}$	(graph: -1 0 1 2 3 4 5 6)	$[3, \infty)$
$\{x \mid x \leq 5 \text{ and } x \geq 3\}$ also $\{x \mid 3 \leq x \leq 5\}$ (see below)	(graph: -1 0 1 2 3 4 5 6)	$[3, 5]$

Since $x \geq 3$ is the same as $3 \leq x$, the compound inequality $3 \leq x$ and $x \leq 5$ can be written in a more compact form as $3 \leq x \leq 5$. The solution set $\{x \mid 3 \leq x \leq 5\}$ includes all numbers that are greater than or equal to 3 and at the same time less than or equal to 5.

In interval notation, the set $\{x \mid x \leq 5 \text{ and } x \geq 3\}$ or the set $\{x \mid 3 \leq x \leq 5\}$ is written as $[3, 5]$.

> **Helpful Hint**
>
> Don't forget that some compound inequalities containing "and" can be written in a more compact form.
>
> | Compound Inequality | Compact Form | Interval Notation |
> |---|---|---|
> | $2 \leq x$ and $x \leq 6$ | $2 \leq x \leq 6$ | $[2, 6]$ |
>
> Graph: 0 1 2 3 4 5 6 7

EXAMPLE 2   Solve: $x - 7 < 2$ and $2x + 1 < 9$

Solution First we solve each inequality separately.

$$x - 7 < 2 \quad and \quad 2x + 1 < 9$$
$$x < 9 \quad and \quad 2x < 8$$
$$x < 9 \quad and \quad x < 4$$

Now we can graph the two intervals on two number lines and find their intersection. Their intersection is shown on the third number line.

$\{x \mid x < 9\}$ $(-\infty, 9)$

$\{x \mid x < 4\}$ $(-\infty, 4)$

$\{x \mid x < 9 \text{ and } x < 4\} = \{x \mid x < 4\}$ $(-\infty, 4)$

The solution set is $(-\infty, 4)$.

PRACTICE
2   Solve $x + 3 < 8$ _and_ $2x - 1 < 3$. Write the solution set in interval notation.

EXAMPLE 3   Solve: $2x \geq 0$ and $4x - 1 \leq -9$

Solution First we solve each inequality separately.

$$2x \geq 0 \quad and \quad 4x - 1 \leq -9$$
$$x \geq 0 \quad and \quad 4x \leq -8$$
$$x \geq 0 \quad and \quad x \leq -2$$

Now we can graph the two intervals and find their intersection.

$\{x \mid x \geq 0\}$ $[0, \infty)$

$\{x \mid x \leq -2\}$ $(-\infty, -2]$

$\{x \mid x \geq 0 \text{ and } x \leq -2\} = \varnothing$ $\varnothing$

There is no number that is greater than or equal to 0 _and_ less than or equal to -2. The solution set can be written as $\{\ \}$ or $\varnothing$.

PRACTICE
3   Solve $4x \leq 0$ _and_ $3x + 2 > 8$. Write the solution set in interval notation.

> **Helpful Hint**
>
> Example 3 shows that some compound inequalities have no solution. Also, some have all real numbers as solutions.

To solve a compound inequality written in a compact form, such as $2 < 4 - x < 7$, we get x alone in the "middle part." Since a compound inequality is really two inequalities in one statement, we must perform the same operations on all three parts of the inequality. For example:

$$2 < 4 - x < 7 \text{ means } 2 < 4 - x \quad and \quad 4 - x < 7,$$

EXAMPLE 4   Solve: $2 < 4 - x < 7$

Solution To get x alone, we first subtract 4 from all three parts.

$$2 < 4 - x < 7$$
$$2 - 4 < 4 - x - 4 < 7 - 4 \qquad \text{Subtract 4 from all three parts.}$$
$$-2 < -x < 3 \qquad\qquad\qquad \text{Simplify.}$$
$$\frac{-2}{-1} > \frac{-x}{-1} > \frac{3}{-1} \qquad\qquad \text{Divide all three parts by } -1 \text{ and}$$
$$\qquad\qquad\qquad\qquad\qquad\qquad \text{reverse the inequality symbols.}$$
$$2 > x > -3$$

Helpful Hint

Don't forget to reverse both inequality symbols.

This is equivalent to $-3 < x < 2$.

The solution set in interval notation is $(-3, 2)$, and its graph is shown.

PRACTICE
4   Solve $3 < 5 - x < 9$. Write the solution set in interval notation.

EXAMPLE 5   Solve: $-1 \le \dfrac{2x}{3} + 5 \le 2$

Solution First, clear the inequality of fractions by multiplying all three parts by the LCD, 3.

$$-1 \le \frac{2x}{3} + 5 \le 2$$
$$3(-1) \le 3\left(\frac{2x}{3} + 5\right) \le 3(2) \qquad \text{Multiply all three parts by the LCD, 3.}$$
$$-3 \le 2x + 15 \le 6 \qquad\qquad \text{Use the distributive property and multiply.}$$
$$-3 - 15 \le 2x + 15 - 15 \le 6 - 15 \quad \text{Subtract 15 from all three parts.}$$
$$-18 \le 2x \le -9 \qquad\qquad\qquad \text{Simplify.}$$
$$\frac{-18}{2} \le \frac{2x}{2} \le \frac{-9}{2} \qquad\qquad\quad \text{Divide all three parts by 2.}$$
$$-9 \le x \le -\frac{9}{2} \qquad\qquad\qquad \text{Simplify.}$$

The graph of the solution is shown.

The solution set in interval notation is $\left[-9, -\dfrac{9}{2}\right]$.

PRACTICE
5   Solve $-4 \le \dfrac{x}{2} - 1 \le 3$. Write the solution set in interval notation.

OBJECTIVE

3 Finding the Union of Two Sets

The solution set of a compound inequality formed by the word **or** is the **union** of the solution sets of the two inequalities. We use the symbol ∪ to denote "union."

Union of Two Sets
The **union** of two sets, A and B, is the set of elements that belong to *either* of the sets. A union B is denoted by $A \cup B$.

$A \cup B$ |

EXAMPLE 6   If $A = \{x \mid x$ is an even number greater than 0 and less than 10$\}$ and $B = \{3, 4, 5, 6\}$, find $A \cup B$.

Solution Recall from Example 1 that $A = \{2, 4, 6, 8\}$. The numbers that are in either set or both sets are $\{2, 3, 4, 5, 6, 8\}$. This set is the union.   □

PRACTICE

6   If $A = \{x \mid x$ is an odd number greater than 0 and less than 10$\}$ and $B = \{2, 3, 4, 5, 6\}$, find $A \cup B$.   ◼

OBJECTIVE

4 Solving Compound Inequalities Containing "or"

A value is a solution of a compound inequality formed by the word **or** if it is a solution of **either** inequality. For example, the solution set of the compound inequality $x \leq 1$ **or** $x \geq 3$ contains all numbers that make the inequality $x \leq 1$ a true statement **or** the inequality $x \geq 3$ a true statement.

$\{x \mid x \leq 1\}$ $(-\infty, 1]$

$\{x \mid x \geq 3\}$ $[3, \infty)$

$\{x \mid x \leq 1 \text{ or } x \geq 3\}$ $(-\infty, 1] \cup [3, \infty)$

In interval notation, the set $\{x \mid x \leq 1 \text{ or } x \geq 3\}$ is written as $(-\infty, 1] \cup [3, \infty)$.

EXAMPLE 7   Solve: $5x - 3 \leq 10 \text{ or } x + 1 \geq 5$

Solution First we solve each inequality separately.

$$5x - 3 \leq 10 \quad \text{or} \quad x + 1 \geq 5$$
$$5x \leq 13 \quad \text{or} \quad x \geq 4$$
$$x \leq \frac{13}{5} \quad \text{or} \quad x \geq 4$$

Now we can graph each interval and find their union.

$\left\{x \mid x \leq \dfrac{13}{5}\right\}$ $\left(-\infty, \dfrac{13}{5}\right]$

$\{x \mid x \geq 4\}$ $[4, \infty)$

$\left\{x \mid x \leq \dfrac{13}{5} \text{ or } x \geq 4\right\}$ $\left(-\infty, \dfrac{13}{5}\right] \cup [4, \infty)$

The solution set is $\left(-\infty, \dfrac{13}{5}\right] \cup [4, \infty)$. ☐

7   Solve $8x + 5 \le 8$ or $x - 1 \ge 2$. Write the solution set in interval notation. ■

EXAMPLE 8   Solve: $-2x - 5 < -3 \ or \ 6x < 0$

Solution First we solve each inequality separately.

$$-2x - 5 < -3 \quad or \quad 6x < 0$$
$$-2x < 2 \quad or \quad x < 0$$
$$x > -1 \quad or \quad x < 0$$

Now we can graph each interval and find their union.

$\{x \mid x > -1\}$ $(-1, \infty)$

$\{x \mid x < 0\}$ $(-\infty, 0)$

$\{x \mid x > -1 \ or \ x < 0\}$ $(-\infty, \infty)$
= all real numbers

The solution set is $(-\infty, \infty)$. ☐

PRACTICE
8   Solve $-3x - 2 > -8 \ or \ 5x > 0$. Write the solution set in interval notation. ■

✔ CONCEPT CHECK
Which of the following is *not* a correct way to represent the set of all numbers between -3 and 5?
a. $\{x \mid -3 < x < 5\}$ **b.** $-3 < x \ or \ x < 5$
c. $(-3, 5)$ **d.** $x > -3 \ and \ x < 5$

Answer to Concept Check:
b is not correct

✔ Vocabulary, Readiness & Video Check

Use the choices below to fill in each blank.

or   ∪   ∅
and   ∩   compound

1. Two inequalities joined by the words "and" or "or" are called _____ inequalities.
2. The word _____ means intersection.
3. The word _____ means union.
4. The symbol _____ represents intersection.
5. The symbol _____ represents union.
6. The symbol _____ is the empty set.

Martin-Gay Interactive Videos

See Video 2.5 🌐

Watch the section lecture video and answer the following questions.

OBJECTIVE 1

7. Based on Example 1 and the lecture before, complete the following statement. For an element to be in the intersection of sets A and B, the element must be in set A _____ in set B.

OBJECTIVE 2

8. In Example 2, how can using three number lines help us find the solution to this "and" compound inequality?

OBJECTIVE 3

9. Based on Example 4 and the lecture before, complete the following statement. For an element to be in the union of sets A and B, the element must be in set A _____ in set B.

OBJECTIVE 4

10. In Example 5, how can using three number lines help us find the solution to this "or" compound inequality?

2.5 Exercise Set MyMathLab® ▶

MIXED PRACTICE

If $A = \{x \mid x \text{ is an even integer}\}$, $B = \{x \mid x \text{ is an odd integer}\}$, $C = \{2, 3, 4, 5\}$, and $D = \{4, 5, 6, 7\}$, list the elements of each set. See Examples 1 and 6.

1. $C \cup D$
2. $C \cap D$
3. $A \cap D$
4. $A \cup D$
5. $A \cup B$
6. $A \cap B$
7. $B \cap D$
8. $B \cup D$
9. $B \cup C$
10. $B \cap C$
11. $A \cap C$
12. $A \cup C$

Solve each compound inequality. Graph the solution set and write it in interval notation. See Examples 2 and 3.

13. $x < 1 \text{ and } x > -3$
14. $x \leq 0 \text{ and } x \geq -2$
15. $x \leq -3 \text{ and } x \geq -2$
16. $x < 2 \text{ and } x > 4$
17. $x < -1 \text{ and } x < 1$
18. $x \geq -4 \text{ and } x > 1$

Solve each compound inequality. Write solutions in interval notation. See Examples 2 and 3.

19. $x + 1 \geq 7 \text{ and } 3x - 1 \geq 5$
20. $x + 2 \geq 3 \text{ and } 5x - 1 \geq 9$
21. $4x + 2 \leq -10 \text{ and } 2x \leq 0$
22. $2x + 4 > 0 \text{ and } 4x > 0$
23. $-2x < -8 \text{ and } x - 5 < 5$
24. $-7x \leq -21 \text{ and } x - 20 \leq -15$

Solve each compound inequality. See Examples 4 and 5.

25. $5 < x - 6 < 11$
26. $-2 \leq x + 3 \leq 0$
27. $-2 \leq 3x - 5 \leq 7$
28. $1 < 4 + 2x < 7$
29. $1 \leq \frac{2}{3}x + 3 \leq 4$
30. $-2 < \frac{1}{2}x - 5 < 1$
31. $-5 \leq \frac{-3x + 1}{4} \leq 2$
32. $-4 \leq \frac{-2x + 5}{3} \leq 1$

Solve each compound inequality. Graph the solution set and write it in interval notation. See Examples 7 and 8.

33. $x < 4 \text{ or } x < 5$
34. $x \geq -2 \text{ or } x \leq 2$
35. $x \leq -4 \text{ or } x \geq 1$
36. $x < 0 \text{ or } x < 1$
37. $x > 0 \text{ or } x < 3$
38. $x \geq -3 \text{ or } x \leq -4$

Solve each compound inequality. Write solutions in interval notation. See Examples 7 and 8.

39. $-2x \leq -4 \text{ or } 5x - 20 \geq 5$
40. $-5x \leq 10 \text{ or } 3x - 5 \geq 1$
41. $x + 4 < 0 \text{ or } 6x > -12$
42. $x + 9 < 0 \text{ or } 4x > -12$
43. $3(x - 1) < 12 \text{ or } x + 7 > 10$
44. $5(x - 1) \geq -5 \text{ or } 5 + x \leq 11$

MIXED PRACTICE

Solve each compound inequality. Write solutions in interval notation. See Examples 1 through 8.

45. $x < \frac{2}{3} \text{ and } x > -\frac{1}{2}$
46. $x < \frac{5}{7} \text{ and } x < 1$
47. $x < \frac{2}{3} \text{ or } x > -\frac{1}{2}$
48. $x < \frac{5}{7} \text{ or } x < 1$
49. $0 \leq 2x - 3 \leq 9$
50. $3 < 5x + 1 < 11$
51. $\frac{1}{2} < x - \frac{3}{4} < 2$

52. $\dfrac{2}{3} < x + \dfrac{1}{2} < 4$

53. $x + 3 \geq 3 \ and \ x + 3 \leq 2$

54. $2x - 1 \geq 3 \ and \ -x > 2$

55. $3x \geq 5 \ or \ -\dfrac{5}{8}x - 6 > 1$

56. $\dfrac{3}{8}x + 1 \leq 0 \ or \ -2x < -4$

57. $0 < \dfrac{5 - 2x}{3} < 5$

58. $-2 < \dfrac{-2x - 1}{3} < 2$

59. $-6 < 3(x - 2) \leq 8$

60. $-5 < 2(x + 4) < 8$

61. $-x + 5 > 6 \ and \ 1 + 2x \leq -5$

62. $5x \leq 0 \ and \ -x + 5 < 8$

▶ **63.** $3x + 2 \leq 5 \ or \ 7x > 29$

64. $-x < 7 \ or \ 3x + 1 < -20$

65. $5 - x > 7 \ and \ 2x + 3 \geq 13$

66. $-2x < -6 \ or \ 1 - x > -2$

67. $-\dfrac{1}{2} \leq \dfrac{4x - 1}{6} < \dfrac{5}{6}$

68. $-\dfrac{1}{2} \leq \dfrac{3x - 1}{10} < \dfrac{1}{2}$

69. $\dfrac{1}{15} < \dfrac{8 - 3x}{15} < \dfrac{4}{5}$

70. $-\dfrac{1}{4} < \dfrac{6 - x}{12} < -\dfrac{1}{6}$

71. $0.3 < 0.2x - 0.9 < 1.5$

72. $-0.7 \leq 0.4x + 0.8 < 0.5$

REVIEW AND PREVIEW

Evaluate the following. See Sections 1.2 and 1.3.

73. $|-7| - |19|$

74. $|-7 - 19|$

75. $-(-6) - |-10|$

76. $|-4| - (-4) + |-20|$

Find by inspection all values for x that make each equation true.

77. $|x| = 7$

78. $|x| = 5$

79. $|x| = 0$

80. $|x| = -2$

CONCEPT EXTENSIONS

Use the graph to answer Exercises 81 and 82.

United States Single-Family Homes Housing Starts vs. Housing Completions

Source: U.S. Census Bureau

81. For which years were the number of single-family housing starts greater than 1500 and the number of single-family home completions greater than 1500?

82. For which years were the number of single-family housing starts less than 500 or the number of single-family housing completions greater than 1500?

83. In your own words, describe how to find the union of two sets.

84. In your own words, describe how to find the intersection of two sets.

Solve each compound inequality for x. See the example below. To solve $x - 6 < 3x < 2x + 5$, notice that this inequality contains a variable not only in the middle but also on the left and the right. When this occurs, we solve by rewriting the inequality using the word **and**.

$$x - 6 < 3x \quad and \quad 3x < 2x + 5$$
$$-6 < 2x \quad and \quad x < 5$$
$$-3 < x$$
$$x > -3 \quad and \quad x < 5$$

$x > -3$

$x < 5$

$-3 < x < 5 \ or \ (-3, 5)$

85. $2x - 3 < 3x + 1 < 4x - 5$

86. $x + 3 < 2x + 1 < 4x + 6$

87. $-3(x - 2) \leq 3 - 2x \leq 10 - 3x$

88. $7x - 1 \leq 7 + 5x \leq 3(1 + 2x)$

89. $5x - 8 < 2(2 + x) < -2(1 + 2x)$

90. $1 + 2x < 3(2 + x) < 1 + 4x$

The formula for converting Fahrenheit temperatures to Celsius temperatures is $C = \dfrac{5}{9}(F - 32)$. Use this formula for Exercises 91 and 92.

91. During a recent year, the temperatures in Chicago ranged from $-29°C$ to $35°C$. Use a compound inequality to convert these temperatures to Fahrenheit temperatures.

92. In Oslo, the average temperature ranges from $-10°C$ to $18°C$. Use a compound inequality to convert these temperatures to the Fahrenheit scale.

Solve.

93. Christian D'Angelo has scores of 68, 65, 75, and 78 on his algebra tests. Use a compound inequality to find the scores he can make on his final exam to receive a C in the course. The final exam counts as two tests, and a C is received if the final course average is from 70 to 79.

94. Wendy Wood has scores of 80, 90, 82, and 75 on her chemistry tests. Use a compound inequality to find the range of scores she can make on her final exam to receive a B in the course. The final exam counts as two tests, and a B is received if the final course average is from 80 to 89.

2.6 Absolute Value Equations

OBJECTIVE

1 Solve Absolute Value Equations.

OBJECTIVE

1   Solving Absolute Value Equations

In Chapter 1, we defined the absolute value of a number as its distance from 0 on a number line.

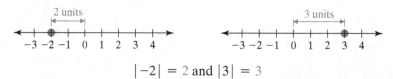

$$|-2| = 2 \text{ and } |3| = 3$$

In this section, we concentrate on solving equations containing the absolute value of a variable or a variable expression. Examples of absolute value equations are

$$|x| = 3 \qquad -5 = |2y + 7| \qquad |z - 6.7| = |3z + 1.2|$$

Since distance and absolute value are so closely related, absolute value equations and inequalities (see Section 2.7) are extremely useful in solving distance-type problems such as calculating the possible error in a measurement.

For the absolute value equation $|x| = 3$, its solution set will contain all numbers whose distance from 0 is 3 units. Two numbers are 3 units away from 0 on the number line: 3 and -3.

Thus, the solution set of the equation $|x| = 3$ is $\{3, -3\}$. This suggests the following:

> **Solving Equations of the Form $|X| = a$**
>
> If a is a positive number, then $|X| = a$ is equivalent to $X = a$ or $X = -a$.

> **EXAMPLE 1**   Solve: $|p| = 2$

Solution Since 2 is positive, $|p| = 2$ is equivalent to $p = 2$ or $p = -2$.

To check, let $p = 2$ and then $p = -2$ in the original equation.

$\|p\| = 2$	Original equation	$\|p\| = 2$	Original equation
$\|2\| \stackrel{?}{=} 2$	Let $p = 2$.	$\|-2\| \stackrel{?}{=} 2$	Let $p = -2$.
$2 = 2$	True	$2 = 2$	True

The solutions are 2 and -2 or the solution set is $\{2, -2\}$. □

PRACTICE

1   Solve: $|q| = 13$ $-13, 13$

If the expression inside the absolute value bars is more complicated than a single variable, we can still apply the absolute value property.

> **Helpful Hint**
>
> For the equation $|X| = a$ in the box on the previous page, X can be a single variable or a variable expression.

EXAMPLE 2 Solve: $|5w + 3| = 7$

Solution Here the expression inside the absolute value bars is $5w + 3$. If we think of the expression $5w + 3$ as X in the absolute value property, we see that $|X| = 7$ is equivalent to

$$X = 7 \quad \text{or} \quad X = -7$$

Then substitute $5w + 3$ for X, and we have

$$5w + 3 = 7 \quad \text{or} \quad 5w + 3 = -7$$

Solve these two equations for w.

$$
\begin{aligned}
5w + 3 &= 7 &\text{or}& \quad 5w + 3 = -7 \\
5w &= 4 &\text{or}& \quad 5w = -10 \\
w &= \frac{4}{5} &\text{or}& \quad w = -2
\end{aligned}
$$

Check: To check, let $w = -2$ and then $w = \frac{4}{5}$ in the original equation.

Let $w = -2$ Let $w = \frac{4}{5}$

$$|5(-2) + 3| \stackrel{?}{=} 7 \qquad\qquad \left|5\left(\frac{4}{5}\right) + 3\right| \stackrel{?}{=} 7$$

$$|-10 + 3| \stackrel{?}{=} 7 \qquad\qquad\qquad |4 + 3| \stackrel{?}{=} 7$$

$$|-7| \stackrel{?}{=} 7 \qquad\qquad\qquad\qquad |7| \stackrel{?}{=} 7$$

$$7 = 7 \quad \text{True} \qquad\qquad\qquad 7 = 7 \quad \text{True}$$

Both solutions check, and the solutions are -2 and $\frac{4}{5}$ or the solution set is $\left\{-2, \frac{4}{5}\right\}$. ☐

PRACTICE
2 Solve: $|2x - 3| = 5$ ∎

EXAMPLE 3 Solve: $\left|\frac{x}{2} - 1\right| = 11$

Solution $\left|\frac{x}{2} - 1\right| = 11$ is equivalent to

$$\frac{x}{2} - 1 = 11 \qquad \text{or} \qquad \frac{x}{2} - 1 = -11$$

$$2\left(\frac{x}{2} - 1\right) = 2(11) \quad \text{or} \quad 2\left(\frac{x}{2} - 1\right) = 2(-11) \quad \text{Clear fractions.}$$

$$x - 2 = 22 \qquad \text{or} \qquad x - 2 = -22 \qquad \text{Apply the distributive property.}$$

$$x = 24 \qquad \text{or} \qquad x = -20$$

The solutions are 24 and -20. ☐

PRACTICE
3 Solve: $\left|\frac{x}{5} + 1\right| = 15$ ∎

To apply the absolute value property, first make sure that the absolute value expression is isolated.

> **Helpful Hint**
>
> If the equation has a single absolute value expression containing variables, isolate the absolute value expression first.

EXAMPLE 4   Solve: $|2x| + 5 = 7$

Solution   We want the absolute value expression alone on one side of the equation, so begin by subtracting 5 from both sides. Then apply the absolute value property.

$$|2x| + 5 = 7$$
$$|2x| = 2 \qquad \text{Subtract 5 from both sides.}$$
$$2x = 2 \quad \text{or} \quad 2x = -2$$
$$x = 1 \quad \text{or} \quad x = -1$$

The solutions are -1 and 1. □

PRACTICE
4   Solve: $|3x| + 8 = 14$

EXAMPLE 5   Solve: $|y| = 0$

Solution   We are looking for all numbers whose distance from 0 is zero units. The only number is 0. The solution is 0. □

PRACTICE
5   Solve: $|z| = 0$

The next two examples illustrate a special case for absolute value equations. This special case occurs when an isolated absolute value is equal to a negative number.

EXAMPLE 6   Solve: $2|x| + 25 = 23$

Solution   First, isolate the absolute value.

$$2|x| + 25 = 23$$
$$2|x| = -2 \quad \text{Subtract 25 from both sides.}$$
$$|x| = -1 \quad \text{Divide both sides by 2.}$$

The absolute value of a number is never negative, so this equation has no solution. The solution set is { } or $\varnothing$. □

PRACTICE
6   Solve: $3|z| + 9 = 7$

EXAMPLE 7   Solve: $\left| \dfrac{3x + 1}{2} \right| = -2$

Solution   Again, the absolute value of any expression is never negative, so no solution exists. The solution set is { } or $\varnothing$. □

PRACTICE
7   Solve: $\left| \dfrac{5x + 3}{4} \right| = -8$

Given two absolute value expressions, we might ask, when are the absolute values of two expressions equal? To see the answer, notice that

$$|2| = |2|, \quad |-2| = |-2|, \quad |-2| = |2|, \quad \text{and} \quad |2| = |-2|$$

same   same   opposites   opposites

Two absolute value expressions are equal when the expressions inside the absolute value bars are equal to or are opposites of each other.

EXAMPLE 8 Solve: $|3x + 2| = |5x - 8|$

Solution This equation is true if the expressions inside the absolute value bars are equal to or are opposites of each other.

$$3x + 2 = 5x - 8 \quad \text{or} \quad 3x + 2 = -(5x - 8)$$

Next, solve each equation.

$$
\begin{aligned}
3x + 2 &= 5x - 8 \quad \text{or} \quad 3x + 2 = -5x + 8 \\
-2x + 2 &= -8 \quad\quad \text{or} \quad 8x + 2 = 8 \\
-2x &= -10 \quad\quad \text{or} \quad\quad 8x = 6 \\
x &= 5 \quad\quad\quad \text{or} \quad\quad\quad x = \frac{3}{4}
\end{aligned}
$$

The solutions are $\frac{3}{4}$ and 5.

PRACTICE
8 Solve: $|2x + 4| = |3x - 1|$

EXAMPLE 9 Solve: $|x - 3| = |5 - x|$

Solution

$$
\begin{aligned}
x - 3 &= 5 - x \quad \text{or} \quad\quad x - 3 = -(5 - x) \\
2x - 3 &= 5 \quad\quad \text{or} \quad\quad x - 3 = -5 + x \\
2x &= 8 \quad\quad \text{or} \quad x - 3 - x = -5 + x - x \\
x &= 4 \quad\quad \text{or} \quad\quad\quad -3 = -5 \quad\quad \text{False}
\end{aligned}
$$

Recall from Section 2.1 that when an equation simplifies to a false statement, the equation has no solution. Thus, the only solution for the original absolute value equation is 4.

PRACTICE
9 Solve: $|x - 2| = |8 - x|$

✔ **CONCEPT CHECK**
True or false? Absolute value equations always have two solutions. Explain your answer.

The following box summarizes the methods shown for solving absolute value equations.

Absolute Value Equations
$|X| = a$ $\begin{cases} \text{If } a \text{ is positive, then solve } X = a \text{ or } X = -a. \\ \text{If } a \text{ is 0, solve } X = 0. \\ \text{If } a \text{ is negative, the equation } |X| = a \text{ has no solution.} \end{cases}$
$|X| = |Y|$ $\quad$ Solve $X = Y$ or $X = -Y$.

Vocabulary, Readiness & Video Check

Match each absolute value equation with an equivalent statement.

1. $|x - 2| = 5$

2. $|x - 2| = 0$

3. $|x - 2| = |x + 3|$

4. $|x + 3| = 5$

5. $|x + 3| = -5$

A. $x - 2 = 0$

B. $x - 2 = x + 3$ or $x - 2 = -(x + 3)$

C. $x - 2 = 5$ or $x - 2 = -5$

D. $\varnothing$

E. $x + 3 = 5$ or $x + 3 = -5$

Martin-Gay Interactive Videos

See Video 2.6

Watch the section lecture videos and answer the following question.

OBJECTIVE
1 **6.** As explained in Example 3, why is *a* positive in the rule "$|X| = a$ is equivalent to $X = a$ or $X = -a$"?

2.6 Exercise Set MyMathLab®

Solve each absolute value equation. See Examples 1 through 7.

1. $|x| = 7$

2. $|y| = 15$

3. $|3x| = 12.6$

4. $|6n| = 12.6$

5. $|2x - 5| = 9$

6. $|6 + 2n| = 4$

7. $\left|\dfrac{x}{2} - 3\right| = 1$

8. $\left|\dfrac{n}{3} + 2\right| = 4$

9. $|z| + 4 = 9$

10. $|x| + 1 = 3$

11. $|3x| + 5 = 14$

12. $|2x| - 6 = 4$

13. $|2x| = 0$

14. $|7z| = 0$

15. $|4n + 1| + 10 = 4$

16. $|3z - 2| + 8 = 1$

17. $|5x - 1| = 0$

18. $|3y + 2| = 0$

Solve. See Examples 8 and 9.

19. $|5x - 7| = |3x + 11|$

20. $|9y + 1| = |6y + 4|$

21. $|z + 8| = |z - 3|$

22. $|2x - 5| = |2x + 5|$

MIXED PRACTICE

Solve each absolute value equation. See Examples 1 through 9.

23. $|x| = 4$

24. $|x| = 1$

25. $|y| = 0$

26. $|y| = 8$

27. $|z| = -2$

28. $|y| = -9$

29. $|7 - 3x| = 7$

30. $|4m + 5| = 5$

31. $|6x| - 1 = 11$

32. $|7z| + 1 = 22$

33. $|4p| = -8$

34. $|5m| = -10$

35. $|x - 3| + 3 = 7$

36. $|x + 4| - 4 = 1$

37. $\left|\dfrac{z}{4} + 5\right| = -7$

38. $\left|\dfrac{c}{5} - 1\right| = -2$

39. $|9v - 3| = -8$

40. $|1 - 3b| = -7$

41. $|8n + 1| = 0$

42. $|5x - 2| = 0$

43. $|1 + 6c| - 7 = -3$

44. $|2 + 3m| - 9 = -7$

45. $|5x + 1| = 11$

46. $|8 - 6c| = 1$

47. $|4x - 2| = |-10|$

48. $|3x + 5| = |-4|$

49. $|5x + 1| = |4x - 7|$

50. $|3 + 6n| = |4n + 11|$

51. $|6 + 2x| = -|-7|$

52. $|4 - 5y| = -|-3|$

53. $|2x - 6| = |10 - 2x|$

54. $|4n + 5| = |4n + 3|$

55. $\left|\dfrac{2x - 5}{3}\right| = 7$

56. $\left|\dfrac{1 + 3n}{4}\right| = 4$

57. $2 + |5n| = 17$

58. $8 + |4m| = 24$

59. $\left|\dfrac{2x - 1}{3}\right| = |-5|$

60. $\left|\dfrac{5x + 2}{2}\right| = |-6|$

61. $|2y - 3| = |9 - 4y|$

62. $|5z - 1| = |7 - z|$

63. $\left|\dfrac{3n + 2}{8}\right| = |-1|$

64. $\left|\dfrac{2r - 6}{5}\right| = |-2|$

65. $|x + 4| = |7 - x|$

66. $|8 - y| = |y + 2|$

67. $\left|\dfrac{8c - 7}{3}\right| = -|-5|$

68. $\left|\dfrac{5d + 1}{6}\right| = -|-9|$

REVIEW AND PREVIEW

The circle graph shows the types of cheese produced in the United States in 2014. Use this graph to answer Exercises 69 through 72. See Section 2.2.

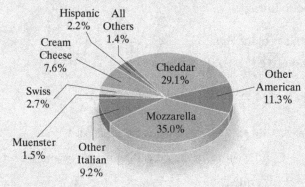

U.S. Cheese¹ Production by Variety, 2014

Hispanic 2.2%
All Others 1.4%
Cream Cheese 7.6%
Swiss 2.7%
Muenster 1.5%
Other Italian 9.2%
Cheddar 29.1%
Other American 11.3%
Mozzarella 35.0%

¹Excludes Cottage Cheese

Source: USDA, *Dairy Products Annual Survey*

69. In 2014, cheddar cheese made up what percent of U.S. cheese production?

70. Which cheese had the highest U.S. production in 2014?

71. A circle contains 360°. Find the number of degrees found in the 9.2% sector for Other Italian Cheese.

72. In 2014, the total production of cheeses above in the United States was 11,201,000,000 pounds. Find the amount of cream cheese produced during that year.

List five integer solutions of each inequality. See Sections 1.2 through 1.4.

73. $|x| \le 3$

74. $|x| \ge -2$

75. $|y| > -10$

76. $|y| < 0$

CONCEPT EXTENSIONS

Without going through a solution procedure, determine the solution of each absolute value equation or inequality.

77. $|x - 7| = -4$ **78.** $|x - 7| < -4$

79. Write an absolute value equation representing all numbers x whose distance from 0 is 5 units.

80. Write an absolute value equation representing all numbers x whose distance from 0 is 2 units.

81. Explain why some absolute value equations have two solutions.

82. Explain why some absolute value equations have one solution.

83. Write an absolute value equation representing all numbers x whose distance from 1 is 5 units.

84. Write an absolute value equation representing all numbers x whose distance from 7 is 2 units.

85. Describe how solving an absolute value equation such as $|2x - 1| = 3$ is similar to solving an absolute value equation such as $|2x - 1| = |x - 5|$.

86. Describe how solving an absolute value equation such as $|2x - 1| = 3$ is different from solving an absolute value equation such as $|2x - 1| = |x - 5|$.

Write each as an equivalent absolute value equation.

87. $x = 6$ or $x = -6$

88. $2x - 1 = 4$ or $2x - 1 = -4$

89. $x - 2 = 3x - 4$ or $x - 2 = -(3x - 4)$

90. For what value(s) of c will an absolute value equation of the form $|ax + b| = c$ have

  a. one solution?

  b. no solution?

  c. two solutions?

2.7 Absolute Value Inequalities

OBJECTIVES

1 Solve Absolute Value Inequalities of the Form $|X| < a$.

2 Solve Absolute Value Inequalities of the Form $|X| > a$.

OBJECTIVE

1 Solving Absolute Value Inequalities of the Form $|X| < a$

The solution set of an absolute value inequality such as $|x| < 2$ contains all numbers whose distance from 0 is less than 2 units, as shown below.

Distance from 0: less than 2 units

Distance from 0: less than 2 units

$-3\ -2\ -1\ \ 0\ \ 1\ \ 2\ \ 3$

The solution set is $\{x \mid -2 < x < 2\}$, or $(-2, 2)$ in interval notation.

EXAMPLE 1 Solve $|x| \le 3$ and graph the solution set.

Solution The solution set of this inequality contains all numbers whose distance from 0 is less than or equal to 3. Thus 3, −3, and all numbers between 3 and −3 are in the solution set.

$$\xleftarrow{\quad\begin{array}{cccccccccc} | & [& | & | & | & | & | &] & | & | \\ -4 & -3 & -2 & -1 & 0 & 1 & 2 & 3 & 4 & 5 \end{array}\quad}\rightarrow$$

The solution set is $[-3, 3]$. □

PRACTICE

1 Solve $|x| < 5$ and graph the solution set. ■

In general, we have the following.

> **Solving Absolute Value Inequalities of the Form $|X| < a$**
> If a is a positive number, then $|X| < a$ is equivalent to $-a < X < a$.

This property also holds true for the inequality symbol $\leq$.

EXAMPLE 2 Solve $|m - 6| < 2$ for m and graph the solution set.

Solution Replace X with $m - 6$ and a with 2 in the preceding property, and we see that

$$|m - 6| < 2 \quad \text{is equivalent to} \quad -2 < m - 6 < 2$$

Solve this compound inequality for m by adding 6 to all three parts.

$$-2 < m - 6 < 2$$
$$-2 + 6 < m - 6 + 6 < 2 + 6 \quad \text{Add 6 to all three parts.}$$
$$4 < m < 8 \quad \text{Simplify.}$$

The solution set is $(4, 8)$, and its graph is shown.

$$\xleftarrow{\quad\begin{array}{ccccccc} | & (& | & | & | &) & | \\ 3 & 4 & 5 & 6 & 7 & 8 & 9 \end{array}\quad}\rightarrow$$ □

PRACTICE

2 Solve $|b + 1| < 3$ for b and graph the solution set. ■

> **Helpful Hint**
>
> Before using an absolute value inequality property, isolate the absolute value expression on one side of the inequality.

EXAMPLE 3 Solve $|5x + 1| + 1 \leq 10$ for x and graph the solution set.

Solution First, isolate the absolute value expression by subtracting 1 from both sides.

$$|5x + 1| + 1 \leq 10$$
$$|5x + 1| \leq 10 - 1 \quad \text{Subtract 1 from both sides.}$$
$$|5x + 1| \leq 9 \quad \text{Simplify.}$$

Since 9 is positive, we apply the absolute value property for $|X| \leq a$.

$$-9 \leq 5x + 1 \leq 9$$
$$-9 - 1 \leq 5x + 1 - 1 \leq 9 - 1 \quad \text{Subtract 1 from all three parts.}$$
$$-10 \leq 5x \leq 8 \quad \text{Simplify.}$$
$$-2 \leq x \leq \frac{8}{5} \quad \text{Divide all three parts by 5.}$$

$$\overset{\frac{8}{5}}{\xleftarrow{\quad\begin{array}{cccccc} | & [& | & | & | &] & | \\ -3 & -2 & -1 & 0 & 1 & 2 \end{array}\quad}\rightarrow}$$

The solution set is $\left[-2, \dfrac{8}{5} \right]$, and the graph is shown above. □

PRACTICE

3 Solve $|3x - 2| + 5 \leq 9$ for x and graph the solution set. ■

EXAMPLE 4   Solve for x: $\left|2x - \dfrac{1}{10}\right| < -13$

Solution   The absolute value of a number is always nonnegative and can never be less than -13. Thus this absolute value inequality has no solution. The solution set is $\{\ \}$ or $\varnothing$.

PRACTICE 4   Solve for x: $\left|3x + \dfrac{5}{8}\right| < -4$

EXAMPLE 5   Solve for x: $\left|\dfrac{2(x+1)}{3}\right| \leq 0$

Solution   Recall that "$\leq$" means "is less than or equal to." The absolute value of any expression will never be less than 0, but it may be equal to 0. Thus, to solve $\left|\dfrac{2(x+1)}{3}\right| \leq 0$, we solve $\left|\dfrac{2(x+1)}{3}\right| = 0$

$$\frac{2(x+1)}{3} = 0$$

$$3\left[\frac{2(x+1)}{3}\right] = 3(0) \quad \text{Clear the equation of fractions.}$$

$$2x + 2 = 0 \qquad \text{Apply the distributive property.}$$

$$2x = -2 \qquad \text{Subtract 2 from both sides.}$$

$$x = -1 \qquad \text{Divide both sides by 2.}$$

The solution set is $\{-1\}$.

PRACTICE 5   Solve for x: $\left|\dfrac{3(x-2)}{5}\right| \leq 0$

OBJECTIVE

2   Solving Absolute Value Inequalities of the Form $|X| > a$

Let us now solve an absolute value inequality of the form $|X| > a$, such as $|x| \geq 3$. The solution set contains all numbers whose distance from 0 is 3 or more units. Thus the graph of the solution set contains 3 and all points to the right of 3 on the number line or -3 and all points to the left of -3 on the number line.

Distance from 0:
greater than or
equal to 3 units

Distance from 0:
greater than or
equal to 3 units

$-3\ -2\ -1\quad 0\quad 1\quad 2\quad 3$

This solution set is written as $\{x \mid x \leq -3 \text{ or } x \geq 3\}$. In interval notation, the solution is $(-\infty, -3] \cup [3, \infty)$, since "or" means "union." In general, we have the following.

Solving Absolute Value Inequalities of the Form $|X| > a$

If a is a positive number, then $|X| > a$ is equivalent to $X < -a$ or $X > a$.

This property also holds true for the inequality symbol $\geq$.

EXAMPLE 6   Solve for y: $|y - 3| > 7$

Solution   Since 7 is positive, we apply the property for $|X| > a$.

$$|y - 3| > 7 \text{ is equivalent to } y - 3 < -7 \text{ or } y - 3 > 7$$

Next, solve the compound inequality.

$$y - 3 < -7 \qquad \text{or} \qquad y - 3 > 7$$
$$y - 3 + 3 < -7 + 3 \quad \text{or} \quad y - 3 + 3 > 7 + 3 \qquad \text{Add 3 to both sides.}$$
$$y < -4 \qquad \text{or} \qquad y > 10 \qquad \text{Simplify.}$$

The solution set is $(-\infty, -4) \cup (10, \infty)$, and its graph is shown.

PRACTICE

6   Solve for y: $|y + 4| \geq 6$

Example 7 illustrates another special case of absolute value inequalities when an isolated absolute value expression is less than, less than or equal to, greater than, or greater than or equal to a negative number or 0.

EXAMPLE 7   Solve: $|2x + 9| + 5 > 3$

Solution First isolate the absolute value expression by subtracting 5 from both sides.

$$|2x + 9| + 5 > 3$$
$$|2x + 9| + 5 - 5 > 3 - 5 \qquad \text{Subtract 5 from both sides.}$$
$$|2x + 9| > -2 \qquad \text{Simplify.}$$

The absolute value of any number is always nonnegative and thus is always greater than -2. This inequality and the original inequality are true for all values of x. The solution set is $\{x \mid x \text{ is a real number}\}$ or $(-\infty, \infty)$, and its graph is shown.

PRACTICE

7   Solve $|4x + 3| + 5 > 3$. Graph the solution set.

✔ **CONCEPT CHECK**

Without taking any solution steps, how do you know that the absolute value inequality $|3x - 2| > -9$ has a solution? What is its solution?

EXAMPLE 8   Solve: $\left|\dfrac{x}{3} - 1\right| - 7 \geq -5$

Solution First, isolate the absolute value expression by adding 7 to both sides.

$$\left|\frac{x}{3} - 1\right| - 7 \geq -5$$

$$\left|\frac{x}{3} - 1\right| - 7 + 7 \geq -5 + 7 \qquad \text{Add 7 to both sides.}$$

$$\left|\frac{x}{3} - 1\right| \geq 2 \qquad \text{Simplify.}$$

Next, write the absolute value inequality as an equivalent compound inequality and solve.

$$\frac{x}{3} - 1 \leq -2 \qquad \text{or} \qquad \frac{x}{3} - 1 \geq 2$$

$$3\left(\frac{x}{3} - 1\right) \leq 3(-2) \qquad \text{or} \qquad 3\left(\frac{x}{3} - 1\right) \geq 3(2) \qquad \text{Clear the inequalities of fractions.}$$

$$x - 3 \leq -6 \qquad \text{or} \qquad x - 3 \geq 6 \qquad \text{Apply the distributive property.}$$

$$x \leq -3 \qquad \text{or} \qquad x \geq 9 \qquad \text{Add 3 to both sides.}$$

Answer to Concept Check:
$(-\infty, \infty)$ since the absolute value is always nonnegative

The solution set is $(-\infty, -3] \cup [9, \infty)$, and its graph is shown.

PRACTICE
8   Solve $\left|\dfrac{x}{2} - 3\right| - 5 > -2$. Graph the solution set.

The following box summarizes the types of absolute value equations and inequalities.

Solving Absolute Value Equations and Inequalities with $a > 0$

Algebraic Solution	Solution Graph
$\|X\| = a$ is equivalent to $X = a$ or $X = -a$.	
$\|X\| < a$ is equivalent to $-a < X < a$.	
$\|X\| > a$ is equivalent to $X < -a$ or $X > a$.	

✔ Vocabulary, Readiness & Video Check

Match each absolute value statement with an equivalent statement.

1. $|2x + 1| = 3$

2. $|2x + 1| \le 3$

3. $|2x + 1| < 3$

4. $|2x + 1| \ge 3$

5. $|2x + 1| > 3$

A. $2x + 1 > 3$ or $2x + 1 < -3$

B. $2x + 1 \ge 3$ or $2x + 1 \le -3$

C. $-3 < 2x + 1 < 3$

D. $2x + 1 = 3$ or $2x + 1 = -3$

E. $-3 \le 2x + 1 \le 3$

Martin-Gay Interactive Videos

See Video 2.7

Watch the section lecture video and answer the following questions.

OBJECTIVE
1   **6.** In Example 3, how can you reason that the inequality has no solution even if you don't know the rule?

OBJECTIVE
2   **7.** In Example 4, why is the union symbol used when the solution is written in interval notation?

2.7   Exercise Set   MyMathLab®

Solve each inequality. Then graph the solution set and write it in interval notation. See Examples 1 through 4.

1. $|x| \le 4$

2. $|x| < 6$

3. $|x - 3| < 2$

4. $|y - 7| \le 5$

5. $|x + 3| < 2$

6. $|x + 4| < 6$

7. $|2x + 7| \le 13$

8. $|5x - 3| \le 18$

9. $|x| + 7 \le 12$

10. $|x| + 6 \le 7$

▶ **11.** $|3x - 1| < -5$

12. $|8x - 3| < -2$

13. $|x - 6| - 7 \le -1$

14. $|z + 2| - 7 < -3$

Solve each inequality. Graph the solution set and write it in interval notation. See Examples 6 through 8.

▶ **15.** $|x| > 3$

16. $|y| \ge 4$

17. $|x + 10| \ge 14$

18. $|x - 9| \ge 2$

19. $|x| + 2 > 6$

20. $|x| - 1 > 3$

21. $|5x| > -4$

22. $|4x - 11| > -1$

23. $|6x - 8| + 3 > 7$

24. $|10 + 3x| + 1 > 2$

Solve each inequality. Graph the solution set and write it in interval notation. See Example 5.

25. $|x| \leq 0$

26. $|x| \geq 0$

27. $|8x + 3| > 0$

28. $|5x - 6| < 0$

MIXED PRACTICE

Solve each inequality. Graph the solution set and write it in interval notation. See Examples 1 through 8.

29. $|x| \leq 2$

30. $|z| < 8$

31. $|y| > 1$

32. $|x| \geq 10$

33. $|x - 3| < 8$

34. $|-3 + x| \leq 10$

35. $|0.6x - 3| > 0.6$

36. $|1 + 0.3x| \geq 0.1$

37. $5 + |x| \leq 2$

38. $8 + |x| < 1$

39. $|x| > -4$

40. $|x| \leq -7$

41. $|2x - 7| \leq 11$

42. $|5x + 2| < 8$

43. $|x + 5| + 2 \geq 8$

44. $|-1 + x| - 6 > 2$

45. $|x| > 0$

46. $|x| < 0$

47. $9 + |x| > 7$

48. $5 + |x| \geq 4$

49. $6 + |4x - 1| \leq 9$

50. $-3 + |5x - 2| \leq 4$

51. $\left|\dfrac{2}{3}x + 1\right| > 1$

52. $\left|\dfrac{3}{4}x - 1\right| \geq 2$

53. $|5x + 3| < -6$

54. $|4 + 9x| \geq -6$

55. $\left|\dfrac{8x - 3}{4}\right| \leq 0$

56. $\left|\dfrac{5x + 6}{2}\right| \leq 0$

57. $|1 + 3x| + 4 < 5$

58. $|7x - 3| - 1 \leq 10$

59. $\left|\dfrac{x + 6}{3}\right| > 2$

60. $\left|\dfrac{7 + x}{2}\right| \geq 4$

61. $-15 + |2x - 7| \leq -6$

62. $-9 + |3 + 4x| < -4$

63. $\left|2x + \dfrac{3}{4}\right| - 7 \leq -2$

64. $\left|\dfrac{3}{5} + 4x\right| - 6 < -1$

MIXED PRACTICE

Solve each equation or inequality for x. (Sections 2.6, 2.7)

65. $|2x - 3| < 7$

66. $|2x - 3| > 7$

67. $|2x - 3| = 7$

68. $|5 - 6x| = 29$

69. $|x - 5| \geq 12$

70. $|x + 4| \geq 20$

71. $|9 + 4x| = 0$

72. $|9 + 4x| \geq 0$

73. $|2x + 1| + 4 < 7$

74. $8 + |5x - 3| \geq 11$

75. $|3x - 5| + 4 = 5$

76. $|5x - 3| + 2 = 4$

77. $|x + 11| = -1$

78. $|4x - 4| = -3$

79. $\left|\dfrac{2x - 1}{3}\right| = 6$

80. $\left|\dfrac{6 - x}{4}\right| = 5$

81. $\left|\dfrac{3x - 5}{6}\right| > 5$

82. $\left|\dfrac{4x - 7}{5}\right| < 2$

REVIEW AND PREVIEW

Recall the formula:

$$\text{Probability of an event} = \frac{\substack{\text{number of ways that} \\ \text{the event can occur}}}{\substack{\text{number of possible} \\ \text{outcomes}}}$$

Find the probability of rolling each number on a single toss of a die. (Recall that a die is a cube with each of its six sides containing 1, 2, 3, 4, 5, and 6 black dots, respectively.) See Section 2.3.

83. $P(\text{rolling a 2})$

84. $P(\text{rolling a 5})$

85. $P(\text{rolling a 7})$

86. $P(\text{rolling a 0})$

87. $P(\text{rolling a 1 or 3})$

88. $P(\text{rolling a 1, 2, 3, 4, 5, or 6})$

Consider the equation $3x - 4y = 12$. For each value of x or y given, find the corresponding value of the other variable that makes the statement true. See Section 2.3.

89. If $x = 2$, find y.

90. If $y = -1$, find x.

91. If $y = -3$, find x.

92. If $x = 4$, find y.

CONCEPT EXTENSIONS

93. Write an absolute value inequality representing all numbers x whose distance from 0 is less than 7 units.

94. Write an absolute value inequality representing all numbers x whose distance from 0 is greater than 4 units.

95. Write $-5 \leq x \leq 5$ as an equivalent inequality containing an absolute value.

96. Write $x > 1$ or $x < -1$ as an equivalent inequality containing an absolute value.

97. Describe how solving $|x - 3| = 5$ is different from solving $|x - 3| < 5$.

98. Describe how solving $|x + 4| = 0$ is similar to solving $|x + 4| \leq 0$.

The expression $|x_T - x|$ is defined to be the absolute error in x, where x_T is the true value of a quantity and x is the measured value or value as stored in a computer.

99. If the true value of a quantity is 3.5 and the absolute error must be less than 0.05, find the acceptable measured values.

100. If the true value of a quantity is 0.2 and the approximate value stored in a computer is $\dfrac{51}{256}$, find the absolute error.

Chapter 2 Vocabulary Check

Fill in each blank with one of the words or phrases listed below.

contradiction	linear inequality in one variable	compound inequality	solution
absolute value	consecutive integers	identity	union
formula	linear equation in one variable	intersection	

1. The statement "$x < 5$ *or* $x > 7$" is called a(n) _____.

2. An equation in one variable that has no solution is called a(n) _____.

3. The _____ of two sets is the set of all elements common to both sets.

4. The _____ of two sets is the set of all elements that belong to either of the sets.

5. An equation in one variable that has every number (for which the equation is defined) as a solution is called a(n) _____.

6. The equation $d = rt$ is also called a(n) _____.

7. A number's distance from 0 is called its _____.

8. When a variable in an equation is replaced by a number and the resulting equation is true, then that number is called a(n) _____ of the equation.

9. The integers 17, 18, 19 are examples of _____.

10. The statement $5x - 0.2 < 7$ is an example of a(n) _____.

11. The statement $5x - 0.2 = 7$ is an example of a(n) _____.

Chapter 2 Highlights

DEFINITIONS AND CONCEPTS	EXAMPLES

Section 2.1   Linear Equations in One Variable

An **equation** is a statement that two expressions are equal.	Equations: $$5 = 5 \qquad 7x + 2 = -14 \qquad 3(x - 1)^2 = 9x^2 - 6$$
A **linear equation in one variable** is an equation that can be written in the form $ax + b = c$, where a, b, and c are real numbers and a is not 0.	Linear equations: $$7x + 2 = -14 \qquad x = -3$$ $$5(2y - 7) = -2(8y - 1)$$
A **solution** of an equation is a value for the variable that makes the equation a true statement.	Check to see that -1 is a solution of $$3(x - 1) = 4x - 2.$$ $$3(-1 - 1) \stackrel{?}{=} 4(-1) - 2$$ $$3(-2) \stackrel{?}{=} -4 - 2$$ $$-6 = -6 \qquad \text{True}$$ Thus, -1 is a solution.
Equivalent equations have the same solution.	$x - 12 = 14$ and $x = 26$ are equivalent equations.

(continued)

DEFINITIONS AND CONCEPTS	EXAMPLES

Section 2.1   Linear Equations in One Variable (continued)

The **addition property of equality** guarantees that the same number may be added to (or subtracted from) both sides of an equation, and the result is an equivalent equation.

Solve for x: $-3x - 2 = 10$

$$-3x - 2 + 2 = 10 + 2 \quad \text{Add 2 to both sides.}$$
$$-3x = 12$$
$$\frac{-3x}{-3} = \frac{12}{-3} \quad \text{Divide both sides by } -3.$$
$$x = -4$$

The **multiplication property of equality** guarantees that both sides of an equation may be multiplied by (or divided by) the same nonzero number, and the result is an equivalent equation.

To Solve a Linear Equation in One Variable

Solve for x:

$$x - \frac{x-2}{6} = \frac{x-7}{3} + \frac{2}{3}$$

1. Clear the equation of fractions.

1. $6\left(x - \dfrac{x-2}{6}\right) = 6\left(\dfrac{x-7}{3} + \dfrac{2}{3}\right)$ Multiply both sides by 6.

$$6x - (x - 2) = 2(x - 7) + 2(2)$$

2. Remove grouping symbols such as parentheses.

3. Simplify by combining like terms.

4. Write variable terms on one side and numbers on the other side using the addition property of equality.

2. $6x - x + 2 = 2x - 14 + 4$ Remove grouping symbols.

3. $5x + 2 = 2x - 10$

4. $5x + 2 - 2 = 2x - 10 - 2$ Subtract 2.

$$5x = 2x - 12$$
$$5x - 2x = 2x - 12 - 2x \quad \text{Subtract } 2x.$$
$$3x = -12$$

5. Isolate the variable using the multiplication property of equality.

5. $\dfrac{3x}{3} = \dfrac{-12}{3}$ Divide by 3.

$$x = -4$$

6. Check the proposed solution in the original equation.

6. $-4 - \dfrac{-4-2}{6} \stackrel{?}{=} \dfrac{-4-7}{3} + \dfrac{2}{3}$ Replace x with -4 in the original equation.

$$-4 - \frac{-6}{6} \stackrel{?}{=} \frac{-11}{3} + \frac{2}{3}$$
$$-4 - (-1) \stackrel{?}{=} \frac{-9}{3}$$
$$-3 = -3 \quad \text{True}$$

Section 2.2   An Introduction to Problem Solving

Problem-Solving Strategy

Colorado is shaped like a rectangle whose length is about 1.3 times its width. If the perimeter of Colorado is 2070 kilometers, find its dimensions.

1. UNDERSTAND the problem.

1. Read and reread the problem. Guess a solution and check your guess.

Let x = width of Colorado in kilometers. Then $1.3x$ = length of Colorado in kilometers.

Colorado x

$1.3x$

DEFINITIONS AND CONCEPTS	EXAMPLES

Section 2.2   An Introduction to Problem Solving (continued)

2. TRANSLATE the problem.

2. In words:

twice the length	+	twice the width	=	perimeter
↘		↓		↓
Translate: $2(1.3x)$	+	$2x$	=	2070

3. SOLVE the equation.

3. $2.6x + 2x = 2070$

$4.6x = 2070$

$x = 450$

4. INTERPRET the results.

4. If $x = 450$ kilometers, then $1.3x = 1.3(450) = 585$ kilometers. *Check*: The perimeter of a rectangle whose width is 450 kilometers and length is 585 kilometers is $2(450) + 2(585) = 2070$ kilometers, the required perimeter. *State*: The dimensions of Colorado are 450 kilometers by 585 kilometers.

Section 2.3   Formulas and Problem Solving

An equation that describes a known relationship among quantities is called a **formula.**

To Solve a Formula for a Specified Variable

To solve a formula for a specified variable, use the steps for solving an equation. Treat the specified variable as the only variable of the equation.

Formulas:

$A = \pi r^2$ (area of a circle)

$I = PRT$ (interest = principal · rate · time)

Solve $A = 2HW + 2LW + 2LH$ for H.

$A - 2LW = 2HW + 2LH$ Subtract $2LW$.

$A - 2LW = H(2W + 2L)$ Factor out H.

$\dfrac{A - 2LW}{2W + 2L} = \dfrac{H(2W + 2L)}{2W + 2L}$ Divide by $2W + 2L$.

$\dfrac{A - 2LW}{2W + 2L} = H$ Simplify.

Section 2.4   Linear Inequalities and Problem Solving

A **linear inequality in one variable** is an inequality that can be written in the form $ax + b < c$, where a, b, and c are real numbers and $a \neq 0$. (The inequality symbols $\leq$, $>$, and $\geq$ also apply here.)

The **addition property of inequality** guarantees that the same number may be added to (or subtracted from) both sides of an inequality, and the resulting inequality will have the same solution set.

The **multiplication property of inequality** guarantees that both sides of an inequality may be multiplied by (or divided by) the same **positive** number, and the resulting inequality will have the same solution set. We may also multiply (or divide) both sides of an inequality by the same **negative** number and **reverse the direction of the inequality symbol**, and the result is an inequality with the same solution set.

Linear inequalities:

$5x - 2 \leq -7$ $3y > 1$ $\dfrac{z}{7} < -9(z - 3)$

$x - 9 \leq -16$

$x - 9 + 9 \leq -16 + 9$ Add 9.

$x \leq -7$

Solve.

$6x < -66$

$\dfrac{6x}{6} < \dfrac{-66}{6}$ Divide by 6. Do not reverse direction of inequality symbol.

$x < -11$

Solve.

$-6x < -66$

$\dfrac{-6x}{-6} > \dfrac{-66}{-6}$ Divide by -6. Reverse direction of inequality symbol.

$x > 11$

(continued)

DEFINITIONS AND CONCEPTS	EXAMPLES

Section 2.4   Linear Inequalities and Problem Solving (continued)

To Solve a Linear Inequality in One Variable

Steps:

1. Clear the inequality of fractions.
2. Remove grouping symbols such as parentheses.
3. Simplify by combining like terms.
4. Write variable terms on one side and numbers on the other side using the addition property of inequality.
5. Isolate the variable using the multiplication property of inequality.

Solve for x.

$$\frac{3}{7}(x - 4) \geq x + 2$$

1. $7\left[\dfrac{3}{7}(x - 4)\right] \geq 7(x + 2)$ Multiply by 7.

$$3(x - 4) \geq 7(x + 2)$$

2. $3x - 12 \geq 7x + 14$ Apply the distributive property.

3. No like terms on each side of the inequality.

4. $-4x - 12 \geq 14$ Subtract $7x$.

$\qquad -4x \geq 26$ Add 12.

5. $\dfrac{-4x}{-4} \leq \dfrac{26}{-4}$ Divide by -4. Reverse direction of inequality symbol.

$$x \leq -\frac{13}{2}$$

Section 2.5   Compound Inequalities

Two inequalities joined by the words **and** or **or** are called **compound inequalities.**

Compound inequalities:

$$x - 7 \leq 4 \quad\quad and \quad\quad x \geq -21$$
$$2x + 7 > x - 3 \quad or \quad 5x + 2 > -3$$

The solution set of a compound inequality formed by the word **and** is the **intersection** $\cap$ of the solution sets of the two inequalities.

Solve for x:

$x < 5$ *and* $x < 3$

$\{x \mid x < 5\}$ $(-\infty, 5)$

$\{x \mid x < 3\}$ $(-\infty, 3)$

$\{x \mid x < 3$ *and* $x < 5\}$ $(-\infty, 3)$

The solution set of a compound inequality formed by the word **or** is the **union**, $\cup$, of the solution sets of the two inequalities.

Solve for x:

$$x - 2 \geq -3 \quad or \quad 2x \leq -4$$
$$x \geq -1 \quad or \quad x \leq -2$$

$\{x \mid x \geq -1\}$ $[-1, \infty)$

$\{x \mid x \leq -2\}$ $(-\infty, -2]$

$\{x \mid x \leq -2$ *or* $x \geq -1\}$ $(-\infty, -2] \cup [-1, \infty)$

Section 2.6 Absolute Value Equations

If a is a positive number, then $|X| = a$ is equivalent to $X = a$ or $X = -a$.

Solve for y:

$$|5y - 1| - 7 = 4$$

$|5y - 1| = 11$

$5y - 1 = 11$ or $5y - 1 = -11$

$5y = 12$ or $\quad 5y = -10$ Add 1.

$y = \dfrac{12}{5}$ or $y = -2$ Divide by 5.

The solutions are -2 and $\dfrac{12}{5}$.

DEFINITIONS AND CONCEPTS	EXAMPLES

Section 2.6 Absolute Value Equations (continued)

If a is negative, then $|X| = a$ has no solution.

Solve for x:

$$\left|\frac{x}{2} - 7\right| = -1$$

The solution set is { } or $\varnothing$.

If an absolute value equation is of the form $|X| = |Y|$, solve $X = Y$ or $X = -Y$.

Solve for x:

$$|x - 7| = |2x + 1|$$

$x - 7 = 2x + 1 \quad$ or $\quad x - 7 = -(2x + 1)$

$\quad x = 2x + 8 \qquad\qquad x - 7 = -2x - 1$

$\quad -x = 8 \qquad\qquad\qquad x = -2x + 6$

$\quad\; x = -8 \quad$ or $\qquad 3x = 6$

$\qquad\qquad\qquad\qquad\qquad x = 2$

The solutions are -8 and 2.

Section 2.7 Absolute Value Inequalities

If a is a positive number, then $|X| < a$ is equivalent to $-a < X < a$.

Solve for y:

$$|y - 5| \le 3$$

$\qquad -3 \le y - 5 \le 3$

$-3 + 5 \le y - 5 + 5 \le 3 + 5 \quad$ Add 5.

$\qquad\quad 2 \le y \le 8$

The solution set is $[2, 8]$.

If a is a positive number, then $|X| > a$ is equivalent to $X < -a$ or $X > a$.

Solve for x:

$$\left|\frac{x}{2} - 3\right| > 7$$

$\dfrac{x}{2} - 3 < -7 \quad$ or $\quad \dfrac{x}{2} - 3 > 7$

$x - 6 < -14 \quad$ or $\quad x - 6 > 14 \quad$ Multiply by 2.

$\quad x < -8 \quad$ or $\quad x > 20 \qquad$ Add 6.

The solution set is $(-\infty, -8) \cup (20, \infty)$.

Chapter 2 Review

(2.1) Solve each linear equation.

1. $4(x - 5) = 2x - 14$

2. $x + 7 = -2(x + 8)$

3. $3(2y - 1) = -8(6 + y)$

4. $-(z + 12) = 5(2z - 1)$

5. $n - (8 + 4n) = 2(3n - 4)$

6. $4(9v + 2) = 6(1 + 6v) - 10$

7. $0.3(x - 2) = 1.2$

8. $1.5 = 0.2(c - 0.3)$

9. $-4(2 - 3x) = 2(3x - 4) + 6x$

10. $6(m - 1) + 3(2 - m) = 0$

11. $6 - 3(2g + 4) - 4g = 5(1 - 2g)$

12. $20 - 5(p + 1) + 3p = -(2p - 15)$

13. $\dfrac{x}{3} - 4 = x - 2$

14. $\dfrac{9}{4}y = \dfrac{2}{3}y$

15. $\dfrac{3n}{8} - 1 = 3 + \dfrac{n}{6}$

16. $\dfrac{z}{6} + 1 = \dfrac{z}{2} + 2$

17. $\dfrac{y}{4} - \dfrac{y}{2} = -8$

18. $\dfrac{2x}{3} - \dfrac{8}{3} = x$

19. $\dfrac{b - 2}{3} = \dfrac{b + 2}{5}$

20. $\dfrac{2t - 1}{3} = \dfrac{3t + 2}{15}$

21. $\dfrac{2(t + 1)}{3} = \dfrac{2(t - 1)}{3}$

22. $\dfrac{3a - 3}{6} = \dfrac{4a + 1}{15} + 2$

(2.2) Solve.

23. Twice the difference of a number and 3 is the same as 1 added to three times the number. Find the number.

24. One number is 5 more than another number. If the sum of the numbers is 285, find the numbers.

25. Find 40% of 130.

26. Find 1.5% of 8.

27. The length of a rectangular playing field is 5 meters less than twice its width. If 230 meters of fencing goes around the field, find the dimensions of the field.

28. In 2013, the median weekly earnings of young adults with bachelor degrees were $1108. This represents a 43% increase over the weekly median earnings of young adults with associate degrees. Find the median weekly earnings of young adults with associate degrees in 2013. Round to the nearest whole dollar. (*Source:* Bureau of Labor Statistics)

29. Find four consecutive integers such that twice the first subtracted from the sum of the other three integers is 16.

30. Determine whether there are two consecutive odd integers such that 5 times the first exceeds 3 times the second by 54.

31. A car rental company charges $19.95 per day for a compact car plus 12 cents per mile for every mile over 100 miles driven per day. If Mr. Woo's bill for 2 days' use is $46.86, find how many miles he drove.

32. The cost C of producing x number of scientific calculators is given by $C = 4.50x + 3000$, and the revenue R from selling them is given by $R = 16.50x$. Find the number of calculators that must be sold to break even. (Recall that to break even, revenue = cost.)

(2.3) Solve each equation for the specified variable.

△ 33. $V = lwh$ for w

△ 34. $C = 2\pi r$ for r

35. $5x - 4y = -12$ for y

36. $5x - 4y = -12$ for x

37. $y - y_1 = m(x - x_1)$ for m

38. $y - y_1 = m(x - x_1)$ for x

39. $E = I(R + r)$ for r

40. $S = vt + gt^2$ for g

41. $T = gr + gvt$ for g

42. $I = Prt + P$ for P

43. A principal of $3000 is invested in an account paying an annual percentage rate of 3%. Find the amount (to the nearest cent) in the account after 7 years if the amount is compounded

　　a. semiannually.

　　b. weekly.

44. The high temperature in Slidell, Louisiana, one day was 90° Fahrenheit. Convert this temperature to degrees Celsius.

△ 45. Angie Applegate has a photograph for which the length is 2 inches longer than the width. If she increases each dimension by 4 inches, the area is increased by 88 square inches. Find the original dimensions.

△ 46. One-square-foot floor tiles come 24 to a package. Find how many packages are needed to cover a rectangular floor 18 feet by 21 feet.

(2.4) Solve each linear inequality. Write your answers in interval notation.

47. $3(x - 5) > -(x + 3)$

48. $-2(x + 7) \geq 3(x + 2)$

49. $4x - (5 + 2x) < 3x - 1$

50. $3(x - 8) < 7x + 2(5 - x)$

51. $24 \geq 6x - 2(3x - 5) + 2x$

52. $\dfrac{x}{3} + \dfrac{1}{2} > \dfrac{2}{3}$

53. $x + \dfrac{3}{4} < -\dfrac{x}{2} + \dfrac{9}{4}$

54. $\dfrac{x - 5}{2} \leq \dfrac{3}{8}(2x + 6)$

Solve.

55. George Boros can pay his housekeeper $15 per week to do his laundry, or he can have the laundromat do it at a cost of 50 cents per pound for the first 10 pounds and 40 cents for each additional pound. Use an inequality to find the weight at which it is more economical to use the housekeeper than the laundromat.

56. In the Olympic gymnastics competition, Nana must average a score of 9.65 to win the silver medal. Seven of the eight judges have reported scores of 9.5, 9.7, 9.9, 9.7, 9.7, 9.6, and 9.5. Use an inequality to find the minimum score that Nana must receive from the last judge to win the silver medal.

(2.5) Solve each inequality. Write your answers in interval notation.

57. $1 \leq 4x - 7 \leq 3$

58. $-2 \leq 8 + 5x < -1$

59. $-3 < 4(2x - 1) < 12$

60. $-6 < x - (3 - 4x) < -3$

61. $\dfrac{1}{6} < \dfrac{4x - 3}{3} \leq \dfrac{4}{5}$

62. $x \leq 2$ and $x > -5$

63. $3x - 5 > 6$ or $-x < -5$

64. Ceramic firing temperatures usually range from 500° to 1000° Fahrenheit. Use a compound inequality to convert this range to the Celsius scale. Round to the nearest degree.

65. Carol would like to pay cash for a car when she graduates from college and estimates that she can afford a car that costs between $4000 and $8000. She has saved $500 so far and plans to earn the rest of the money by working the next two summers. If Carol plans to save the same amount each summer, use a compound inequality to find the range of money she must save each summer to buy the car.

(2.6) *Solve each absolute value equation.*

66. $|x - 7| = 9$

67. $|8 - x| = 3$

68. $|2x + 9| = 9$

69. $|-3x + 4| = 7$

70. $|3x - 2| + 6 = 10$

71. $5 + |6x + 1| = 5$

72. $-5 = |4x - 3|$

73. $|5 - 6x| + 8 = 3$

74. $-8 = |x - 3| - 10$

75. $\left|\dfrac{3x - 7}{4}\right| = 2$

76. $|6x + 1| = |15 + 4x|$

(2.7) *Solve each absolute value inequality. Graph the solution set and write it in interval notation.*

77. $|5x - 1| < 9$

78. $|6 + 4x| \geq 10$

79. $|3x| - 8 > 1$

80. $9 + |5x| < 24$

81. $|6x - 5| \leq -1$

82. $\left|3x + \dfrac{2}{5}\right| \geq 4$

83. $\left|\dfrac{x}{3} + 6\right| - 8 > -5$

84. $\left|\dfrac{4(x - 1)}{7}\right| + 10 < 2$

MIXED REVIEW

Solve.

85. $\dfrac{x - 2}{5} + \dfrac{x + 2}{2} = \dfrac{x + 4}{3}$

86. $\dfrac{2z - 3}{4} - \dfrac{4 - z}{2} = \dfrac{z + 1}{3}$

△ **87.** $A = \dfrac{h}{2}(B + b)$ for B

△ **88.** $V = \dfrac{1}{3}\pi r^2 h$ for h

89. China, the United States, and France are predicted to be the top tourist destinations by 2020. In this year, the United States is predicted to have 9 million more tourists than France, and China is predicted to have 44 million more tourists than France. If the total number of tourists predicted for these three countries is 332 million, find the number predicted for each country in 2020.

90. Erasmos Gonzalez left Los Angeles at 11 a.m. and drove nonstop to San Diego, 130 miles away. If he arrived at 1:15 p.m., find his average speed, rounded to the nearest mile per hour.

△ **91.** Determine which container holds more ice cream, an 8 inch × 5 inch × 3 inch box or a cylinder with radius of 3 inches and height of 6 inches.

Solve. If an inequality, write your solutions in interval notation.

92. $48 + x \geq 5(2x + 4) - 2x$

93. $\dfrac{3(x - 2)}{5} > \dfrac{-5(x - 2)}{3}$

94. $0 \leq \dfrac{2(3x + 4)}{5} \leq 3$

95. $x \leq 2 \ or \ x > -5$

96. $-2x \leq 6 \ and \ -2x + 3 < -7$

97. $|7x| - 26 = -5$

98. $\left|\dfrac{9 - 2x}{5}\right| = -3$

99. $|x - 3| = |7 + 2x|$

100. $|6x - 5| \geq -1$

101. $\left|\dfrac{4x - 3}{5}\right| < 1$

1c

Chapter 2   Getting Ready for the Test

MATCHING *Match each equation with its solution. Letters may be used more than once or not at all.*

▶ **1.** $x - 9 = -6x - 9$

▶ **2.** $4x + 8 = 2(x + 4)$

▶ **3.** $5(2x - 4) = 10(x - 2)$

▶ **4.** $3(x + 2) + x = 4(x - 1) + 1$

    A. all real numbers

    B. no solution

    C. the solution is 0

MULTIPLE CHOICE *For Exercises 5 and 6, choose the correct interval notation for each set.*

▶ **5.** $\{x \mid x \leq -11\}$

    A. $(-\infty, -11]$ **B.** $[-11, \infty)$ **C.** $[-11, 11]$ **D.** $(-\infty, -11)$

▶ **6.** $\{x \mid -5 < x\}$

    A. $(-\infty, -5)$ **B.** $(-5, \infty)$ **C.** $(-5, 5)$ **D.** $(-\infty, -5]$

▶ **7.** Choose the solutions of $|x - 3| = 7$ by checking the given numbers in the original equation.

    A. $\{-7, 7\}$ **B.** $\{-10, 10\}$ **C.** $\{4, 10\}$ **D.** $\{-4, 10\}$

MATCHING *Match each equation or inequality in the first column with an equivalent statement in the second column. Letters may be used more than once or not at all.*

8. $|5x - 2| \le 4$

9. $|5x - 2| = 4$

10. $|5x - 2| \ge 4$

11. $|5x| - 2 = 4$

A. $5x - 2 = 4$ or $5x - 2 = -4$

B. $5x = 6$ or $5x = -6$

C. $-4 \le 5x - 2 \le 4$

D. $-6 \le 5x \le 6$

E. $5x - 2 \ge 4$ or $5x - 2 \le -4$

F. $5x \ge 6$ or $5x \le -6$

MATCHING *Match each equation or inequality with its solution. Letters may be used more than once or not at all.*

12. $|x + 3| = -9$

13. $|x + 3| < -9$

14. $|x + 3| > -9$

A. no solution, or $\varnothing$

B. $(-\infty, \infty)$

Chapter 2 Test   MyMathLab® You Tube

Solve each equation.

1. $8x + 14 = 5x + 44$

2. $9(x + 2) = 5[11 - 2(2 - x) + 3]$

3. $3(y - 4) + y = 2(6 + 2y)$

4. $7n - 6 + n = 2(4n - 3)$

5. $\dfrac{7w}{4} + 5 = \dfrac{3w}{10} + 1$

6. $\dfrac{z + 7}{9} + 1 = \dfrac{2z + 1}{6}$

7. $|6x - 5| - 3 = -2$

8. $|8 - 2t| = -6$

9. $|2x - 3| = |4x + 5|$

10. $|x - 5| = |x + 2|$

Solve each equation for the specified variable.

11. $3x - 4y = 8$ for y

12. $S = gt^2 + gvt$ for g

13. $F = \dfrac{9}{5}C + 32$ for C

Solve each inequality. Write your solutions in interval notation.

14. $3(2x - 7) - 4x > -(x + 6)$

15. $\dfrac{3x - 2}{3} - \dfrac{5x + 1}{4} \ge 0$

16. $-3 < 2(x - 3) \le 4$

17. $|3x + 1| > 5$

18. $|x - 5| - 4 < -2$

19. $x \ge 5$ *and* $x \ge 4$

20. $x \ge 5$ *or* $x \ge 4$

21. $-1 \le \dfrac{2x - 5}{3} < 2$

22. $6x + 1 > 5x + 4$ *or* $1 - x > -4$

23. Find 12% of 80.

Solve.

24. In 2014, Ford sold 2,480,942 new vehicles in America. This represents a 29.1% increase over the number of new vehicles sold by Ford in 2010. Use this information to find the number of new vehicles sold by Ford in 2010. Round to the nearest thousand. (*Source:* Ford Motor Company)

25. A circular dog pen has a circumference of 78.5 feet. Approximate π by 3.14 and estimate how many hunting dogs could be safely kept in the pen if each dog needs at least 60 square feet of room.

26. In 2022, the number of people employed as registered nurses in the United States is expected to be 3,240,000. This represents a 19% increase over the number of people employed as registered nurses in 2012. Find the number of registered nurses employed in 2012. Round to the nearest thousand. (*Source:* Bureau of Labor Statistics)

27. Find the amount of money in an account after 10 years if a principal of $2500 is invested at 3.5% interest compounded quarterly. (Round to the nearest cent.)

28. The three states where international travelers spend the most money are Florida, California, and New York. International travelers spend $4 billion more money in California than New York, and in Florida they spend $1 billion less than twice the amount spent in New York. If total international spending in these three states is $39 billion, find the amount spent in each state. (*Source:* Travel Industry Association of America)

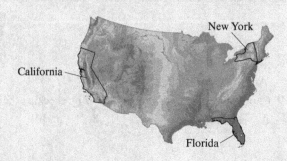

Chapter 2 Cumulative Review

List the elements in each set.

1. **a.** $\{x \mid x \text{ is a natural number greater than } 100\}$
   b. $\{x \mid x \text{ is a whole number between } 1 \text{ and } 6\}$

2. **a.** $\{x \mid x \text{ is an integer between } -3 \text{ and } 5\}$
   b. $\{x \mid x \text{ is a whole number between } 3 \text{ and } 5\}$

3. Find each absolute value.
   a. $|3|$ **b.** $\left|-\dfrac{1}{7}\right|$
   c. $-|2.7|$ **d.** $-|-8|$
   e. $|0|$

4. Find the opposite of each number.
   a. $\dfrac{2}{3}$ **b.** -9 **c.** 1.5

5. Add.
   a. $-3 + (-11)$ **b.** $3 + (-7)$
   c. $-10 + 15$ **d.** $-8.3 + (-1.9)$
   e. $-\dfrac{1}{4} + \dfrac{1}{2}$ **f.** $-\dfrac{2}{3} + \dfrac{3}{7}$

6. Subtract.
   a. $-2 - (-10)$ **b.** $1.7 - 8.9$
   c. $-\dfrac{1}{2} - \dfrac{1}{4}$

7. Find the square roots.
   a. $\sqrt{9}$ **b.** $\sqrt{25}$
   c. $\sqrt{\dfrac{1}{4}}$ **d.** $-\sqrt{36}$
   e. $\sqrt{-36}$

8. Multiply or divide.
   a. $-3(-2)$ **b.** $-\dfrac{3}{4}\left(-\dfrac{4}{7}\right)$
   c. $\dfrac{0}{-2}$ **d.** $\dfrac{-20}{-2}$

9. Evaluate each algebraic expression when $x = 4$ and $y = -3$.
   a. $3x - 7y$ **b.** $-2y^2$
   c. $\dfrac{\sqrt{x}}{y} - \dfrac{y}{x}$

10. Find the roots.
   a. $\sqrt[4]{1}$ **b.** $\sqrt[3]{8}$ **c.** $\sqrt[4]{81}$

11. Write each sentence as an equation.
   a. The sum of x and 5 is 20.
   b. Two times the sum of 3 and y amounts to 4.
   c. The difference of 8 and x is the same as the product of 2 and x.
   d. The quotient of z and 9 amounts to 9 plus z.

12. Insert $<$, $>$, or $=$ between each pair of numbers to form a true statement.
   a. $-3 \quad -5$ **b.** $\dfrac{-12}{-4} \quad 3$
   c. $0 \quad -2$

13. Use the commutative property of addition to write an expression equivalent to $7x + 5$.

14. Use the associative property of multiplication to write an expression equivalent to $5 \cdot (7x)$. Then simplify the expression.

Solve for x.

15. $2x + 5 = 9$

16. $11.2 = 1.2 - 5x$

17. $6x - 4 = 2 + 6(x - 1)$

18. $2x + 1.5 = -0.2 + 1.6x$

19. Write the following as algebraic expressions. Then simplify.
   a. The sum of three consecutive integers if x is the first consecutive integer
   b. The perimeter of a triangle with sides of length x, $5x$, and $6x - 3$

20. Write the following as algebraic expressions. Then simplify.
   a. The sum of three consecutive even integers if x is the first consecutive even integer
   b. The perimeter of a square with side length $3x + 1$

21. Find three numbers such that the second number is 3 more than twice the first number, and the third number is four times the first number. The sum of the three numbers is 164.

22. Find two numbers such that the second number is 2 more than three times the first number, and the difference of the two numbers is 24.

23. Solve $3y - 2x = 7$ for y.

24. Solve $7x - 4y = 10$ for x.

25. Solve $A = \dfrac{1}{2}(B + b)h$ for b.

26. Solve $P = 2l + 2w$ for l.

27. Graph each set on a number line and then write in interval notation.
   a. $\{x \mid x \geq 2\}$
   b. $\{x \mid x < -1\}$
   c. $\{x \mid 0.5 < x \leq 3\}$

28. Graph each set on a number line and then write in interval notation.
   a. $\{x \mid x \leq -3\}$
   b. $\{x \mid -2 \leq x < 0.1\}$

Solve.

29. $-(x - 3) + 2 \leq 3(2x - 5) + x$

30. $2(7x - 1) - 5x > -(-7x) + 4$

31. $2(x + 3) > 2x + 1$

32. $4(x + 1) - 3 < 4x + 1$

33. If $A = \{x \mid x$ is an even number greater than 0 and less than 10$\}$ and $B = \{3, 4, 5, 6\}$, find $A \cap B$.

34. Find the union: $\{-2, 0, 2, 4\} \cup \{-1, 1, 3, 5\}$

35. Solve: $x - 7 < 2 \text{ and } 2x + 1 < 9$

36. Solve: $x + 3 \leq 1 \text{ or } 3x - 1 < 8$

37. If $A = \{x \mid x$ is an even number greater than 0 and less than 10$\}$ and $B = \{3, 4, 5, 6\}$, find $A \cup B$.

38. Find the intersection: $\{-2, 0, 2, 4\} \cap \{-1, 1, 3, 5\}$

39. Solve: $-2x - 5 < -3 \text{ or } 6x < 0$

40. Solve: $-2x - 5 < -3 \text{ and } 6x < 0$

Solve.

41. $|p| = 2$

42. $|x| = 5$

43. $\left| \dfrac{x}{2} - 1 \right| = 11$

44. $\left| \dfrac{y}{3} + 2 \right| = 10$

45. $|x - 3| = |5 - x|$

46. $|x + 3| = |7 - x|$

47. $|x| \leq 3$

48. $|x| > 1$

49. $|2x + 9| + 5 > 3$

50. $|3x + 1| + 9 < 1$

Graphs and Functions

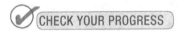

The linear equations and inequalities we explored in Chapter 2 are statements about a single variable. This chapter examines statements about two variables: linear equations and inequalities in two variables. We focus particularly on graphs of those equations and inequalities that lead to the notion of relation and to the notion of function, perhaps the single most important and useful concept in all of mathematics.

If Any of these New Technologies Interest You, Research and Read More

GPS Running Watches

New 3D Printers Could Build Implants, Electronics

New Smart Sensors Constantly Monitor Stresses on Bridge Structures

The EOscc2 Has a Top Speed of 40 mph and Can Travel 30–44 Miles on a 4-hour Battery Charge

The world is changing at an ever faster rate and new technology requires ever more knowledge and education to be ready for future innovations. The bar graph below shows the increase in the percent of Americans age 25 and older who have completed at least a high school education. Notice that the two functions $f(x)$ and $g(x)$ both approximate the percent of Americans who have completed at least high school. Also, for both functions, x is the number of years since 2008. In Section 3.2, Exercises 81–86, we use these functions to predict the growth in the number of Americans improving their educational achievements. Remember: Education is the key to our future.

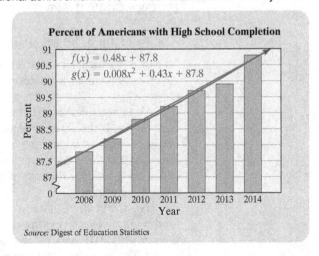

Percent of Americans with High School Completion

$f(x) = 0.48x + 87.8$

$g(x) = 0.008x^2 + 0.43x + 87.8$

Source: Digest of Education Statistics

3.1 Graphing Equations

OBJECTIVES

1 Plot Ordered Pairs.

2 Determine Whether an Ordered Pair of Numbers Is a Solution of an Equation in Two Variables.

3 Graph Linear Equations.

4 Graph Nonlinear Equations.

Graphs are widely used today in newspapers, magazines, and all forms of newsletters. A few examples of graphs are shown here.

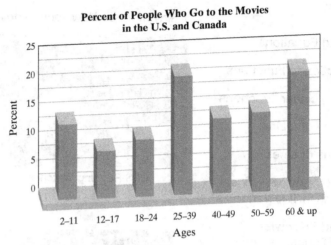

Percent of People Who Go to the Movies in the U.S. and Canada

Source: Motion Picture Association of America

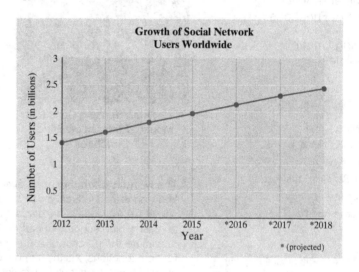

Growth of Social Network Users Worldwide

* (projected)

To help us understand how to read these graphs, we will review their basis—the rectangular coordinate system.

OBJECTIVE

1 Plotting Ordered Pairs on a Rectangular Coordinate System

One way to locate points on a plane is by using a **rectangular coordinate system,** which is also called a **Cartesian coordinate system** after its inventor, René Descartes (1596–1650).

A rectangular coordinate system consists of two number lines that intersect at right angles at their 0 coordinates. We position these axes on paper such that one number line is horizontal and the other number line is then vertical. The horizontal number line is called the **x-axis** (or the axis of the **abscissa**), and the vertical number line is called the **y-axis** (or the axis of the **ordinate**). The point of intersection of these axes is named the **origin.**

Notice in the left figure on the next page that the axes divide the plane into four regions. These regions are called **quadrants.** The top-right region is quadrant I. Quadrants II, III, and IV are numbered counterclockwise from the first quadrant as shown. The x-axis and the y-axis are not in any quadrant.

Each point in the plane can be located, or **plotted,** or graphed by describing its position in terms of distances along each axis from the origin. An **ordered pair,** represented by the notation (x, y), records these distances.

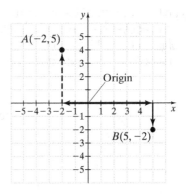

For example, the location of point A in the above figure on the right is described as 2 units to the left of the origin along the x-axis and 5 units upward parallel to the y-axis. Thus, we identify point A with the ordered pair $(-2, 5)$. Notice that the order of these numbers is *critical*. The x-value -2 is called the **x-coordinate** and is associated with the x-axis. The y-value 5 is called the **y-coordinate** and is associated with the y-axis.

Compare the location of point A with the location of point B, which corresponds to the ordered pair $(5, -2)$. Can you see that the order of the coordinates of an ordered pair matters? Also, two ordered pairs are considered equal and correspond to the same point if and only if their x-coordinates are equal and their y-coordinates are equal.

Keep in mind that **each ordered pair corresponds to exactly one point in the real plane and that each point in the plane corresponds to exactly one ordered pair.** Thus, we may refer to the ordered pair (x, y) as the point (x, y).

EXAMPLE 1   Plot each ordered pair on a Cartesian coordinate system and name the quadrant or axis in which the point is located.

a. $(2, -1)$ **b.** $(0, 5)$ **c.** $(-3, 5)$ **d.** $(-2, 0)$ **e.** $\left(-\dfrac{1}{2}, -4\right)$ **f.** $(1.5, 1.5)$

Solution The six points are graphed as shown.

a. $(2, -1)$ lies in quadrant IV.

b. $(0, 5)$ is on the y-axis.

c. $(-3, 5)$ lies in quadrant II.

d. $(-2, 0)$ is on the x-axis.

e. $\left(-\dfrac{1}{2}, -4\right)$ is in quadrant III.

f. $(1.5, 1.5)$ is in quadrant I.

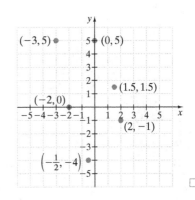

PRACTICE

1   Plot each ordered pair on a Cartesian coordinate system and name the quadrant or axis in which the point is located.

a. $(3, -4)$ **b.** $(0, -2)$ **c.** $(-2, 4)$ **d.** $(4, 0)$ **e.** $\left(-1\dfrac{1}{2}, -2\right)$ **f.** $(2.5, 3.5)$

Notice that the y-coordinate of any point on the x-axis is 0. For example, the point with coordinates $(-2, 0)$ lies on the x-axis. Also, the x-coordinate of any point on the y-axis is 0. For example, the point with coordinates $(0, 5)$ lies on the y-axis. These points that lie on the axes do not lie in any quadrants.

✔ CONCEPT CHECK

Which of the following correctly describes the location of the point $(3, -6)$ in a rectangular coordinate system?

a. 3 units to the left of the y-axis and 6 units above the x-axis
b. 3 units above the x-axis and 6 units to the left of the y-axis
c. 3 units to the right of the y-axis and 6 units below the x-axis
d. 3 units below the x-axis and 6 units to the right of the y-axis

Many types of real-world data occur in pairs. Study the graph below and notice the paired data $(2015, 143)$ and the corresponding plotted point, both in blue.

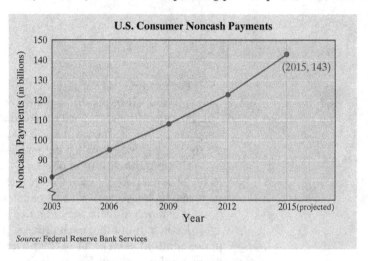

Source: Federal Reserve Bank Services

The paired data point, $(2015, 143)$, means that in the year 2015, it is predicted that 143 billion dollars of payments in the United States will be made cashlessly. This includes credit cards, debit cards, EBT (electronic benefits transfer), and checks. (This data does not include prepaid cards, such as gift cards.)

OBJECTIVE

2 Determining Whether an Ordered Pair Is a Solution

Solutions of equations in two variables consist of two numbers that form a true statement when substituted into the equation. A convenient notation for writing these numbers is as ordered pairs. A solution of an equation containing the variables x and y is written as a pair of numbers in the order (x, y). If the equation contains other variables, we will write ordered pair solutions in alphabetical order.

EXAMPLE 2 Determine whether $(0, -12)$, $(1, 9)$, and $(2, -6)$ are solutions of the equation $3x - y = 12$.

Solution To check each ordered pair, replace x with the x-coordinate and y with the y-coordinate and see whether a true statement results.

Let $x = 0$ and $y = -12$.

$$3x - y = 12$$
$$3(0) - (-12) \stackrel{?}{=} 12$$
$$0 + 12 \stackrel{?}{=} 12$$
$$12 = 12 \quad \text{True}$$

Let $x = 1$ and $y = 9$.

$$3x - y = 12$$
$$3(1) - 9 \stackrel{?}{=} 12$$
$$3 - 9 \stackrel{?}{=} 12$$
$$-6 = 12 \quad \text{False}$$

Let $x = 2$ and $y = -6$.

$$3x - y = 12$$
$$3(2) - (-6) \stackrel{?}{=} 12$$
$$6 + 6 \stackrel{?}{=} 12$$
$$12 = 12 \quad \text{True}$$

Thus, $(1, 9)$ is not a solution of $3x - y = 12$, but both $(0, -12)$ and $(2, -6)$ are solutions. ☐

PRACTICE

2 Determine whether $(1, 4)$, $(0, 6)$, and $(3, -4)$ are solutions of the equation $4x + y = 8$.

OBJECTIVE

3 Graphing Linear Equations

The equation $3x - y = 12$, from Example 2, actually has an infinite number of ordered pair solutions. Since it is impossible to list all solutions, we visualize them by graphing.

A few more ordered pairs that satisfy $3x - y = 12$ are $(4, 0)$, $(3, -3)$, $(5, 3)$, and $(1, -9)$. These ordered pair solutions along with the ordered pair solutions from Example 2 are plotted on the following graph. The graph of $3x - y = 12$ is the single line containing these points. Every ordered pair solution of the equation corresponds to a point on this line, and every point on this line corresponds to an ordered pair solution.

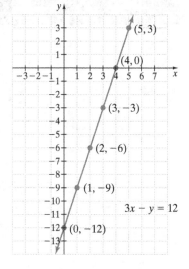

x	y	$3x - y = 12$
5	3	$3 \cdot 5 - 3 = 12$
4	0	$3 \cdot 4 - 0 = 12$
3	-3	$3 \cdot 3 - (-3) = 12$
2	-6	$3 \cdot 2 - (-6) = 12$
1	-9	$3 \cdot 1 - (-9) = 12$
0	-12	$3 \cdot 0 - (-12) = 12$

The equation $3x - y = 12$ is called a linear equation in two variables, and **the graph of every linear equation in two variables is a line.**

Linear Equation in Two Variables

A **linear equation in two variables** is an equation that can be written in the form

$$Ax + By = C$$

where A and B are not both 0. This form is called **standard form.**

Some examples of equations in standard form:

$$3x - y = 12$$
$$-2.1x + 5.6y = 0$$

Helpful Hint

Remember: A linear equation is written in standard form when all of the variable terms are on one side of the equation and the constant is on the other side.

Many real-life applications are modeled by linear equations. Suppose you have a part-time job at a store that sells office products.

Your pay is $3000 plus 20% or $\frac{1}{5}$ of the price of the products you sell. If we let *x* represent products sold **and** *y* represent monthly salary, the linear equation that models your salary is

$$y = 3000 + \frac{1}{5}x$$

(Although this equation is not written in standard form, it is a linear equation. To see this, subtract $\frac{1}{5}x$ from both sides.)

Some ordered pair solutions of this equation are below.

Products Sold	x	0	1000	2000	3000	4000	10,000
Monthly Salary	y	3000	3200	3400	3600	3800	5000

For example, we say that the ordered pair (1000, 3200) is a solution of the equation $y = 3000 + \frac{1}{5}x$ because when x is replaced with 1000 and y is replaced with 3200, a true statement results.

$$y = 3000 + \frac{1}{5}x$$

$$3200 \stackrel{?}{=} 3000 + \frac{1}{5}(1000) \quad \text{Let } x = 1000 \text{ and } y = 3200.$$

$$3200 \stackrel{?}{=} 3000 + 200$$

$$3200 = 3200 \qquad \text{True}$$

A portion of the graph of $y = 3000 + \frac{1}{5}x$ is shown in the next example.

Since we assume that the smallest amount of product sold is none, or 0, then x must be greater than or equal to 0. Therefore, only the part of the graph that lies in quadrant I is shown. Notice that the graph gives a visual picture of the correspondence between products sold and salary.

> **Helpful Hint**
>
> A line contains an infinite number of points and each point corresponds to an ordered pair that is a solution of its corresponding equation.

EXAMPLE 3 Use the graph of $y = 3000 + \frac{1}{5}x$ to answer the following questions.

a. If the salesperson sells $8000 of products in a particular month, what is the salary for that month?

b. If the salesperson wants to make more than $5000 per month, what must be the total amount of products sold?

Solution

a. Since x is products sold, find 8000 along the x-axis and move vertically up until you reach a point on the line. From this point on the line, move horizontally to the left until you reach the y-axis. Its value on the y-axis is 4600, which means if $8000 worth of products is sold, the salary for the month is $4600.

b. Since y is monthly salary, find 5000 along the y-axis and move horizontally to the right until you reach a point on the line. Either read the corresponding x-value from the labeled ordered pair or move vertically downward until you reach the *x*-axis. The corresponding *x*-value is 10,000. This means that $10,000 worth of products sold gives a salary of $5000 for the month. For the salary to be greater than $5000, products sold must be greater than $10,000.   □

PRACTICE
3   Use the graph in Example 3 to answer the following questions.

a. If the salesperson sells $6000 of products in a particular month, what is the salary for that month?

b. If the salesperson wants to make more than $4800 per month, what must be the total amount of products sold?   ■

Recall from geometry that a line is determined by two points. This means that to graph a linear equation in two variables, just two solutions are needed. We will find a third solution, just to check our work. To find ordered pair solutions of linear equations in two variables, we can choose an *x*-value and find its corresponding *y*-value, or we can choose a *y*-value and find its corresponding *x*-value. The number 0 is often a convenient value to choose for *x* or for *y*.

EXAMPLE 4   Graph the equation $y = -2x + 3$.

Solution   This is a linear equation. (In standard form it is $2x + y = 3$.) Find three ordered pair solutions, and plot the ordered pairs. The line through the plotted points is the graph. Since the equation is solved for *y*, let's choose three *x*-values. We'll choose 0, 2, and then −1 for *x* to find our three ordered pair solutions.

Let $x = 0$	Let $x = 2$	Let $x = -1$
$y = -2x + 3$	$y = -2x + 3$	$y = -2x + 3$
$y = -2 \cdot 0 + 3$	$y = -2 \cdot 2 + 3$	$y = -2(-1) + 3$
$y = 3$ Simplify.	$y = -1$ Simplify.	$y = 5$ Simplify.

The three ordered pairs $(0, 3)$, $(2, -1)$, and $(-1, 5)$ are listed in the table, and the graph is shown.

x	y
0	3
2	−1
−1	5

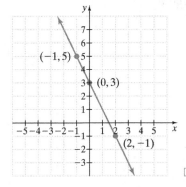

PRACTICE
4   Graph the equation $y = -3x - 2$.   ■

Notice that the graph crosses the *y*-axis at the point $(0, 3)$. This point is called the **y-intercept.** (You may sometimes see just the number 3 called the *y*-intercept.) This graph also crosses the *x*-axis at the point $\left(\frac{3}{2}, 0\right)$. This point is called the **x-intercept.** (You may also see just the number $\frac{3}{2}$ called the *x*-intercept.)

Since every point on the *y*-axis has an *x*-value of 0, we can find the *y*-intercept of a graph by letting $x = 0$ and solving for *y*. Also, every point on the *x*-axis has a *y*-value of 0. To find the *x*-intercept, we let $y = 0$ and solve for *x*.

Finding x- and y-Intercepts

To find an x-intercept, let $y = 0$ and solve for x.
To find a y-intercept, let $x = 0$ and solve for y.

We will study intercepts further in Section 3.3.

EXAMPLE 5 Graph the linear equation $y = \dfrac{1}{3}x$.

Solution To graph, we find ordered pair solutions, plot the ordered pairs, and draw a line through the plotted points. We will choose x-values and substitute in the equation. To avoid fractions, we choose x-values that are multiples of 3. To find the y-intercept, we let $x = 0$.

If $x = 0$, then $y = \dfrac{1}{3}(0)$, or 0.

If $x = 6$, then $y = \dfrac{1}{3}(6)$, or 2.

If $x = -3$, then $y = \dfrac{1}{3}(-3)$, or -1.

$y = \dfrac{1}{3}x$

x	y
0	0
6	2
-3	-1

This graph crosses the x-axis at $(0, 0)$ and the y-axis at $(0, 0)$. This means that the x-intercept is $(0, 0)$ and that the y-intercept is $(0, 0)$.

> **Helpful Hint**
> Notice that by using multiples of 3 for x, we avoid fractions.

> **Helpful Hint**
> Since the equation $y = \dfrac{1}{3}x$ is solved for y, we choose x-values for finding points. This way, we simply need to evaluate an expression to find the y-value, as shown.

PRACTICE
5 Graph the linear equation $y = -\dfrac{1}{2}x$.

OBJECTIVE
4 Graphing Nonlinear Equations

Not all equations in two variables are linear equations, and not all graphs of equations in two variables are lines.

EXAMPLE 6 Graph $y = x^2$.

Solution This equation is not linear because the x^2 term does not allow us to write it in the form $Ax + By = C$. Its graph is not a line. We begin by finding ordered pair solutions. Because this graph is solved for y, we choose x-values and find corresponding y-values.

If $x = -3$, then $y = (-3)^2$, or 9.

If $x = -2$, then $y = (-2)^2$, or 4.

If $x = -1$, then $y = (-1)^2$, or 1.

If $x = 0$, then $y = 0^2$, or 0.

If $x = 1$, then $y = 1^2$, or 1.

If $x = 2$, then $y = 2^2$, or 4.

If $x = 3$, then $y = 3^2$, or 9.

x	y
-3	9
-2	4
-1	1
0	0
1	1
2	4
3	9

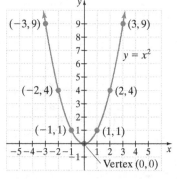

Study the table a moment and look for patterns. Notice that the ordered pair solution $(0, 0)$ contains the smallest y-value because any other x-value squared will give a positive result. This means that the point $(0, 0)$ will be the lowest point on the graph. Also notice that all other y-values correspond to two different x-values. For example, $3^2 = 9$, and also $(-3)^2 = 9$. This means that the graph will be a mirror image of itself across the y-axis. Connect the plotted points with a smooth curve to sketch the graph.

This curve is given a special name, **a parabola.** We will study more about parabolas in later chapters. □

PRACTICE
6   Graph $y = 4x^2$. ■

EXAMPLE 7   Graph the equation $y = |x|$.

Solution This is not a linear equation since it cannot be written in the form $Ax + By = C$. Its graph is not a line. Because we do not know the shape of this graph, we find many ordered pair solutions. We will choose x-values and substitute to find corresponding y-values.

If $x = -3$, then $y = |-3|$, or 3.
If $x = -2$, then $y = |-2|$, or 2.
If $x = -1$, then $y = |-1|$, or 1.
If $x = 0$, then $y = |0|$, or 0.
If $x = 1$, then $y = |1|$, or 1.
If $x = 2$, then $y = |2|$, or 2.
If $x = 3$, then $y = |3|$, or 3.

x	y
-3	3
-2	2
-1	1
0	0
1	1
2	2
3	3

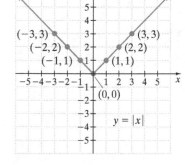

Again, study the table of values for a moment and notice any patterns.

From the plotted ordered pairs, we see that the graph of this absolute value equation is V-shaped. □

PRACTICE
7   Graph $y = -|x|$. ■

Graphing Calculator Explorations

In this section, we begin a study of graphing calculators and graphing software packages for computers. These graphers use the same point plotting technique that we introduced in this section. The advantage of this graphing technology is, of course, that graphing calculators and computers can find and plot ordered pair solutions much faster than we can. Note, however, that the features described in these boxes may not be available on all graphing calculators.

The rectangular screen where a portion of the rectangular coordinate system is displayed is called a **window.** We call it a **standard window** for graphing when both the x- and y-axes display coordinates between -10 and 10. This information is often displayed in the window menu on a graphing calculator as

Xmin $= -10$
Xmax $= 10$
 Xscl $= 1$ The scale on the x-axis is one unit per tick mark.
Ymin $= -10$
Ymax $= 10$
 Yscl $= 1$ The scale on the y-axis is one unit per tick mark.

To use a graphing calculator to graph the equation $y = -5x + 4$, press the
$\boxed{Y =}$ key and enter the keystrokes

↑

(Check your owner's manual to make sure the "negative" key is pressed here and not the "subtraction" key.)

The top row should now read $Y_1 = -5x + 4$. Next, press the GRAPH key, and the graphed display should look like this:

Use a standard window and graph the following equations. (Unless otherwise stated, we will use a standard window when graphing.)

1. $y = -3.2x + 7.9$

2. $y = -x + 5.85$

3. $y = \frac{1}{4}x - \frac{2}{3}$

4. $y = \frac{2}{3}x - \frac{1}{5}$

5. $y = |x - 3| + 2$

6. $y = |x + 1| - 1$

7. $y = x^2 + 3$

8. $y = (x + 3)^2$

Vocabulary, Readiness & Video Check

Use the choices below to fill in each blank. Some choices may not be used.

line	parabola	1	3
origin	V-shaped	2	4

1. The intersection of the x-axis and y-axis is a point called the _____.

2. The rectangular coordinate system has _____ quadrants and _____ axes.

3. The graph of a single ordered pair of numbers is how many points? _____

4. The graph of $Ax + By = C$, where A and B are not both 0, is a(n) _____.

5. The graph of $y = |x|$ looks _____.

6. The graph of $y = x^2$ is a _____.

Martin-Gay Interactive Videos

See Video 3.1

Watch the section lecture video and answer the following questions.

OBJECTIVE
1

7. Several points are plotted in ▤ Examples 1–3. Where do you start when using this method to plot a point? How does the 1st coordinate tell you to move? How does the 2nd coordinate tell you to move? Include the role of signs in your answer.

OBJECTIVE
2

8. Based on ▤ Examples 4 and 5, complete the following statement. An ordered pair is a solution of an equation in _____ variables if, when the variables are replaced with their ordered pair values, a _____ statement results.

OBJECTIVE
3

9. From ▤ Example 6 and the lecture before, what is the graph of an equation? If you need only two points to determine a line, why are three ordered pair solutions or points found for a linear equation?

OBJECTIVE
4

10. Based on ▤ Examples 7 and 8, complete the following statements. When graphing a nonlinear equation, first recognize it as a nonlinear equation and know that the graph is _____ a line. If you don't know the _____ of the graph, plot enough points until you see a pattern.

3.1 Exercise Set MyMathLab®

Plot each point and name the quadrant or axis in which the point lies. See Example 1.

1. $(3, 2)$ **2.** $(2, -1)$

3. $(-5, 3)$ **4.** $(-3, -1)$

5. $\left(5\frac{1}{2}, -4\right)$ **6.** $\left(-2, 6\frac{1}{3}\right)$

7. $(0, 3.5)$ **8.** $(-5.2, 0)$

9. $(-2, -4)$ **10.** $(-4.2, 0)$

Determine the coordinates of each point on the graph. See Example 1.

11. Point C

12. Point D

13. Point E

14. Point F

15. Point B

16. Point A

Determine whether each ordered pair is a solution of the given equation. See Example 2.

17. $y = 3x - 5; (0, 5), (-1, -8)$

18. $y = -2x + 7; (1, 5), (-2, 3)$

19. $-6x + 5y = -6; (1, 0), \left(2, \frac{6}{5}\right)$

20. $5x - 3y = 9; (0, 3), \left(\frac{12}{5}, -1\right)$

21. $y = 2x^2; (1, 2), (3, 18)$

22. $y = 2|x|; (-1, 2), (0, 2)$

23. $y = x^3; (2, 8), (3, 9)$

24. $y = x^4; (-1, 1), (2, 16)$

25. $y = \sqrt{x} + 2; (1, 3), (4, 4)$

26. $y = \sqrt[3]{x} - 4; (1, -3), (8, 6)$

MIXED PRACTICE

Determine whether each equation is linear or not. Then graph the equation by finding and plotting ordered pair solutions. See Examples 3 through 7.

27. $x + y = 3$ **28.** $y - x = 8$

29. $y = 4x$ **30.** $y = 6x$

31. $y = 4x - 2$ **32.** $y = 6x - 5$

33. $y = |x| + 3$ **34.** $y = |x| + 2$

35. $2x - y = 5$ **36.** $4x - y = 7$

37. $y = 2x^2$ **38.** $y = 3x^2$

39. $y = x^2 - 3$ **40.** $y = x^2 + 3$

41. $y = -2x$ **42.** $y = -3x$

43. $y = -2x + 3$ **44.** $y = -3x + 2$

45. $y = |x + 2|$ **46.** $y = |x - 1|$

47. $y = x^3$

(*Hint*: Let $x = -3, -2, -1, 0, 1, 2$.)

48. $y = x^3 - 2$

(*Hint*: Let $x = -3, -2, -1, 0, 1, 2$.)

49. $y = -|x|$ **50.** $y = -x^2$

51. $y = \frac{1}{3}x - 1$ **52.** $y = \frac{1}{2}x - 3$

53. $y = -\frac{3}{2}x + 1$ **54.** $y = -\frac{2}{3}x + 1$

REVIEW AND PREVIEW

Solve the following equations. See Section 2.1.

55. $3(x - 2) + 5x = 6x - 16$

56. $5 + 7(x + 1) = 12 + 10x$

57. $3x + \frac{2}{5} = \frac{1}{10}$ **58.** $\frac{1}{6} + 2x = \frac{2}{3}$

Solve the following inequalities. See Section 2.4.

59. $3x \leq -15$

60. $-3x > 18$

61. $2x - 5 > 4x + 3$

62. $9x + 8 \leq 6x - 4$

CONCEPT EXTENSIONS

Without graphing, visualize the location of each point. Then give its location by quadrant or x- or y-axis.

63. $(4, -2)$ **64.** $(-42, 17)$

65. $(0, -100)$ **66.** $(-87, 0)$

67. $(-10, -30)$ **68.** $(0, 0)$

Given that x is a positive number and that y is a positive number, determine the quadrant or axis in which each point lies.

69. $(x, -y)$ **70.** $(-x, y)$

71. $(x, 0)$ **72.** $(0, -y)$

73. $(-x, -y)$ **74.** $(0, 0)$

Solve. See the Concept Check in this section.

75. Which correctly describes the location of the point $(-1, 5.3)$ in a rectangular coordinate system?

   a. 1 unit to the right of the y-axis and 5.3 units above the x-axis

   b. 1 unit to the left of the y-axis and 5.3 units above the x-axis

   c. 1 unit to the left of the y-axis and 5.3 units below the x-axis

   d. 1 unit to the right of the y-axis and 5.3 units below the x-axis

76. Which correctly describes the location of the point $\left(0, -\frac{3}{4}\right)$ in a rectangular coordinate system?

   a. on the x-axis and $\frac{3}{4}$ unit to the left of the y-axis

   b. on the x-axis and $\frac{3}{4}$ unit to the right of the y-axis

   c. on the y-axis and $\frac{3}{4}$ unit above the x-axis

   d. on the y-axis and $\frac{3}{4}$ unit below the x-axis

For Exercises 77 through 80, match each description with the graph that best illustrates it.

77. Moe worked 40 hours per week until the fall semester started. He quit and didn't work again until he worked 60 hours a week during the holiday season starting mid-December.

78. Kawana worked 40 hours a week for her father during the summer. She slowly cut back her hours to not working at all during the fall semester. In December, she started working again and increased her hours to 60 hours per week.

79. Wendy worked from July through February, never quitting. She worked between 10 and 30 hours per week.

80. Bartholomew worked from July through February. During the holiday season between mid-November and the beginning of January, he worked 40 hours per week. The rest of the time, he worked between 10 and 40 hours per week.

This broken-line graph shows the hourly minimum wage and the years it increased. Use this graph for Exercises 81 through 84.

Source: U.S. Department of Labor

81. What was the first year that the minimum hourly wage rose above $5.00?

82. What was the first year that the minimum hourly wage rose above $6.00?

83. Why do you think that this graph is shaped the way it is?

84. The federal hourly minimum wage started in 1938 at $0.25. How much will it have increased by 2011?

85. Graph $y = x^2 - 4x + 7$. Let $x = 0, 1, 2, 3, 4$ to generate ordered pair solutions.

86. Graph $y = x^2 + 2x + 3$. Let $x = -3, -2, -1, 0, 1$ to generate ordered pair solutions.

△ 87. The perimeter y of a rectangle whose width is a constant 3 inches and whose length is x inches is given by the equation

$$y = 2x + 6$$

a. Draw a graph of this equation.

b. Read from the graph the perimeter y of a rectangle whose length x is 4 inches.

88. The distance y traveled in a train moving at a constant speed of 50 miles per hour is given by the equation

$$y = 50x$$

where x is the time in hours traveled.

a. Draw a graph of this equation.

b. Read from the graph the distance y traveled after 6 hours.

*For income tax purposes, the owner of Copy Services uses a method called **straight-line depreciation** to show the loss in value of a copy machine he recently purchased. He assumes that he can use the machine for 7 years. The following graph shows the value of the machine over the years. Use this graph to answer Exercises 89 through 94.*

89. What was the purchase price of the copy machine?

90. What is the depreciated value of the machine in 7 years?

91. What loss in value occurred during the first year?

92. What loss in value occurred during the second year?

93. Why do you think that this method of depreciating is called straight-line depreciation?

94. Why is the line tilted downward?

95. On the same set of axes, graph $y = 2x, y = 2x - 5$, and $y = 2x + 5$. What patterns do you see in these graphs?

96. On the same set of axes, graph $y = 2x, y = x$, and $y = -2x$. Describe the differences and similarities in these graphs.

Write each statement as an equation in two variables. Then graph each equation.

97. The *y*-value is 5 more than three times the *x*-value.

98. The *y*-value is −3 decreased by twice the *x*-value.

99. The *y*-value is 2 more than the square of the *x*-value.

100. The *y*-value is 5 decreased by the square of the *x*-value.

Use a graphing calculator to verify the graphs of the following exercises.

101. Exercise 39

102. Exercise 40

103. Exercise 47

104. Exercise 48

3.2 | Introduction to Functions

OBJECTIVES

1 Define Relation, Domain, and Range.

2 Identify Functions.

3 Use the Vertical Line Test for Functions.

4 Find the Domain and Range of a Function.

5 Use Function Notation.

OBJECTIVE

1 Defining Relation, Domain, and Range

Recall our example from the last section about products sold and monthly salary. We modeled the data given by the equation $y = 3000 + \frac{1}{5}x$. This equation describes a relationship between *x*-values and *y*-values. For example, if $x = 1000$, then this equation describes how to find the *y*-value related to $x = 1000$. In words, the equation $y = 3000 + \frac{1}{5}x$ says that 3000 plus $\frac{1}{5}$ of the *x*-value gives the corresponding *y*-value. The *x*-value of 1000 corresponds to the *y*-value of $3000 + \frac{1}{5} \cdot 1000 = 3200$ for this equation, and we have the ordered pair $(1000, 3200)$.

There are other ways of describing relations or correspondences between two numbers or, in general, a first set (sometimes called the set of *inputs*) and a second set (sometimes called the set of *outputs*). For example,

First Set: Input	⟶	*Correspondence*	⟶	*Second Set: Output*
People in a certain city		Each person's age, to the nearest year		The set of nonnegative integers

A few examples of ordered pairs from this relation might be (Ana, 4), (Bob, 36), (Trey, 21), and so on.

Below are just a few other ways of describing relations between two sets and the ordered pairs that they generate.

Ordered Pairs
$(a, 3), (c, 3), (e, 1)$

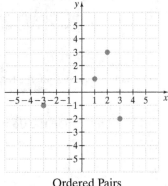

Ordered Pairs
$(-3, -1), (1, 1), (2, 3), (3, -2)$

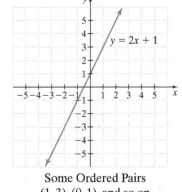

Some Ordered Pairs
$(1, 3), (0, 1),$ and so on

Relation, Domain, and Range

A **relation** is a set of ordered pairs.

The **domain** of the relation is the set of all first components of the ordered pairs.

The **range** of the relation is the set of all second components of the ordered pairs.

For example, the domain for our relation on the left above is $\{a, c, e\}$ and the range is $\{1, 3\}$. Notice that the range does not include the element 2 of the second set.

This is because no element of the first set is assigned to this element. If a relation is defined in terms of x- and y-values, we will agree that the domain corresponds to x-values and that the range corresponds to y-values that have x-values assigned to them.

> **Helpful Hint**
>
> Remember that the range includes only elements that are paired with domain values. For the correspondence to the right, the range is $\{a\}$.
>
>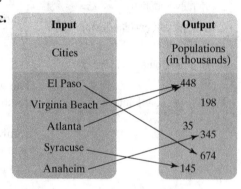

EXAMPLE 1   Determine the domain and range of each relation.

     a. $\{(2,3),(2,4),(0,-1),(3,-1)\}$

     b.

     c.

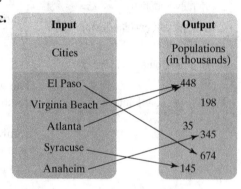

Solution

     a. The domain is the set of all first coordinates of the ordered pairs, $\{2,0,3\}$. The range is the set of all second coordinates, $\{3,4,-1\}$.

     b. Ordered pairs are not listed here but are given in graph form. The relation is $\{(-4,1),(-3,1),(-2,1),(-1,1),(0,1),(1,1),(2,1),(3,1)\}$. The domain is $\{-4,-3,-2,-1,0,1,2,3\}$. The range is $\{1\}$.

     c. The domain is the set of inputs, {El Paso, Virginia Beach, Atlanta, Syracuse, Anaheim}. The range is the numbers in the set of outputs that correspond to elements in the set of inputs {448, 345, 674, 145}.

> **Helpful Hint**
>
> Domain or range elements that occur more than once need to be listed only once.

PRACTICE

   1   Determine the domain and range of each relation.

a. $\{(4,1),(4,-3),(5,-2),(5,6)\}$

b.

c.

OBJECTIVE

2 Identifying Functions

Now we consider a special kind of relation called a function.

Function

A **function** is a relation in which each first component in the ordered pairs corresponds to *exactly* one second component.

Helpful Hint

A function is a special type of relation, so all functions are relations, but not all relations are functions.

EXAMPLE 2   Determine whether the following relations are also functions.

a. $\{(-2,5),(2,7),(-3,5),(9,9)\}$

b.

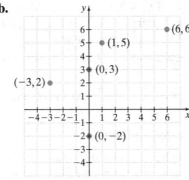

c.

Input	Correspondence	Output
People in a certain city	Each person's age	The set of nonnegative integers

Solution

    a. Although the ordered pairs $(-2,5)$ and $(-3,5)$ have the same y-value, each x-value is assigned to only one y-value, so this set of ordered pairs is a function.

    b. The x-value 0 is assigned to two y-values, -2 and 3, in this graph, so this relation does not define a function.

    c. This relation is a function because although two people may have the same age, each person has only one age. This means that each element in the first set is assigned to only one element in the second set.

PRACTICE

2   Determine whether the following relations are also functions.

a. $\{(3,1),(-3,-4),(8,5),(9,1)\}$ **b.**

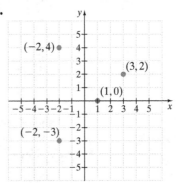

c.

Input	Correspondence	Output
People in a certain city	Birth date (day of month)	set of nonnegative integers

---

✔ **CONCEPT CHECK**

Explain why a function can contain both the ordered pairs $(1, 3)$ and $(2, 3)$ but not both $(3, 1)$ and $(3, 2)$.

We will call an equation such as $y = 2x + 1$ a **relation** since this equation defines a set of ordered pair solutions.

EXAMPLE 3 Is the relation $y = 2x + 1$ also a function?*

Solution The relation $y = 2x + 1$ is a function if each x-value corresponds to just one y-value. For each x-value substituted in the equation $y = 2x + 1$, the multiplication and addition performed on each gives a single result, so only one y-value will be associated with each x-value. Thus, $y = 2x + 1$ is a function.   □

*For further discussion including the graph, see Objective 3 below.

PRACTICE
3 Is the relation $y = -3x + 5$ also a function?

EXAMPLE 4 Is the relation $x = y^2$ also a function?*

Solution In $x = y^2$, if $y = 3$, then $x = 9$. Also, if $y = -3$, then $x = 9$. In other words, we have the ordered pairs $(9, 3)$ and $(9, -3)$. Since the x-value 9 corresponds to two y-values, 3 and -3, $x = y^2$ is not a function.   □

*For further discussion including the graph, see Objective 3 below.

PRACTICE
4 Is the relation $y = -x^2$ also a function?

OBJECTIVE
3 Using the Vertical Line Test

As we have seen so far, not all relations are functions. Consider the graphs of $y = 2x + 1$ and $x = y^2$ shown next. For the graph of $y = 2x + 1$, notice that each x-value corresponds to only one y-value. Recall from Example 3 that $y = 2x + 1$ is a function.

Graph of Example 3: $y = 2x + 1$

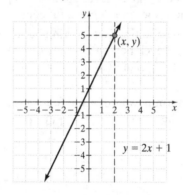

Graph of Example 4: $x = y^2$

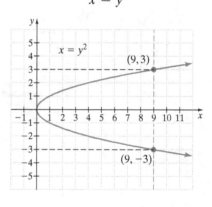

For the graph of $x = y^2$ the x-value 9, for example, corresponds to two y-values, 3 and -3, as shown by the vertical line. Recall from Example 4 that $x = y^2$ is not a function.

Graphs can be used to help determine whether a relation is also a function by the following **vertical line test.**

Vertical Line Test

If no vertical line can be drawn so that it intersects a graph more than once, the graph is the graph of a function.

EXAMPLE 5 Determine whether the following graphs are graphs of functions.

a.

b.

c.

Solution

Yes, this is the graph of a function since no vertical line will intersect this graph more than once.

Yes, this is the graph of a function.

No, this is not the graph of a function. Note that vertical lines can be drawn that intersect the graph in two points.

d.

e.

Solution

Yes, this is the graph of a function.

No, this is not the graph of a function. A vertical line can be drawn that intersects this line at every point.

PRACTICE

5 Determine whether the following relations are also functions.

a.

b.

c.

d.

e.

Recall that the graph of a linear equation in two variables is a line, and a line that is not vertical will pass the vertical line test. Thus, **all linear equations are functions except those whose graph is a vertical line.**

✔ **CONCEPT CHECK**

Determine which equations represent functions. Explain your answer.

a. $y = |x|$ **b.** $y = x^2$ **c.** $x + y = 6$

OBJECTIVE

4 Finding the Domain and Range of a Function ▶

Next, we practice finding the domain and range of a relation from its graph.

EXAMPLE 6 Find the domain and range of each relation. Determine whether the relation is also a function.

a.

b.

c.

d.

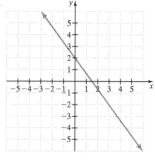

Solution By the vertical line test, graphs **a**, **c**, and **d** are graphs of functions. The domain is the set of values of x and the range is the set of values of y. We read these values from each graph.

a.

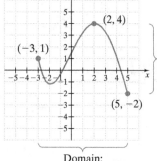

Range: The y-values graphed are from -2 to 4, or $[-2, 4]$.

Domain: The x-values graphed are from -3 to 5, or $[-3, 5]$.

b.

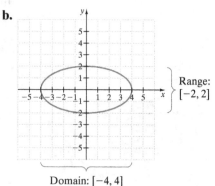

Range: $[-2, 2]$

Domain: $[-4, 4]$

Helpful Hint

In Example 6(a), notice that the graph contains the endpoints $(-3, 1)$ and $(5, -2)$ whereas the graphs in Examples 6(c) and 6(d) contain arrows that indicate that they continue forever.

Answer to Concept Check:
a, b, c; answers may vary

c.

Range: $[0, \infty)$

Domain: $(-\infty, \infty)$

d.

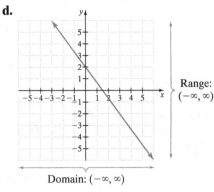

Range: $(-\infty, \infty)$

Domain: $(-\infty, \infty)$

PRACTICE

6 Find the domain and range of each relation. Determine whether the relation is also a function.

a.

b.

c.

d.

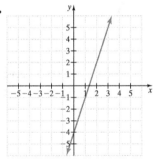

OBJECTIVE

5 **Using Function Notation**

Many times letters such as f, g, and h are used to name functions.

Function Notation

To denote that y is a function of x, we can write

$$y = \underbrace{f(x)}_{\textbf{Function Notation}} \quad \text{(Read "} f \text{ of } x\text{.")}$$

This notation means that **y is a function of x** or that y *depends on x.* For this reason, y is called the **dependent variable** and x the **independent variable.**

For example, to use function notation with the function $y = 4x + 3$, we write $f(x) = 4x + 3$. The notation $f(1)$ means to replace x with 1 and find the resulting y or function value. Since

$$f(x) = 4x + 3$$

then

$$f(1) = 4(1) + 3 = 7$$

This means that when $x = 1$, y or $f(x) = 7$. The corresponding ordered pair is $(1, 7)$. Here, the input is 1 and the output is $f(1)$ or 7. Now let's find $f(2), f(0)$, and $f(-1)$.

$$f(x) = 4x + 3$$
$$f(2) = 4(2) + 3$$
$$= 8 + 3$$
$$= 11$$

$$f(x) = 4x + 3$$
$$f(0) = 4(0) + 3$$
$$= 0 + 3$$
$$= 3$$

$$f(x) = 4(x) + 3$$
$$f(-1) = 4(-1) + 3$$
$$= -4 + 3$$
$$= -1$$

> **Helpful Hint**
>
> Make sure you remember that $f(2) = 11$ corresponds to the ordered pair $(2, 11)$.

Ordered Pairs:

$(2, 11)$ $(0, 3)$ $(-1, -1)$

> **Helpful Hint**
>
> Note that $f(x)$ is a special symbol in mathematics used to denote a function. The symbol $f(x)$ is read "f of x." It does *not* mean $f \cdot x$ (f times x).

EXAMPLE 7   If $f(x) = 7x^2 - 3x + 1$ and $g(x) = 8x - 2$, find the following.

   a. $f(1)$ **b.** $g(1)$ **c.** $f(-2)$ **d.** $g(0)$

Solution

a. Substitute 1 for x in $f(x) = 7x^2 - 3x + 1$ and simplify.
$$f(x) = 7x^2 - 3x + 1$$
$$f(1) = 7(1)^2 - 3(1) + 1 = 5$$

b. $g(x) = 8x - 2$
$$g(1) = 8(1) - 2 = 6$$

c. $f(x) = 7x^2 - 3x + 1$
$$f(-2) = 7(-2)^2 - 3(-2) + 1 = 35$$

d. $g(x) = 8x - 2$
$$g(0) = 8(0) - 2 = -2$$

PRACTICE
7   If $f(x) = 3x - 2$ and $g(x) = 5x^2 + 2x - 1$, Find the following.

   a. $f(1)$ **b.** $g(1)$ **c.** $f(0)$ **d.** $g(-2)$

✔ **CONCEPT CHECK**

Suppose $y = f(x)$ and we are told that $f(3) = 9$. Which is not true?

a. When $x = 3$, $y = 9$.
b. A possible function is $f(x) = x^2$.
c. A point on the graph of the function is $(3, 9)$.
d. A possible function is $f(x) = 2x + 4$.

If it helps, think of a function, f, as a machine that has been programmed with a certain correspondence or rule. An input value (a member of the domain) is then fed into the machine, the machine does the correspondence or rule, and the result is the output (a member of the range).

EXAMPLE 8   Given the graphs of the functions *f* and *g*, find each function value by inspecting the graphs.

a. $f(4)$ **b.** $f(-2)$ **c.** $g(5)$ **d.** $g(0)$

e. Find all *x*-values such that $f(x) = 1$.

f. Find all *x*-values such that $g(x) = 0$.

Solution

a. To find $f(4)$, find the *y*-value when $x = 4$. We see from the graph that when $x = 4$, *y* or $f(x) = 2$. Thus, $f(4) = 2$.

b. $f(-2) = 1$ from the ordered pair $(-2, 1)$.

c. $g(5) = 3$ from the ordered pair $(5, 3)$.

d. $g(0) = 0$ from the ordered pair $(0, 0)$.

e. To find *x*-values such that $f(x) = 1$, we are looking for any ordered pairs on the graph of *f* whose $f(x)$ or *y*-value is 1. They are $(2, 1)$ and $(-2, 1)$. Thus $f(2) = 1$ and $f(-2) = 1$. The *x*-values are 2 and -2.

f. Find ordered pairs on the graph of *g* whose $g(x)$ or *y*-value is 0. They are $(3, 0), (0, 0)$, and $(-4, 0)$. Thus $g(3) = 0, g(0) = 0$, and $g(-4) = 0$. The *x*-values are 3, 0, and -4.   ☐

PRACTICE

8   Given the graphs of the functions *f* and *g*, find each function value by inspecting the graphs.

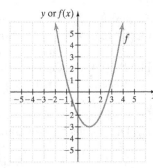

a. $f(1)$ **b.** $f(0)$ **c.** $g(-2)$ **d.** $g(0)$

e. Find all *x*-values such that $f(x) = 1$.

f. Find all *x*-values such that $g(x) = -2$.   ■

Many types of real-world paired data form functions. The broken-line graphs on the next page show the 4-year and 2-year enrollments in postsecondary institutions.

EXAMPLE 9   The following graph shows the 2-year and 4-year enrollments in postsecondary institutions as functions of time.

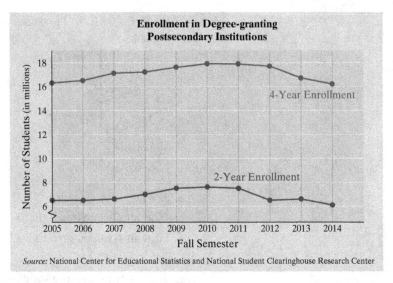

Enrollment in Degree-granting Postsecondary Institutions

Source: National Center for Educational Statistics and National Student Clearinghouse Research Center

a. Approximate the 2-year enrollment in 2013.

b. In Fall 2007, the enrollment in 4-year colleges was 17.1 million students. Find the increase in 4-year college enrollment from Fall 2007 to Fall 2011.

Solution

a. Find the semester Fall 2013 and move upward until you reach the bottom broken-line graph. From this point on the graph, move horizontally to the left until the vertical axis is reached. In Fall 2013, approximately 6.6 million students, or 6,600,000 students, were enrolled in 2-year degree-granting institutions.

b. The increase in enrollment in 4-year postsecondary institutions from Fall 2007 to Fall 2011 is 17.9 million − 17.1 million = 0.8 million or 800,000 students. □

PRACTICE

9 Use the graph in Example 9 and approximate the 2-year enrollment in Fall 2010. ▪

Notice that each graph separately in Example 9 is the graph of a function since for each year there is only one 4-year institution enrollment figure and only one 2-year enrollment figure. Often, businesses depend on equations that closely fit data-defined functions like these to model the data and predict future trends. For example, the function $f(x) = -0.08x^2 + 1.5x + 10.3$ approximates the data for the red graph and the function $g(x) = -0.06x^2 + 1.1x + 2.2$ approximates the data for the blue graph. For each function, x is the number of years since 2000, and $f(x)$ is the number of students (in millions). The graphs and the data functions are shown next.

> **Helpful Hint**
> Each function graphed is the graph of a function and passes the vertical line test.

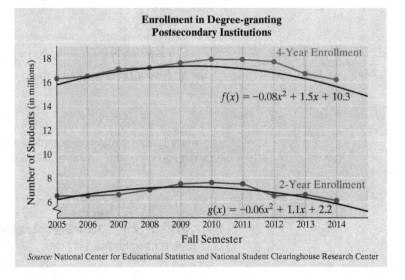

Enrollment in Degree-granting Postsecondary Institutions

$f(x) = -0.08x^2 + 1.5x + 10.3$

$g(x) = -0.06x^2 + 1.1x + 2.2$

Source: National Center for Educational Statistics and National Student Clearinghouse Research Center

EXAMPLE 10   Use the function $f(x) = -0.07x^2 + 1.5x + 10.3$ and the discussion following Example 9 to predict the enrollment in 4-year degree-granting institutions in Fall 2015.

Solution To predict the 4-year enrollment in Fall 2015, remember that x represents the number of years since 2000, so $x = 15$. Use $f(x) = -0.07x^2 + 1.5x + 10.3$ and find $f(15)$.

$$f(x) = -0.07x^2 + 1.5x + 10.3$$
$$f(15) = -0.07(15)^2 + 1.5(15) + 10.3$$
$$= 17.05$$

We predict that in Fall 2015, the total enrollment in 4-year degree-granting institutions was 17.05 million, or 17,050,000 students.   □

PRACTICE

10   Use $f(x) = -0.05x^2 + 1.1x + 2.2$ to approximate 2-year institution enrollment in Fall 2015.

Graphing Calculator Explorations

It is possible to use a graphing calculator to sketch the graph of more than one equation on the same set of axes. For example, graph the functions $f(x) = x^2$ and $g(x) = x^2 + 4$ on the same set of axes.

To graph on the same set of axes, press the $\boxed{Y =}$ key and enter the equations on the first two lines.

$$Y_1 = x^2$$
$$Y_2 = x^2 + 4$$

Then press the $\boxed{\text{GRAPH}}$ key as usual. The screen should look like this.

Notice that the graph of y or $g(x) = x^2 + 4$ is the graph of $y = x^2$ moved 4 units upward.

Graph each pair of functions on the same set of axes. Describe the similarities and differences in their graphs.

1. $f(x) = |x|$
   $g(x) = |x| + 1$

2. $f(x) = x^2$
   $h(x) = x^2 - 5$

3. $f(x) = x$
   $H(x) = x - 6$

4. $f(x) = |x|$
   $G(x) = |x| + 3$

5. $f(x) = -x^2$
   $F(x) = -x^2 + 7$

6. $f(x) = x$
   $F(x) = x + 2$

Vocabulary, Readiness & Video Check

Use the choices below to fill in each blank. Some choices may not be used.

domain	vertical	relation	$(1.7, -2)$
range	horizontal	function	$(-2, 1.7)$

1. A _____ is a set of ordered pairs.

2. The _____ of a relation is the set of all second components of the ordered pairs.

3. The _____ of a relation is the set of all first components of the ordered pairs.

4. A _____ is a relation in which each first component in the ordered pairs corresponds to *exactly* one second component.

5. By the vertical line test, all linear equations are functions except those whose graphs are _____ lines.

6. If $f(-2) = 1.7$, the corresponding ordered pair is _____.

Martin-Gay Interactive Videos

See Video 3.2

Watch the section lecture video and answer the following questions.

OBJECTIVE 1
7. Based on the lecture before ▦ Example 1, why can an equation in two variables define a relation?

OBJECTIVE 2
8. Based on the lecture before ▦ Example 2, can a relation in which a second component corresponds to more than one first component be a function?

OBJECTIVE 3
9. Based on ▦ Example 3 and the lecture before, explain why the vertical line test works.

OBJECTIVE 4
10. From ▦ Example 8, do all linear equations in two variables define functions? Explain.

OBJECTIVE 5
11. From ▦ Examples 9 and 10, what is the connection between function notation to evaluate a function at certain values and ordered pair solutions of the function?

3.2 Exercise Set MyMathLab▸

Find the domain and the range of each relation. Also determine whether the relation is a function. See Examples 1 and 2.

▸ 1. $\{(-1, 7), (0, 6), (-2, 2), (5, 6)\}$

2. $\{(4, 9), (-4, 9), (2, 3), (10, -5)\}$

3. $\{(-2, 4), (6, 4), (-2, -3), (-7, -8)\}$

4. $\{(6, 6), (5, 6), (5, -2), (7, 6)\}$

5. $\{(1, 1), (1, 2), (1, 3), (1, 4)\}$

6. $\{(1, 1), (2, 1), (3, 1), (4, 1)\}$

7. $\left\{\left(\dfrac{3}{2}, \dfrac{1}{2}\right), \left(1\dfrac{1}{2}, -7\right), \left(0, \dfrac{4}{5}\right)\right\}$

8. $\{(\pi, 0), (0, \pi), (-2, 4), (4, -2)\}$

9. $\{(-3, -3), (0, 0), (3, 3)\}$

10. $\left\{\left(\dfrac{1}{2}, \dfrac{1}{4}\right), \left(0, \dfrac{7}{8}\right), (0.5, \pi)\right\}$

▸ 11.

12.

13.

14.

15.

16.

17.

18.

In Exercises 19 through 22, determine whether the relation is a function. See Example 2.

	First Set: Input	*Correspondence*	*Second Set: Output*
19.	Class of algebra students	Final grade average	nonnegative numbers
20.	People who live in Cincinnati, Ohio	Birth date	days of the year
21.	blue, green, brown	Eye color	People who live in Cincinnati, Ohio
22.	Whole numbers from 0 to 4	Number of children	50 women in a cybersecurity seminar

Use the vertical line test to determine whether each graph is the graph of a function. See Example 5.

23.   **24.**

25.   **26.**

27.   **28.**

Find the domain and the range of each relation. Use the vertical line test to determine whether each graph is the graph of a function. See Example 6.

29.

30.

31.

32.

33.

34.

35.

36.

37.

38.

39.

40.

MIXED PRACTICE

Decide whether each is a function. See Examples 3 through 6.

41. $y = x + 1$ **42.** $y = x - 1$

43. $x = 2y^2$ **44.** $y = x^2$

45. $y - x = 7$ **46.** $2x - 3y = 9$

47. $y = \dfrac{1}{x}$ **48.** $y = \dfrac{1}{x - 3}$

49. $y = 5x - 12$ **50.** $y = \dfrac{1}{2}x + 4$

51. $x = y^2$ **52.** $x = |y|$

If $f(x) = 3x + 3$, $g(x) = 4x^2 - 6x + 3$, and $h(x) = 5x^2 - 7$, find the following. See Example 7.

53. $f(4)$ **54.** $f(-1)$

55. $h(-3)$ **56.** $h(0)$

57. $g(2)$ **58.** $g(1)$

59. $g(0)$ **60.** $h(-2)$

Given the following functions, find the indicated values. See Example 7.

61. $f(x) = \dfrac{1}{2}x$

    a. $f(0)$ **b.** $f(2)$ **c.** $f(-2)$

62. $g(x) = -\dfrac{1}{3}x$

    a. $g(0)$ **b.** $g(-1)$ **c.** $g(3)$

63. $g(x) = 2x^2 + 4$

    a. $g(-11)$ **b.** $g(-1)$ **c.** $g\left(\dfrac{1}{2}\right)$

64. $h(x) = -x^2$

   a. $h(-5)$ **b.** $h\left(-\dfrac{1}{3}\right)$ **c.** $h\left(\dfrac{1}{3}\right)$

65. $f(x) = -5$

   a. $f(2)$ **b.** $f(0)$ **c.** $f(606)$

66. $h(x) = 7$

   a. $h(7)$ **b.** $h(542)$ **c.** $h\left(-\dfrac{3}{4}\right)$

67. $f(x) = 1.3x^2 - 2.6x + 5.1$

   a. $f(2)$ **b.** $f(-2)$ **c.** $f(3.1)$

68. $g(x) = 2.7x^2 + 6.8x - 10.2$

   a. $g(1)$ **b.** $g(-5)$ **c.** $g(7.2)$

Use the graphs of the functions below to answer Exercises 69 through 80. See Example 8.

69. If $f(1) = -10$, write the corresponding ordered pair.

70. If $f(-5) = -10$, write the corresponding ordered pair.

71. If $g(4) = 56$, write the corresponding ordered pair.

72. If $g(-2) = 8$, write the corresponding ordered pair.

73. Find $f(-1)$.

74. Find $f(-2)$.

75. Find $g(2)$.

76. Find $g(-4)$.

77. Find all values of x such that $f(x) = -5$.

78. Find all values of x such that $f(x) = -2$.

79. Find all positive values of x such that $g(x) = 4$.

80. Find all values of x such that $g(x) = 0$.

From the Chapter 3 opener, we have two functions to describe the percent of Americans 25 and older who have completed at least high school. For both functions, x is the number of years since 2008, any y (or f(x) or g(x)) is the percent of Americans completing at least high school.

$$f(x) = 0.48x + 87.8 \quad \text{or} \quad g(x) = 0.008x^2 + 0.43x + 87.8$$

Use this for Exercises 81–86. See Examples 9 and 10.

81. Find $f(6)$ and describe in words what this means.

82. Find $g(6)$ and describe in words what this means.

83. Assume the trend of $g(x)$ continues. Find $g(12)$ and describe in words what this means.

84. Assume the trend of $f(x)$ continues. Find $f(12)$ and describe in words what this means.

85. Use Exercises 81–84 and compare $f(6)$ and $g(6)$, then $f(12)$ and $g(12)$. As x increases, are the function values staying about the same or not? Explain your answer.

86. Use the Chapter 3 opener graph and study the graphs of $f(x)$ and $g(x)$. Use these graphs to answer Exercise 85. Explain your answer.

The function $f(x) = 0.42x + 10.5$ can be used to predict diamond production. For this function, x is the number of years after 2000, and f(x) is the value (in billions of dollars) of the year's diamond production.

87. Use the function to predict diamond production in 2012.

88. Use the function to predict diamond production in 2015.

89. Since $y = x + 7$ describes a function, rewrite the equation using function notation.

90. In your own words, explain how to find the domain of a function given its graph.

The function $A(r) = \pi r^2$ may be used to find the area of a circle if we are given its radius.

△ **91.** Find the area of a circle whose radius is 5 centimeters. (Do not approximate π.)

△ **92.** Find the area of a circular garden whose radius is 8 feet. (Do not approximate π.)

The function $V(x) = x^3$ may be used to find the volume of a cube if we are given the length x of a side.

93. Find the volume of a cube whose side is 14 inches.

94. Find the volume of a die whose side is 1.7 centimeters.

Forensic scientists use the following functions to find the height of a woman if they are given the length of her femur bone f or her tibia bone t in centimeters.

$$H(f) = 2.59f + 47.24.$$
$$H(t) = 2.72t + 61.28$$

|← 46 cm Femur →|← 35 cm Tibia →|

95. Find the height of a woman whose femur measures 46 centimeters.

96. Find the height of a woman whose tibia measures 35 centimeters.

The dosage in milligrams D of Ivermectin, a heartworm preventive, for a dog who weighs x pounds is given by

$$D(x) = \frac{136}{25}x$$

97. Find the proper dosage for a dog that weighs 30 pounds.

98. Find the proper dosage for a dog that weighs 50 pounds.

99. The per capita consumption (in pounds) of all beef in the United States is given by the function $C(x) = -1.17x + 61.7$, where x is the number of years since 2008. (*Source:* U.S. Department of Agriculture and Cattle Network)

  a. Find and interpret $C(6)$.

  b. Estimate the per capita consumption of beef in the United States in 2019.

100. The amount of money (in billions of dollars) spent by the Boeing Company and subsidiaries on research and development annually is represented by the function $R(x) = -0.3x + 4.1$, where x is the number of years after 2010. (*Source:* Boeing Corporation)

  a. Find and interpret $R(3)$.

  b. Estimate the amount of money spent on research and development by Boeing in 2018.

REVIEW AND PREVIEW

Complete the given table and use the table to graph the linear equation. See Section 3.1.

101. $x - y = -5$

x	0		1
y		0	

102. $2x + 3y = 10$

x	0		
y		0	2

103. $7x + 4y = 8$

x	0		
y		0	-1

104. $5y - x = -15$

x	0		-2
y		0	

105. $y = 6x$

x	0		-1
y		0	

106. $y = -2x$

x	0		-2
y		0	

△ **107.** Is it possible to find the perimeter of the following geometric figure? If so, find the perimeter.

45 meters

40 meters

108. Is it possible to find the area of the figure in Exercise 107? If so, find the area.

CONCEPT EXTENSIONS

For Exercises 109 through 112, suppose that $y = f(x)$ and it is true that $f(7) = 50$. Determine whether each is true or false. See the third Concept Check in this section.

109. An ordered pair solution of the function is $(7, 50)$.

110. When x is 50, y is 7.

111. A possible function is $f(x) = x^2 + 1$.

112. A possible function is $f(x) = 10x - 20$.

Given the following functions, find the indicated values.

113. $h(x) = x^2 + 7$

  a. $h(3)$ **b.** $h(a)$

114. $f(x) = x^2 - 12$

  a. $f(12)$ **b.** $f(a)$

115. $f(x) = 3x - 12$

  a. $f(4)$
  b. $f(a)$
  c. $f(-x)$
  d. $f(x + h)$

116. $f(x) = 2x + 7$

  a. $f(2)$
  b. $f(a)$
  c. $f(-x)$
  d. $f(x + h)$

117. What is the greatest number of x-intercepts that a function may have? Explain your answer.

118. What is the greatest number of y-intercepts that a function may have? Explain your answer.

119. In your own words, explain how to find the domain of a function given its graph.

120. Explain the vertical line test and how it is used.

121. Describe a function whose domain is the set of people in your hometown.

122. Describe a function whose domain is the set of people in your algebra class.

3.3 Graphing Linear Functions

OBJECTIVES

1 Graph Linear Functions.

2 Graph Linear Functions by Using Intercepts.

3 Graph Vertical and Horizontal Lines.

OBJECTIVE

1 Graphing Linear Functions

In this section, we identify and graph linear functions. By the vertical line test, we know that all linear equations except those whose graphs are vertical lines are functions. For example, we know from Section 3.1 that $y = 2x$ is a linear equation in two variables. Its graph is shown.

x	$y = 2x$
1	2
0	0
−1	−2

Because this graph passes the vertical line test, we know that $y = 2x$ is a function. If we want to emphasize that this equation describes a function, we may write $y = 2x$ as $f(x) = 2x$.

EXAMPLE 1   Graph $g(x) = 2x + 1$. Compare this graph with the graph of $f(x) = 2x$.

<u>Solution</u> To graph $g(x) = 2x + 1$, find three ordered pair solutions.

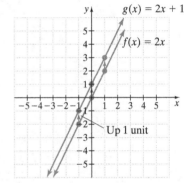

x	$f(x) = 2x$	$g(x) = 2x + 1$
0	0	1
−1	−2	−1
1	2	3

Notice that y-values for the graph of $g(x) = 2x + 1$ are obtained by adding 1 to each y-value of each corresponding point of the graph of $f(x) = 2x$. The graph of $g(x) = 2x + 1$ is the same as the graph of $f(x) = 2x$ shifted upward 1 unit. □

PRACTICE

1   Graph $g(x) = 4x - 3$ and $f(x) = 4x$ on the same axes. ■

In general, a **linear function** is a function that can be written in the form $f(x) = mx + b$. For example, $g(x) = 2x + 1$ is in this form, with $m = 2$ and $b = 1$.

EXAMPLE 2   Graph the linear functions $f(x) = -3x$ and $g(x) = -3x - 6$ on the same set of axes.

<u>Solution</u> To graph $f(x)$ and $g(x)$, find ordered pair solutions.

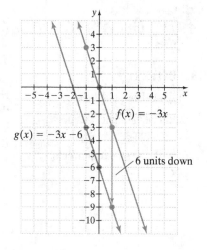

x	$f(x) = -3x$	$g(x) = -3x - 6$
0	0	−6
1	−3	−9
−1	3	−3
−2	6	0

subtract 6

subtract 6

Each y-value for the graph of $g(x) = -3x - 6$ is obtained by subtracting 6 from the y-value of the corresponding point of the graph of $f(x) = -3x$. The graph of $g(x) = -3x - 6$ is the same as the graph of $f(x) = -3x$ shifted down 6 units.   □

PRACTICE
2   Graph the linear functions $f(x) = -2x$ and $g(x) = -2x + 5$ on the same set of axes.   ▪

OBJECTIVE
2   Graphing Linear Functions by Using Intercepts

Notice that the y-intercept of the graph of $g(x) = -3x - 6$ in the preceding figure is $(0, -6)$. In general, if *a linear function is written in the form* $f(x) = mx + b$ *or* $y = mx + b$, *the* y-*intercept is* $(0, b)$. This is because if x is 0, then $f(x) = mx + b$ becomes $f(0) = m \cdot 0 + b = b$, and we have the ordered pair solution $(0, b)$. We will study this form more in the next section.

EXAMPLE 3   Find the y-intercept of the graph of each equation.

$$\textbf{a. } f(x) = \frac{1}{2}x + \frac{3}{7} \qquad\qquad \textbf{b. } y = -2.5x - 3.2$$

Solution

a. The y-intercept of $f(x) = \frac{1}{2}x + \frac{3}{7}$ is $\left(0, \frac{3}{7}\right)$.

b. The y-intercept of $y = -2.5x - 3.2$ is $(0, -3.2)$.   □

PRACTICE
3   Find the y-intercept of the graph of each equation.

$$\textbf{a. } f(x) = \frac{3}{4}x - \frac{2}{5} \qquad\qquad \textbf{b. } y = 2.6x + 4.1$$ ▪

In general, to find the y-intercept of the graph of an equation not in the form $y = mx + b$, let $x = 0$ since any point on the y-axis has an x-coordinate of 0. To find the x-intercept of a line, let $y = 0$ or $f(x) = 0$ since any point on the x-axis has a y-coordinate of 0.

> **Finding x- and y-Intercepts**
>
> To find an x-intercept, let $y = 0$ or $f(x) = 0$ and solve for x.
> To find a y-intercept, let $x = 0$ and solve for y.

Intercepts are usually easy to find and plot since one coordinate is 0.

EXAMPLE 4 Find the intercepts of and then graph $3x + 4y = -12$.

Solution To find the *y*-intercept, we let $x = 0$ and solve for *y*. To find the *x*-intercept, we let $y = 0$ and solve for *x*. Let's let $x = 0$, then $y = 0$; and then let $x = 2$ to find a third point as a check.

Let $x = 0$.	Let $y = 0$.	Let $x = 2$.
$3x + 4y = -12$	$3x + 4y = -12$	$3x + 4y = -12$
$3 \cdot 0 + 4y = -12$	$3x + 4 \cdot 0 = -12$	$3 \cdot 2 + 4y = -12$
$4y = -12$	$3x = -12$	$6 + 4y = -12$
$y = -3$	$x = -4$	$4y = -18$
		$y = -\dfrac{18}{4} = -4\dfrac{1}{2}$
$(0, -3)$	$(-4, 0)$	$\left(2, -4\dfrac{1}{2}\right)$

The ordered pairs are in the table below. The graph of $3x + 4y = -12$ is the line drawn through these points, as shown.

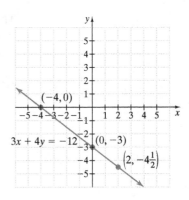

	x	y	
	0	−3	← *y*-intercept
x-intercept →	−4	0	
	2	$-4\dfrac{1}{2}$	

PRACTICE
4 Find the intercepts of and then graph $4x - 5y = -20$.

Notice that the equation $3x + 4y = -12$ describes a linear function—"linear" because its graph is a line and "function" because the graph passes the vertical line test.

If we want to emphasize that the equation $3x + 4y = -12$ from Example 4 describes a function, first solve the equation for *y*.

$$3x + 4y = -12$$
$$4y = -3x - 12 \quad \text{Subtract } 3x \text{ from both sides.}$$
$$\frac{4y}{4} = \frac{-3x}{4} - \frac{12}{4} \quad \text{Divide both sides by 4.}$$
$$y = -\frac{3}{4}x - 3 \quad \text{Simplify.}$$

Next, since $y = f(x)$, replace *y* with $f(x)$.

$$f(x) = -\frac{3}{4}x - 3$$

Helpful Hint

Any linear equation that describes a function can be written using function notation. To do so,

1. solve the equation for *y* and then
2. replace *y* with $f(x)$, as we did above.

EXAMPLE 5 Graph $x = -2y$ by plotting intercepts.

Solution Let $y = 0$ to find the x-intercept and $x = 0$ to find the y-intercept.

$$
\begin{array}{ll}
\text{If } y = 0 \quad \text{then} & \text{If } x = 0 \quad \text{then} \\
x = -2(0) \quad \text{or} & 0 = -2y \quad \text{or} \\
x = 0 & 0 = y \\
(0, 0) & (0, 0)
\end{array}
$$

Ordered pairs Both the x-intercept and y-intercept are $(0, 0)$. This happens when the graph passes through the origin. Since two points are needed to determine a line, we must find at least one more ordered pair that satisfies $x = -2y$. Let $y = -1$ to find a second ordered pair solution and let $y = 1$ as a check point.

$$
\begin{array}{ll}
\text{If } y = -1 \quad \text{then} & \text{If } y = 1 \quad \text{then} \\
x = -2(-1) \quad \text{or} & x = -2(1) \quad \text{or} \\
x = 2 & x = -2
\end{array}
$$

The ordered pairs are $(0, 0)$, $(2, -1)$, and $(-2, 1)$. Plot these points to graph $x = -2y$.

x	y
0	0
2	-1
-2	1

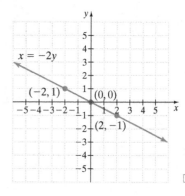

PRACTICE
5 Graph $y = -3x$ by plotting intercepts.

OBJECTIVE
3 Graphing Vertical and Horizontal Lines

The equations $x = c$ and $y = c$, where c is a real number constant, are both linear equations in two variables. Why? Because $x = c$ can be written as $x + 0y = c$ and $y = c$ can be written as $0x + y = c$. We graph these two special linear equations in the next two examples.

EXAMPLE 6 Graph $x = 2$.

Solution The equation $x = 2$ can be written as $x + 0y = 2$. For any y-value chosen, notice that x is 2. No other value for x satisfies $x + 0y = 2$. Any ordered pair whose x-coordinate is 2 is a solution to $x + 0y = 2$ because 2 added to 0 times any value of y is $2 + 0$, or 2. We will use the ordered pairs $(2, 3)$, $(2, 0)$, and $(2, -3)$ to graph $x = 2$.

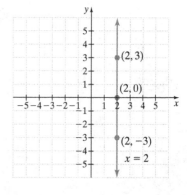

x	y
2	3
x-intercept → 2	0
2	-3

The graph is a vertical line with x-intercept $(2, 0)$. Notice that this graph **is not the graph of a function,** and it has no y-intercept because x is never 0.

PRACTICE
6 Graph $x = -4$.

EXAMPLE 7   Graph $y = -3$.

Solution The equation $y = -3$ can be written as $0x + y = -3$. For any x-value chosen, y is -3. If we choose 4, 0, and -2 as x-values, the ordered pair solutions are $(4, -3)$, $(0, -3)$, and $(-2, -3)$. We will use these ordered pairs to graph $y = -3$.

x	y
4	−3
0	−3 ← y-intercept
−2	−3

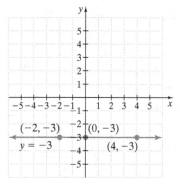

The graph is a horizontal line with y-intercept $(0, -3)$ and no x-intercept. Notice that this graph **is the graph of a function**.   □

PRACTICE
7   Graph $y = 4$.   ■

From Examples 6 and 7, we have the following generalization.

Graphing Vertical and Horizontal Lines

The graph of $x = c$, where c is a real number, is a vertical line with x-intercept $(c, 0)$.

The graph of $y = c$, where c is a real number, is a horizontal line with y-intercept $(0, c)$.

not a function

a function

✔ CONCEPT CHECK
Determine which equations represent functions. Explain your answer.
a. $y = 14$ b. $x = -5$

Concept Check Answer
a; answers may vary

 Graphing Calculator Explorations

You may have noticed by now that to use the $\boxed{Y =}$ key on a graphing calculator to graph an equation, the equation must be solved for y.

Graph each function by first solving the function for y.

1. $x = 3.5y$ **2.** $-2.7y = x$

3. $5.78x + 2.31y = 10.98$ **4.** $-7.22x + 3.89y = 12.57$

5. $y - |x| = 3.78$ **6.** $3y - 5x^2 = 6x - 4$

7. $y - 5.6x^2 = 7.7x + 1.5$ **8.** $y + 2.6|x| = -3.2$

✔ Vocabulary, Readiness & Video Check

Use the choices below to fill in each blank. Some choices may be used more than once and some not at all.

horizontal	y	$(c, 0)$	$(b, 0)$	$(m, 0)$	linear
vertical	x	$(0, c)$	$(0, b)$	$(0, m)$	$f(x)$

1. A(n) _____ function can be written in the form $f(x) = mx + b$.

2. In the form $f(x) = mx + b$, the y-intercept is _____.

3. The graph of $x = c$ is a(n) _____ line with x-intercept _____.

4. The graph of $y = c$ is a(n) _____ line with y-intercept _____.

5. To find an x-intercept, let _____ = 0 or _____ = 0 and solve for _____.

6. To find a y-intercept, let _____ = 0 and solve for _____.

Martin-Gay Interactive Videos

See Video 3.3 ◉

Watch the section lecture video and answer the following questions.

OBJECTIVE
1
7. Based on the lecture before ▣ Example 1, in what form can a linear function be written?

OBJECTIVE
2
8. In ▣ Example 2, the goal is to use the x- and y-intercepts to graph a line. Yet once two intercepts are found, a third point is also found before the line is graphed. Why?

OBJECTIVE
3
9. From ▣ Examples 3 and 4, what can you say about the coefficients of the variable terms when the equation of a horizontal line is written in the form $Ax + By = C$? Of a vertical line?

3.3 Exercise Set MyMathLab® ◉

Graph each linear function. See Examples 1 and 2.

1. $f(x) = -2x$

2. $f(x) = 2x$

▶ 3. $f(x) = -2x + 3$

4. $f(x) = 2x + 6$

5. $f(x) = \frac{1}{2}x$

6. $f(x) = \frac{1}{3}x$

7. $f(x) = \frac{1}{2}x - 4$

8. $f(x) = \frac{1}{3}x - 2$

The graph of $f(x) = 5x$ follows. Use this graph for exercises 9 through 12 to match each linear function with its graph. See Examples 1 through 3.

$y = 5x$

9. $f(x) = 5x - 3$

10. $f(x) = 5x - 2$

11. $f(x) = 5x + 1$

12. $f(x) = 5x + 3$

A.

B.

C.

D.

Graph each linear function by finding x- and y-intercepts. Then write each equation using function notation. See Examples 4 and 5.

13. $x - y = 3$

14. $x - y = -4$

15. $x = 5y$

16. $2x = y$

17. $-x + 2y = 6$

18. $x - 2y = -8$

19. $2x - 4y = 8$

20. $4x + 6y = 12$

Graph each linear equation. See Examples 6 and 7.

21. $x = -1$ **22.** $y = 5$

23. $y = 0$ **24.** $x = 0$

25. $y + 7 = 0$ **26.** $x - 3 = 0$

Match each equation below with its graph.

A.   **B.**

C.   **D.**

27. $y = 2$ **28.** $x = -3$

29. $x - 2 = 0$ **30.** $y + 1 = 0$

MIXED PRACTICE

Graph each linear equation. See Examples 1 through 7.

31. $x + 2y = 8$ **32.** $x - 3y = 3$

33. $3x + 5y = 7$ **34.** $3x - 2y = 5$

35. $x + 8y = 8$ **36.** $x - 3y = 9$

37. $5 = 6x - y$ **38.** $4 = x - 3y$

39. $-x + 10y = 11$ **40.** $-x + 9 = -y$

41. $y = \dfrac{3}{2}$ **42.** $x = \dfrac{3}{2}$

43. $2x + 3y = 6$ **44.** $4x + y = 5$

45. $x + 3 = 0$ **46.** $y - 6 = 0$

47. $f(x) = \dfrac{3}{4}x + 2$ **48.** $f(x) = \dfrac{4}{3}x + 2$

49. $f(x) = x$ **50.** $f(x) = -x$

51. $f(x) = \dfrac{1}{2}x$ **52.** $f(x) = -2x$

53. $f(x) = 4x - \dfrac{1}{3}$ **54.** $f(x) = -3x + \dfrac{3}{4}$

55. $x = -3$ **56.** $f(x) = 3$

REVIEW AND PREVIEW

Solve the following. See Sections 2.6 and 2.7

57. $|x - 3| = 6$

58. $|x + 2| < 4$

59. $|2x + 5| > 3$

60. $|5x| = 10$

61. $|3x - 4| \leq 2$

62. $|7x - 2| \geq 5$

Simplify. See Section 1.3.

63. $\dfrac{-6 - 3}{2 - 8}$ **64.** $\dfrac{4 - 5}{-1 - 0}$ **65.** $\dfrac{-8 - (-2)}{-3 - (-2)}$

66. $\dfrac{-12 - (-3)}{-10 - (-9)}$ **67.** $\dfrac{0 - 6}{5 - 0}$ **68.** $\dfrac{2 - 2}{3 - 5}$

CONCEPT EXTENSIONS

Think about the appearance of each graph. Without graphing, determine which equations represent functions. Explain each answer. See the Concept Check in this section.

69. $x = -1$

70. $y = 5$

71. $y = 2x$

72. $x + y = -5$

Solve.

73. Broyhill Furniture found that it takes 2 hours to manufacture each table for one of its special dining room sets. Each chair takes 3 hours to manufacture. A total of 1500 hours is available to produce tables and chairs of this style. The linear equation that models this situation is $2x + 3y = 1500$, where x represents the number of tables produced and y the number of chairs produced.

  a. Complete the ordered pair solution $(0, \quad)$ of this equation. Describe the manufacturing situation this solution corresponds to.

  b. Complete the ordered pair solution $(\quad, 0)$ for this equation. Describe the manufacturing situation this solution corresponds to.

  c. If 50 tables are produced, find the greatest number of chairs the company can make.

74. While manufacturing two different digital camera models, Kodak found that the basic model costs \$55 to produce, whereas the deluxe model costs \$75. The weekly budget for these two models is limited to \$33,000 in production costs. The linear equation that models this situation is

$55x + 75y = 33,000$, where x represents the number of basic models and y the number of deluxe models.

a. Complete the ordered pair solution $(0, \quad)$ of this equation. Describe the manufacturing situation this solution corresponds to.

b. Complete the ordered pair solution $(\quad, 0)$ of this equation. Describe the manufacturing situation this solution corresponds to.

c. If 350 deluxe models are produced, find the greatest number of basic models that can be made in one week.

75. The cost of renting a car for a day is given by the linear function $C(x) = 0.2x + 24$, where $C(x)$ is in dollars and x is the number of miles driven.

a. Find the cost of driving the car 200 miles.

b. Graph $C(x) = 0.2x + 24$.

c. How can you tell from the graph of $C(x)$ that as the number of miles driven increases, the total cost increases also?

76. The cost of renting a piece of machinery is given by the linear function $C(x) = 4x + 10$, where $C(x)$ is in dollars and x is given in hours.

a. Find the cost of renting the piece of machinery for 8 hours.

b. Graph $C(x) = 4x + 10$.

c. How can you tell from the graph of $C(x)$ that as the number of hours increases, the total cost increases also?

77. The yearly cost of tuition (in-state), fees, and room and board for attending a public two-year college full time can be estimated by the linear function $f(x) = 502x + 7180$, where x is the number of years after 2007 and $f(x)$ is the total cost. (*Source*: National Center for Educational Statistics and The College Board)

a. Use this function to approximate the yearly cost of attending a two-year college in the year 2020. [*Hint*: Find $f(13)$.]

b. Use the given function to predict in what year the yearly cost of tuition, fees, and room and board will exceed $15,000. [*Hint*: Let $f(x) = 15,000$, solve for x, then round your solution up to the next whole year.]

c. Use this function to approximate the yearly cost of attending a two-year college in the present year. If you attend a two-year college, is this amount greater than or less than the amount that is currently charged by the college you attend?

78. The yearly cost of tuition (in-state), fees, and room and board for attending a public four-year college full time can be estimated by the linear function $f(x) = 639x + 14,436$, where x is the number of years after 2007 and $f(x)$ is the total cost in dollars. (*Source*: National Center for Educational Statistics and The College Board)

a. Use this function to approximate the yearly cost of attending a four-year college in the year 2020. [*Hint*: Find $f(13)$.]

b. Use the given function to predict in what year the yearly cost of tuition, fees, and room and board will exceed $25,000. [*Hint*: Let $f(x) = 25,000$, solve for x, then round your solution up to the next whole year.]

c. Use this function to approximate the yearly cost of attending a four-year college in the present year. If you attend a four-year college, is this amount greater than or less than the amount that is currently charged by the college you attend?

79. In your own words, explain how to find x- and y-intercepts.

80. Explain why it is a good idea to use three points to graph a linear equation.

81. Discuss whether a vertical line ever has a y-intercept.

82. Discuss whether a horizontal line ever has an x-intercept.

The graph of $f(x)$ or $y = -4x$ is given below. Without actually graphing, describe the shape and location of

83. $y = -4x + 2$

84. $y = -4x - 5$

It is true that for any function $f(x)$, the graph of $f(x) + k$ is the same as the graph of $f(x)$ shifted k units up if k is positive and $|k|$ units down if k is negative. (We study this further in Section 3.7.)

The graph of $y = |x|$ is

Match each graph with its equation.

85.

86.

87.

88.

A. $y = |x| - 1$

B. $y = |x| + 1$

C. $y = |x| - 3$

D. $y = |x| + 3$

Use a graphing calculator to verify the results of each exercise.

89. Exercise 9

90. Exercise 10

91. Exercise 17

92. Exercise 18

3.4 | The Slope of a Line

OBJECTIVES

1 Find the Slope of a Line Given Two Points on the Line.

2 Find the Slope of a Line Given the Equation of a Line.

3 Interpret the Slope–Intercept Form in an Application.

4 Find the Slopes of Horizontal and Vertical Lines.

5 Compare the Slopes of Parallel and Perpendicular Lines.

OBJECTIVE

1 ▸ **Finding Slope Given Two Points**

You may have noticed by now that different lines often tilt differently. It is very important in many fields to be able to measure and compare the tilt, or **slope,** of lines. For example, a wheelchair ramp with a slope of $\frac{1}{12}$ means that the ramp rises 1 foot for every 12 horizontal feet. A road with a slope or grade of 11% $\left(\text{or } \frac{11}{100} \right)$ means that the road rises 11 feet for every 100 horizontal feet.

We measure the slope of a line as a ratio of **vertical change** to **horizontal change.** Slope is usually designated by the letter m.

Suppose that we want to measure the slope of the following line.

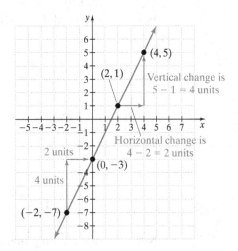

The vertical change between *both* pairs of points on the line is 4 units per horizontal change of 2 units. Then

$$\text{slope } m = \frac{\text{change in } y \text{ (vertical change)}}{\text{change in } x \text{ (horizontal change)}} = \frac{4}{2} = 2.$$

Notice that slope is a **rate of change** between points. A slope of 2 or $\frac{2}{1}$ means that between pairs of points on the line, the rate of change is a vertical change of 2 units per horizontal change of 1 unit.

Consider the line in the box on the next page, which passes through the points (x_1, y_1) and (x_2, y_2). (The notation x_1 is read "*x*-sub-one.") The vertical change, or *rise*, between these points is the difference of the *y*-coordinates: $y_2 - y_1$. The horizontal change, or *run*, between the points is the difference of the *x*-coordinates: $x_2 - x_1$.

Slope of a Line

Given a line passing through points (x_1, y_1) and (x_2, y_2), the **slope** m of the line is

$$m = \frac{\text{rise}}{\text{run}} = \frac{y_2 - y_1}{x_2 - x_1}, \text{ as long as}$$

$$x_2 \neq x_1.$$

✔ **CONCEPT CHECK**

In the definition of slope, we state that $x_2 \neq x_1$. Explain why.

EXAMPLE 1   Find the slope of the line containing the points $(0, 3)$ and $(2, 5)$. Graph the line.

<u>Solution</u> We use the slope formula. It does not matter which point we call (x_1, y_1) and which point we call (x_2, y_2). We'll let $(x_1, y_1) = (0, 3)$ and $(x_2, y_2) = (2, 5)$.

$$m = \frac{y_2 - y_1}{x_2 - x_1}$$

$$= \frac{5 - 3}{2 - 0} = \frac{2}{2} = 1$$

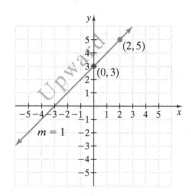

Notice in this example that the slope is *positive* and that the graph of the line containing $(0, 3)$ and $(2, 5)$ moves *upward*—that is, the y-values increase—as we go from left to right.   □

PRACTICE

1   Find the slope of the line containing the points $(4, 0)$ and $(-2, 3)$. Graph the line.   ■

Helpful Hint

The slope of a line is the same no matter which 2 points of a line you choose to calculate slope. The line in Example 1 also contains the point $(-3, 0)$. Below, we calculate the slope of the line using $(0, 3)$ as (x_1, y_1) and $(-3, 0)$ as (x_2, y_2).

$$m = \frac{y_2 - y_1}{x_2 - x_1} = \frac{0 - 3}{-3 - 0} = \frac{-3}{-3} = 1 \quad \text{Same slope as found in Example 1.}$$

EXAMPLE 2 Find the slope of the line containing the points $(5, -4)$ and $(-3, 3)$. Graph the line.

Solution We use the slope formula and let $(x_1, y_1) = (5, -4)$ and $(x_2, y_2) = (-3, 3)$.

$$m = \frac{y_2 - y_1}{x_2 - x_1}$$

$$= \frac{3 - (-4)}{-3 - 5} = \frac{7}{-8} = -\frac{7}{8}$$

Notice in this example that the slope is negative and that the graph of the line through $(5, -4)$ and $(-3, 3)$ moves downward—that is, the y-values decrease—as we go from left to right. □

PRACTICE

2 Find the slope of the line containing the points $(-5, -4)$ and $(5, 2)$. Graph the line. ■

> **Helpful Hint**
>
> When we are trying to find the slope of a line through two given points, it makes no difference which given point is called (x_1, y_1) and which is called (x_2, y_2). Once an x-coordinate is called x_1, however, make sure its corresponding y-coordinate is called y_1.

✔ **CONCEPT CHECK**

Find and correct the error in the following calculation of slope of the line containing the points $(12, 2)$ and $(4, 7)$.

$$m = \cancel{\frac{12 - 4}{2 - 7}} = \cancel{\frac{8}{-5}} = \cancel{-\frac{8}{5}}$$

OBJECTIVE

2 Finding Slope Given an Equation

As we have seen, the slope of a line is defined by two points on the line. Thus, if we know the equation of a line, we can find its slope.

EXAMPLE 3 Find the slope of the line whose equation is $f(x) = \frac{2}{3}x + 4$.

Solution Two points are needed on the line defined by $f(x) = \frac{2}{3}x + 4$ or $y = \frac{2}{3}x + 4$ to find its slope. We will use intercepts as our two points.

If $x = 0$, then   If $y = 0$, then

$$y = \frac{2}{3} \cdot 0 + 4 \qquad\qquad 0 = \frac{2}{3}x + 4$$

$$y = 4 \qquad\qquad\qquad -4 = \frac{2}{3}x \qquad \text{Subtract 4.}$$

$$\frac{3}{2}(-4) = \frac{3}{2} \cdot \frac{2}{3}x \qquad \text{Multiply by } \frac{3}{2}.$$

$$-6 = x$$

Use the points $(0, 4)$ and $(-6, 0)$ to find the slope. Let (x_1, y_1) be $(0, 4)$ and (x_2, y_2) be $(-6, 0)$. Then

$$m = \frac{y_2 - y_1}{x_2 - x_1} = \frac{0 - 4}{-6 - 0} = \frac{-4}{-6} = \frac{2}{3}.$$

PRACTICE
3   Find the slope of the line whose equation is $f(x) = -4x + 6$.

Analyzing the results of Example 3, you may notice a striking pattern:

The slope of $y = \frac{2}{3}x + 4$ is $\frac{2}{3}$, the same as the coefficient of x.

Also, the y-intercept is $(0, 4)$, as expected.

When a linear equation is written in the form $f(x) = mx + b$ or $y = mx + b$, m is the slope of the line and $(0, b)$ is its y-intercept. The form $y = mx + b$ is appropriately called the **slope–intercept form.**

> **Slope–Intercept Form**
>
> When a linear equation in two variables is written in slope–intercept form,
>
> slope y-intercept is $(0, b)$
>   ↓   ↓
> $$y = mx + b$$
>
> then m is the slope of the line and $(0, b)$ is the y-intercept of the line.
>
> *Note:* As mentioned in Section 3.1, the y-intercept may also be noted as just b.

EXAMPLE 4   Find the slope and the y-intercept of the line $3x - 4y = 4$.

Solution We write the equation in slope–intercept form by solving for y.

$$3x - 4y = 4$$
$$-4y = -3x + 4 \qquad \text{Subtract } 3x \text{ from both sides.}$$
$$\frac{-4y}{-4} = \frac{-3x}{-4} + \frac{4}{-4} \qquad \text{Divide both sides by } -4.$$
$$y = \frac{3}{4}x - 1 \qquad \text{Simplify.}$$

The coefficient of x, $\frac{3}{4}$, is the slope, and the y-intercept is $(0, -1)$.

PRACTICE
4   Find the slope and the y-intercept of the line $2x - 3y = 9$.

OBJECTIVE
3   Interpreting Slope–Intercept Form

On the following page is the graph of one-day ticket prices at Disney World for the years shown.

Notice that the graph resembles the graph of a line. Recall that businesses often depend on equations that closely fit graphs like this one to model the data and to predict future trends. By the **least squares** method, the linear function $f(x) = 3.53x + 67.39$ approximates the data shown, where x is the number of years since 2006 and y is the ticket price for that year.

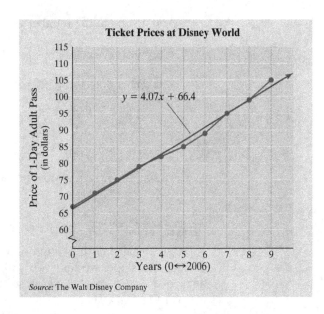

Ticket Prices at Disney World

$y = 4.07x + 66.4$

Years (0 ↔ 2006)

Source: The Walt Disney Company

Helpful Hint

The notation $0 \leftrightarrow 2006$ means that the number 0 corresponds to the year 2006, 1 corresponds to the year 2007, and so on.

EXAMPLE 5   Predicting Future Prices

The adult one-day pass price y for Disney World is given by

$$y = 4.07x + 66.4$$

where x is the number of years since 2006.

    a. Use this equation to predict the ticket prices for 2021.

    b. What does the slope of this equation mean?

    c. What does the y-intercept of this equation mean?

Solution:

    a. To predict the price of a pass in 2021, we need to find y when x is 15. (Since the year 2006 corresponds to $x = 0$, the year 2021 corresponds to the year $2021 - 2006 = 15$.)

$$y = 4.07x + 66.4$$
$$= 4.07(15) + 66.4 \quad \text{Let } x = 15$$
$$= 127.45$$

We predict that in the year 2021, the price of an adult one-day pass to Disney World will be about $127.45.

    b. The slope of $y = 4.07x + 66.4$ is 4.07. We can think of this number as $\dfrac{\text{rise}}{\text{run}}$, or $\dfrac{4.07}{1}$. This means that the ticket price increases on average by $4.07 each year.

    c. The y-intercept of $y = 4.07x + 66.4$ is 66.4. Notice that it corresponds to the point $(0, 66.4)$ on the graph.

                    ↑ ↑
                Year price

That means that at year $x = 0$, or 2006, the ticket price was about $66.40. □

PRACTICE

5   For the period 2010 through 2040, the number of people y age 85 or older living in the United States is given by the equation $y = 269{,}370x + 4{,}869{,}700$, where x is the number of years since 2010. (*Source:* Based on data and estimates from the U.S. Census Bureau)

a. Estimate the number of people age 85 or older living in the United States in 2015.

b. What does the slope of this equation mean?

c. What does the y-intercept of this equation mean?

OBJECTIVE

4 Finding Slopes of Horizontal and Vertical Lines

Next we find the slopes of two special types of lines: vertical lines and horizontal lines.

EXAMPLE 6 Find the slope of the line $x = -5$.

Solution Recall that the graph of $x = -5$ is a vertical line with x-intercept $(-5, 0)$. To find the slope, we find two ordered pair solutions of $x = -5$. Of course, solutions of $x = -5$ must have an x-value of -5. We will let $(x_1, y_1) = (-5, 0)$ and $(x_2, y_2) = (-5, 4)$. Then

$$m = \frac{y_2 - y_1}{x_2 - x_1}$$

$$= \frac{4 - 0}{-5 - (-5)}$$

$$= \frac{4}{0}$$

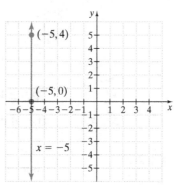

Since $\frac{4}{0}$ is undefined, we say that the slope of the vertical line $x = -5$ is undefined. □

PRACTICE

6 Find the slope of the line $x = 4$.

EXAMPLE 7 Find the slope of the line $y = 2$.

Solution Recall that the graph of $y = 2$ is a horizontal line with y-intercept $(0, 2)$. To find the slope, we find two points on the line, such as $(0, 2)$ and $(1, 2)$, and use these points to find the slope.

$$m = \frac{2 - 2}{1 - 0}$$

$$= \frac{0}{1}$$

$$= 0$$

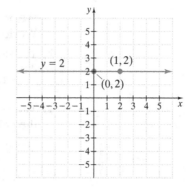

The slope of the horizontal line $y = 2$ is 0. □

PRACTICE

7 Find the slope of the line $y = -3$.

From the previous two examples, we have the following generalization.

> The slope of any vertical line is undefined.
> The slope of any horizontal line is 0.

> **Helpful Hint**
>
> Slope of 0 and undefined slope are not the same. Vertical lines have undefined slope, whereas horizontal lines have a slope of 0.

The following four graphs summarize the overall appearance of lines with positive, negative, zero, or undefined slopes.

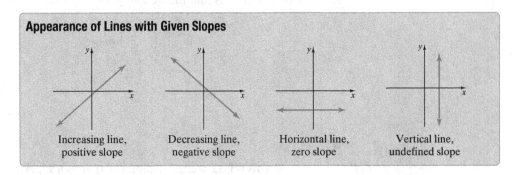

Appearance of Lines with Given Slopes

Increasing line, positive slope

Decreasing line, negative slope

Horizontal line, zero slope

Vertical line, undefined slope

The appearance of a line can give us further information about its slope.

The graphs of $y = \frac{1}{2}x + 1$ and $y = 5x + 1$ are shown to the right. Recall that the graph of $y = \frac{1}{2}x + 1$ has a slope of $\frac{1}{2}$ and that the graph of $y = 5x + 1$ has a slope of 5.

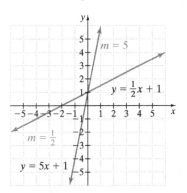

Notice that the line with the slope of 5 is steeper than the line with the slope of $\frac{1}{2}$. This is true in general for positive slopes.

> For a line with positive slope m, as m increases, the line becomes steeper.

To see why this is so, compare the slopes from above. $\frac{1}{2}$ means a vertical change of 1 unit per horizontal change of 2 units; 5 or $\frac{10}{2}$ means a vertical change of 10 units per horizontal change of 2 units.

For larger positive slopes, the vertical change is greater for the same horizontal change. Thus, larger positive slopes mean steeper lines.

OBJECTIVE

5   Comparing Slopes of Parallel and Perpendicular Lines

Slopes of lines can help us determine whether lines are parallel. Parallel lines are distinct lines with the same steepness, so it follows that they have the same slope.

Parallel Lines

Two nonvertical lines are parallel if they have the same slope and different y-intercepts.

Different y-intercepts

Same slope

How do the slopes of perpendicular lines compare? (Two lines intersecting at right angles are called **perpendicular lines.**) Suppose that a line has a slope of $\frac{a}{b}$. If the line is rotated 90°, the rise and run are now switched, except that the run is now negative. This means that the new slope is $-\frac{b}{a}$. Notice that

$$\left(\frac{a}{b}\right) \cdot \left(-\frac{b}{a}\right) = -1$$

This is how we tell whether two lines are perpendicular.

Perpendicular Lines

Two nonvertical lines are perpendicular if the product of their slopes is -1.

$m = -\frac{b}{a}$ $m = \frac{a}{b}$

In other words, two nonvertical lines are perpendicular if the slope of one is the negative reciprocal of the slope of the other.

EXAMPLE 8   Are the following pairs of lines parallel, perpendicular, or neither?

a. $3x + 7y = 4$ **b.** $-x + 3y = 2$
       $6x + 14y = 7$ $2x + 6y = 5$

Solution Find the slope of each line by solving each equation for y.

a. $3x + 7y = 4$ $6x + 14y = 7$

$7y = -3x + 4$ $14y = -6x + 7$

$\dfrac{7y}{7} = \dfrac{-3x}{7} + \dfrac{4}{7}$ $\dfrac{14y}{14} = \dfrac{-6x}{14} + \dfrac{7}{14}$

$y = -\dfrac{3}{7}x + \dfrac{4}{7}$ $y = -\dfrac{3}{7}x + \dfrac{1}{2}$

    ↑   ↖   ↑   ↖

slope y-intercept   slope y-intercept

$\left(0, \dfrac{4}{7}\right)$ $\left(0, \dfrac{1}{2}\right)$

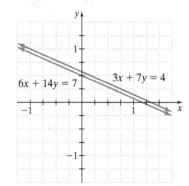

$6x + 14y = 7$ $3x + 7y = 4$

The slopes of both lines are $-\dfrac{3}{7}$.

The y-intercepts are different, so the lines are not the same. Therefore, the lines are parallel. (Their graphs are shown in the margin.)

b.
$$-x + 3y = 2 \qquad\qquad 2x + 6y = 5$$
$$3y = x + 2 \qquad\qquad 6y = -2x + 5$$
$$\frac{3y}{3} = \frac{x}{3} + \frac{2}{3} \qquad\qquad \frac{6y}{6} = \frac{-2x}{6} + \frac{5}{6}$$
$$y = \frac{1}{3}x + \frac{2}{3} \qquad\qquad y = -\frac{1}{3}x + \frac{5}{6}$$

slope   y-intercept   slope   y-intercept

$$\left(0, \frac{2}{3}\right) \qquad\qquad \left(0, \frac{5}{6}\right)$$

The slopes are not the same and their product is not -1. $\left[\left(\frac{1}{3}\right) \cdot \left(-\frac{1}{3}\right) = -\frac{1}{9}\right]$

Therefore, the lines are neither parallel nor perpendicular. (Their graphs are shown in the margin.)

PRACTICE
8   Are the following pairs of lines parallel, perpendicular, or neither?

a. $x - 2y = 3$
$\quad\ 2x + y = 3$

b. $4x - 3y = 2$
$\quad\ -8x + 6y = -6$

✔ **CONCEPT CHECK**
What is *different* about the equations of two parallel lines?

Answer to Concept Check:
y-intercepts are different

 Graphing Calculator Explorations

Many graphing calculators have a TRACE feature. This feature allows you to trace along a graph and see the corresponding *x*- and *y*-coordinates appear on the screen. Use this feature for the following exercises.

Graph each function and then use the TRACE feature to complete each ordered pair solution. (Many times, the tracer will not show an exact *x*- or *y*-value asked for. In each case, trace as closely as you can to the given *x*- or *y*-coordinate and approximate the other, unknown coordinate to one decimal place.)

1. $y = 2.3x + 6.7$
$\quad x = 5.1, y = ?$

2. $y = -4.8x + 2.9$
$\quad x = -1.8, y = ?$

3. $y = -5.9x - 1.6$
$\quad x = ?, y = 7.2$

4. $y = 0.4x - 8.6$
$\quad x = ?, y = -4.4$

5. $y = x^2 + 5.2x - 3.3$
$\quad x = 2.3, y = ?$
$\quad x = ?, y = 36$
(There will be two answers here.)

6. $y = 5x^2 - 6.2x - 8.3$
$\quad x = 3.2, y = ?$
$\quad x = ?, y = 12$
(There will be two answers here.)

✓ **Vocabulary, Readiness & Video Check**

Use the choices below to fill in each blank. Some choices may be used more than once and some not at all.

horizontal   the same -1 y-intercepts $(0, b)$ slope
vertical   different m x-intercepts $(b, 0)$ slope–intercept

1. The measure of the steepness or tilt of a line is called _____.

2. The slope of a line through two points is measured by the ratio of _____ change to _____ change.

3. If a linear equation is in the form $y = mx + b$, or $f(x) = mx + b$, the slope of the line is _____ and the y-intercept is _____.

4. The form $y = mx + b$ or $f(x) = mx + b$ is the _____ form.

5. The slope of _____ a line is 0.

6. The slope of a _____ line is undefined.

7. Two nonvertical perpendicular lines have slopes whose product is _____.

8. Two nonvertical lines are parallel if they have _____ slope and different _____.

Martin-Gay Interactive Videos

See Video 3.4 🌐

Watch the section lecture video and answer the following questions.

OBJECTIVE 1
9. Based on ▤ Examples 1 and 2, complete the following statements. A positive slope means the line _____ from left to right. A negative slope means the line _____ from left to right.

OBJECTIVE 2
10. From ▤ Example 3, how do you write an equation in slope–intercept form? Once the equation is in slope–intercept form, how do you determine the slope?

OBJECTIVE 3
11. ▤ Example 4 gives a linear equation that models a real-life application. The equation is rewritten in slope-intercept form. How does this help us better understand how the equation relates to the application? What specific information is discovered?

OBJECTIVE 4
12. In the lecture after ▤ Example 6, different slopes are summarized. What's the difference between zero slope and undefined slope? What does "no slope" mean?

OBJECTIVE 5
13. From the lecture before ▤ Example 7, why do the slope rules for parallel or perpendicular lines indicate nonvertical lines only?

3.4 **Exercise Set** MyMathLab ▸

Find the slope of the line that goes through the given points. See Examples 1 and 2.

1. $(3, 2), (8, 11)$

2. $(1, 6), (7, 11)$

3. $(3, 1), (1, 8)$

4. $(2, 9), (6, 4)$

5. $(-2, 8), (4, 3)$

6. $(3, 7), (-2, 11)$

▸ 7. $(-2, -6), (4, -4)$

8. $(-3, -4), (-1, 6)$

9. $(-3, -1), (-12, 11)$

10. $(3, -1), (-6, 5)$

11. $(-2, 5), (3, 5)$

12. $(4, 2), (4, 0)$

13. $(-1, 1), (-1, -5)$

14. $(-2, -5), (3, -5)$

15. $(0, 6), (-3, 0)$

16. $(5, 2), (0, 5)$

▸ 17. $(-1, 2), (-3, 4)$

18. $(3, -2), (-1, -6)$

Decide whether a line with the given slope slants upward or downward from left to right or is horizontal or vertical.

19. $m = \dfrac{7}{6}$

20. $m = -3$

21. $m = 0$

22. m is undefined

Two lines are graphed on each set of axes. Decide whether l_1 or l_2 has the greater slope. See the boxed material on page 161.

23.

24.

25.

26.

27.

28.

Find the slope and the y-intercept of each line. See Examples 3 and 4.

29. $f(x) = 5x - 2$

30. $f(x) = -2x + 6$

31. $2x + y = 7$

32. $-5x + y = 10$

▶ **33.** $2x - 3y = 10$

34. $-3x - 4y = 6$

35. $f(x) = \dfrac{1}{2}x$

36. $f(x) = -\dfrac{1}{4}x$

Match each equation in Exercises 37 through 40 with its graph. See Examples 1 and 2.

A.

B.

C.

D.

37. $f(x) = 2x + 3$ **38.** $f(x) = 2x - 3$

39. $f(x) = -2x + 3$ **40.** $f(x) = -2x - 3$

Find the slope of each line. See Examples 6 and 7.

▶ **41.** $x = 1$ **42.** $y = -2$

▶ **43.** $y = -3$ **44.** $x = 4$

45. $x + 2 = 0$ **46.** $y - 7 = 0$

MIXED PRACTICE

Find the slope and the y-intercept of each line. See Examples 3 through 7.

47. $f(x) = -x + 5$

48. $f(x) = x + 2$

49. $-6x + 5y = 30$

50. $4x - 7y = 28$

51. $3x + 9 = y$

52. $2y - 7 = x$

53. $y = 4$ **54.** $x = 7$

55. $f(x) = 7x$ **56.** $f(x) = \dfrac{1}{7}x$

57. $6 + y = 0$ **58.** $x - 7 = 0$

59. $2 - x = 3$ **60.** $2y + 4 = -7$

Decide whether the lines are parallel, perpendicular, or neither. See Example 8.

61. $y = 12x + 6$ **62.** $y = 5x + 8$
    $y = 12x - 2$ $y = 5x - 8$

▶ **63.** $y = -9x + 3$ **64.** $y = 2x - 12$
    $y = \dfrac{3}{2}x - 7$ $y = \dfrac{1}{2}x - 6$

65. $f(x) = -3x + 6$ **66.** $f(x) = 7x - 6$
    $g(x) = \dfrac{1}{3}x + 5$ $g(x) = -\dfrac{1}{7}x + 2$

67. $-4x + 2y = 5$ **68.** $-8x + 20y = 7$
    $2x - y = 7$ $2x - 5y = 0$

69. $-2x + 3y = 1$ **70.** $2x - y = -10$
    $3x + 2y = 12$ $2x + 4y = 2$

Use the points shown on the graphs to determine the slope of each line. See Examples 1 and 2.

71.

72.

73.

74.

Find each slope. See Examples 1 and 2.

75. Find the pitch, or slope, of the roof shown.

76. Upon takeoff, a Delta Airlines jet climbs to 3 miles as it passes over 25 miles of land below it. Find the slope of its climb.

77. Driving down Bald Mountain in Wyoming, Bob Dean finds that he descends 1600 feet in elevation by the time he is 2.5 miles (horizontally) away from the high point on the mountain road. Find the slope of his descent rounded to two decimal places (1 mile = 5280 feet).

78. Find the grade, or slope, of the road shown.

Solve. See Example 5.

79. The life expectancy at birth y for females born in the United States is given by the equation $y = 0.15x + 71.5$, where x is the number of years after 1950. (*Source:* National Center for Health Statistics)

   a. Find the life expectancy for an American female born in 1990.

   b. Find and interpret the slope of the equation.

   c. Find and interpret the y-intercept of the equation.

80. The number of women completing bachelor degrees surpassed the number of men completing bachelor degrees in 1982. The number of women completing bachelor degrees (in thousands) is given by the equation $y = 23.3x + 708.7$, where x is the number of years since 2000. (*Source:* National Center for Educational Statistics)

   a. Find the number of women completing bachelor degrees in 2015.

   b. Find and interpret the slope of the equation.

   c. Find and interpret the y-intercept of the equation.

81. One of the top 10 occupations in terms of job growth in the next few years is expected to be registered nurses. The number of people, y, in thousands, employed as registered nurses in the United States can be estimated by the linear equation $527x - 10y = -27,110$, where x is the number of years after 2012. (*Source:* Based on data from the U.S. Bureau of Labor Statistics)

   a. Find the slope and the y-intercept of the linear equation.

   b. What does the slope mean in this context?

   c. What does the y-intercept mean in this context?

82. One of the fastest growing occupations over the next few years is expected to be interpreters or translators. The number of people, y, in thousands, employed as interpreters or translators in the United States can be estimated by the linear equation $293x - 100y = -6360$, where x is the number of years after 2012. (*Source:* Based on data from the U.S. Bureau of Labor Statistics)

   a. Find the slope and the y-intercept of the linear equation.
   b. What does the slope mean in this context?
   c. What does the y-intercept mean in this context?

83. The Converse Company (maker of the famous Chuck Taylors) almost went bankrupt when they tried to enter the competitive, high-cost athletic shoe market. They regrouped, and went back to their roots, creating their All-Star shoes for the casual market. The equation $y = 0.18x + 0.95$ approximates their annual sales y (in billions of dollars) where x is the number of years since 2010. (*Source:* Converse)

   a. Use this equation to estimate the annual sales of Converse in 2014.
   b. Use this equation to predict in what year the annual sales of Converse will be above \$2 billion. (*Hint:* Let $y = 2$ and solve for x.)
   c. Use this equation to estimate the annual sales for Converse in the current year.

84. The number of U.S. and Canadian admissions y (in billions) to movie theaters can be estimated by the linear equation $y = -0.014x + 1.38$, where x is the number of years after 2009. (*Source:* Motion Picture Association of America)

   a. Use this equation to estimate the number of movie admissions in the United States and Canada in 2011. Round to the nearest hundredth of a billion.
   b. Use this equation to predict in what year the number of movie admissions in the United States and Canada will be below 1.25 billion. (*Hint:* Let $y = 1.25$ and solve for x.)
   c. Use this equation to estimate the number of movie admissions in the present year. Do you go to the movies? Do your friends?

REVIEW AND PREVIEW

Simplify and solve for y. See Section 2.3.

85. $y - 2 = 5(x + 6)$ **86.** $y - 0 = -3[x - (-10)]$

87. $y - (-1) = 2(x - 0)$ **88.** $y - 9 = -8[x - (-4)]$

CONCEPT EXTENSIONS

Each slope calculation is incorrect. Find the error and correct the calculation. See the second Concept Check in this section.

89. $(-2, 6)$ and $(7, -14)$

$$m = \frac{-14 - 6}{7 - 2} = \frac{-20}{5} = -4$$

90. $(-1, 4)$ and $(-3, 9)$

$$m = \frac{9 - 4}{-3 - 1} = \frac{5}{-4} \text{ or } -\frac{5}{4}$$

91. $(-8, -10)$ and $(-11, -5)$

$$m = \frac{-10 - 5}{-8 - 11} = \frac{-15}{-19} = \frac{15}{19}$$

92. $(0, -4)$ and $(-6, -6)$

$$m = \frac{0 - (-6)}{-4 - (-6)} = \frac{6}{2} = 3$$

93. Find the slope of a line parallel to the line $f(x) = -\dfrac{7}{2}x - 6$.

94. Find the slope of a line parallel to the line $f(x) = x$.

95. Find the slope of a line perpendicular to the line
$$f(x) = -\frac{7}{2}x - 6.$$

96. Find the slope of a line perpendicular to the line $f(x) = x$.

97. Find the slope of a line parallel to the line $5x - 2y = 6$.

98. Find the slope of a line parallel to the line $-3x + 4y = 10$.

99. Find the slope of a line perpendicular to the line $5x - 2y = 6$.

100. Find the slope of a line perpendicular to the line $-3x + 4y = 10$.

Each line below has negative slope.

101. Find the slope of each line.

102. Use the result of Exercise 101 to fill in the blank. For lines with negative slopes, the steeper line has the _____ (greater/lesser) slope.

The following graph shows the altitude of a seagull in flight over a time period of 30 seconds.

103. Find the coordinates of point B.

104. Find the coordinates of point C.

105. Find the rate of change of altitude between points B and C. (Recall that the rate of change between points is the slope between points. This rate of change will be in yards per second.)

106. Find the rate of change of altitude (in yards per second) between points F and G.

107. Explain how merely looking at a line can tell us whether its slope is negative, positive, undefined, or zero.

108. Explain why the graph of $y = b$ is a horizontal line.

109. Explain whether two lines, both with positive slopes, can be perpendicular.

110. Explain why it is reasonable that nonvertical parallel lines have the same slope.

111. Professional plumbers suggest that a sewer pipe should be sloped 0.25 inch for every foot. Find the recommended slope for a sewer pipe. (*Source: Rules of Thumb* by Tom Parker, Houghton Mifflin Company)

112. a. On a single screen, graph $y = \frac{1}{2}x + 1$, $y = x + 1$, and $y = 2x + 1$. Notice the change in slope for each graph.

b. On a single screen, graph $y = -\frac{1}{2}x + 1$, $y = -x + 1$, and $y = -2x + 1$. Notice the change in slope for each graph.

c. Determine whether the following statement is true or false for slope m of a given line. As $|m|$ becomes greater, the line becomes steeper.

113. Support the result of Exercise 67 by graphing the pair of equations on a graphing calculator.

114. Support the result of Exercise 70 by graphing the pair of equations on a graphing calculator. (*Hint:* Use the window showing $[-15, 15]$ on the x-axis and $[-10, 10]$ on the y-axis.)

3.5 Equations of Lines

OBJECTIVES

1. Graph a Line Using Its Slope and y-Intercept.
2. Use the Slope–Intercept Form to Write the Equation of a Line.
3. Use the Point–Slope Form to Write the Equation of a Line.
4. Write Equations of Vertical and Horizontal Lines.
5. Find Equations of Parallel and Perpendicular Lines.

OBJECTIVE

1 Graphing a Line Using Its Slope and y-Intercept

In the last section, we learned that the slope–intercept form of a linear equation is $y = mx + b$. Recall that when an equation is written in this form, the slope of the line is the same as the coefficient m of x. Also, the y-intercept of the line is $(0, b)$. For example, the slope of the line defined by $y = 2x + 3$ is 2 and its y-intercept is $(0, 3)$.

We may also use the slope–intercept form to graph a linear equation.

EXAMPLE 1 Graph $y = \frac{1}{4}x - 3$.

Solution Recall that the slope of the graph of $y = \frac{1}{4}x - 3$ is $\frac{1}{4}$ and the y-intercept is $(0, -3)$. To graph the line, we first plot the y-intercept $(0, -3)$. To find another point on the line, we recall that slope is $\frac{\text{rise}}{\text{run}} = \frac{1}{4}$. Another point may then be plotted by starting at $(0, -3)$, rising 1 unit up, and then running 4 units to the right. We are now at the point $(4, -2)$. The graph is the line through these two points.

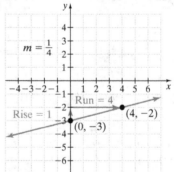

Notice that the line does have a y-intercept of $(0, -3)$ and a slope of $\frac{1}{4}$.

PRACTICE 1 Graph $y = \frac{3}{4}x + 2$.

EXAMPLE 2 Graph $2x + 3y = 12$.

Solution First, we solve the equation for y to write it in slope–intercept form. In slope–intercept form, the equation is $y = -\frac{2}{3}x + 4$. Next we plot the y-intercept $(0, 4)$. To find another point on the line, we use the slope $-\frac{2}{3}$, which can be written as $\frac{\text{rise}}{\text{run}} = \frac{-2}{3}$. We start at $(0, 4)$ and move down 2 units since the numerator of the slope is -2;

then we move 3 units to the right since the denominator of the slope is 3. We arrive at the point $(3, 2)$. The line through these points is the graph, shown below to the left.

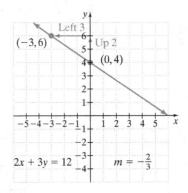

The slope $-\dfrac{2}{3}$ can also be written as $\dfrac{2}{-3}$, so to find another point, we could start at $(0, 4)$ and move up 2 units and then 3 units to the left. We would arrive at the point $(-3, 6)$. The line through $(-3, 6)$ and $(0, 4)$ is the same line as shown previously through $(3, 2)$ and $(0, 4)$. See the graph above to the right.   □

PRACTICE

2   Graph $x + 2y = 6$.   ■

OBJECTIVE

2   Using Slope–Intercept Form to Write Equations of Lines   ▶

We may also use the slope–intercept form to write the equation of a line given its slope and y-intercept. The equation of a line is a linear equation in two variables that, if graphed, would produce the line described.

EXAMPLE 3   Write an equation of the line with y-intercept $(0, -3)$ and a slope of $\dfrac{1}{4}$.

Solution We want to write a linear equation in two variables that describes the line with y-intercept $(0, -3)$ and has a slope of $\dfrac{1}{4}$. We are given the slope and the y-intercept. Let $m = \dfrac{1}{4}$ and $b = -3$ and write the equation in slope–intercept form, $y = mx + b$.

$$y = mx + b$$
$$y = \frac{1}{4}x + (-3) \quad \text{Let } m = \frac{1}{4} \text{ and } b = -3.$$
$$y = \frac{1}{4}x - 3 \qquad \text{Simplify.} \qquad □$$

PRACTICE

3   Write an equation of the line with y-intercept $(0, 4)$ and a slope of $-\dfrac{3}{4}$.   ■

✔ **CONCEPT CHECK**

What is wrong with the following equation of a line with y-intercept $(0, 4)$ and slope 2?

$$y = 4x + 2$$

Answer to Concept Check:
y-intercept and slope were switched, should be $y = 2x + 4$

OBJECTIVE

3 Using Point–Slope Form to Write Equations of Lines

When the slope of a line and a point on the line are known, the equation of the line can also be found. To do this, use the slope formula to write the slope of a line that passes through points (x_1, y_1) and (x, y). We have

$$m = \frac{y - y_1}{x - x_1}$$

Multiply both sides of this equation by $x - x_1$ to obtain

$$y - y_1 = m(x - x_1)$$

This form is called the **point–slope form** of the equation of a line.

> **Point–Slope Form of the Equation of a Line**
>
> The **point–slope form** of the equation of a line is
>
> $$\overset{\text{slope}}{\underset{\text{point}}{y - y_1 = m(x - x_1)}}$$
>
> where m is the slope of the line and (x_1, y_1) is a point on the line.

EXAMPLE 4 Find an equation of the line with slope -3 containing the point $(1, -5)$. Write the equation in slope–intercept form $y = mx + b$.

Solution Because we know the slope and a point of the line, we use the point–slope form with $m = -3$ and $(x_1, y_1) = (1, -5)$.

$$
\begin{aligned}
y - y_1 &= m(x - x_1) && \text{Point–slope form} \\
y - (-5) &= -3(x - 1) && \text{Let } m = -3 \text{ and } (x_1, y_1) = (1, -5). \\
y + 5 &= -3x + 3 && \text{Apply the distributive property.} \\
y &= -3x - 2 && \text{Write in slope–intercept form.}
\end{aligned}
$$

In slope–intercept form, the equation is $y = -3x - 2$. □

PRACTICE

4 Find an equation of the line with slope -4 containing the point $(-2, 5)$. Write the equation in slope–intercept form $y = mx + b$. ∎

> **Helpful Hint**
>
> Remember, "slope–intercept form" means the equation is "solved for y."

EXAMPLE 5 Find an equation of the line through points $(4, 0)$ and $(-4, -5)$. Write the equation using function notation.

Solution First, find the slope of the line.

$$m = \frac{-5 - 0}{-4 - 4} = \frac{-5}{-8} = \frac{5}{8}$$

Next, use the point–slope form. Replace (x_1, y_1) by either $(4, 0)$ or $(-4, -5)$ in the point–slope equation. We will choose the point $(4, 0)$. The line through $(4, 0)$ with slope $\frac{5}{8}$ is

$$
\begin{aligned}
y - y_1 &= m(x - x_1) && \text{Point–slope form.} \\
y - 0 &= \frac{5}{8}(x - 4) && \text{Let } m = \frac{5}{8} \text{ and } (x_1, y_1) = (4, 0). \\
8y &= 5(x - 4) && \text{Multiply both sides by 8.} \\
8y &= 5x - 20 && \text{Apply the distributive property.}
\end{aligned}
$$

To write the equation using function notation, we solve for y, then replace y with $f(x)$.

$$8y = 5x - 20$$

$$y = \frac{5}{8}x - \frac{20}{8} \quad \text{Divide both sides by 8.}$$

$$f(x) = \frac{5}{8}x - \frac{5}{2} \quad \text{Write using function notation.} \qquad \square$$

PRACTICE
5   Find an equation of the line through points $(-1, 2)$ and $(2, 0)$. Write the equation using function notation. ▪

> **Helpful Hint**
>
> If two points of a line are given, either one may be used with the point–slope form to write an equation of the line.

EXAMPLE 6   Find an equation of the line graphed. Write the equation in standard form.

<u>Solution</u> First, find the slope of the line by identifying the coordinates of the noted points on the graph.

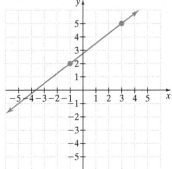

The points have coordinates $(-1, 2)$ and $(3, 5)$.

$$m = \frac{5 - 2}{3 - (-1)} = \frac{3}{4}$$

Next, use the point–slope form. We will choose $(3, 5)$ for (x_1, y_1), although it makes no difference which point we choose. The line through $(3, 5)$ with slope $\frac{3}{4}$ is

$$y - y_1 = m(x - x_1) \quad \text{Point–slope form}$$

$$y - 5 = \frac{3}{4}(x - 3) \quad \text{Let } m = \frac{3}{4} \text{ and } (x_1, y_1) = (3, 5).$$

$$4(y - 5) = 3(x - 3) \quad \text{Multiply both sides by 4.}$$

$$4y - 20 = 3x - 9 \quad \text{Apply the distributive property.}$$

To write the equation in standard form, move x- and y-terms to one side of the equation and any numbers (constants) to the other side.

$$4y - 20 = 3x - 9$$

$$-3x + 4y = 11 \quad \text{Subtract } 3x \text{ from both sides and add 20 to both sides.}$$

The equation of the graphed line is $-3x + 4y = 11$. $\qquad \square$

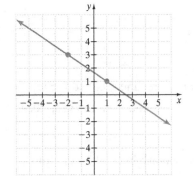

PRACTICE
6   Find an equation of the line graphed in the margin. Write the equation in standard form. ▪

The point–slope form of an equation is very useful for solving real-world problems.

EXAMPLE 7   **Predicting Sales**

Southern Star Realty is an established real estate company that has enjoyed constant growth in sales since 2008. In 2010, the company sold 200 houses, and in 2015, the company sold 275 houses. Use these figures to predict the number of houses this company will sell in the year 2024.

Solution

1. UNDERSTAND. Read and reread the problem. Then let

x = the number of years after 2008 and

y = the number of houses sold in the year corresponding to x.

The information provided then gives the ordered pairs $(2, 200)$ and $(7, 275)$. To better visualize the sales of Southern Star Realty, we graph the linear equation that passes through the points $(2, 200)$ and $(7, 275)$.

2. TRANSLATE. We write a linear equation that passes through the points $(2, 200)$ and $(7, 275)$. To do so, we first find the slope of the line.

$$m = \frac{275 - 200}{7 - 2} = \frac{75}{5} = 15$$

Then, using the point–slope form and the point $(2, 200)$ to write the equation, we have

$$y - y_1 = m(x - x_1)$$
$$y - 200 = 15(x - 2) \quad \text{Let } m = 15 \text{ and } (x_1, y_1) = (2, 200).$$
$$y - 200 = 15x - 30 \quad \text{Multiply.}$$
$$y = 15x + 170 \quad \text{Add 200 to both sides.}$$

3. SOLVE. To predict the number of houses sold in the year 2024, we use $y = 15x + 170$ and complete the ordered pair $(16, \ )$, since $2024 - 2008 = 16$.

$$y = 15(16) + 170 \quad \text{Let } x = 16.$$
$$y = 410$$

4. INTERPRET.

Check: Verify that the point $(16, 410)$ is a point on the line graphed in Step 1.

State: Southern Star Realty should expect to sell 410 houses in the year 2024.

□

PRACTICE

7 The Las Vegas area was hit hard after the housing crash in 2009. In the fourth quarter of 2009, there were 15,710 home sales, and in the fourth quarter of 2014, there were 12,680 home sales. Use these figures to predict the number of home sales in the fourth quarter of 2020. Round to the nearest whole number.

OBJECTIVE

4 Writing Equations of Vertical and Horizontal Lines

Two special types of linear equations are linear equations whose graphs are either vertical or horizontal lines.

EXAMPLE 8 Find an equation of the horizontal line containing the point (2, 3).

Solution Recall that a horizontal line has an equation of the form $y = b$. Since the line contains the point (2, 3), the equation is $y = 3$, as shown to the right.

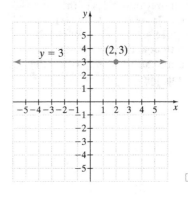

PRACTICE
8 Find the equation of the horizontal line containing the point $(6, -2)$.

EXAMPLE 9 Find an equation of the line containing the point (2, 3) with undefined slope.

Solution Since the line has undefined slope, the line must be vertical. A vertical line has an equation of the form $x = c$. Since the line contains the point (2, 3), the equation is $x = 2$, as shown to the right.

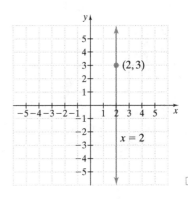

PRACTICE
9 Find an equation of the line containing the point $(6, -2)$ with undefined slope.

OBJECTIVE
5 Finding Equations of Parallel and Perpendicular Lines

Next, we find equations of parallel and perpendicular lines.

  EXAMPLE 10 Find an equation of the line containing the point (4, 4) and parallel to the line $2x + 3y = -6$. Write the equation in standard form.

Solution Because the line we want to find is *parallel* to the line $2x + 3y = -6$, the two lines must have equal slopes. Find the slope of $2x + 3y = -6$ by writing it in the form $y = mx + b$. In other words, solve the equation for y.

$$2x + 3y = -6$$
$$3y = -2x - 6 \quad \text{Subtract } 2x \text{ from both sides.}$$
$$y = \frac{-2x}{3} - \frac{6}{3} \quad \text{Divide by 3.}$$
$$y = -\frac{2}{3}x - 2 \quad \text{Write in slope–intercept form.}$$

The slope of this line is $-\frac{2}{3}$. Thus, a line parallel to this line will also have a slope of $-\frac{2}{3}$.

The equation we are asked to find describes a line containing the point (4, 4) with a slope of $-\frac{2}{3}$. We use the point–slope form.

$$y - y_1 = m(x - x_1)$$
$$y - 4 = -\frac{2}{3}(x - 4) \quad \text{Let } m = -\frac{2}{3}, x_1 = 4, \text{ and } y_1 = 4.$$
$$3(y - 4) = -2(x - 4) \quad \text{Multiply both sides by 3.}$$
$$3y - 12 = -2x + 8 \quad \text{Apply the distributive property.}$$
$$2x + 3y = 20 \quad \text{Write in standard form.} \qquad \square$$

PRACTICE

10 Find an equation of the line containing the point $(8, -3)$ and parallel to the line $3x + 4y = 1$. Write the equation in standard form. ■

EXAMPLE 11 Write a function that describes the line containing the point $(4, 4)$ that is perpendicular to the line $2x + 3y = -6$.

Solution In the previous example, we found that the slope of the line $2x + 3y = -6$ is $-\frac{2}{3}$. A line perpendicular to this line will have a slope that is the negative reciprocal of $-\frac{2}{3}$, or $\frac{3}{2}$. From the point–slope equation, we have

$$y - y_1 = m(x - x_1)$$
$$y - 4 = \frac{3}{2}(x - 4) \quad \text{Let } x_1 = 4, y_1 = 4, \text{ and } m = \frac{3}{2}.$$
$$2(y - 4) = 3(x - 4) \quad \text{Multiply both sides by 2.}$$
$$2y - 8 = 3x - 12 \quad \text{Apply the distributive property.}$$
$$2y = 3x - 4 \quad \text{Add 8 to both sides.}$$
$$y = \frac{3}{2}x - 2 \quad \text{Divide both sides by 2.}$$
$$f(x) = \frac{3}{2}x - 2 \quad \text{Write using function notation.} \qquad \square$$

PRACTICE

11 Write a function that describes the line containing the point $(8, -3)$ that is perpendicular to the line $3x + 4y = 1$. ■

Forms of Linear Equations

$Ax + By = C$	**Standard form** of a linear equation A and B are not both 0.
$y = mx + b$	**Slope–intercept form** of a linear equation The slope is m, and the y-intercept is $(0, b)$.
$y - y_1 = m(x - x_1)$	**Point–slope form** of a linear equation The slope is m, and (x_1, y_1) is a point on the line.
$y = c$	**Horizontal line** The slope is 0, and the y-intercept is $(0, c)$.
$x = c$	**Vertical line** The slope is undefined, and the x-intercept is $(c, 0)$.

Parallel and Perpendicular Lines

Nonvertical parallel lines have the same slope. The product of the slopes of two nonvertical perpendicular lines is -1.

✔ Vocabulary, Readiness & Video Check

State the slope and the y-intercept of each line with the given equation.

1. $y = -4x + 12$

2. $y = \frac{2}{3}x - \frac{7}{2}$

3. $y = 5x$

4. $y = -x$

5. $y = \frac{1}{2}x + 6$

6. $y = -\frac{2}{3}x + 5$

Decide whether the lines are parallel, perpendicular, or neither.

7. $y = 12x + 6$
   $y = 12x - 2$

8. $y = -5x + 8$
   $y = -5x - 8$

9. $y = -9x + 3$
   $y = \frac{3}{2}x - 7$

10. $y = 2x - 12$
   $y = \frac{1}{2}x - 6$

Martin-Gay Interactive Videos

See Video 3.5 🔘

Watch the section lecture video and answer the following questions.

OBJECTIVE 1

11. Complete these statements based on ⊞ Example 1. To graph a line using its slope and y-intercept, first write the equation in _____ form. Graph the one point you now know, the _____. Use the _____ to find a second point.

OBJECTIVE 2

12. From ⊞ Example 2, given a y-intercept point, how do you know which value to use for *b* in the slope–intercept form?

OBJECTIVE 3

13. ⊞ Example 4 discusses how to find an equation of a line given two points. Under what circumstances might the slope–intercept form be chosen over the point–slope form to find an equation?

OBJECTIVE 4

14. Solve ⊞ Examples 5 and 6 again, this time using the point $(-1, 3)$ in each exercise.

OBJECTIVE 5

15. Solve ⊞ Example 7 again, this time writing the equation of the line in function notation, *parallel* to the given line through the given point.

3.5   Exercise Set   MyMathLab® ▸

Graph each linear equation. See Examples 1 and 2.

1. $y = 5x - 2$

2. $y = 2x + 1$

▸ **3.** $4x + y = 7$

4. $3x + y = 9$

5. $-3x + 2y = 3$

6. $-2x + 5y = -16$

Use the slope–intercept form of a linear equation to write an equation of each line with the given slope and y-intercept. See Example 3.

▸ **7.** Slope -1; y-intercept $(0, 1)$

8. Slope $\frac{1}{2}$; y-intercept $(0, -6)$

9. Slope 2; y-intercept $\left(0, \frac{3}{4}\right)$

10. Slope -3; y-intercept $\left(0, -\frac{1}{5}\right)$

11. Slope $\frac{2}{7}$; y-intercept $(0, 0)$

12. Slope $-\frac{4}{5}$; y-intercept $(0, 0)$

Find an equation of the line with the given slope and containing the given point. Write the equation in slope–intercept form. See Example 4.

▸ **13.** Slope 3; through $(1, 2)$

14. Slope 4; through $(5, 1)$

15. Slope -2; through $(1, -3)$

16. Slope -4; through $(2, -4)$

17. Slope $\frac{1}{2}$; through $(-6, 2)$

18. Slope $\frac{2}{3}$; through $(-9, 4)$

19. Slope $-\frac{9}{10}$; through $(-3, 0)$

20. Slope $-\frac{1}{5}$; through $(4, -6)$

Find an equation of the line passing through the given points. Use function notation to write the equation. See Example 5.

21. $(2, 0), (4, 6)$

22. $(3, 0), (7, 8)$

23. $(-2, 5), (-6, 13)$

24. $(7, -4), (2, 6)$

25. $(-2, -4), (-4, -3)$

26. $(-9, -2), (-3, 10)$

▶ **27.** $(-3, -8), (-6, -9)$

28. $(8, -3), (4, -8)$

29. $\left(\frac{3}{5}, \frac{2}{5}\right)$ and $\left(-\frac{1}{5}, \frac{7}{10}\right)$

30. $\left(\frac{1}{2}, -\frac{1}{4}\right)$ and $\left(\frac{3}{2}, \frac{3}{4}\right)$

Find an equation of each line graphed. Write the equation in standard form. See Example 6.

31.

32.

33.

34.

Use the graph of the following function $f(x)$ to find each value.

35. $f(0)$

36. $f(-1)$

37. $f(2)$

38. $f(1)$

39. Find x such that $f(x) = -6$.

40. Find x such that $f(x) = 4$.

Write an equation of each line. See Examples 8 and 9.

▶ **41.** Slope 0; through $(-2, -4)$

42. Horizontal; through $(-3, 1)$

▶ **43.** Vertical; through $(4, 7)$

44. Vertical; through $(2, 6)$

45. Horizontal; through $(0, 5)$

46. Undefined slope; through $(0, 5)$

△ *Find an equation of each line. Write the equation using function notation. See Examples 10 and 11.*

47. Through $(3, 8)$; parallel to $f(x) = 4x - 2$

48. Through $(1, 5)$; parallel to $f(x) = 3x - 4$

▶ **49.** Through $(2, -5)$; perpendicular to $3y = x - 6$

50. Through $(-4, 8)$; perpendicular to $2x - 3y = 1$

51. Through $(-2, -3)$; parallel to $3x + 2y = 5$

52. Through $(-2, -3)$; perpendicular to $3x + 2y = 5$

MIXED PRACTICE

Find the equation of each line. Write the equation in standard form unless indicated otherwise. See Examples 3 through 5, and 8 through 11.

53. Slope 2; through $(-2, 3)$

54. Slope 3; through $(-4, 2)$

55. Through $(1, 6)$ and $(5, 2)$; use function notation.

56. Through $(2, 9)$ and $(8, 6)$

57. With slope $-\frac{1}{2}$; y-intercept 11

58. With slope -4; y-intercept $\frac{2}{9}$; use function notation.

59. Through $(-7, -4)$ and $(0, -6)$

60. Through $(2, -8)$ and $(-4, -3)$

61. Slope $-\frac{4}{3}$; through $(-5, 0)$

62. Slope $-\frac{3}{5}$; through $(4, -1)$

63. Vertical line; through $(-2, -10)$

64. Horizontal line; through $(1, 0)$

△ **65.** Through $(6, -2)$; parallel to the line $2x + 4y = 9$

△ **66.** Through $(8, -3)$; parallel to the line $6x + 2y = 5$

67. Slope 0; through $(-9, 12)$

68. Undefined slope; through $(10, -8)$

△ **69.** Through $(6, 1)$; parallel to the line $8x - y = 9$

△ **70.** Through $(3, 5)$; perpendicular to the line $2x - y = 8$

△ **71.** Through $(5, -6)$; perpendicular to $y = 9$

△ **72.** Through $(-3, -5)$; parallel to $y = 9$

73. Through $(2, -8)$ and $(-6, -5)$; use function notation.

74. Through $(-4, -2)$ and $(-6, 5)$; use function notation.

Solve. See Example 7.

75. A rock is dropped from the top of a 400-foot building. After 1 second, the rock is traveling 32 feet per second. After 3 seconds, the rock is traveling 96 feet per second. Let *y* be the rate of descent and *x* be the number of seconds since the rock was dropped.

  a. Write a linear equation that relates time *x* to rate *y*. [*Hint:* Use the ordered pairs (1, 32) and (3, 96).]

  b. Use this equation to determine the rate of travel of the rock 4 seconds after it was dropped.

76. A fruit company recently released a new applesauce. By the end of its first year, profits on this product amounted to $30,000. The anticipated profit for the end of the fourth year is $66,000. The ratio of change in time to change in profit is constant. Let *x* be years and *y* be profit.

  a. Write a linear equation that relates profit and time. [*Hint:* Use the ordered pairs (1, 30,000) and (4, 66,000).]

  b. Use this equation to predict the company's profit at the end of the seventh year.

  c. Predict when the profit should reach $126,000.

77. The Whammo Company has learned that by pricing a newly released Frisbee at $6, sales will reach 2000 per day. Raising the price to $8 will cause the sales to fall to 1500 per day. Assume that the ratio of change in price to change in daily sales is constant and let *x* be the price of the Frisbee and *y* be number of sales.

  a. Find the linear equation that models the price–sales relationship for this Frisbee. [*Hint:* The line must pass through (6, 2000) and (8, 1500).]

  b. Use this equation to predict the daily sales of Frisbees if the price is set at $7.50.

78. The Pool Fun Company has learned that, by pricing a newly released Fun Noodle at $3, sales will reach 10,000 Fun Noodles per day during the summer. Raising the price to $5 will cause the sales to fall to 8000 Fun Noodles per day. Let *x* be price and *y* be the number sold.

  a. Assume that the relationship between sales price and number of Fun Noodles sold is linear and write an equation describing this relationship. [*Hint:* The line must pass through (3, 10,000) and (5, 8000).]

  b. Use this equation to predict the daily sales of Fun Noodles if the price is $3.50.

79. The number of people employed in the United States as registered nurses was 2711 thousand in 2012. By 2022, this number is expected to rise to 3238 thousand. Let *y* be the number of registered nurses (in thousands) employed in the United States in the year *x*, where *x* = 0 represents 2012. (*Source:* U.S. Bureau of Labor Statistics)

  a. Write a linear equation that models the number of people (in thousands) employed as registered nurses in year *x*.

  b. Use this equation to estimate the number of people employed as registered nurses in 2017.

80. In 2010, IBM had 426,750 employees worldwide. By 2014, this number had increased to 431,200. Let *y* be the number of IBM employees worldwide in the year *x*, where *x* = 0 represents 2010. (*Source:* IBM Corporation)

  a. Write a linear equation that models the growth in the number of IBM employees worldwide, in terms of the year *x*.

  b. Use this equation to predict the number of IBM employees worldwide in 2018.

81. In 2014, the average price of a new home sold in the United States was $342,800. In 2009, the average price of a new home in the United States was $268,200. Let *y* be the average price of a new home in the year *x*, where *x* = 0 represents the year 2009. (*Source:* Based on data from U.S. census)

  a. Write a linear equation that models the average price of a new home in terms of the year *x*. [*Hint:* The line must pass through the points (0, 268,200) and (5, 342,800).]

  b. Use this equation to predict the average price of a new home in 2018.

82. The number of McDonald's restaurants worldwide in 2014 was 36,258. In 2009, there were 32,478 McDonald's restaurants worldwide. Let *y* be the number of McDonald's restaurants in the year *x*, where *x* = 0 represents the year 2009. (*Source:* McDonald's Corporation)

  a. Write a linear equation that models the growth in the number of McDonald's restaurants worldwide in terms of the year *x*. [*Hint:* The line must pass through the points (0, 32,478) and (5, 36,258).]

  b. Use this equation to predict the number of McDonald's restaurants worldwide in 2018.

REVIEW AND PREVIEW

Solve. Write the solution in interval notation. See Section 2.4.

83. $2x - 7 \le 21$

84. $-3x + 1 > 0$

85. $5(x - 2) \ge 3(x - 1)$

86. $-2(x + 1) \le -x + 10$

87. $\dfrac{x}{2} + \dfrac{1}{4} < \dfrac{1}{8}$

88. $\dfrac{x}{5} - \dfrac{3}{10} \ge \dfrac{x}{2} - 1$

CONCEPT EXTENSIONS

Answer true or false.

89. A vertical line is always perpendicular to a horizontal line.

90. A vertical line is always parallel to a vertical line.

Example

Find an equation of the perpendicular bisector of the line segment whose endpoints are (2, 6) and (0, −2).

Solution:

A perpendicular bisector is a line that contains the midpoint of the given segment and is perpendicular to the segment.

Step 1. The midpoint of the segment with endpoints $(2, 6)$ and $(0, -2)$ is $(1, 2)$.

Step 2. The slope of the segment containing points $(2, 6)$ and $(0, -2)$ is 4.

Step 3. A line perpendicular to this line segment will have slope of $-\frac{1}{4}$.

Step 4. The equation of the line through the midpoint $(1, 2)$ with a slope of $-\frac{1}{4}$ will be the equation of the perpendicular bisector. This equation in standard form is $x + 4y = 9$.

Find an equation of the perpendicular bisector of the line segment whose endpoints are given. See the previous example.

91. $(3, -1); (-5, 1)$

92. $(-6, -3); (-8, -1)$

93. $(-2, 6); (-22, -4)$

94. $(5, 8); (7, 2)$

95. $(2, 3); (-4, 7)$

96. $(-6, 8); (-4, -2)$

97. Describe how to see if the graph of $2x - 4y = 7$ passes through the points $(1.4, -1.05)$ and $(0, -1.75)$. Then follow your directions and check these points.

Use a graphing calculator with a TRACE feature to see the results of each exercise.

98. Exercise 56; graph the equation and verify that it passes through $(2, 9)$ and $(8, 6)$.

99. Exercise 55; graph the function and verify that it passes through $(1, 6)$ and $(5, 2)$.

100. Exercise 62; graph the equation. See that it has a negative slope and passes through $(4, -1)$.

101. Exercise 61; graph the equation. See that it has a negative slope and passes through $(-5, 0)$.

102. Exercise 48: Graph the equation and verify that it passes through $(1, 5)$ and is parallel to $y = 3x - 4$.

103. Exercise 47: Graph the equation and verify that it passes through $(3, 8)$ and is parallel to $y = 4x - 2$.

Integrated Review Linear Equations in Two Variables

Sections 3.1–3.5

Below is a review of equations of lines.

Forms of Linear Equations

$Ax + By = C$	**Standard form** of a linear equation. A and B are not both 0.
$y = mx + b$	**Slope–intercept form** of a linear equation. The slope is m, and the y-intercept is $(0, b)$.
$y - y_1 = m(x - x_1)$	**Point–slope form** of a linear equation. The slope is m, and (x_1, y_1) is a point on the line.
$y = c$	**Horizontal line** The slope is 0, and the y-intercept is $(0, c)$.
$x = c$	**Vertical line** The slope is undefined and the x-intercept is $(c, 0)$.

Parallel and Perpendicular Lines

Nonvertical parallel lines have the same slope. The product of the slopes of two nonvertical perpendicular lines is -1.

Graph each linear equation.

1. $y = -2x$ **2.** $3x - 2y = 6$

3. $x = -3$ **4.** $y = 1.5$

Find the slope of the line containing each pair of points.

5. $(-2, -5), (3, -5)$ **6.** $(5, 2), (0, 5)$

Find the slope and y-intercept of each line.

7. $y = 3x - 5$ **8.** $5x - 2y = 7$

Determine whether each pair of lines is parallel, perpendicular, or neither.

9. $y = 8x - 6$
$y = 8x + 6$

10. $y = \frac{2}{3}x + 1$
$2y + 3x = 1$

Find an equation of each line. Write the equation in the form $x = a$, $y = b$, or $y = mx + b$. For Exercises 14 through 17, write the equation in the form $f(x) = mx + b$.

11. Through $(1, 6)$ and $(5, 2)$

12. Vertical line; through $(-2, -10)$

13. Horizontal line; through $(1, 0)$

14. Through $(2, -9)$ and $(-6, -5)$

15. Through $(-2, 4)$ with slope -5

16. Slope -4; y-intercept $\left(0, \dfrac{1}{3}\right)$

17. Slope $\dfrac{1}{2}$; y-intercept $(0, -1)$

18. Through $\left(\dfrac{1}{2}, 0\right)$ with slope 3

19. Through $(-1, -5)$; parallel to $3x - y = 5$

20. Through $(0, 4)$; perpendicular to $4x - 5y = 10$

21. Through $(2, -3)$; perpendicular to $4x + y = \dfrac{2}{3}$

22. Through $(-1, 0)$; parallel to $5x + 2y = 2$

23. Undefined slope; through $(-1, 3)$

24. $m = 0$; through $(-1, 3)$

3.6 Graphing Piecewise-Defined Functions and Shifting and Reflecting Graphs of Functions

OBJECTIVES

1 Graph Piecewise-Defined Functions.

2 Vertical and Horizontal Shifts.

3 Reflect Graphs.

OBJECTIVE

1   Graphing Piecewise-Defined Functions

Throughout Chapter 3, we have graphed functions. There are many special functions. In this objective, we study functions defined by two or more expressions. The expression used to complete the function varies with and depends upon the value of x. Before we actually graph these piecewise-defined functions, let's practice finding function values.

EXAMPLE 1   Evaluate $f(2)$, $f(-6)$, and $f(0)$ for the function

$$f(x) = \begin{cases} 2x + 3 & \text{if } x \le 0 \\ -x - 1 & \text{if } x > 0 \end{cases}$$

Then write your results in ordered pair form.

<u>Solution</u> Take a moment and study this function. It is a single function defined by two expressions depending on the value of x. From above, if $x \le 0$, use $f(x) = 2x + 3$. If $x > 0$, use $f(x) = -x - 1$. Thus

$f(2) = -(2) - 1$	$f(-6) = 2(-6) + 3$	$f(0) = 2(0) + 3$
$\quad = -3 \;\; \text{since } 2 > 0$	$\quad = -9 \;\; \text{since } -6 \le 0$	$\quad = 3 \;\; \text{since } 0 \le 0$
$f(2) = -3$	$f(-6) = -9$	$f(0) = 3$
Ordered pairs: $(2, -3)$	$(-6, -9)$	$(0, 3)$

PRACTICE

1   Evaluate $f(4)$, $f(-2)$, and $f(0)$ for the function

$$f(x) = \begin{cases} -4x - 2 & \text{if } x \le 0 \\ x + 1 & \text{if } x > 0 \end{cases}$$

Now, let's graph a piecewise-defined function.

EXAMPLE 2 Graph $f(x) = \begin{cases} 2x + 3 & \text{if } x \leq 0 \\ -x - 1 & \text{if } x > 0 \end{cases}$

Solution Let's graph each piece.

If $x \leq 0$,
$f(x) = 2x + 3$

Values ≤ 0
x	$f(x) = 2x + 3$
0	3 Closed circle
−1	1
−2	−1

If $x > 0$,
$f(x) = -x - 1$

Values > 0
x	$f(x) = -x - 1$
1	−2
2	−3
3	−4

The graph of the first part of $f(x)$ listed will look like a ray with a closed-circle end point at $(0, 3)$. The graph of the second part of $f(x)$ listed will look like a ray with an open-circle end point. To find the exact location of the open-circle end point, use $f(x) = -x - 1$ and find $f(0)$. Since $f(0) = -0 - 1 = -1$, we graph the values from the second table and place an open circle at $(0, -1)$.

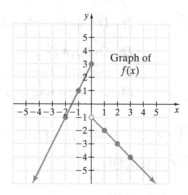

Graph of $f(x)$

Notice that this graph is the graph of a function because it passes the vertical line test. The domain of this function is $(-\infty, \infty)$ and the range is $(-\infty, 3]$. □

PRACTICE
2 Graph

$$f(x) = \begin{cases} -4x - 2 & \text{if } x \leq 0 \\ x + 1 & \text{if } x > 0 \end{cases}$$

OBJECTIVE
2 Vertical and Horizontal Shifting

Review of Common Graphs

We now take common graphs and learn how more complicated graphs are actually formed by shifting and reflecting these common graphs. These shifts and reflections are called transformations, and it is possible to combine transformations. A knowledge of these transformations will help you simplify future graphs.

Let's begin with a review of the graphs of four common functions. Many of these functions we graphed in earlier sections.

First, **let's graph the linear function $f(x) = x$ or** $y = x$. Ordered pair solutions of this graph consist of ordered pairs whose x- and y-values are the same.

x	y or $f(x) = x$
−3	−3
0	0
1	1
4	4

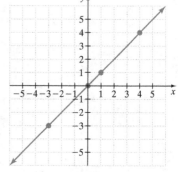

Next, **let's graph the nonlinear function** $f(x) = x^2$ **or** $y = x^2$.

This equation is not linear because the x^2 term does not allow us to write it in the form $Ax + By = C$. Its graph is not a line. We begin by finding ordered pair solutions. Because this graph is solved for $f(x)$, or y, we choose x-values and find corresponding $f(x)$, or y-values.

If $x = -3$, then $y = (-3)^2$, or 9.

If $x = -2$, then $y = (-2)^2$, or 4.

If $x = -1$, then $y = (-1)^2$, or 1.

If $x = 0$, then $y = 0^2$, or 0.

If $x = 1$, then $y = 1^2$, or 1.

If $x = 2$, then $y = 2^2$, or 4.

If $x = 3$, then $y = 3^2$, or 9.

x	$f(x)$ or y
-3	9
-2	4
-1	1
0	0
1	1
2	4
3	9

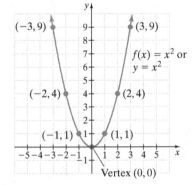

Study the table for a moment and look for patterns. Notice that the ordered pair solution $(0, 0)$ contains the smallest y-value because any other x-value squared will give a positive result. This means that the point $(0, 0)$ will be the lowest point on the graph. Also notice that all other y-values correspond to two different x-values, for example, $3^2 = 9$ and $(-3)^2 = 9$. This means that the graph will be a mirror image of itself across the y-axis. Connect the plotted points with a smooth curve to sketch its graph.

This curve is given a special name, a **parabola**. We will study more about parabolas in later chapters.

Next, **let's graph another nonlinear function,** $f(x) = |x|$ **or** $y = |x|$.

This is not a linear equation since it cannot be written in the form $Ax + By = C$. Its graph is not a line. Because we do not know the shape of this graph, we find many ordered pair solutions. We will choose x-values and substitute to find corresponding y-values.

If $x = -3$, then $y = |-3|$, or 3.

If $x = -2$, then $y = |-2|$, or 2.

If $x = -1$, then $y = |-1|$, or 1.

If $x = 0$, then $y = |0|$, or 0.

If $x = 1$, then $y = |1|$, or 1.

If $x = 2$, then $y = |2|$, or 2.

If $x = 3$, then $y = |3|$, or 3.

x	y
-3	3
-2	2
-1	1
0	0
1	1
2	2
3	3

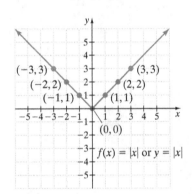

Again, study the table of values for a moment and notice any patterns.

From the plotted ordered pairs, we see that the graph of this absolute value equation is V-shaped.

Finally, consider a fourth common function, $f(x) = \sqrt{x}$ or $y = \sqrt{x}$. For this graph, you need to recall basic facts about square roots and use your calculator to approximate some square roots to help locate points. Recall also that the square root of a negative number is not a real number, so be careful when finding your domain.

Now **let's graph the square root function** $f(x) = \sqrt{x}$ **or** $y = \sqrt{x}$.

To graph, we identify the domain, evaluate the function for several values of x, plot the resulting points, and connect the points with a smooth curve. Since $\sqrt{x}$ represents the nonnegative square root of x, the domain of this function is the set of all nonnegative numbers, $\{x \mid x \geq 0\}$, or $[0, \infty)$. We have approximated $\sqrt{3}$ on the next page to help us locate the point corresponding to $(3, \sqrt{3})$.

If $x = 0$, then $y = \sqrt{0}$, or 0.

If $x = 1$, then $y = \sqrt{1}$, or 1.

If $x = 3$, then $y = \sqrt{3}$, or 1.7.

If $x = 4$, then $y = \sqrt{4}$, or 2.

If $x = 9$, then $y = \sqrt{9}$, or 3.

x	$f(x) = \sqrt{x}$
0	0
1	1
3	$\sqrt{3} \approx 1.7$
4	2
9	3

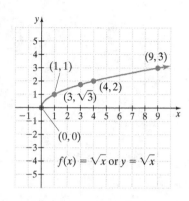

Notice that the graph of this function passes the vertical line test, as expected.

Below is a summary of our four common graphs. Take a moment and study these graphs. Your success in the rest of this section depends on your knowledge of these graphs.

Common Graphs

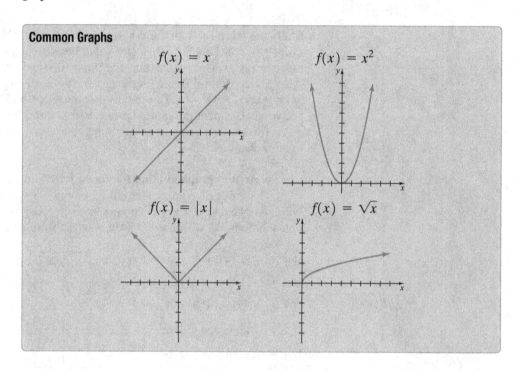

$f(x) = x$

$f(x) = x^2$

$f(x) = |x|$

$f(x) = \sqrt{x}$

Your knowledge of the slope–intercept form, $f(x) = mx + b$, will help you understand simple shifting or transformations such as vertical shifts. For example, what is the difference between the graphs of $f(x) = x$ and $g(x) = x + 3$?

$$f(x) = x$$
slope, $m = 1$
y-intercept is $(0, 0)$

$$g(x) = x + 3$$
slope, $m = 1$
y-intercept is $(0, 3)$

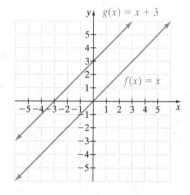

Notice that the graph of $g(x) = x + 3$ is the same as the graph of $f(x) = x$, but moved upward 3 units. This is an example of a **vertical shift** and is true for graphs in general.

Vertical Shifts (Upward and Downward)
Let *k* be a Positive Number

Graph of	Same As	Moved
$g(x) = f(x) + k$	$f(x)$	k units upward
$g(x) = f(x) - k$	$f(x)$	k units downward

EXAMPLES   Without plotting points, sketch the graph of each pair of functions on the same set of axes.

3. $f(x) = x^2$ and $g(x) = x^2 + 2$ **4.** $f(x) = \sqrt{x}$ and $g(x) = \sqrt{x} - 3$

 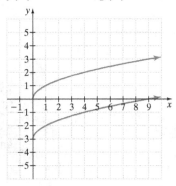

PRACTICE

3-4   Without plotting points, sketch the graphs of each pair of functions on the same set of axes.

3. $f(x) = x^2$ and $g(x) = x^2 - 3$ **4.** $f(x) = \sqrt{x}$ and $g(x) = \sqrt{x} + 1$ ▪

A horizontal shift to the left or right may be slightly more difficult to understand. Let's graph $g(x) = |x - 2|$ and compare it with $f(x) = |x|$.

EXAMPLE 5   Sketch the graphs of $f(x) = |x|$ and $g(x) = |x - 2|$ on the same set of axes.

Solution Study the table below to understand the placement of both graphs.

x	$f(x) = |x|$	$g(x) = |x - 2|$
-3	3	5
-2	2	4
-1	1	3
0	0	2
1	1	1
2	2	0
3	3	1

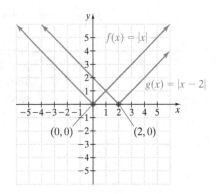

PRACTICE

5   Sketch the graphs of $f(x) = |x|$ and $g(x) = |x - 3|$ on the same set of axes. ▪

The graph of $g(x) = |x - 2|$ is the same as the graph of $f(x) = |x|$, but moved 2 units to the right. This is an example of a **horizontal shift** and is true for graphs in general.

Horizontal Shift (To the Left or Right)
Let *h* be a Positive Number

Graph of	Same as	Moved
$g(x) = f(x - h)$	$f(x)$	*h* units to the right
$g(x) = f(x + h)$	$f(x)$	*h* units to the left

Helpful Hint

Notice that $f(x - h)$ corresponds to a shift to the right and $f(x + h)$ corresponds to a shift to the left.

Vertical and horizontal shifts can be combined.

EXAMPLE 6 Sketch the graphs of $f(x) = x^2$ and $g(x) = (x - 2)^2 + 1$ on the same set of axes.

Solution The graph of $g(x)$ is the same as the graph of $f(x)$ shifted 2 units to the right and 1 unit up.

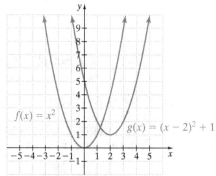

PRACTICE

6 Sketch the graphs of $f(x) = |x|$ and $g(x) = |x - 2| + 3$ on the same set of axes.

OBJECTIVE

3 Reflecting Graphs

Another type of transformation is called a **reflection.** In this section, we will study reflections (mirror images) about the *x*-axis only. For example, take a moment and study these two graphs. The graph of $g(x) = -x^2$ can be verified, as usual, by plotting points.

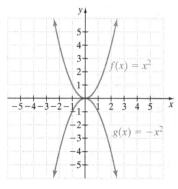

Reflection about the *x*-Axis

The graph of $g(x) = -f(x)$ is the graph of $f(x)$ reflected about the *x*-axis.

EXAMPLE 7   Sketch the graph of $h(x) = -|x - 3| + 2$.

Solution The graph of $h(x) = -|x - 3| + 2$ is the same as the graph of $f(x) = |x|$ reflected about the x-axis, then moved three units to the right and two units upward.

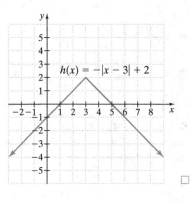

PRACTICE
7   Sketch the graph of $h(x) = -(x + 2)^2 - 1$.

There are other transformations, such as stretching, that won't be covered in this section. For a review of this transformation, see the Appendix.

Vocabulary, Readiness & Video Check

Match each equation with its graph.

1. $y = \sqrt{x}$ **2.** $y = x^2$ **3.** $y = x$ **4.** $y = |x|$

A.   **B.**   **C.**   **D.**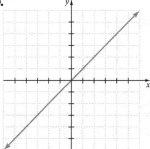

Martin-Gay Interactive Videos

Watch the section lecture video and answer the following questions.

OBJECTIVE 1
5. In Example 1, only one piece of the function is defined for the value $x = -1$. Why do we find $f(-1)$ for $f(x) = x + 3$?

OBJECTIVE 2
6. For Examples 2–8, why is it helpful to be familiar with common graphs and their basic shapes?

OBJECTIVE 3
7. Based on the lecture before Example 9, complete the following statement. The graph of $f(x) = -\sqrt{x} + 6$ has the same shape as the graph of $f(x) = \sqrt{x} + 6$ but it is reflected about the ____.

See Video 3.6

See video answer section.

3.6   Exercise Set MyMathLab°

Graph each piecewise-defined function. See Examples 1 and 2.

1. $f(x) = \begin{cases} 2x & \text{if } x < 0 \\ x + 1 & \text{if } x \geq 0 \end{cases}$

2. $f(x) = \begin{cases} 3x & \text{if } x < 0 \\ x + 2 & \text{if } x \geq 0 \end{cases}$

3. $f(x) = \begin{cases} 4x + 5 & \text{if } x \leq 0 \\ \frac{1}{4}x + 2 & \text{if } x > 0 \end{cases}$

4. $f(x) = \begin{cases} 5x + 4 & \text{if } x \leq 0 \\ \frac{1}{3}x - 1 & \text{if } x > 0 \end{cases}$

5. $g(x) = \begin{cases} -x & \text{if } x \leq 1 \\ 2x + 1 & \text{if } x > 1 \end{cases}$

6. $g(x) = \begin{cases} 3x - 1 & \text{if } x \leq 2 \\ -x & \text{if } x > 2 \end{cases}$

7. $f(x) = \begin{cases} 5 & \text{if } x < -2 \\ 3 & \text{if } x \geq -2 \end{cases}$ **8.** $f(x) = \begin{cases} 4 & \text{if } x < -3 \\ -2 & \text{if } x \geq -3 \end{cases}$

MIXED PRACTICE

(Sections 3.2, 3.6) Graph each piecewise-defined function. Use the graph to determine the domain and range of the function. See Examples 1 and 2.

9. $f(x) = \begin{cases} -2x & \text{if } x \leq 0 \\ 2x + 1 & \text{if } x > 0 \end{cases}$

10. $g(x) = \begin{cases} -3x & \text{if } x \leq 0 \\ 3x + 2 & \text{if } x > 0 \end{cases}$

11. $h(x) = \begin{cases} 5x - 5 & \text{if } x < 2 \\ -x + 3 & \text{if } x \geq 2 \end{cases}$

12. $f(x) = \begin{cases} 4x - 4 & \text{if } x < 2 \\ -x + 1 & \text{if } x \geq 2 \end{cases}$

▶ 13. $f(x) = \begin{cases} x + 3 & \text{if } x < -1 \\ -2x + 4 & \text{if } x \geq -1 \end{cases}$

14. $h(x) = \begin{cases} x + 2 & \text{if } x < 1 \\ 2x + 1 & \text{if } x \geq 1 \end{cases}$

15. $g(x) = \begin{cases} -2 & \text{if } x \leq 0 \\ -4 & \text{if } x \geq 1 \end{cases}$

16. $f(x) = \begin{cases} -1 & \text{if } x \leq 0 \\ -3 & \text{if } x \geq 2 \end{cases}$

MIXED PRACTICE

Sketch the graph of each function. See Examples 3 through 6.

▶ 17. $f(x) = |x| + 3$ **18.** $f(x) = |x| - 2$

▶ 19. $f(x) = \sqrt{x} - 2$ **20.** $f(x) = \sqrt{x} + 3$

▶ 21. $f(x) = |x - 4|$ **22.** $f(x) = |x + 3|$

23. $f(x) = \sqrt{x + 2}$ **24.** $f(x) = \sqrt{x - 2}$

▶ 25. $y = (x - 4)^2$ **26.** $y = (x + 4)^2$

27. $f(x) = x^2 + 4$ **28.** $f(x) = x^2 - 4$

29. $f(x) = \sqrt{x - 2} + 3$ **30.** $f(x) = \sqrt{x - 1} + 3$

31. $f(x) = |x - 1| + 5$ **32.** $f(x) = |x - 3| + 2$

▶ 33. $f(x) = \sqrt{x + 1} + 1$ **34.** $f(x) = \sqrt{x + 3} + 2$

▶ 35. $f(x) = |x + 3| - 1$ **36.** $f(x) = |x + 1| - 4$

▶ 37. $g(x) = (x - 1)^2 - 1$ **38.** $h(x) = (x + 2)^2 + 2$

39. $f(x) = (x + 3)^2 - 2$ **40.** $f(x) = (x + 2)^2 + 4$

Sketch the graph of each function. See Examples 3 through 7.

▶ 41. $f(x) = -(x - 1)^2$ **42.** $g(x) = -(x + 2)^2$

43. $h(x) = -\sqrt{x} + 3$ **44.** $f(x) = -\sqrt{x + 3}$

▶ 45. $h(x) = -|x + 2| + 3$ **46.** $g(x) = -|x + 1| + 1$

47. $f(x) = (x - 3) + 2$ **48.** $f(x) = (x - 1) + 4$

REVIEW AND PREVIEW

Match each equation with its graph. See Section 3.3.

49. $y = -1$ **50.** $x = -1$

51. $x = 3$ **52.** $y = 3$

A.

B.

C.

D.

CONCEPT EXTENSIONS

53. Draw a graph whose domain is $(-\infty, 5]$ and whose range is $[2, \infty)$.

54. In your own words, describe how to graph a piecewise-defined function.

55. Graph: $f(x) = \begin{cases} -\dfrac{1}{2}x & \text{if } x \leq 0 \\ x + 1 & \text{if } 0 < x \leq 2 \\ 2x - 1 & \text{if } x > 2 \end{cases}$

56. Graph: $f(x) = \begin{cases} -\dfrac{1}{3}x & \text{if } x \leq 0 \\ x + 2 & \text{if } 0 < x \leq 4 \\ 3x - 4 & \text{if } x > 4 \end{cases}$

Write the domain and range of the following exercises.

57. Exercise 29   **58.** Exercise 30

59. Exercise 45   **60.** Exercise 46

Without graphing, find the domain of each function.

61. $f(x) = 5\sqrt{x - 20} + 1$

62. $g(x) = -3\sqrt{x + 5}$

63. $h(x) = 5|x - 20| + 1$

64. $f(x) = -3|x + 5.7|$

65. $g(x) = 9 - \sqrt{x + 103}$

66. $h(x) = \sqrt{x - 17} - 3$

Sketch the graph of each piecewise-defined function. Write the domain and range of each function.

67. $f(x) = \begin{cases} |x| & \text{if } x \leq 0 \\ x^2 & \text{if } x > 0 \end{cases}$ **68.** $f(x) = \begin{cases} x^2 & \text{if } x < 0 \\ \sqrt{x} & \text{if } x \geq 0 \end{cases}$

69. $g(x) = \begin{cases} |x - 2| & \text{if } x < 0 \\ -x^2 & \text{if } x \geq 0 \end{cases}$

70. $g(x) = \begin{cases} -|x + 1| - 1 & \text{if } x < -2 \\ \sqrt{x + 2} - 4 & \text{if } x \geq -2 \end{cases}$

3.7 Graphing Linear Inequalities

OBJECTIVES

1 Graph Linear Inequalities.
2 Graph the Intersection or Union of Two Linear Inequalities.

1   Graphing Linear Inequalities

Recall that the graph of a linear equation in two variables is the graph of all ordered pairs that satisfy the equation, and we determined that the graph is a line. Here we graph **linear inequalities** in two variables; that is, we graph all the ordered pairs that satisfy the inequality.

If the equal sign in a linear equation in two variables is replaced with an inequality symbol, the result is a linear inequality in two variables.

Examples of Linear Inequalities in Two Variables

$$3x + 5y \geq 6 \qquad 2x - 4y < -3$$
$$4x > 2 \qquad\qquad y \leq 5$$

To graph the linear inequality $x + y < 3$, for example, we first graph the related **boundary** equation $x + y = 3$. The resulting boundary line contains all ordered pairs the sum of whose coordinates is 3. This line separates the plane into two **half-planes.** All points "above" the boundary line $x + y = 3$ have coordinates that satisfy the inequality $x + y > 3$, and all points "below" the line have coordinates that satisfy the inequality $x + y < 3$.

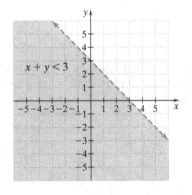

The graph, or **solution region,** for $x + y < 3$, then, is the half-plane below the boundary line and is shown shaded in the graph on the left. The boundary line is shown dashed since it is not a part of the solution region. These ordered pairs on this line satisfy $x + y = 3$ and not $x + y < 3$.

The following steps may be used to graph linear inequalities in two variables.

Graphing a Linear Inequality in Two Variables

Step 1. Graph the boundary line found by replacing the inequality sign with an equal sign. If the inequality sign is < or >, graph a dashed line indicating that points on the line are not solutions of the inequality. If the inequality sign is ≤ or ≥, graph a solid line indicating that points on the line are solutions of the inequality.

Step 2. Choose a **test point not on the boundary line** and substitute the coordinates of this test point into the **original inequality.**

Step 3. If a true statement is obtained in Step 2, shade the half-plane that contains the test point. If a false statement is obtained, shade the half-plane that does not contain the test point.

EXAMPLE 1 Graph: $2x - y < 6$

Solution First, the boundary line for this inequality is the graph of $2x - y = 6$. Graph a dashed boundary line because the inequality symbol is $<$. Next, choose a test point on either side of the boundary line. The point $(0, 0)$ is not on the boundary line, so we use this point. Replacing x with 0 and y with 0 in the _original inequality_ $2x - y < 6$ leads to the following:

$$2x - y < 6$$
$$2(0) - 0 < 6 \quad \text{Let } x = 0 \text{ and } y = 0.$$
$$0 < 6 \quad \text{True}$$

Because $(0, 0)$ satisfies the inequality, so does every point on the same side of the boundary line as $(0, 0)$. Shade the half-plane that contains $(0, 0)$. The half-plane graph of the inequality is shown at the right.

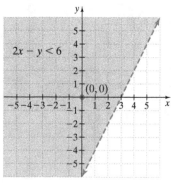

Every point in the shaded half-plane satisfies the original inequality. Notice that the inequality $2x - y < 6$ does not describe a function since its graph does not pass the vertical line test. □

PRACTICE

1 Graph: $3x + y < 8$

In general, linear inequalities of the form $Ax + By \leq C$, where A and B are not both 0, do not describe functions.

EXAMPLE 2 Graph: $3x \geq y$

Solution First, graph the boundary line $3x = y$. Graph a solid boundary line because the inequality symbol is $\geq$. Test a point not on the boundary line to determine which half-plane contains points that satisfy the inequality. We choose $(0, 1)$ as our test point.

$$3x \geq y$$
$$3(0) \geq 1 \quad \text{Let } x = 0 \text{ and } y = 1.$$
$$0 \geq 1 \quad \text{False}$$

This point does not satisfy the inequality, so the correct half-plane is on the opposite side of the boundary line from $(0, 1)$. The graph of $3x \geq y$ is the boundary line together with the shaded region shown.

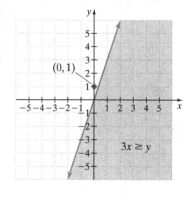

PRACTICE

2 Graph: $x \geq 3y$

✔ **CONCEPT CHECK**

If a point on the boundary line is included in the solution of an inequality in two variables, should the graph of the boundary line be solid or dashed?

OBJECTIVE

2 Graphing Intersections or Unions of Linear Inequalities

The intersection and the union of linear inequalities can also be graphed, as shown in the next two examples. Recall from Section 2.5 that the graph of two inequalities joined by *and* is the intersection of the graphs of the two inequalities. Also, the graph of two inequalities joined by *or* is the union of the graphs of the two inequalities.

EXAMPLE 3 Graph $x \geq 1$ and $y \geq 2x - 1$.

Solution Graph each inequality. The word *and* means the intersection. The intersection of the two graphs is all points common to both regions, as shown by the dark pink shading in the third graph.

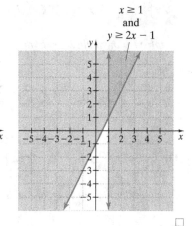

PRACTICE

3 Graph the intersection of $x \leq 3$ and $y \leq x - 2$.

EXAMPLE 4 Graph $x + \frac{1}{2}y \geq -4$ or $y \leq -2$.

Solution Graph each inequality. The word *or* means the union. The union of the two inequalities is both shaded regions, including the solid boundary lines shown in the third graph.

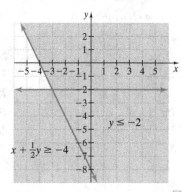

Answer to Concept Check:
solid

PRACTICE

4 Graph $2x - 3y \leq -2$ or $y \geq 1$.

✔ Vocabulary, Readiness & Video Check

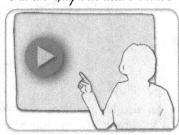

Martin-Gay Interactive Videos

Watch the section lecture video and answer the following questions.

OBJECTIVE 1

1. From Example 1 and the lecture before, how do you find the equation of the boundary line? How do you determine if the points on the boundary line are solutions to the inequality?

OBJECTIVE 2

2. Based on Example 2, describe how you find the intersection of two linear inequalities in two variables.

See Video 3.7

3.7 Exercise Set MyMathLab®

Graph each inequality. See Examples 1 and 2.

1. $x < 2$
2. $x > -3$
3. $x - y \geq 7$
4. $3x + y \leq 1$
▶ 5. $3x + y > 6$
6. $2x + y > 2$
7. $y \leq -2x$
8. $y \leq 3x$
9. $2x + 4y \geq 8$
10. $2x + 6y \leq 12$
11. $5x + 3y > -15$
12. $2x + 5y < -20$

Graph each union or intersection. See Examples 3 and 4.

13. $x \geq 3$ and $y \leq -2$
14. $x \geq 3$ or $y \leq -2$
15. $x \leq -2$ or $y \geq 4$
16. $x \leq -2$ and $y \geq 4$
17. $x - y < 3$ and $x > 4$
18. $2x > y$ and $y > x + 2$
19. $x + y \leq 3$ or $x - y \geq 5$
20. $x - y \leq 3$ or $x + y > -1$

MIXED PRACTICE

Graph each inequality.

21. $y \geq -2$
22. $y \leq 4$
23. $x - 6y < 12$
24. $x - 4y < 8$
25. $x > 5$
26. $y \geq -2$
27. $-2x + y \leq 4$
28. $-3x + y \leq 9$
29. $x - 3y < 0$
30. $x + 2y > 0$
31. $3x - 2y \leq 12$
32. $2x - 3y \leq 9$
33. $x - y > 2$ or $y < 5$
34. $x - y < 3$ or $x > 4$
▶ 35. $x + y \leq 1$ and $y \leq -1$

36. $y \geq x$ and $2x - 4y \geq 6$
37. $2x + y > 4$ or $x \geq 1$
38. $3x + y < 9$ or $y \leq 2$
39. $x \geq -2$ and $x \leq 1$
40. $x \geq -4$ and $x \leq 3$
41. $x + y \leq 0$ or $3x - 6y \geq 12$
42. $x + y \leq 0$ and $3x - 6y \geq 12$
43. $2x - y > 3$ and $x > 0$
44. $2x - y > 3$ or $x > 0$

Match each inequality with its graph.

45. $y \leq 2x + 3$
46. $y < 2x + 3$
47. $y > 2x + 3$
48. $y \geq 2x + 3$

A. B.

C. D.

Write the inequality whose graph is given.

49.

50.

51.

52.

53.

54.

55.

56.

Find the domain and the range of each relation. Determine whether the relation is also a function. See Section 3.2.

65.

66.

CONCEPT EXTENSIONS

67. Explain when a dashed boundary line should be used in the graph of an inequality.

68. Explain why, after the boundary line is sketched, we test a point on either side of this boundary in the original inequality.

Solve.

69. Chris-Craft manufactures boats out of Fiberglas and wood. Fiberglas hulls require 2 hours of work, whereas wood hulls require 4 hours of work. Employees work at most 40 hours a week. The following inequalities model these restrictions, where x represents the number of Fiberglas hulls produced and y represents the number of wood hulls produced.

$$\begin{cases} x \geq 0 \\ y \geq 0 \\ 2x + 4y \leq 40 \end{cases}$$

Graph the intersection of these inequalities.

70. Rheem Abo-Zahrah decides that she will study at most 20 hours every week and that she must work at least 10 hours every week. Let x represent the hours studying and y represent the hours working. Write two inequalities in addition to $x \geq 0$ and $y \geq 0$ that model this situation and graph their intersection.

REVIEW AND PREVIEW

Evaluate each expression. See Sections 1.3 and 1.4.

57. 2^3

58. 3^2

59. -5^2

60. $(-5)^2$

61. $(-2)^4$

62. -2^4

63. $\left(\dfrac{3}{5}\right)^3$

64. $\left(\dfrac{2}{7}\right)^2$

Chapter 3 Vocabulary Check

Fill in each blank with one of the words or phrases listed below.

relation	standard	slope-intercept	range	point–slope
line	slope	x	parallel	perpendicular
function	domain	y	linear function	linear inequality

1. A(n) _____ is a set of ordered pairs.

2. The graph of every linear equation in two variables is a(n) _____.

3. The statement $-x + 2y > 0$ is called a(n) _____ in two variables.

4. _____ form of a linear equation in two variables is $Ax + By = C$.

5. The _____ of a relation is the set of all second components of the ordered pairs of the relation.

6. _____ lines have the same slope and different y-intercepts.

7. _____ form of a linear equation in two variables is $y = mx + b$.

8. A(n) _____ is a relation in which each first component in the ordered pairs corresponds to exactly one second component.

9. In the equation $y = 4x - 2$, the coefficient of x is the _____ of its corresponding graph.

10. Two lines are _____ if the product of their slopes is -1.

11. To find the x-intercept of a linear equation, let _____ = 0 and solve for the other variable.

12. The _____ of a relation is the set of all first components of the ordered pairs of the relation.

13. A(n) _____ is a function that can be written in the form $f(x) = mx + b$.

14. To find the y-intercept of a linear equation, let _____ = 0 and solve for the other variable.

15. The equation $y - 8 = -5(x + 1)$ is written in _____ form.

Chapter 3 Highlights

DEFINITIONS AND CONCEPTS	EXAMPLES
Section 3.1 Graphing Equations	

The **rectangular coordinate system,** or **Cartesian coordinate system,** consists of a vertical and a horizontal number line intersecting at their 0 coordinates. The vertical number line is called the **y-axis,** and the horizontal number line is called the **x-axis.** The point of intersection of the axes is called the **origin.** The axes divide the plane into four regions called **quadrants.**

DEFINITIONS AND CONCEPTS	EXAMPLES

Section 3.1   Graphing Equations (continued)

To **plot** or **graph** an ordered pair means to find its corresponding point on a rectangular coordinate system.

To plot or graph the ordered pair $(-2, 5)$, start at the origin. Move 2 units to the left along the x-axis, then 5 units upward parallel to the y-axis.

An ordered pair is a **solution** of an equation in two variables if replacing the variables by the corresponding coordinates results in a true statement.

Determine whether $(-2, 3)$ is a solution of

$$3x + 2y = 0$$
$$3(-2) + 2(3) = 0$$
$$-6 + 6 = 0$$
$$0 = 0 \quad \text{True}$$

$(-2, 3)$ is a solution.

A **linear equation in two variables** is an equation that can be written in the form $Ax + By = C$, where A, B, and C are real numbers and A and B are not both 0. The form $Ax + By = C$ is called **standard form.**

Linear Equations in Two Variables

$$y = -2x + 5, \quad x = 7$$
$$y - 3 = 0, \quad 6x - 4y = 10$$

$6x - 4y = 10$ is in standard form.

The graph of a linear equation in two variables is a line. To graph a linear equation in two variables, find three ordered pair solutions. (Use the third ordered pair to check.) Plot the solution points and draw the line connecting the points.

Graph $3x + y = -6$.

x	y
0	−6
−2	0
−3	3

To graph an equation that is not linear, find a sufficient number of ordered pair solutions so that a pattern may be discovered.

Graph $y = x^3 + 2$.

x	y
−2	−6
−1	1
0	2
1	3
2	10

DEFINITIONS AND CONCEPTS	EXAMPLES

Section 3.2 Introduction to Functions

A **relation** is a set of ordered pairs. The **domain** of the relation is the set of all first components of the ordered pairs. The **range** of the relation is the set of all second components of the ordered pairs.

Relation

Domain: {cat, dog, too, give}
Range: {1, 2}

A **function** is a relation in which each element of the first set corresponds to exactly one element of the second set.

The previous relation is a function. Each word contains exactly one number of vowels.

Vertical Line Test

If no vertical line can be drawn so that it intersects a graph more than once, the graph is the graph of a function.

Find the domain and the range of the relation. Also determine whether the relation is a function.

Range: $(-\infty, 0]$

Domain: $(-\infty, \infty)$

By the vertical line test, this graph is the graph of a function.

The symbol $f(x)$ means **function of x** and is called **function notation**.

If $f(x) = 2x^2 - 5$, find $f(-3)$.

$$f(-3) = 2(-3)^2 - 5 = 2(9) - 5 = 13$$

Section 3.3 Graphing Linear Functions

A **linear function** is a function that can be written in the form $f(x) = mx + b$.

Linear Functions

$$f(x) = -3, g(x) = 5x, h(x) = -\frac{1}{3}x - 7$$

To graph a linear function, find three ordered pair solutions. (Use the third ordered pair to check.) Graph the solutions and draw a line through the plotted points.

Graph $f(x) = -2x$.

x	y or $f(x)$
-1	2
0	0
2	-4

DEFINITIONS AND CONCEPTS	EXAMPLES

Section 3.3   Graphing Linear Functions (continued)

The graph of $y = mx + b$ is the same as the graph of $y = mx$ but shifted b units up if b is positive and $|b|$ units down if b is negative.

Graph $g(x) = -2x + 3$.

This is the same as the graph of $f(x) = -2x$ shifted 3 units up.

The x-coordinate of a point where a graph crosses the x-axis is called an **x-intercept.** The y-coordinate of a point where a graph crosses the y-axis is called a **y-intercept.**

To find an x-intercept, let $y = 0$ or $f(x) = 0$ and solve for x.

To find a y-intercept, let $x = 0$ and solve for y.

Graph $5x - y = -5$ by finding intercepts.

$$
\begin{array}{ll}
\text{If } x = 0, \text{ then} & \text{If } y = 0, \text{ then} \\
5x - y = -5 & 5x - y = -5 \\
5 \cdot 0 - y = -5 & 5x - 0 = -5 \\
-y = -5 & 5x = -5 \\
y = 5 & x = -1 \\
(0, 5) & (-1, 0)
\end{array}
$$

Ordered pairs are $(0, 5)$ and $(-1, 0)$.

The graph of $x = c$ is a vertical line with x-intercept $(c, 0)$.

The graph of $y = c$ is a horizontal line with y-intercept $(0, c)$.

Section 3.4   The Slope of a Line

The **slope** m of the line through (x_1, y_1) and (x_2, y_2) is given by

$$m = \frac{y_2 - y_1}{x_2 - x_1} \text{ as long } x_2 \neq x_1$$

Find the slope of the line through $(-1, 7)$ and $(-2, -3)$.

$$m = \frac{y_2 - y_1}{x_2 - x_1} = \frac{-3 - 7}{-2 - (-1)} = \frac{-10}{-1} = 10$$

(continued)

DEFINITIONS AND CONCEPTS	EXAMPLES

Section 3.4   The Slope of a Line (continued)

The **slope-intercept form** of a linear equation is $y = mx + b$, where m is the slope of the line and $(0, b)$ is the y-intercept.

Find the slope and y-intercept of $-3x + 2y = -8$.

$$2y = 3x - 8$$

$$\frac{2y}{2} = \frac{3x}{2} - \frac{8}{2}$$

$$y = \frac{3}{2}x - 4$$

The slope of the line is $\frac{3}{2}$, and the y-intercept is $(0, -4)$.

Nonvertical parallel lines have the same slope.

If the product of the slopes of two lines is -1, the lines are perpendicular.

The slope of a horizontal line is 0.

The slope of a vertical line is undefined.

The slope of $y = -2$ is 0.

The slope of $x = 5$ is undefined.

Section 3.5   Equations of Lines

We can use the slope–intercept form to write an equation of a line given its slope and y-intercept.

Write an equation of the line with y-intercept $(0, -1)$ and slope $\frac{2}{3}$.

$$y = mx + b$$

$$y = \frac{2}{3}x - 1$$

The point–slope form of the equation of a line is $y - y_1 = m(x - x_1)$, where m is the slope of the line and (x_1, y_1) is a point on the line.

Find an equation of the line with slope 2 containing the point $(1, -4)$. Write the equation in standard form: $Ax + By = C$.

$$y - y_1 = m(x - x_1)$$

$$y - (-4) = 2(x - 1)$$

$$y + 4 = 2x - 2$$

$$-2x + y = -6 \qquad \text{Standard form}$$

Section 3.6   Graphing Piecewise-Defined Functions and Shifting and Reflecting Graphs of Functions

Vertical Shifts (Upward and Downward)
Let k be a positive number.

Graph of	Same as	Moved
$g(x) = f(x) + k$	$f(x)$	k units upward
$g(x) = f(x) - k$	$f(x)$	k units downward

The graph of $h(x) = -|x - 3| + 1$ is the same as the graph of $f(x) = |x|$, reflected about the x-axis, shifted 3 units right, and 1 unit up.

DEFINITIONS AND CONCEPTS	EXAMPLES

Section 3.6   Graphing Piecewise-Defined Functions and Shifting and Reflecting Graphs of Functions (continued)

Horizontal Shifts (Left or Right)
Let h be a positive number.

Graph of	Same as	Moved
$g(x) = f(x - h)$	$f(x)$	h units to the right
$g(x) = f(x + h)$	$f(x)$	h units to the left

Reflection about the x-Axis

The graph of $g(x) = -f(x)$ is the graph of $f(x)$ reflected about the x-axis.

Section 3.7 Graphing Linear Inequalities

If the equal sign in a linear equation in two variables is replaced with an inequality symbol, the result is a **linear inequality in two variables.**

To Graph a Linear Inequality

1. Graph the boundary line by graphing the related equation. Draw the line solid if the inequality symbol is $\leq$ or $\geq$. Draw the line dashed if the inequality symbol is $<$ or $>$.

2. Choose a test point not on the line. Substitute its coordinates into the original inequality.

3. If the resulting inequality is true, shade the **half-plane** that contains the test point. If the inequality is not true, shade the half-plane that does not contain the test point.

Linear Inequalities in Two Variables

$$x \leq -5 \quad y \geq 2$$
$$3x - 2y > 7 \quad x < -5$$

Graph $2x - 4y > 4$.

1. Graph $2x - 4y = 4$. Draw a dashed line because the inequality symbol is $>$.

2. Check the test point $(0, 0)$ in the inequality $2x - 4y > 4$.

$$2 \cdot 0 - 4 \cdot 0 > 4 \quad \text{Let } x = 0 \text{ and } y = 0.$$
$$0 > 4 \quad \text{False}$$

3. The inequality is false, so we shade the half-plane that does not contain $(0, 0)$.

Chapter 3 Review

(3.1) Plot the points and name the quadrant or axis in which each point lies.

1. $A(2, -1), B(-2, 1), C(0, 3), D(-3, -5)$
2. $A(-3, 4), B(4, -3), C(-2, 0), D(-4, 1)$

Determine whether each ordered pair is a solution of the given equation.

3. $7x - 8y = 56; (0, 56), (8, 0)$
4. $-2x + 5y = 10; (-5, 0), (1, 1)$

5. $x = 13; (13, 5), (13, 13)$
6. $y = 2; (7, 2), (2, 7)$

Determine whether each equation is linear or not. Then graph the equation.

7. $y = 3x$
8. $y = 5x$
9. $3x - y = 4$
10. $x - 3y = 2$
11. $y = |x| + 4$
12. $y = x^2 + 4$

13. $y = -\dfrac{1}{2}x + 2$

14. $y = -x + 5$

15. $y = 2x - 1$

16. $y = \dfrac{1}{3}x + 1$

17. $y = -1.36x$

18. $y = 2.1x + 5.9$

(3.2) Find the domain and range of each relation. Also determine whether the relation is a function.

19. $\left\{\left(-\dfrac{1}{2}, \dfrac{3}{4}\right), (6, 0.75), (0, -12), (25, 25)\right\}$

20. $\left\{\left(\dfrac{3}{4}, -\dfrac{1}{2}\right), (0.75, 6), (-12, 0), (25, 25)\right\}$

21.

22.

23.

24.

25.

26.

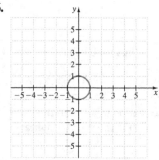

If $f(x) = x - 5$, $g(x) = -3x$, and $h(x) = 2x^2 - 6x + 1$, find the following.

27. $f(2)$ **28.** $g(0)$

29. $g(-6)$ **30.** $h(-1)$

31. $h(1)$ **32.** $f(5)$

The function $J(x) = 2.54x$ may be used to calculate the weight of an object on Jupiter J given its weight on Earth x.

33. If a person weighs 150 pounds on Earth, find the equivalent weight on Jupiter.

34. A 2000-pound probe on Earth weighs how many pounds on Jupiter?

Use the graph of the function below to answer Exercises 35 through 38.

35. Find $f(-1)$.   **36.** Find $f(1)$.

37. Find all values of x such that $f(x) = 1$.

38. Find all values of x such that $f(x) = -1$.

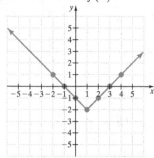

(3.3) Graph each linear function.

39. $f(x) = \dfrac{1}{5}x$

40. $f(x) = -\dfrac{1}{3}x$

41. $g(x) = -2x + 3$

42. $g(x) = 4x - 1$

The graph of $f(x) = 3x$ is sketched below. Use this graph to match each linear function with its graph.

43. $f(x) = 3x + 1$ **44.** $f(x) = 3x - 2$

45. $f(x) = 3x + 2$ **46.** $f(x) = 3x - 5$

A.

B.

C.

D.

Graph each linear equation by finding intercepts if possible.

47. $4x + 5y = 20$ **48.** $3x - 2y = -9$

49. $4x - y = 3$ **50.** $2x + 6y = 9$

51. $y = 5$ **52.** $x = -2$

Graph each linear equation.

53. $x - 2 = 0$ **54.** $y + 3 = 0$

(3.4) Find the slope of the line through each pair of points.

55. $(2, 8)$ and $(6, -4)$ **56.** $(-3, 9)$ and $(5, 13)$

57. $(-7, -4)$ and $(-3, 6)$ **58.** $(7, -2)$ and $(-5, 7)$

Find the slope and y-intercept of each line.

59. $f(x) = -3x + \dfrac{1}{2}$

60. $g(x) = 2x + 4$

61. $6x - 15y = 20$

62. $4x + 14y = 21$

Find the slope of each line.

63. $y - 3 = 0$ **64.** $x = -5$

Two lines are graphed on each set of axes. Decide whether l_1 or l_2 has the greater slope.

65.

66.

67.

68.

69. The cost C, in dollars, of renting a minivan for a day is given by the linear equation $C = 0.3x + 42$, where x is number of miles driven.

  a. Find the cost of renting the minivan for a day and driving it 150 miles.

  b. Find and interpret the slope of this equation.

  c. Find and interpret the y-intercept of this equation.

70. The cost C, in dollars, of renting a compact car for a day is given by the linear equation $C = 0.4x + 19$, where x is the number of miles driven.

  a. Find the cost of renting the compact car for a day and driving it 325 miles.

  b. Find and interpret the slope of this equation.

  c. Find and interpret the y-intercept of this equation.

△ *Decide whether the lines are parallel, perpendicular, or neither.*

71. $f(x) = -2x + 6$ **72.** $y = \dfrac{3}{4}x + 1$

  $g(x) = 2x - 1$ $y = -\dfrac{4}{3}x + 1$

73. $-x + 3y = 2$ **74.** $x - 2y = 6$

  $6x - 18y = 3$ $4x + y = 8$

(3.5) Graph each line passing through the given point with the given slope.

75. Through $(2, -3)$ with slope $\dfrac{2}{3}$

76. Through $(-2, 0)$ with slope -3

Graph each linear equation using the slope and y-intercept.

77. $y = -x + 1$ **78.** $y = 4x - 3$

79. $3x - y = 6$ **80.** $y = -5x$

Find an equation of the line satisfying the given conditions.

81. Horizontal; through $(3, -1)$

82. Vertical; through $(-2, -4)$

△ **83.** Parallel to the line $x = 6$; through $(-4, -3)$

84. Slope 0; through $(2, 5)$

Find the standard form equation of each line satisfying the given conditions.

85. Through $(-3, 5)$; slope 3

86. Slope 2; through $(5, -2)$

87. Through $(-6, -1)$ and $(-4, -2)$

88. Through $(-5, 3)$ and $(-4, -8)$

△ **89.** Through $(-2, 3)$; perpendicular to $x = 4$

△ **90.** Through $(-2, -5)$; parallel to $y = 8$

Find an equation of each line satisfying the given conditions. Write each equation using function notation.

91. Slope $-\dfrac{2}{3}$; y-intercept $(0, 4)$

92. Slope -1; y-intercept $(0, -2)$

△ **93.** Through $(2, -6)$; parallel to $6x + 3y = 5$

△ **94.** Through $(-4, -2)$; parallel to $3x + 2y = 8$

△ **95.** Through $(-6, -1)$; perpendicular to $4x + 3y = 5$

△ **96.** Through $(-4, 5)$; perpendicular to $2x - 3y = 6$

97. The value of a building bought in 2000 continues to increase as time passes. Seven years after the building was bought, it was worth \$210,000; 12 years after it was bought, it was worth \$270,000.

 a. Assuming that this relationship between the number of years past 2000 and the value of the building is linear, write an equation describing this relationship. [*Hint:* Use ordered pairs of the form (years past 2000, value of the building).]

 b. Use this equation to estimate the value of the building in 2018.

98. The value of an automobile bought in 2012 continues to decrease as time passes. Two years after the car was bought, it was worth \$20,600; four years after it was bought, it was worth \$14,600.

 a. Assuming that this relationship between the number of years past 2012 and the value of the car is linear, write an equation describing this relationship. [*Hint:* Use ordered pairs of the form (years past 2012, value of the automobile).]

 b. Use this equation to estimate the value of the automobile in 2018.

(3.6) Graph each function.

99. $f(x) = \begin{cases} -3x & \text{if } x < 0 \\ x - 3 & \text{if } x \geq 0 \end{cases}$

100. $g(x) = \begin{cases} -\dfrac{1}{5}x & \text{if } x \leq -1 \\ -4x + 2 & \text{if } x > -1 \end{cases}$

Graph each function.

101. $y = \sqrt{x} - 4$

102. $f(x) = \sqrt{x - 4}$

103. $g(x) = |x - 2| - 2$

104. $h(x) = -(x + 3)^2 - 1$

(3.7) Graph each linear inequality.

105. $3x + y > 4$ **106.** $\dfrac{1}{2}x - y < 2$

107. $5x - 2y \leq 9$ **108.** $2x \leq 6y$

109. $y < 1$ **110.** $x > -2$

111. Graph $y > 2x + 3$ or $x \leq -3$.

112. Graph $2x < 3y + 8$ and $y \geq -2$.

MIXED REVIEW

Graph each linear equation or inequality.

113. $3x - 2y = -9$ **114.** $5x - 3y < 10$

115. $3y \geq x$ **116.** $x = -4y$

Write an equation of the line satisfying each set of conditions. If possible, write the equation in the form $y = mx + b$.

117. Vertical; through $\left(-7, -\dfrac{1}{2}\right)$

118. Slope 0; through $\left(-4, \dfrac{9}{2}\right)$

119. Slope $\dfrac{3}{4}$; through $(-8, -4)$

120. Through $(-3, 8)$ and $(-2, 3)$

△ **121.** Through $(-6, 1)$; parallel to $y = -\dfrac{3}{2}x + 11$

△ **122.** Through $(-5, 7)$; perpendicular to $5x - 4y = 10$

Graph each piecewise-defined function.

123. $f(x) = \begin{cases} x - 2 & \text{if } x \leq 0 \\ -\dfrac{x}{3} & \text{if } x \geq 3 \end{cases}$

124. $g(x) = \begin{cases} 4x - 3 & \text{if } x \leq 1 \\ 2x & \text{if } x > 1 \end{cases}$

Graph each function.

125. $f(x) = \sqrt{x - 2}$ **126.** $f(x) = |x + 1| - 3$

Chapter 3 Getting Ready for the Test

1c

MATCHING *Given that a is a positive number and b is a positive number, match each ordered pair with the quadrant or axis that each lies.*

1. (a,b) **2.** $(-a,-b)$

3. $(0,b)$ **4.** $(a,0)$

5. $(-a,b)$ **6.** $(a,-b)$

A. Quadrant I   **D.** Quadrant IV
B. Quadrant II   **E.** x-axis
C. Quadrant III   **F.** y-axis

MULTIPLE CHOICE *Use the diagram to the right for Exercises 7 and 8. Choose the best answer.*

7. Is the relation diagramed also a function?

    A. Yes   **B.** No   **C.** there is not enough information given

8. What is the range of the relation?

    A. $\{1,2,3\}$ **B.** $\{1,3\}$ **C.** $\{m,t,r\}$ **D.** there is not enough information given

Input → Output: $m \rightarrow 1$, t, 2, $r \rightarrow 3$

MULTIPLE CHOICE *For Exercises 9 through 12, choose the best answer.*

9. If $f(x) = -x^2$, find the value of $f(-3)$.

    A. 6   **B.** -6 **C.** 9   **D.** -9

10. If $f(x) = 2x - 3$, find the value of $f(a + h)$.

    A. $2a + h - 3$ **B.** $2x(a + h) - 3$ **C.** $2a + 2h - 3$ **D.** $2a + 2h$

11. An ordered pair solution for the function $g(x)$ is $(-6,0)$. This solution written using function notation is:

    A. $g(0) = -6$ **B.** $g(-6) = 0$ **C.** $g(-6) = g(0)$ **D.** $-6 = 0$

12. Given: $(0,4)$ and $(5,0)$. Final answer: $f(x) = -\dfrac{4}{5}x + 4$. Select the correct directions.

    A. Find the slope of the line through the two points.
    B. Find an equation of the line through the two points. Write the equation in standard form.
    C. Find an equation of the line through the two points. Write the equation using function notation.

MULTIPLE CHOICE *Without graphing, identify each linear equation as:*

    A. A function   **B.** Not a function

13. $y = -3x + 13$ **14.** $y = 5$ **15.** $x = -4$ **16.** $y = 4x$

MULTIPLE CHOICE *For Exercises 17 through 22 use the given graph to fill in each blank using the choices below. Letters may be used more than once or not at all.*

    A. $f(3) = 4$ **B.** $f(4) = 3$ **C.** 6   **D.** -9 **E.** 2
    F. 0   **G.** $(-\infty,\infty)$ **H.** $(-\infty,4]$ **I.** $(-\infty,3]$

17. The vertex written in function notation is _____.

18. $f(0) =$ ____   **19.** If $f(x) = 0$, then $x =$ _____ or $x =$ _____.

20. $f(8) =$ ____   **21.** The domain of $f(x)$ is ____.   **22.** The range of $f(x)$ is ___.

MULTIPLE CHOICE *Use the letters on the graph to the right to fill in the blanks for Exercises 23 and 24.*

23. The line with the greatest slope is line _____.   **24.** The line with the least slope is line ____.

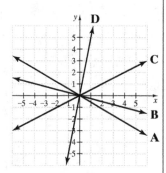

Chapter 3 Test   MyMathLab® You Tube

1. Plot the points and name the quadrant or axis in which each is located: $A(6, -2)$, $B(4, 0)$, $C(-1, 6)$.

Graph each line.

2. $2x - 3y = -6$

3. $4x + 6y = 7$

4. $f(x) = \dfrac{2}{3}x$

5. $y = -3$

6. Find the slope of the line that passes through $(5, -8)$ and $(-7, 10)$.

7. Find the slope and the y-intercept of the line $3x + 12y = 8$.

Graph each nonlinear function. Suggested x-values have been given for ordered pair solutions.

8. $f(x) = (x - 1)^2$ Let $x = -2, -1, 0, 1, 2, 3, 4$.

9. $g(x) = |x| + 2$ Let $x = -3, -2, -1, 0, 1, 2, 3$.

Find an equation of each line satisfying the given conditions. Write Exercises 10–14 in standard form. Write Exercises 15–17 using function notation.

10. Horizontal; through $(2, -8)$

11. Vertical; through $(-4, -3)$

12. Perpendicular to $x = 5$; through $(3, -2)$

13. Through $(4, -1)$; slope -3

14. Through $(0, -2)$; slope 5

15. Through $(4, -2)$ and $(6, -3)$

16. Through $(-1, 2)$; perpendicular to $3x - y = 4$

17. Parallel to $2y + x = 3$; through $(3, -2)$

18. Line L_1 has the equation $2x - 5y = 8$. Line L_2 passes through the points $(1, 4)$ and $(-1, -1)$. Determine whether these lines are parallel lines, perpendicular lines, or neither.

Graph each inequality.

19. $x \le -4$

20. $2x - y > 5$

21. The intersection of $2x + 4y < 6$ and $y \le -4$

Find the domain and range of each relation. Also determine whether the relation is a function.

22.

23.

24.

25.

26. Although some sports experts debunk this theory, many people believe that the amount of money a baseball team spends on payroll affects the number of wins, and thus its standing in the league. For the 2014 Major League Baseball season, the following linear equation can be used to describe the relationship between an American League team's payroll x (in millions of dollars) and the number of games y that team won during the regular season.

$$y = 0.024x + 79.44$$

Round each answer to the nearest whole. (*Source:* Major League Baseball)

a. According to this equation, how many games would have been won in 2014 by a team with a payroll of $90 million?

b. The New York Yankees had a payroll of $204 million in 2014. According to this equation, how many games should they have won during the season?

c. According to this equation, what payroll would have been necessary in 2014 to have won 95 games during the season?

d. Find and interpret the slope of the equation.

Graph each function. For Exercises 27 and 29, state the domain and the range of the function.

27. $f(x) = \begin{cases} -\dfrac{1}{2}x & \text{if } x \le 0 \\ 2x - 3 & \text{if } x > 0 \end{cases}$

28. $f(x) = (x - 4)^2$

29. $g(x) = -|x + 2| - 1$

30. $h(x) = \sqrt{x} - 1$

Chapter 3 Cumulative Review

1. Evaluate $3x - y$ when $x = 15$ and $y = 4$.

2. Add.
   a. $-4 + (-3)$
   b. $\dfrac{1}{2} - \left(-\dfrac{1}{3}\right)$
   c. $7 - 20$

3. Determine whether the following statements are true or false.
   a. 3 is a real number.
   b. $\frac{1}{5}$ is an irrational number.
   c. Every rational number is an integer.
   d. $\{1, 5\} \subseteq \{2, 3, 4, 5\}$

4. Write the opposite of each number.
   a. -7
   b. 0
   c. $\dfrac{1}{4}$

5. Subtract.
   a. $2 - 8$ b. $-8 - (-1)$
   c. $-11 - 5$ d. $10.7 - (-9.8)$
   e. $-\dfrac{2}{3} - \dfrac{1}{2}$ f. $1 - 0.06$
   g. Subtract 7 from 4.

6. Multiply or divide.
   a. $\dfrac{-42}{-6}$
   b. $\dfrac{0}{14}$
   c. $-1(-5)(-2)$

7. Evaluate each expression.
   a. 3^2
   b. $\left(\dfrac{1}{2}\right)^4$
   c. -5^2
   d. $(-5)^2$
   e. -5^3
   f. $(-5)^3$

8. Which property is illustrated?
   a. $5(x + 7) = 5 \cdot x + 5 \cdot 7$
   b. $5(x + 7) = 5(7 + x)$

9. Insert $<, >,$ or $=$ between each pair of numbers to form a true statement.
   a. $-1 \quad -2$ b. $\dfrac{12}{4} \quad 3$
   c. $-5 \quad 0$ d. $-3.5 \quad -3.05$
   e. $\dfrac{5}{8} \quad \dfrac{3}{8}$ f. $\dfrac{2}{3} \quad \dfrac{3}{4}$

10. Evaluate $2x^2$ for
    a. $x = 7$
    b. $x = -7$

11. Write the multiplicative inverse, or reciprocal, of each.
    a. 11 b. -9
    c. $\dfrac{7}{4}$

12. Simplify: $-2 + 3[5 - (7 - 10)]$

13. Solve: $0.6 = 2 - 3.5c$

14. Solve: $2(x - 3) = -40$

15. Solve: $3x + 5 = 3(x + 2)$

16. Solve: $5(x - 7) = 4x - 35 + x$

17. Write the following as algebraic expressions. Then simplify.
    a. The sum of three consecutive integers if x is the first consecutive integer
    b. The perimeter of a triangle with sides of length $x, 5x$, and $6x - 3$.

18. Find 25% of 16.

19. Kelsey Ohleger was helping her friend Benji Burnstine study for an algebra exam. Kelsey told Benji that her three latest art history quiz scores are three consecutive even integers whose sum is 264. Help Benji find the scores.

20. Find 3 consecutive odd integers whose sum is 213.

21. Solve $V = lwh$ for h.

22. Solve $7x + 3y = 21$ for y.

23. Solve: $x - 2 < 5$

24. Solve: $-x - 17 \geq 9$

25. Solve: $\dfrac{2}{5}(x - 6) \geq x - 1$

26. Solve: $3x + 10 > \dfrac{5}{2}(x - 1)$

27. Solve: $2x \geq 0$ and $4x - 1 \leq -9$

28. Solve: $x - 2 < 6$ and $3x + 1 > 1$

29. Solve: $5x - 3 \leq 10$ or $x + 1 \geq 5$

30. Solve: $x - 2 < 6$ or $3x + 1 > 1$

31. Solve: $|5w + 3| = 7$

32. Solve: $|5x - 2| = 3$

33. Solve: $|3x + 2| = |5x - 8|$

34. Solve: $|7x - 2| = |7x + 4|$

35. Solve: $|5x + 1| + 1 \leq 10$

36. Solve: $|-x + 8| - 2 \leq 8$

37. Solve: $|y - 3| > 7$ for y

38. Solve: $|x + 3| > 1$ for x

39. Determine whether $(0, -12)$, $(1, 9)$, and $(2, -6)$ are solutions of the equation $3x - y = 12$.

40. Find the slope and y-intercept of $7x + 2y = 10$.

41. Is the relation $y = 2x + 1$ also a function?

42. Determine whether the graph below is the graph of a function.

43. Find the y-intercept of the graph of each equation.

   a. $f(x) = \dfrac{1}{2}x + \dfrac{3}{7}$

   b. $y = -2.5x - 3.2$

44. Find the slope of the line through $(-1, 6)$ and $(0, 9)$.

45. Find the slope of the line whose equation is $f(x) = \dfrac{2}{3}x + 4$.

46. Find an equation of the vertical line through $\left(-2, -\dfrac{3}{4}\right)$.

47. Write an equation of the line with y-intercept $(0, -3)$ and slope of $\dfrac{1}{4}$.

48. Find an equation of the horizontal line through $\left(-2, -\dfrac{3}{4}\right)$.

49. Graph $2x - y < 6$.

50. Write an equation of the line through $(-2, 5)$ and $(-4, 7)$.

Systems of Equations

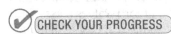

CHECK YOUR PROGRESS

Vocabulary Check
Chapter Highlights
Chapter Review
Getting Ready for the Test
Chapter Test
Cumulative Review

In this chapter, two or more equations in two or more variables are solved simultaneously. Such a collection of equations is called a **system of equations.** Systems of equations are good mathematical models for many real-world problems because these problems may involve several related patterns.

Bottled Water vs. Soda Consumption

Since 2009, the sale of bottled water has steadily increased, while the sale of carbonated beverages, or soda, has decreased. In Section 4.3, Exercises 57 and 58, we will use the functions graphed below to solve the system of equations.

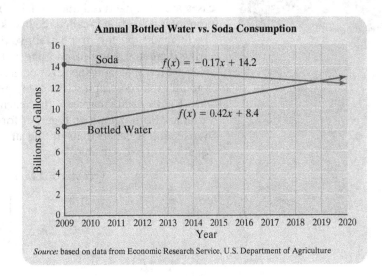

Annual Bottled Water vs. Soda Consumption

Source: based on data from Economic Research Service, U.S. Department of Agriculture

4.1 Solving Systems of Linear Equations in Two Variables

OBJECTIVES

1 Determine Whether an Ordered Pair Is a Solution of a System of Two Linear Equations.

2 Solve a System by Graphing.

3 Solve a System by Substitution.

4 Solve a System by Elimination.

An important problem that often occurs in the fields of business and economics concerns the concepts of revenue and cost. For example, suppose that a small manufacturing company begins to manufacture and sell iPad protective cases. The revenue of a company is the company's income from selling these cases, and the cost is the amount of money that a company spends to manufacture these cases. The following coordinate system shows the graphs of revenue and cost for the protective cases.

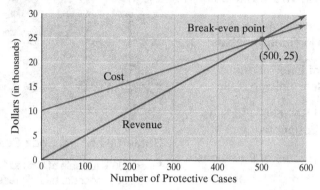

These lines intersect at the point $(500, 25)$. This means that when 500 protective cases are manufactured and sold, both cost and revenue are $25,000. In business, this point of intersection is called the **break-even point.** Notice that for x-values (cases sold) less than 500, the cost graph is above the revenue graph, meaning that cost of manufacturing is greater than revenue, and so the company is losing money. For x-values (cases sold) greater than 500, the revenue graph is above the cost graph, meaning that revenue is greater than cost, and so the company is making money.

Recall from Chapter 3 that each line is a graph of some linear equation in two variables. Both equations together form a **system of equations.** The common point of intersection is called the **solution of the system.** Some examples of systems of linear equations in two variables are

Systems of Linear Equations in Two Variables

$$\begin{cases} x - 2y = -7 \\ 3x + y = 0 \end{cases} \qquad \begin{cases} x = 5 \\ x + \dfrac{y}{2} = 9 \end{cases} \qquad \begin{cases} x - 3 = 2y + 6 \\ y = 1 \end{cases}$$

OBJECTIVE

1 Determining Whether an Ordered Pair Is a Solution

Recall that a solution of an equation in two variables is an ordered pair (x, y) that makes the equation true. A **solution of a system** of two equations in two variables is an ordered pair (x, y) that makes both equations true.

EXAMPLE 1 Determine whether the given ordered pair is a solution of the system.

a. $\begin{cases} -x + y = 2 \\ 2x - y = -3 \end{cases} \quad (-1, 1)$

b. $\begin{cases} 5x + 3y = -1 \\ x - y = 1 \end{cases} \quad (-2, 3)$

Solution

a. We replace x with -1 and y with 1 in each equation.

$-x + y = 2$ First equation $2x - y = -3$ Second equation

$-(-1) + (1) \overset{?}{=} 2$ Let $x = -1$ and $y = 1$. $2(-1) - (1) \overset{?}{=} -3$ Let $x = -1$ and $y = 1$.

$1 + 1 \overset{?}{=} 2$ $-2 - 1 \overset{?}{=} -3$

$2 = 2$ True $-3 = -3$ True

Since $(-1, 1)$ makes *both* equations true, it is a solution.

b. We replace x with -2 and y with 3 in each equation.

$5x + 3y = -1$ First equation

$5(-2) + 3(3) \stackrel{?}{=} -1$ Let $x = -2$ and $y = 3$.

$-10 + 9 \stackrel{?}{=} -1$

$-1 = -1$ True

$x - y = 1$ Second equation

$(-2) - (3) \stackrel{?}{=} 1$ Let $x = -2$ and $y = 3$.

$-5 = 1$ False

Since the ordered pair $(-2, 3)$ does not make *both* equations true, it is not a solution of the system. □

PRACTICE

1   Determine whether the given ordered pair is a solution of the system.

a. $\begin{cases} -x - 4y = 1 \\ 2x + y = 5 \end{cases}$ $(3, -1)$

b. $\begin{cases} 4x + y = -4 \\ -x + 3y = 8 \end{cases}$ $(-2, 4)$

OBJECTIVE

2   Solving a System by Graphing ▶

We can *estimate* the solutions of a system by graphing each equation on the same coordinate system and estimating the coordinates of any point of intersection.

EXAMPLE 2   Solve the system by graphing.

$$\begin{cases} x + y = 2 \\ 3x - y = -2 \end{cases}$$

Solution   First we graph the linear equations on the same rectangular coordinate system. These lines intersect at one point as shown. The coordinates of the point of intersection appear to be $(0, 2)$. We check this estimated solution by replacing x with 0 and y with 2 in *both* equations.

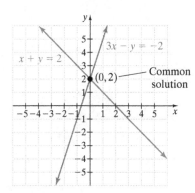

$x + y = 2$ First equation

$0 + 2 \stackrel{?}{=} 2$ Let $x = 0$ and $y = 2$.

$2 = 2$ True

$3x - y = -2$ Second equation

$3(0) - 2 \stackrel{?}{=} -2$ Let $x = 0$ and $y = 2$.

$-2 = -2$ True

Helpful Hint

Using set notation, we may write the solution set as $\{(0, 2)\}$.

The ordered pair $(0, 2)$ is the solution of the system. A system that has at least one solution, such as this one, is said to be **consistent.** □

PRACTICE

2   Solve the system by graphing. $\begin{cases} y = 5x \\ 2x + y = 7 \end{cases}$

Helpful Hint

Reading values from graphs may not be accurate. Until a proposed solution is checked in both equations of the system, we can only assume that we have *estimated* a solution.

In Example 2, we have a **consistent system.** To review, a system that has at least one solution is said to be consistent.

Later, we will talk about **dependent equations.** For now, we define an **independent equation** to be an equation in a system of equations that cannot be algebraically derived from any other equation in the system.

Thus:

One solution

Consistent System: **The system has at least one solution.**

Independent Equations: **Each equation in the system cannot be algebraically derived from the other. (Note: Their graphs are not the same.)**

EXAMPLE 3   Solve the system by graphing.

$$\begin{cases} x - 2y = 4 \\ x \quad\;\; = 2y \end{cases}$$

Solution We graph each linear equation.

The lines appear to be parallel. To be sure, let's write each equation in slope-intercept form, $y = mx + b$. To do so, we solve for y.

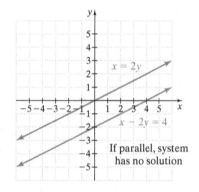

$x - 2y = 4$	First equation
$-2y = -x + 4$	Subtract x from both sides.
$y = \dfrac{1}{2}x - 2$	Divide both sides by -2

$x = 2y$	Second equation
$\dfrac{1}{2}x = y$	Divide both sides by 2.
$y = \dfrac{1}{2}x$	

If parallel, system has no solution

The graphs of these equations have the same slope, $\dfrac{1}{2}$, but different y-intercepts, so these lines are parallel. Therefore, the system has no solution since the equations have no common solution (there are no intersection points). A system that has no solution is said to be **inconsistent.**   □

PRACTICE
3   Solve the system by graphing. $\begin{cases} y = \dfrac{3}{4}x + 1 \\ 3x - 4y = 12 \end{cases}$ ■

In Example 3, we have an **inconsistent system.** To review, a system that has no solution is said to be inconsistent.

Let's now talk about the equations in this system. Each equation in this system cannot be algebraically derived from the other, so each equation is independent of the other.

Thus:

No solution

Inconsistent System: **The system has no solution.**

Independent Equations: **Each equation in the system cannot be algebraically derived from the other. (Note: Their graphs are not the same.)**

- If a system of equations has *at least one solution*, the system is *consistent.*
- If a system of equations has *no solution*, the system is *inconsistent.*

The pairs of equations in Examples 2 and 3 are called independent because their graphs differ. In Example 4, we see an example of dependent equations.

EXAMPLE 4 Solve the system by graphing.

$$\begin{cases} 2x + 4y = 10 \\ x + 2y = 5 \end{cases}$$

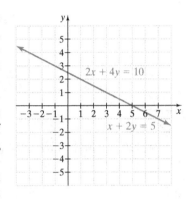

Solution We graph each linear equation. We see that the graphs of the equations are the same line. To confirm this, notice that if both sides of the second equation are multiplied by 2, the result is the first equation. This means that the equations have identical solutions. Any ordered pair solution of one equation satisfies the other equation also. These equations are said to be **dependent equations.** The solution set of the system is $\{(x, y) \mid x + 2y = 5\}$ or, equivalently, $\{(x, y) \mid 2x + 4y = 10\}$ since the lines describe identical ordered pairs. Written the second way, the solution set is read "the set of all ordered pairs (x, y), such that $2x + 4y = 10$." There is an infinite number of solutions to this system.

PRACTICE
4 Solve the system by graphing. $\begin{cases} 3x - 2y = 4 \\ -9x + 6y = -12 \end{cases}$

In Example 4, we have a **consistent system.** To review, a system that has at least one solution is said to be consistent. In fact, the system in Example 4 has an infinite number of solutions.

Let's now define **dependent equations.** We define a **dependent equation** to be an equation in a system of equations that can be algebraically derived from another equation in the system.

Thus:

> Consistent System: The system has at least one solution.
>
> Infinite number of solutions
>
> Dependent Equations: An equation in a system of equations can be algebraically derived from another. (Note: Their graphs are the same.)

- If the graphs of two equations *differ,* they are *independent* equations.
- If the graphs of two equations are the *same,* they are *dependent* equations.

✔ CONCEPT CHECK

The equations in the system are dependent and the system has an infinite number of solutions. Which ordered pairs below are solutions?

$$\begin{cases} -x + 3y = 4 \\ 2x + 8 = 6y \end{cases}$$

a. $(4, 0)$ **b.** $(-4, 0)$ **c.** $(-1, 1)$

Answer to Concept Check: **b, c**

We can summarize the information discovered in Examples 2 through 4 as follows.

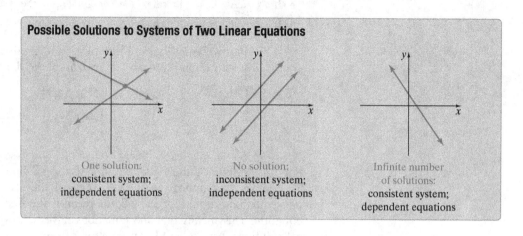

Possible Solutions to Systems of Two Linear Equations

One solution:
consistent system;
independent equations

No solution:
inconsistent system;
independent equations

Infinite number
of solutions:
consistent system;
dependent equations

✔ **CONCEPT CHECK**

How can you tell just by looking at the following system that it has no solution?

$$\begin{cases} y = 3x + 5 \\ y = 3x - 7 \end{cases}$$

How can you tell just by looking at the following system that it has infinitely many solutions?

$$\begin{cases} x + y = 5 \\ 2x + 2y = 10 \end{cases}$$

OBJECTIVE

3 Solving a System by Substitution ▶

Graphing the equations of a system by hand is often a good method of finding approximate solutions of a system, but it is not a reliable method of finding exact solutions of a system. We turn instead to two algebraic methods of solving systems. We use the first method, the **substitution method,** to solve the system

$$\begin{cases} 2x + 4y = -6 & \text{First equation} \\ \quad\ x = 2y - 5 & \text{Second equation} \end{cases}$$

EXAMPLE 5 Use the substitution method to solve the system.

$$\begin{cases} 2x + 4y = -6 & \text{First equation} \\ \quad\ x = 2y - 5 & \text{Second equation} \end{cases}$$

Solution In the second equation, we are told that x is equal to $2y - 5$. Since they are equal, we can *substitute* $2y - 5$ for x in the first equation. This will give us an equation in one variable, which we can solve for y.

$$2x + 4y = -6 \qquad \text{First equation}$$

$$2(\overbrace{2y - 5}) + 4y = -6 \qquad \text{Substitute } 2y - 5 \text{ for } x.$$

$$4y - 10 + 4y = -6$$

$$8y = 4$$

$$y = \frac{4}{8} = \frac{1}{2} \qquad \text{Solve for } y.$$

The y-coordinate of the solution is $\frac{1}{2}$. To find the x-coordinate, we replace y with $\frac{1}{2}$ in the second equation, $x = 2y - 5$.

$$x = 2y - 5$$

$$x = 2\left(\frac{1}{2}\right) - 5 = 1 - 5 = -4$$

The ordered pair solution is $\left(-4, \frac{1}{2}\right)$. Check to see that $\left(-4, \frac{1}{2}\right)$ satisfies both equations of the system. □

PRACTICE

5 Use the substitution method to solve the system.

$$\begin{cases} y = 4x + 7 \\ 2x + y = 4 \end{cases}$$

Solving a System of Two Equations Using the Substitution Method

Step 1. Solve one of the equations for one of its variables.

Step 2. Substitute the expression for the variable found in Step 1 into the other equation.

Step 3. Find the value of one variable by solving the equation from Step 2.

Step 4. Find the value of the other variable by substituting the value found in Step 3 into the equation from Step 1.

Step 5. Check the ordered pair solution in *both* original equations.

Helpful Hint

If a system of equations contains equations with fractions, the first step is to clear the equations of fractions.

EXAMPLE 6 Use the substitution method to solve the system.

$$\begin{cases} -\dfrac{x}{6} + \dfrac{y}{2} = \dfrac{1}{2} \\ \dfrac{x}{3} - \dfrac{y}{6} = -\dfrac{3}{4} \end{cases}$$

Solution First we multiply each equation by its least common denominator to clear the system of fractions. We multiply the first equation by 6 and the second equation by 12.

$$\begin{cases} 6\left(-\dfrac{x}{6} + \dfrac{y}{2}\right) = 6\left(\dfrac{1}{2}\right) \\ 12\left(\dfrac{x}{3} - \dfrac{y}{6}\right) = 12\left(-\dfrac{3}{4}\right) \end{cases}$$

simplifies to

$$\begin{cases} -x + 3y = 3 \quad \text{First equation} \\ 4x - 2y = -9 \quad \text{Second equation} \end{cases}$$

Helpful Hint

To avoid tedious fractions, solve for a variable whose coefficient is 1 or −1 if possible.

To use the substitution method, we now solve the first equation for x.

$$-x + 3y = 3 \quad \text{First equation}$$
$$3y - 3 = x \quad \text{Solve for } x.$$

Next we replace x with $3y - 3$ in the second equation.

$$4x - 2y = -9 \quad \text{Second equation}$$
$$4(\overline{3y - 3}) - 2y = -9$$
$$12y - 12 - 2y = -9$$
$$10y = 3$$
$$y = \frac{3}{10} \quad \text{Solve for } y.$$

To find the corresponding x-coordinate, we replace y with $\dfrac{3}{10}$ in the equation $x = 3y - 3$. Then

$$x = 3\left(\frac{3}{10}\right) - 3 = \frac{9}{10} - 3 = \frac{9}{10} - \frac{30}{10} = -\frac{21}{10}$$

The ordered pair solution is $\left(-\dfrac{21}{10}, \dfrac{3}{10}\right)$. Check to see that this solution satisfies both original equations. □

PRACTICE
6 Use the substitution method to solve the system.

$$\begin{cases} -\dfrac{x}{3} + \dfrac{y}{4} = \dfrac{1}{2} \\ \dfrac{x}{4} - \dfrac{y}{2} = -\dfrac{1}{4} \end{cases}$$

OBJECTIVE
4 Solving a System by Elimination

The **elimination method,** or **addition method,** is a second algebraic technique for solving systems of equations. For this method, we rely on a version of the addition property of equality, which states that "equals added to equals are equal."

If $A = B$ and $C = D$ then $A + C = B + D$.

EXAMPLE 7 Use the elimination method to solve the system.

$$\begin{cases} x - 5y = -12 & \text{First equation} \\ -x + y = 4 & \text{Second equation} \end{cases}$$

Solution Since the left side of each equation is equal to the right side, we add equal quantities by adding the left sides of the equations and the right sides of the equations. This sum gives us an equation in one variable, y, which we can solve for y.

$$\begin{array}{ll} x - 5y = -12 & \text{First equation} \\ \underline{-x + y = 4} & \text{Second equation} \\ -4y = -8 & \text{Add} \\ y = 2 & \text{Solve for } y. \end{array}$$

The y-coordinate of the solution is 2. To find the corresponding x-coordinate, we replace y with 2 in either original equation of the system. Let's use the second equation.

$$\begin{array}{ll} -x + y = 4 & \text{Second equation} \\ -x + 2 = 4 & \text{Let } y = 2. \\ -x = 2 \\ x = -2 \end{array}$$

The ordered pair solution is $(-2, 2)$. Check to see that $(-2, 2)$ satisfies both equations of the system. □

PRACTICE
7 Use the elimination method to solve the system.

$$\begin{cases} 3x - y = 5 \\ 5x + y = 11 \end{cases}$$

The steps below summarize the elimination method.

Solving a System of Two Linear Equations Using the Elimination Method

Step 1. Rewrite each equation in standard form, $Ax + By = C$.

Step 2. If necessary, multiply one or both equations by some nonzero number so that the coefficients of a variable are opposites of each other.

Step 3. Add the equations.

Step 4. Find the value of one variable by solving the equation from Step 3.

Step 5. Find the value of the second variable by substituting the value found in Step 4 into either original equation.

Step 6. Check the proposed ordered pair solution in *both* original equations.

EXAMPLE 8   Use the elimination method to solve the system.

$$\begin{cases} 3x - 2y = 10 \\ 4x - 3y = 15 \end{cases}$$

Solution If we add the two equations, the sum will still be an equation in two variables. Notice, however, that we can eliminate y when the equations are added if we multiply both sides of the first equation by 3 and both sides of the second equation by -2. Then

$$\begin{cases} 3(3x - 2y) = 3(10) \\ -2(4x - 3y) = -2(15) \end{cases} \quad \text{simplifies to} \quad \begin{cases} 9x - 6y = 30 \\ -8x + 6y = -30 \end{cases}$$

Next we add the left sides and add the right sides.

$$\begin{array}{r} 9x - 6y = 30 \\ -8x + 6y = -30 \\ \hline x \qquad\quad = 0 \end{array}$$

To find y, we let $x = 0$ in either equation of the system.

$$\begin{aligned} 3x - 2y &= 10 & \text{First equation} \\ 3(0) - 2y &= 10 & \text{Let } x = 0. \\ -2y &= 10 \\ y &= -5 \end{aligned}$$

The ordered pair solution is $(0, -5)$. Check to see that $(0, -5)$ satisfies both equations of the system.   □

PRACTICE

8   Use the elimination method to solve the system.

$$\begin{cases} 3x - 2y = -6 \\ 4x + 5y = -8 \end{cases}$$

EXAMPLE 9   Use the elimination method to solve the system.

$$\begin{cases} 3x + \dfrac{y}{2} = 2 \\ 6x + y = 5 \end{cases}$$

Solution If we multiply both sides of the first equation by -2, the coefficients of x in the two equations will be opposites. Then

$$\begin{cases} -2\left(3x + \dfrac{y}{2}\right) = -2(2) \\ 6x + y = 5 \end{cases} \quad \text{simplifies to} \quad \begin{cases} -6x - y = -4 \\ 6x + y = 5 \end{cases}$$

Now we can add the left sides and add the right sides.

$$-6x - y = -4$$
$$\underline{6x + y = 5}$$
$$0 = 1 \quad \text{False}$$

The resulting equation, $0 = 1$, is false for all values of y or x. Thus, the system has no solution. The solution set is $\{\ \}$ or $\varnothing$. This system is inconsistent, and the graphs of the equations are parallel lines. □

PRACTICE
9 Use the elimination method to solve the system.

$$\begin{cases} 8x + y = 6 \\ 2x + \dfrac{y}{4} = -2 \end{cases}$$

EXAMPLE 10 Use the elimination method to solve the system.

$$\begin{cases} -5x - 3y = 9 \\ 10x + 6y = -18 \end{cases}$$

Solution To eliminate x when the equations are added, we multiply both sides of the first equation by 2. Then

$$\begin{cases} 2(-5x - 3y) = 2(9) \\ 10x + 6y = -18 \end{cases} \quad \text{simplifies to} \quad \begin{cases} -10x - 6y = 18 \\ 10x + 6y = -18 \end{cases}$$

Next we add the equations.

$$-10x - 6y = 18$$
$$\underline{10x + 6y = -18}$$
$$0 = 0$$

The resulting equation, $0 = 0$, is true for all possible values of y or x. Notice in the original system that if both sides of the first equation are multiplied by -2, the result is the second equation. This means that the two equations are equivalent. They have the same solution set and there is an infinite number of solutions. Thus, the equations of this system are dependent, and the solution set of the system is

$$\{(x, y) | -5x - 3y = 9\} \quad \text{or, equivalently,} \quad \{(x, y) | 10x + 6y = -18\}. \quad \square$$

PRACTICE
10 Use the elimination method to solve the system.

$$\begin{cases} -3x + 2y = -1 \\ 9x - 6y = 3 \end{cases}$$

Helpful Hint

Remember that not all ordered pairs are solutions of the system in Example 10, only the infinite number of ordered pairs that satisfy $-5x - 3y = 9$ or, equivalently, $10x + 6y = -18$.

Graphing Calculator Explorations

A graphing calculator may be used to approximate solutions of systems of equations by graphing each equation on the same set of axes and approximating any points of intersection. For example, approximate the solution of the system

$$\begin{cases} y = -2.6x + 5.6 \\ y = 4.3x - 4.9 \end{cases}$$

First use a standard window and graph both equations on a single screen.

The two lines intersect. To approximate the point of intersection, trace to the point of intersection and use an Intersect feature of the graphing calculator or a Zoom In feature.

Using either method, we find that the approximate point of intersection is $(1.52, 1.64)$.

Solve each system of equations. Approximate the solutions to two decimal places.

1. $y = -1.65x + 3.65$
   $y = 4.56x - 9.44$

2. $y = 7.61x + 3.48$
   $y = -1.26x - 6.43$

3. $2.33x - 4.72y = 10.61$
   $5.86x + 6.22y = -8.89$

4. $-7.89x - 5.68y = 3.26$
   $-3.65x + 4.98y = 11.77$

 Vocabulary, Readiness & Video Check

Match each graph with the solution of the corresponding system.

A.   B.   C.   D.

1. no solution   2. Infinite number of solutions   3. $(1, -2)$ 4. $(-3, 0)$

Martin-Gay Interactive Videos

See Video 4.1

Watch the section lecture video and answer the following questions.

OBJECTIVE 1
5. In ▦ Example 1, the ordered pair is a solution of the first equation of the system. Why is this not enough to determine if the ordered pair is a solution of the system?

OBJECTIVE 2
6. From ▦ Example 2, what potential drawbacks does the graphing method have?

OBJECTIVE 3
7. The system in ▦ Example 3 needs one of its equations solved for a variable as a first step. What important point is then emphasized?

OBJECTIVE 4
8. Why is Step 2 in Solving a System by Elimination skipped in ▦ Example 5?

4.1 Exercise Set MyMathLab®

Determine whether each given ordered pair is a solution of each system. See Example 1.

1. $\begin{cases} x - y = 3 \\ 2x - 4y = 8 \end{cases}$ $(2, -1)$

2. $\begin{cases} x - y = -4 \\ 2x + 10y = 4 \end{cases}$ $(-3, 1)$

3. $\begin{cases} 2x - 3y = -9 \\ 4x + 2y = -2 \end{cases}$ $(3, 5)$

4. $\begin{cases} 2x - 5y = -2 \\ 3x + 4y = 4 \end{cases}$ $(4, 2)$

5. $\begin{cases} y = -5x \\ x = -2 \end{cases}$ $(-2, 10)$

6. $\begin{cases} y = 6 \\ x = -2y \end{cases}$ $(-12, 6)$

7. $\begin{cases} 3x + 7y = -19 \\ -6x = 5y + 8 \end{cases}$ $\left(\dfrac{2}{3}, -3\right)$

8. $\begin{cases} 4x + 5y = -7 \\ -8x = 3y - 1 \end{cases}$ $\left(\dfrac{3}{4}, -2\right)$

Solve each system by graphing. See Examples 2 through 4.

9. $\begin{cases} x + y = 1 \\ x - 2y = 4 \end{cases}$

10. $\begin{cases} 2x - y = 8 \\ x + 3y = 11 \end{cases}$

11. $\begin{cases} 2y - 4x = 0 \\ x + 2y = 5 \end{cases}$

12. $\begin{cases} 4x - y = 6 \\ x - y = 0 \end{cases}$

13. $\begin{cases} 3x - y = 4 \\ 6x - 2y = 4 \end{cases}$

14. $\begin{cases} -x + 3y = 6 \\ 3x - 9y = 9 \end{cases}$

Solve each system of equations by the substitution method. See Examples 5 and 6.

15. $\begin{cases} x + y = 10 \\ y = 4x \end{cases}$

16. $\begin{cases} 5x + 2y = -17 \\ x = 3y \end{cases}$

17. $\begin{cases} 4x - y = 9 \\ 2x + 3y = -27 \end{cases}$

18. $\begin{cases} 3x - y = 6 \\ -4x + 2y = -8 \end{cases}$

19. $\begin{cases} \dfrac{1}{2}x + \dfrac{3}{4}y = -\dfrac{1}{4} \\ \dfrac{3}{4}x - \dfrac{1}{4}y = 1 \end{cases}$

20. $\begin{cases} \dfrac{2}{5}x + \dfrac{1}{5}y = -1 \\ x + \dfrac{2}{5}y = -\dfrac{8}{5} \end{cases}$

21. $\begin{cases} \dfrac{x}{3} + y = \dfrac{4}{3} \\ -x + 2y = 11 \end{cases}$

22. $\begin{cases} \dfrac{x}{8} - \dfrac{y}{2} = 1 \\ \dfrac{x}{3} - y = 2 \end{cases}$

Solve each system of equations by the elimination method. See Examples 7 through 10.

23. $\begin{cases} -x + 2y = 0 \\ x + 2y = 5 \end{cases}$

24. $\begin{cases} -2x + 3y = 0 \\ 2x + 6y = 3 \end{cases}$

25. $\begin{cases} 5x + 2y = 1 \\ x - 3y = 7 \end{cases}$

26. $\begin{cases} 6x - y = -5 \\ 4x - 2y = 6 \end{cases}$

27. $\begin{cases} \dfrac{3}{4}x + \dfrac{5}{2}y = 11 \\ \dfrac{1}{16}x - \dfrac{3}{4}y = -1 \end{cases}$

28. $\begin{cases} \dfrac{2}{3}x + \dfrac{1}{4}y = -\dfrac{3}{2} \\ \dfrac{1}{2}x - \dfrac{1}{4}y = -2 \end{cases}$

29. $\begin{cases} 3x - 5y = 11 \\ 2x - 6y = 2 \end{cases}$

30. $\begin{cases} 6x - 3y = -3 \\ 4x + 5y = -9 \end{cases}$

31. $\begin{cases} x - 2y = 4 \\ 2x - 4y = 4 \end{cases}$

32. $\begin{cases} -x + 3y = 6 \\ 3x - 9y = 9 \end{cases}$

33. $\begin{cases} 3x + y = 1 \\ 2y = 2 - 6x \end{cases}$

34. $\begin{cases} y = 2x - 5 \\ 8x - 4y = 20 \end{cases}$

MIXED PRACTICE

Solve each system of equations.

35. $\begin{cases} 2x + 5y = 8 \\ 6x + y = 10 \end{cases}$

36. $\begin{cases} x - 4y = -5 \\ -3x - 8y = 0 \end{cases}$

37. $\begin{cases} 2x + 3y = 1 \\ x - 2y = 4 \end{cases}$

38. $\begin{cases} -2x + y = -8 \\ x + 3y = 11 \end{cases}$

39. $\begin{cases} \dfrac{1}{3}x + y = \dfrac{4}{3} \\ -\dfrac{1}{4}x - \dfrac{1}{2}y = -\dfrac{1}{4} \end{cases}$

40. $\begin{cases} \dfrac{3}{4}x - \dfrac{1}{2}y = -\dfrac{1}{2} \\ x + y = -\dfrac{3}{2} \end{cases}$

41. $\begin{cases} 2x + 6y = 8 \\ 3x + 9y = 12 \end{cases}$

42. $\begin{cases} x = 3y - 1 \\ 2x - 6y = -2 \end{cases}$

43. $\begin{cases} 4x + 2y = 5 \\ 2x + y = -1 \end{cases}$

44. $\begin{cases} 3x + 6y = 15 \\ 2x + 4y = 3 \end{cases}$

45. $\begin{cases} 10y - 2x = 1 \\ 5y = 4 - 6x \end{cases}$

46. $\begin{cases} 3x + 4y = 0 \\ 7x = 3y \end{cases}$

47. $\begin{cases} 5x - 2y = 27 \\ -3x + 5y = 18 \end{cases}$

48. $\begin{cases} 3x + 4y = 2 \\ 2x + 5y = -1 \end{cases}$

49. $\begin{cases} x = 3y + 2 \\ 5x - 15y = 10 \end{cases}$

50. $\begin{cases} y = \dfrac{1}{7}x + 3 \\ x - 7y = -21 \end{cases}$

51. $\begin{cases} 2x - y = -1 \\ y = -2x \end{cases}$

52. $\begin{cases} x = \dfrac{1}{5}y \\ x - y = -4 \end{cases}$

53. $\begin{cases} 2x = 6 \\ y = 5 - x \end{cases}$

54. $\begin{cases} x = 3y + 4 \\ -y = 5 \end{cases}$

55. $\begin{cases} \dfrac{x + 5}{2} = \dfrac{6 - 4y}{3} \\ \dfrac{3x}{5} = \dfrac{21 - 7y}{10} \end{cases}$

56. $\begin{cases} \dfrac{y}{5} = \dfrac{8 - x}{2} \\ x = \dfrac{2y - 8}{3} \end{cases}$

57. $\begin{cases} 4x - 7y = 7 \\ 12x - 21y = 24 \end{cases}$

58. $\begin{cases} 2x - 5y = 12 \\ -4x + 10y = 20 \end{cases}$

59. $\begin{cases} \dfrac{2}{3}x - \dfrac{3}{4}y = -1 \\ -\dfrac{1}{6}x + \dfrac{3}{8}y = 1 \end{cases}$

60. $\begin{cases} \dfrac{1}{2}x - \dfrac{1}{3}y = -3 \\ \dfrac{1}{8}x + \dfrac{1}{6}y = 0 \end{cases}$

61. $\begin{cases} 0.7x - 0.2y = -1.6 \\ 0.2x - y = -1.4 \end{cases}$

62. $\begin{cases} -0.7x + 0.6y = 1.3 \\ 0.5x - 0.3y = -0.8 \end{cases}$

63. $\begin{cases} 4x - 1.5y = 10.2 \\ 2x + 7.8y = -25.68 \end{cases}$

64. $\begin{cases} x - 3y = -5.3 \\ 6.3x + 6y = 3.96 \end{cases}$

REVIEW AND PREVIEW

Determine whether the given replacement values make each equation true or false. See Section 1.3.

65. $3x - 4y + 2z = 5$; $x = 1$, $y = 2$, and $z = 5$

66. $x + 2y - z = 7$; $x = 2$, $y = -3$, and $z = 3$

67. $-x - 5y + 3z = 15$; $x = 0$, $y = -1$, and $z = 5$

68. $-4x + y - 8z = 4$; $x = 1$, $y = 0$, and $z = -1$

Add the equations. See Section 4.1.

69.
$$3x + 2y - 5z = 10$$
$$-3x + 4y + z = 15$$

70.
$$x + 4y - 5z = 20$$
$$2x - 4y - 2z = -17$$

71.
$$10x + 5y + 6z = 14$$
$$-9x + 5y - 6z = -12$$

72.
$$-9x - 8y - z = 31$$
$$9x + 4y - z = 12$$

CONCEPT EXTENSIONS

Without graphing, determine whether each system has one solution, no solution, or an infinite number of solutions. See the second Concept Check in this section.

73. $\begin{cases} y = 2x - 5 \\ y = 2x + 1 \end{cases}$

74. $\begin{cases} y = 3x - \dfrac{1}{2} \\ y = -2x + \dfrac{1}{5} \end{cases}$

75. $\begin{cases} x + y = 3 \\ 5x + 5y = 15 \end{cases}$

76. $\begin{cases} y = 5x - 2 \\ y = -\dfrac{1}{5}x - 2 \end{cases}$

77. Can a system consisting of two linear equations have exactly two solutions? Explain why or why not.

78. Suppose the graph of the equations in a system of two equations in two variables consists of a circle and a line. Discuss the possible number of solutions for this system.

The concept of supply and demand is used often in business. In general, as the unit price of a commodity increases, the demand for that commodity decreases. Also, as a commodity's unit price increases, the manufacturer normally increases the supply. The point where supply is equal to demand is called the equilibrium point. The following shows the graph of a demand equation and the graph of a supply equation for previously rented DVDs. The x-axis represents the number of DVDs in thousands, and the y-axis represents the cost of a DVD. Use this graph to answer Exercises 79 through 82.

79. Find the number of DVDs and the price per DVD when supply equals demand.

80. When x is between 3 and 4, is supply greater than demand or is demand greater than supply?

81. When x is greater than 6, is supply greater than demand or is demand greater than supply?

82. For what x-values are the y-values corresponding to the supply equation greater than the y-values corresponding to the demand equation?

The revenue equation for a certain brand of toothpaste is $y = 2.5x$, where x is the number of tubes of toothpaste sold and y is the total income for selling x tubes. The cost equation is $y = 0.9x + 3000$, where x is the number of tubes of toothpaste manufactured and y is the cost of producing x tubes. The following set of axes shows the graph of the cost and revenue equations. Use this graph for Exercises 83 through 88.

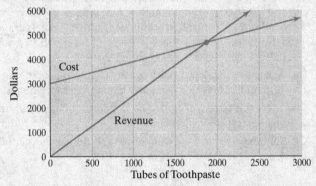

83. Find the coordinates of the point of intersection, or break-even point, by solving the system

$$\begin{cases} y = 2.5x \\ y = 0.9x + 3000 \end{cases}$$

84. Explain the meaning of the x-value of the point of intersection.

85. If the company sells 2000 tubes of toothpaste, does the company make money or lose money?

86. If the company sells 1000 tubes of toothpaste, does the company make money or lose money?

87. For what x-values will the company make a profit? (*Hint:* For what x-values is the revenue graph "higher" than the cost graph?)

88. For what x-values will the company lose money? (*Hint:* For what x-values is the revenue graph "lower" than the cost graph?)

89. Write a system of two linear equations in x and y that has the ordered pair solution $(2, 5)$.

90. Which method would you use to solve the system?

$$\begin{cases} 5x - 2y = 6 \\ 2x + 3y = 5 \end{cases}$$

Explain your choice.

91. The number of mobile phone subscriptions has been growing steadily since 2000, while the number of landline accounts has been decreasing. The number per hundred people y of mobile phone subscriptions in the United States can be modeled by the linear equation $y = 3.9x + 44.1$. The number per hundred people y of landline phone subscriptions in the United States can be modeled by $y = -1.8x + 67.3$. In both models, $x = 0$ represents the year 2000. (*Source:* World Tele-communications/ICT Indicators Database)

   a. What does the slope of each equation tell you about the patterns of mobile phone and landline subscriptions?

   b. Solve this system of equations. Round your final results to the nearest whole numbers.

   c. Explain the meaning of your answer to part **b.**

92. The amount of U.S. federal government income y (in trillions of dollars), for fiscal year x from 2012 to 2015 ($x = 0$ represents 2012), can be modeled by the linear equation $y = 0.35x + 5.04$. The amount of U.S. federal government expenditures y (in trillions of dollars) for the same period can be modeled by $y = 0.03x + 6.03$. (*Source:* Based on data from U.S. Department of the Treasury)

   a. What does the slope of each equation tell you about the patterns of U.S. federal government income and expenditures?

   b. Solve this system of equations. Round your final results to the nearest whole numbers.

   c. Did expenditures ever equal income during the period from 2012 to 2015? If so, in what year?

Solve each system. To do so, you may want to let $a = \dfrac{1}{x}$ (if x is in the denominator) and let $b = \dfrac{1}{y}$ (if y is in the denominator.)

93. $\begin{cases} \dfrac{1}{x} + y = 12 \\ \dfrac{3}{x} - y = 4 \end{cases}$

94. $\begin{cases} x + \dfrac{2}{y} = 7 \\ 3x + \dfrac{3}{y} = 6 \end{cases}$

95. $\begin{cases} \dfrac{1}{x} + \dfrac{1}{y} = 5 \\ \dfrac{1}{x} - \dfrac{1}{y} = 1 \end{cases}$

96. $\begin{cases} \dfrac{2}{x} + \dfrac{3}{y} = 5 \\ \dfrac{5}{x} - \dfrac{3}{y} = 2 \end{cases}$

97. $\begin{cases} \dfrac{2}{x} - \dfrac{4}{y} = 5 \\ \dfrac{1}{x} - \dfrac{2}{y} = \dfrac{3}{2} \end{cases}$

98. $\begin{cases} \dfrac{2}{x} + \dfrac{3}{y} = -1 \\ \dfrac{3}{x} - \dfrac{2}{y} = 18 \end{cases}$

99. $\begin{cases} \dfrac{3}{x} - \dfrac{2}{y} = -18 \\ \dfrac{2}{x} + \dfrac{3}{y} = 1 \end{cases}$

100. $\begin{cases} \dfrac{5}{x} + \dfrac{7}{y} = 1 \\ -\dfrac{10}{x} - \dfrac{14}{y} = 0 \end{cases}$

4.2 Solving Systems of Linear Equations in Three Variables

OBJECTIVE

1 Solve a System of Three Linear Equations in Three Variables.

In this section, the algebraic methods of solving systems of two linear equations in two variables are extended to systems of three linear equations in three variables. We call the equation $3x - y + z = -15$, for example, a **linear equation in three variables** since there are three variables and each variable is raised only to the power 1. A solution of this equation is an **ordered triple (x, y, z)** that makes the equation a true statement. For example, the ordered triple $(2, 0, -21)$ is a solution of $3x - y + z = -15$ since replacing x with 2, y with 0, and z with -21 yields the true statement $3(2) - 0 + (-21) = -15$. The graph of this equation is a plane in three-dimensional space, just as the graph of a linear equation in two variables is a line in two-dimensional space.

Although we will not discuss the techniques for graphing equations in three variables, visualizing the possible patterns of intersecting planes gives us insight into the possible patterns of solutions of a system of three three-variable linear equations. There are four possible patterns.

   1. Three planes have a single point in common. This point represents the single solution of the system. This system is **consistent.**

2. Three planes intersect at no point common to all three. This system has no solution. A few ways that this can occur are shown. This system is **inconsistent.**

3. Three planes intersect at all the points of a single line. The system has infinitely many solutions. This system is **consistent.**

4. Three planes coincide at all points on the plane. The system is consistent, and the equations are **dependent.**

OBJECTIVE

1   **Solving a System of Three Linear Equations in Three Variables**

Just as with systems of two equations in two variables, we can use the elimination or substitution method to solve a system of three equations in three variables. To use the elimination method, we eliminate a variable and obtain a system of two equations in two variables. Then we use the methods we learned in the previous section to solve the system of two equations.

EXAMPLE 1   Solve the system.

$$\begin{cases} 3x - y + z = -15 & \text{Equation (1)} \\ x + 2y - z = 1 & \text{Equation (2)} \\ 2x + 3y - 2z = 0 & \text{Equation (3)} \end{cases}$$

Solution Add equations (1) and (2) to eliminate z.

$$\begin{array}{r} 3x - y + z = -15 \\ \underline{x + 2y - z = 1} \\ 4x + y \phantom{{}- 2z} = -14 \quad \text{Equation (4)} \end{array}$$

Next, add two *other* equations and *eliminate z again*. To do so, multiply both sides of equation (1) by 2 and add this resulting equation to equation (3). Then

$$\begin{cases} 2(3x - y + z) = 2(-15) \\ 2x + 3y - 2z = 0 \end{cases} \quad \text{simplifies to} \quad \begin{cases} 6x - 2y + 2z = -30 \\ \underline{2x + 3y - 2z = 0} \\ 8x + y \phantom{{}- 2z} = -30 \quad \text{Equation (5)} \end{cases}$$

> **Helpful Hint**
>
> Don't forget to add two other equations besides equations (1) and (2) *and* to **eliminate the same variable.**

(Continued on next page)

Now solve equations (4) and (5) for x and y. To solve by elimination, multiply both sides of equation (4) by -1 and add this resulting equation to equation (5). Then

$$\begin{cases} -1(4x + y) = -1(-14) \\ 8x + y = -30 \end{cases} \text{ simplifies to } \begin{cases} -4x - y = 14 \\ \underline{8x + y = -30} \\ 4x = -16 \quad \text{Add the equations.} \\ x = -4 \quad \text{Solve for } x. \end{cases}$$

Replace x with -4 in equation (4) or (5).

$$\begin{aligned} 4x + y &= -14 \quad \text{Equation (4)} \\ 4(-4) + y &= -14 \quad \text{Let } x = -4. \\ y &= 2 \quad \text{Solve for } y. \end{aligned}$$

Finally, replace x with -4 and y with 2 in equation (1), (2), or (3).

$$\begin{aligned} x + 2y - z &= 1 \quad \text{Equation (2)} \\ -4 + 2(2) - z &= 1 \quad \text{Let } x = -4 \text{ and } y = 2. \\ -4 + 4 - z &= 1 \\ -z &= 1 \\ z &= -1 \end{aligned}$$

The solution is $(-4, 2, -1)$. To check, let $x = -4$, $y = 2$, and $z = -1$ in all three original equations of the system.

Equation (1)	**Equation (2)**	**Equation (3)**
$3x - y + z = -15$	$x + 2y - z = 1$	$2x + 3y - 2z = 0$
$3(-4) - 2 + (-1) \stackrel{?}{=} -15$	$-4 + 2(2) - (-1) \stackrel{?}{=} 1$	$2(-4) + 3(2) - 2(-1) \stackrel{?}{=} 0$
$-12 - 2 - 1 \stackrel{?}{=} -15$	$-4 + 4 + 1 \stackrel{?}{=} 1$	$-8 + 6 + 2 \stackrel{?}{=} 0$
$-15 = -15$ True	$1 = 1$ True	$0 = 0$ True

All three statements are true, so the solution is $(-4, 2, -1)$. ☐

PRACTICE 1 Solve the system. $\begin{cases} 3x + 2y - z = 0 \\ x - y + 5z = 2 \\ 2x + 3y + 3z = 7 \end{cases}$ ■

EXAMPLE 2 Solve the system.

$$\begin{cases} 2x - 4y + 8z = 2 & (1) \\ -x - 3y + z = 11 & (2) \\ x - 2y + 4z = 0 & (3) \end{cases}$$

Solution Add equations (2) and (3) to eliminate x, and the new equation is

$$-5y + 5z = 11 \quad (4)$$

To eliminate x again, multiply both sides of equation (2) by 2 and add the resulting equation to equation (1). Then

$$\begin{cases} 2x - 4y + 8z = 2 \\ 2(-x - 3y + z) = 2(11) \end{cases} \begin{array}{c} \text{simplifies} \\ \text{to} \end{array} \begin{cases} 2x - 4y + 8z = 2 \\ \underline{-2x - 6y + 2z = 22} \\ -10y + 10z = 24 \quad (5) \end{cases}$$

Next, solve for y and z using equations (4) and (5). Multiply both sides of equation (4) by -2 and add the resulting equation to equation (5).

$$\begin{cases} -2(-5y + 5z) = -2(11) \\ -10y + 10z = 24 \end{cases} \quad \begin{array}{c} \text{simplifies} \\ \text{to} \end{array} \quad \begin{cases} 10y - 10z = -22 \\ \underline{-10y + 10z = 24} \\ 0 = 2 \quad \text{False} \end{cases}$$

Since the statement is false, this system is inconsistent and has no solution. The solution set is the empty set $\{\ \}$ or $\varnothing$.   □

PRACTICE
2   Solve the system. $\begin{cases} 6x - 3y + 12z = 4 \\ -6x + 4y - 2z = 7 \\ -2x + y - 4z = 3 \end{cases}$ ▪

The elimination method is summarized next.

Solving a System of Three Linear Equations by the Elimination Method

Step 1. Write each equation in standard form $Ax + By + Cz = D$.

Step 2. Choose a pair of equations and use the equations to eliminate a variable.

Step 3. Choose any **other** pair of equations and eliminate the **same variable** as in Step 2.

Step 4. Two equations in two variables should be obtained from Step 2 and Step 3. Use methods from Section 4.1 to solve this system for both variables.

Step 5. To solve for the third variable, substitute the values of the variables found in Step 4 into any of the original equations containing the third variable.

Step 6. Check the ordered triple solution in *all three* original equations.

> **Helpful Hint**
> Make sure you read closely and follow Step 3.

✔ **CONCEPT CHECK**

In the system

$$\begin{cases} x + y + z = 6 & \text{Equation (1)} \\ 2x - y + z = 3 & \text{Equation (2)} \\ x + 2y + 3z = 14 & \text{Equation (3)} \end{cases}$$

equations (1) and (2) are used to eliminate y. Which action could best be used to finish solving? Why?

a. Use (1) and (2) to eliminate z.   **b.** Use (2) and (3) to eliminate y.
c. Use (1) and (3) to eliminate x.

EXAMPLE 3   Solve the system.

$$\begin{cases} 2x + 4y = 1 & (1) \\ 4x - 4z = -1 & (2) \\ y - 4z = -3 & (3) \end{cases}$$

Solution Notice that equation (2) has no term containing the variable y. Let us eliminate y using equations (1) and (3). Multiply both sides of equation (3) by -4 and add the resulting equation to equation (1). Then

$$\begin{cases} 2x + 4y = 1 \\ -4(y - 4z) = -4(-3) \end{cases} \quad \text{simplifies to} \quad \begin{cases} 2x + 4y = 1 \\ \underline{ -4y + 16z = 12} \\ 2x + 16z = 13 \quad (4) \end{cases}$$

(Continued on next page)

Next, solve for z using equations (4) and (2). Multiply both sides of equation (4) by -2 and add the resulting equation to equation (2).

$$\begin{cases} -2(2x + 16z) = -2(13) \\ 4x - 4z = -1 \end{cases} \quad \text{simplifies to} \quad \begin{cases} -4x - 32z = -26 \\ \underline{4x - 4z = -1} \\ -36z = -27 \\ z = \dfrac{3}{4} \end{cases}$$

Replace z with $\dfrac{3}{4}$ in equation (3) and solve for y.

$$y - 4\left(\frac{3}{4}\right) = -3 \quad \text{Let } z = \frac{3}{4} \text{ in equation (3).}$$
$$y - 3 = -3$$
$$y = 0$$

Replace y with 0 in equation (1) and solve for x.

$$2x + 4(0) = 1$$
$$2x = 1$$
$$x = \frac{1}{2}$$

The solution is $\left(\dfrac{1}{2}, 0, \dfrac{3}{4}\right)$. Check to see that this solution satisfies all three equations of the system. □

PRACTICE
3 Solve the system. $\begin{cases} 3x + 4y = 0 \\ 9x - 4z = 6 \\ -2y + 7z = 1 \end{cases}$ ■

EXAMPLE 4 Solve the system.

$$\begin{cases} x - 5y - 2z = 6 & (1) \\ -2x + 10y + 4z = -12 & (2) \\ \dfrac{1}{2}x - \dfrac{5}{2}y - z = 3 & (3) \end{cases}$$

Solution Multiply both sides of equation (3) by 2 to eliminate fractions and multiply both sides of equation (2) by $-\dfrac{1}{2}$ so that the coefficient of x is 1. The resulting system is then

$$\begin{cases} x - 5y - 2z = 6 & (1) \\ x - 5y - 2z = 6 & \text{Multiply (2) by } -\dfrac{1}{2}. \\ x - 5y - 2z = 6 & \text{Multiply (3) by 2.} \end{cases}$$

All three equations are identical, and therefore equations (1), (2), and (3) are all equivalent. There are infinitely many solutions of this system. The equations are dependent. The solution set can be written as $\{(x, y, z) \mid x - 5y - 2z = 6\}$. □

PRACTICE
4 Solve the system. $\begin{cases} 2x + y - 3z = 6 \\ x + \dfrac{1}{2}y - \dfrac{3}{2}z = 3 \\ -4x - 2y + 6z = -12 \end{cases}$ ■

As mentioned earlier, we can also use the substitution method to solve a system of linear equations in three variables.

EXAMPLE 5   Solve the system.

$$\begin{cases} x - 4y - 5z = 35 & (1) \\ x - 3y = 0 & (2) \\ -y + z = -55 & (3) \end{cases}$$

Solution   Notice in equations (2) and (3) that a variable is missing. Also notice that both equations contain the variable y. Let's use the substitution method by solving equation (2) for x and equation (3) for z and substituting the results in equation (1).

$$x - 3y = 0 \qquad (2)$$
$$x = 3y \qquad \text{Solve equation (2) for } x.$$
$$-y + z = -55 \qquad (3)$$
$$z = y - 55 \qquad \text{Solve equation (3) for } z.$$

Now substitute $3y$ for x and $y - 55$ for z in equation (1).

$$x - 4y - 5z = 35 \qquad (1)$$

Helpful Hint

Do not forget to distribute.

$$3y - 4y - 5(y - 55) = 35 \qquad \text{Let } x = 3y \text{ and } z = y - 55.$$
$$3y - 4y - 5y + 275 = 35 \qquad \text{Use the distributive law and multiply.}$$
$$-6y + 275 = 35 \qquad \text{Combine like terms.}$$
$$-6y = -240 \qquad \text{Subtract 275 from both sides.}$$
$$y = 40 \qquad \text{Solve.}$$

To find x, recall that $x = 3y$ and substitute 40 for y. Then $x = 3y$ becomes $x = 3 \cdot 40 = 120$. To find z, recall that $z = y - 55$ and substitute 40 for y, also. Then $z = y - 55$ becomes $z = 40 - 55 = -15$. The solution is $(120, 40, -15)$.   □

PRACTICE
5   Solve the system. $\begin{cases} x + 2y + 4z = 16 \\ x + 2z = -4 \\ y - 3z = 30 \end{cases}$ ■

 Vocabulary, Readiness & Video Check

Solve.

1. Choose the equation(s) that has $(-1, 3, 1)$ as a solution.
   a. $x + y + z = 3$ **b.** $-x + y + z = 5$ **c.** $-x + y + 2z = 0$ **d.** $x + 2y - 3z = 2$

2. Choose the equation(s) that has $(2, 1, -4)$ as a solution.
   a. $x + y + z = -1$ **b.** $x - y - z = -3$ **c.** $2x - y + z = -1$ **d.** $-x - 3y - z = -1$

3. Use the result of Exercise 1 to determine whether $(-1, 3, 1)$ is a solution of the system below. Explain your answer.
   $$\begin{cases} x + y + z = 3 \\ -x + y + z = 5 \\ x + 2y - 3z = 2 \end{cases}$$

4. Use the result of Exercise 2 to determine whether $(2, 1, -4)$ is a solution of the system below. Explain your answer.
   $$\begin{cases} x + y + z = -1 \\ x - y - z = -3 \\ 2x - y + z = -1 \end{cases}$$

Martin-Gay Interactive Videos

Watch the section lecture video and answer the following question.

OBJECTIVE

1

5. From Example 1 and the lecture before, why does Step 3 stress that the same variable be eliminated from two other equations?

See Video 4.2

4.2 Exercise Set MyMathLab®

Solve each system. See Examples 1 through 5.

1. $\begin{cases} x - y + z = -4 \\ 3x + 2y - z = 5 \\ -2x + 3y - z = 15 \end{cases}$

2. $\begin{cases} x + y - z = -1 \\ -4x - y + 2z = -7 \\ 2x - 2y - 5z = 7 \end{cases}$

3. $\begin{cases} x + y = 3 \\ 2y = 10 \\ 3x + 2y - 3z = 1 \end{cases}$

4. $\begin{cases} 5x = 5 \\ 2x + y = 4 \\ 3x + y - 4z = -15 \end{cases}$

5. $\begin{cases} 2x + 2y + z = 1 \\ -x + y + 2z = 3 \\ x + 2y + 4z = 0 \end{cases}$

6. $\begin{cases} 2x - 3y + z = 5 \\ x + y + z = 0 \\ 4x + 2y + 4z = 4 \end{cases}$

7. $\begin{cases} x - 2y + z = -5 \\ -3x + 6y - 3z = 15 \\ 2x - 4y + 2z = -10 \end{cases}$

8. $\begin{cases} 3x + y - 2z = 2 \\ -6x - 2y + 4z = -4 \\ 9x + 3y - 6z = 6 \end{cases}$

9. $\begin{cases} 4x - y + 2z = 5 \\ 2y + z = 4 \\ 4x + y + 3z = 10 \end{cases}$

10. $\begin{cases} 5y - 7z = 14 \\ 2x + y + 4z = 10 \\ 2x + 6y - 3z = 30 \end{cases}$

11. $\begin{cases} x + 5z = 0 \\ 5x + y = 0 \\ y - 3z = 0 \end{cases}$

12. $\begin{cases} x - 5y = 0 \\ x - z = 0 \\ -x + 5z = 0 \end{cases}$

13. $\begin{cases} 6x - 5z = 17 \\ 5x - y + 3z = -1 \\ 2x + y = -41 \end{cases}$

14. $\begin{cases} x + 2y = 6 \\ 7x + 3y + z = -33 \\ x - z = 16 \end{cases}$

15. $\begin{cases} x + y + z = 8 \\ 2x - y - z = 10 \\ x - 2y - 3z = 22 \end{cases}$

16. $\begin{cases} 5x + y + 3z = 1 \\ x - y + 3z = -7 \\ -x + y = 1 \end{cases}$

17. $\begin{cases} x + 2y - z = 5 \\ 6x + y + z = 7 \\ 2x + 4y - 2z = 5 \end{cases}$

18. $\begin{cases} 4x - y + 3z = 10 \\ x + y - z = 5 \\ 8x - 2y + 6z = 10 \end{cases}$

19. $\begin{cases} 2x - 3y + z = 2 \\ x - 5y + 5z = 3 \\ 3x + y - 3z = 5 \end{cases}$

20. $\begin{cases} 4x + y - z = 8 \\ x - y + 2z = 3 \\ 3x - y + z = 6 \end{cases}$

21. $\begin{cases} -2x - 4y + 6z = -8 \\ x + 2y - 3z = 4 \\ 4x + 8y - 12z = 16 \end{cases}$

22. $\begin{cases} -6x + 12y + 3z = -6 \\ 2x - 4y - z = 2 \\ -x + 2y + \dfrac{z}{2} = -1 \end{cases}$

23. $\begin{cases} 2x + 2y - 3z = 1 \\ y + 2z = -14 \\ 3x - 2y = -1 \end{cases}$

24. $\begin{cases} 7x + 4y = 10 \\ x - 4y + 2z = 6 \\ y - 2z = -1 \end{cases}$

25. $\begin{cases} x + 2y - z = 5 \\ -3x - 2y - 3z = 11 \\ 4x + 4y + 5z = -18 \end{cases}$

26. $\begin{cases} 3x - 3y + z = -1 \\ 3x - y - z = 3 \\ -6x + 4y + 3z = -8 \end{cases}$

27. $\begin{cases} \dfrac{3}{4}x - \dfrac{1}{3}y + \dfrac{1}{2}z = 9 \\ \dfrac{1}{6}x + \dfrac{1}{3}y - \dfrac{1}{2}z = 2 \\ \dfrac{1}{2}x - y + \dfrac{1}{2}z = 2 \end{cases}$

28. $\begin{cases} \dfrac{1}{3}x - \dfrac{1}{4}y + z = -9 \\ \dfrac{1}{2}x - \dfrac{1}{3}y - \dfrac{1}{4}z = -6 \\ x - \dfrac{1}{2}y - z = -8 \end{cases}$

REVIEW AND PREVIEW

Translating Solve. See Section 2.2.

29. The sum of two numbers is 45 and one number is twice the other. Find the numbers.

30. The difference of two numbers is 5. Twice the smaller number added to five times the larger number is 53. Find the numbers.

Solve. See Section 2.1.

31. $2(x - 1) - 3x = x - 12$

32. $7(2x - 1) + 4 = 11(3x - 2)$

33. $-y - 5(y + 5) = 3y - 10$

34. $z - 3(z + 7) = 6(2z + 1)$

CONCEPT EXTENSIONS

35. Write a single linear equation in three variables that has $(-1, 2, -4)$ as a solution. (There are many possibilities.) Explain the process you used to write an equation.

36. Write a system of three linear equations in three variables that has $(2, 1, 5)$ as a solution. (There are many possibilities.) Explain the process you used to write an equation.

37. Write a system of linear equations in three variables that has the solution $(-1, 2, -4)$. Explain the process you used to write your system.

38. When solving a system of three equation in three unknowns, explain how to determine that a system has no solution.

39. The fraction $\dfrac{1}{24}$ can be written as the following sum:

$$\frac{1}{24} = \frac{x}{8} + \frac{y}{4} + \frac{z}{3}$$

where the numbers x, y, and z are solutions of

$$\begin{cases} x + y + z = 1 \\ 2x - y + z = 0 \\ -x + 2y + 2z = -1 \end{cases}$$

Solve the system and see that the sum of the fractions is $\dfrac{1}{24}$.

40. The fraction $\dfrac{1}{18}$ can be written as the following sum:

$$\frac{1}{18} = \frac{x}{2} + \frac{y}{3} + \frac{z}{9}$$

where the numbers x, y, and z are solutions of

$$\begin{cases} x + 3y + z = -3 \\ -x + y + 2z = -14 \\ 3x + 2y - z = 12 \end{cases}$$

Solve the system and see that the sum of the fractions is $\dfrac{1}{18}$.

Solving systems involving more than three variables can be accomplished with methods similar to those encountered in this section. Apply what you already know to solve each system of equations in four variables.

41.
$$\begin{cases} x + y \quad\quad - w = 0 \\ y + 2z + w = 3 \\ x \quad - z \quad\quad = 1 \\ 2x - y \quad\quad - w = -1 \end{cases}$$

42.
$$\begin{cases} 5x + 4y \quad\quad = 29 \\ y + z - w = -2 \\ 5x \quad + z \quad\quad = 23 \\ y - z + w = 4 \end{cases}$$

43.
$$\begin{cases} x + y + z + w = 5 \\ 2x + y + z + w = 6 \\ x + y + z \quad = 2 \\ x + y \quad\quad = 0 \end{cases}$$

44.
$$\begin{cases} 2x \quad - z \quad\quad = -1 \\ y + z + w = 9 \\ y \quad - 2w = -6 \\ x + y \quad\quad = 3 \end{cases}$$

45. Write a system of three linear equations in three variables that are dependent equations.

46. How many solutions are there to the system in Exercise 45?

4.3   Systems of Linear Equations and Problem Solving

OBJECTIVES

1 Solve Problems That Can Be Modeled by a System of Two Linear Equations.

2 Solve Problems with Cost and Revenue Functions.

3 Solve Problems That Can Be Modeled by a System of Three Linear Equations.

OBJECTIVE

1   Solving Problems Modeled by Systems of Two Equations

Thus far, we have solved problems by writing one-variable equations and solving for the variable. Some of these problems can be solved, perhaps more easily, by writing a system of equations, as illustrated in this section.

EXAMPLE 1   **Predicting Equal Consumption of Red Meat and Poultry**

America's consumption of red meat has decreased most years since 2005, while consumption of poultry has decreased also, but to a much lesser amount. The function $y = -2.03x + 119.05$ approximates the annual pounds of red meat consumed per capita, where x is the number of years since 2005. The function $y = -0.41x + 103.21$ approximates the annual pounds of poultry consumed per capita, where x is also the number of years since 2005. Based on this trend, determine the year when the annual consumption of red meat and poultry is equal. (*Source:* USDA: Economic Research Service)

(Continued on next page)

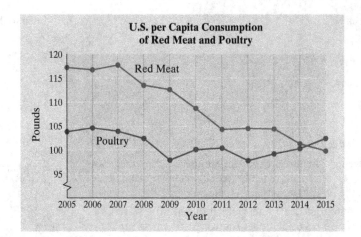

Solution

1. UNDERSTAND. Read and reread the problem and guess a year. Without using the graph for assistance, guess the year 2025. This year is 20 years since 2005, so $x = 20$. Now let $x = 20$ in each given function.

   Red meat: $y = -2.03x + 119.05 = -2.03(20) + 119.05 = 78.45$ pounds

   Poultry: $y = -0.41x + 103.21 = -0.41(20) + 103.21 = 95.01$ pounds

   Since the projected pounds in 2025 for red meat and poultry are not the same, we guessed incorrectly, but we do have a better understanding of the problem. We know that the year is earlier than 2025. Why? Because consumption of red meat for 2025 is less than consumption of poultry.

2. TRANSLATE. We are already given the system of equations.

3. SOLVE. We want to know the year x in which pounds y are the same, so we solve the system

$$\begin{cases} y = -2.03x + 119.05 \\ y = -0.41x + 103.21 \end{cases}$$

   Since both equations are solved for y, one way to solve is to use the substitution method.

   $$y = -0.41x + 103.21 \quad \text{Second equation}$$

   $$-2.03x + 119.05 = -0.41x + 103.21 \quad \text{Let } y = -2.03x + 119.05.$$

   $$-1.62x = -15.84$$

   $$x = \frac{-15.84}{-1.62} \approx 9.78$$

4. INTERPRET. Since we are only asked to find the year, we need only solve for x.

Check: To check, see whether $x \approx 9.78$ gives approximately the same number of pounds of red meat and poultry.

Red meat: $y = -2.03x + 119.05 = -2.03(9.78) + 119.05 = 99.1966$ pounds

Poultry: $y = -0.41x + 103.21 = -0.41(9.78) + 103.21 = 99.2002$ pounds

Since we rounded the number of years, the numbers of pounds do differ slightly. They differ only by 0.0036, so we can assume we solved correctly.

State: The consumption of red meat and poultry will be the same about 9.78 years after 2005, or 2014.78. Thus, in the year 2014, we calculate the consumption is the same. □

PRACTICE
1 Read Example 1. If we use the years 2012, 2013, 2014, and 2015 only to write functions approximating the consumption of red meat and poultry, we have the following:

$$\text{Red meat: } y = -0.91x + 110.45$$
$$\text{Poultry: } \quad y = 0.11x + 98.6$$

where x is the number of years since 2005 and y is the pounds per year per capita consumed.

a. Assuming this trend continues, predict the year when consumption of red meat and poultry will be the same. Round to the nearest year.

b. Does your answer differ from the answer to Example 1? Why or why not?

■

EXAMPLE 2   **Finding Unknown Numbers**

A first number is 4 less than a second number. Four times the first number is 6 more than twice the second. Find the numbers.

Solution

1. UNDERSTAND. Read and reread the problem and guess a solution. If a first number is 10 and this is 4 less than a second number, the second number is 14. Four times the first number is 4(10), or 40. This is not equal to 6 more than twice the second number, which is $2(14) + 6$ or 34. Although we guessed incorrectly, we now have a better understanding of the problem. Since we are looking for two numbers, we will let

$$x = \text{first number}$$
$$y = \text{second number}$$

2. TRANSLATE. Since we have assigned two variables to this problem, we will translate the given facts into two equations. For the first statement we have

In words:	the first number	is	4 less than the second number
	↓	↓	↓
Translate:	x	$=$	$y - 4$

Next we translate the second statement into an equation.

In words:	four times the first number	is	6 more than twice the second number
	↓	↓	↓
Translate:	$4x$	$=$	$2y + 6$

3. SOLVE. Here we solve the system

$$\begin{cases} x = y - 4 \\ 4x = 2y + 6 \end{cases}$$

Since the first equation expresses x in terms of y, we will use substitution. We substitute $y - 4$ for x in the second equation and solve for y.

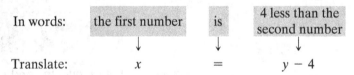

$$4x = 2y + 6 \quad \text{Second equation}$$
$$4(y - 4) = 2y + 6 \quad \text{Let } x = y - 4.$$
$$4y - 16 = 2y + 6$$
$$2y = 22$$
$$y = 11$$

(Continued on next page)

Now we replace y with 11 in the equation $x = y - 4$ and solve for x. Then $x = y - 4$ becomes $x = 11 - 4 = 7$. The ordered pair solution of the system is $(7, 11)$.

4. **INTERPRET.** Since the solution of the system is $(7, 11)$, then the first number we are looking for is 7 and the second number is 11.

Check: Notice that 7 *is* 4 less than 11, and 4 times 7 *is* 6 more than twice 11. The proposed numbers, 7 and 11, are correct.

State: The numbers are 7 and 11. □

PRACTICE

2 A first number is 5 more than a second number. Twice the first number is 2 less than 3 times the second number. Find the numbers. ■

EXAMPLE 3 Finding the Rate of Speed

Two cars leave Indianapolis, one traveling east and the other west. After 3 hours, they are 297 miles apart. If one car is traveling 5 mph faster than the other, what is the speed of each?

Solution

1. **UNDERSTAND.** Read and reread the problem. Let's guess a solution and use the formula $d = rt$ (distance = rate · time) to check. Suppose that one car is traveling at a rate of 55 miles per hour. This means that the other car is traveling at a rate of 50 miles per hour since we are told that one car is traveling 5 mph faster than the other. To find the distance apart after 3 hours, we will first find the distance traveled by each car. One car's distance is rate · time = $55(3) = 165$ miles. The other car's distance is rate · time = $50(3) = 150$ miles. Since one car is traveling east and the other west, their distance apart is the sum of their distances, or 165 miles + 150 miles = 315 miles. Although this distance apart is not the required distance of 297 miles, we now have a better understanding of the problem.

Let's model the problem with a system of equations. We will let

$$x = \text{speed of one car and}$$
$$y = \text{speed of the other car.}$$

We summarize the information on the following chart. Both cars have traveled 3 hours. Since distance = rate · time, their distances are $3x$ and $3y$ miles, respectively.

	Rate ·	Time	=	Distance
One Car	x	3		$3x$
Other Car	y	3		$3y$

2. **TRANSLATE.** We can now translate the stated conditions into two equations.

In words:	one car's distance	added to	the other car's distance	is	297
Translate:	$3x$	$+$	$3y$	$=$	297

In words:	one car's speed	is	5 mph faster than the other
Translate:	x	$=$	$y + 5$

3. SOLVE. Here we solve the system

$$\begin{cases} 3x + 3y = 297 \\ x \quad\;\; = y + 5 \end{cases}$$

Again, the substitution method is appropriate. We replace x with $y + 5$ in the first equation and solve for y.

$$3x + 3y = 297 \quad \text{\small First equation}$$
$$3(y + 5) + 3y = 297 \quad \text{\small Let } x = y + 5.$$
$$3y + 15 + 3y = 297$$
$$6y = 282$$
$$y = 47$$

To find x, we replace y with 47 in the equation $x = y + 5$. Then $x = 47 + 5 = 52$. The ordered pair solution of the system is $(52, 47)$.

4. INTERPRET. The solution $(52, 47)$ means that the cars are traveling at 52 mph and 47 mph, respectively.

Check: Notice that one car is traveling 5 mph faster than the other. Also, if one car travels 52 mph for 3 hours, the distance is $3(52) = 156$ miles. The other car traveling for 3 hours at 47 mph travels a distance of $3(47) = 141$ miles. The sum of the distances $156 + 141$ is 297 miles, the required distance.

Helpful Hint
Don't forget to attach units if appropriate.

State: The cars are traveling at 52 mph and 47 mph. □

PRACTICE
3

In 2007, the French train TGV V150 became the fastest conventional rail train in the world. It broke the 1990 record of the next fastest conventional rail train, the French TGV Atlantique. Assume the V150 and the Atlantique left the same station in Paris, with one heading west and one heading east. After 2 hours, they were 2150 kilometers apart. If the V150 is 75 kph faster than the Atlantique, what is the speed of each? ■

EXAMPLE 4   **Mixing Solutions**

Lynn Pike, a pharmacist, needs 70 liters of a 50% alcohol solution. She has available a 30% alcohol solution and an 80% alcohol solution. How many liters of each solution should she mix to obtain 70 liters of a 50% alcohol solution?

Solution

1. UNDERSTAND. Read and reread the problem. Next, guess the solution. Suppose that we need 20 liters of the 30% solution. Then we need $70 - 20 = 50$ liters of the 80% solution. To see if this gives us 70 liters of a 50% alcohol solution, let's find the amount of pure alcohol in each solution.

number of liters	×	alcohol strength	=	amount of pure alcohol
20 liters	×	0.30	=	6 liters
50 liters	×	0.80	=	40 liters
70 liters	×	0.50	=	35 liters

Since 6 liters + 40 liters = 46 liters and not 35 liters, our guess is incorrect, but we have gained some insight as to how to model and check this problem.

We will let

x = amount of 30% solution, in liters, and

y = amount of 80% solution, in liters

(Continued on next page)

and use a table to organize the given data.

	Number of Liters	Alcohol Strength	Amount of Pure Alcohol
30% Solution	x	30%	$0.30x$
80% Solution	y	80%	$0.80y$
50% Solution Needed	70	50%	$(0.50)(70)$

2. TRANSLATE. We translate the stated conditions into two equations.

In words: | amount of 30% solution | + | amount of 80% solution | = | 70 |

Translate: x + y = 70

In words: | amount of pure alcohol in 30% solution | + | amount of pure alcohol in 80% solution | = | amount of pure alcohol in 50% solution |

Translate: $0.30x$ + $0.80y$ = $(0.50)(70)$

3. SOLVE. Here we solve the system

$$\begin{cases} x + y = 70 \\ 0.30x + 0.80y = (0.50)(70) \end{cases}$$

To solve this system, we use the elimination method. We multiply both sides of the first equation by -3 and both sides of the second equation by 10. Then

$$\begin{cases} -3(x + y) = -3(70) \\ 10(0.30x + 0.80y) = 10(0.50)(70) \end{cases} \quad \begin{matrix} \text{simplifies} \\ \text{to} \end{matrix} \quad \begin{cases} -3x - 3y = -210 \\ \underline{3x + 8y = 350} \\ \quad 5y = 140 \\ \quad y = 28 \end{cases}$$

Now we replace y with 28 in the equation $x + y = 70$ and find that $x + 28 = 70$, or $x = 42$.
The ordered pair solution of the system is $(42, 28)$.

4. INTERPRET.

Check: Check the solution in the same way that we checked our guess.

State: The pharmacist needs to mix 42 liters of 30% solution and 28 liters of 80% solution to obtain 70 liters of 50% solution. □

PRACTICE
4 Keith Robinson is a chemistry teacher who needs 1 liter of a solution of 5% hydrochloric acid (HCl) to carry out an experiment. If he only has a stock solution of 99% HCl, how much water (0% acid) and how much stock solution (99%) of HCl must he mix to get 1 liter of 5% solution? Round answers to the nearest hundredth of a liter.

Suppose you mix an amount of 25% acid solution with an amount of 60% acid solution. You then calculate the acid strength of the resulting acid mixture. For which of the following results should you suspect an error in your calculation? Why?

a. 14%   **b.** 32%   **c.** 55%

OBJECTIVE

2   Solving Problems with Cost and Revenue Functions

Recall that businesses are often computing cost and revenue functions or equations to predict sales, to determine whether prices need to be adjusted, and to see whether the company is making or losing money. Recall also that the value at which revenue equals cost is called the break-even point. When revenue is less than cost, the company is losing money; when revenue is greater than cost, the company is making money.

EXAMPLE 5   **Finding a Break-Even Point**

A manufacturing company recently purchased $3000 worth of new equipment to offer new personalized stationery to its customers. The cost of producing a package of personalized stationery is $3.00, and it is sold for $5.50. Find the number of packages that must be sold for the company to break even.

Solution

1. UNDERSTAND. Read and reread the problem. Notice that the cost to the company will include a one-time cost of $3000 for the equipment and then $3.00 per package produced. The revenue will be $5.50 per package sold. To model this problem, we will let

x = number of packages of personalized stationery

$C(x)$ = total cost of producing x packages of stationery

$R(x)$ = total revenue from selling x packages of stationery

2. TRANSLATE. The revenue equation is

In words:	revenue for selling x packages of stationery	=	price per package	·	number of packages
Translate:	$R(x)$	=	5.5	·	x

The cost equation is

In words:	cost for producing x packages of stationery	=	cost per package	·	number of packages	+	cost for equipment
Translate:	$C(x)$	=	3	·	x	+	3000

Since the break-even point is when $R(x) = C(x)$, we solve the equation

$$5.5x = 3x + 3000$$

(Continued on next page)

3. SOLVE.

$$5.5x = 3x + 3000$$

$$2.5x = 3000 \qquad \text{Subtract } 3x \text{ from both sides.}$$

$$x = 1200 \qquad \text{Divide both sides by 2.5.}$$

4. INTERPRET.

Check: To see whether the break-even point occurs when 1200 packages are produced and sold, see if revenue equals cost when $x = 1200$. When $x = 1200$, $R(x) = 5.5x = 5.5(1200) = 6600$ and $C(x) = 3x + 3000 = 3(1200) + 3000 = 6600$. Since $R(1200) = C(1200) = 6600$, the break-even point is 1200.

State: The company must sell 1200 packages of stationery to break even. The graph of this system is shown.

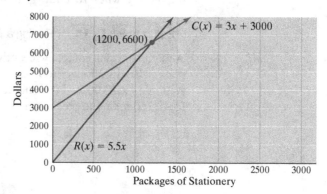

PRACTICE

5 An online-only electronics firm recently purchased $3000 worth of new equipment to create shock-proof packaging for its products. The cost of producing one shock-proof package is $2.50, and the firm charges the customer $4.50 for the packaging. Find the number of packages that must be sold for the company to break even.

OBJECTIVE

3 Solving Problems Modeled by Systems of Three Equations

To introduce problem solving by writing a system of three linear equations in three variables, we solve a problem about triangles.

EXAMPLE 6 Finding Angle Measures

The measure of the largest angle of a triangle is 80° more than the measure of the smallest angle, and the measure of the remaining angle is 10° more than the measure of the smallest angle. Find the measure of each angle.

Solution

1. UNDERSTAND. Read and reread the problem. Recall that the sum of the measures of the angles of a triangle is 180°. Then guess a solution. If the smallest angle measures 20°, the measure of the largest angle is 80° more, or $20° + 80° = 100°$. The measure of the remaining angle is 10° more than the measure of the smallest angle, or $20° + 10° = 30°$. The sum of these three angles is $20° + 100° + 30° = 150°$, not the required 180°. We now know that the measure of the smallest angle is greater than 20°.

To model this problem, we will let

$x =$ degree measure of the smallest angle

$y =$ degree measure of the largest angle

$z =$ degree measure of the remaining angle

2. TRANSLATE. We translate the given information into three equations.

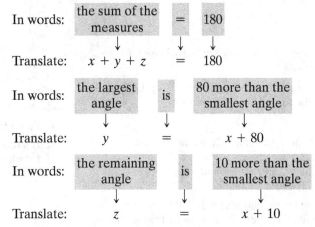

In words: | the sum of the measures | = | 180

Translate: $x + y + z = 180$

In words: | the largest angle | is | 80 more than the smallest angle

Translate: $y = x + 80$

In words: | the remaining angle | is | 10 more than the smallest angle

Translate: $z = x + 10$

3. SOLVE. We solve the system

$$\begin{cases} x + y + z = 180 \\ y = x + 80 \\ z = x + 10 \end{cases}$$

Since y and z are both expressed in terms of x, we will solve using the substitution method. We substitute $y = x + 80$ and $z = x + 10$ in the first equation. Then

$$x + y + z = 180 \quad \text{First equation}$$
$$x + (x + 80) + (x + 10) = 180 \quad \text{Let } y = x + 80 \text{ and } z = x + 10.$$
$$3x + 90 = 180$$
$$3x = 90$$
$$x = 30$$

Then $y = x + 80 = 30 + 80 = 110$, and $z = x + 10 = 30 + 10 = 40$. The ordered triple solution is $(30, 110, 40)$.

4. INTERPRET.

Check: Notice that $30° + 40° + 110° = 180°$. Also, the measure of the largest angle, $110°$, is $80°$ more than the measure of the smallest angle, $30°$. The measure of the remaining angle, $40°$, is $10°$ more than the measure of the smallest angle, $30°$. □

PRACTICE
6 The measure of the largest angle of a triangle is $40°$ more than the measure of the smallest angle, and the measure of the remaining angle is $20°$ more than the measure of the smallest angle. Find the measure of each angle.

✔ Vocabulary, Readiness & Video Check

Martin-Gay Interactive Videos

See Video 4.3 🌐

Watch the section lecture video and answer the following questions.

OBJECTIVE 1
1. In ▦ Example 1 and the lecture before, the problem-solving steps for solving applications are mentioned. What is the difference here from when we've used these steps in the past?

OBJECTIVE 2
2. Based on ▦ Example 2, explain the meaning of a break-even point. How do you find the break-even point algebraically?

OBJECTIVE 3
3. In ▦ Example 3, why is the ordered triple not the final stated solution of the application?

4.3 Exercise Set MyMathLab®

MIXED PRACTICE

Solve. See Examples 1 through 4. For Exercises 1 and 2, the solutions have been started for you.

1. One number is two more than a second number. Twice the first is 4 less than 3 times the second. Find the numbers.

Start the solution:

1. UNDERSTAND the problem. Since we are looking for two numbers, let

x = one number and
y = second number.

2. TRANSLATE. Since we have assigned two variables, we will translate the facts into two equations. (Fill in the blanks.)

First equation:

In words: One number | is | two | more than | second number

Translate: x = ___ ___ ___

Second equation:

In words: Twice the first number | is | 4 | less than | 3 times the second number

Translate: $2x$ = ___ ___ ___

Finish with:

3. SOLVE the system and

4. INTERPRET the results.

2. Three times one number minus a second is 8, and the sum of the numbers is 12. Find the numbers.

Start the solution:

1. UNDERSTAND the problem. Since we are looking for two numbers, let

x = one number and
y = second number.

2. TRANSLATE. Since we have assigned two variables, we will translate the facts into two equations. (Fill in the blanks.)

First equation:

In words: Three times one number | minus | a second number | is | 8

Translate: $3x$ ___ ___ = 8

Second equation:

In words: The sum of the numbers | is | 12

Translate: x + ___ ___ 12

Finish with:

3. SOLVE the system and

4. INTERPRET the results.

3. The United States has the world's only large-deck aircraft carriers that can hold up to 72 aircraft. The Enterprise class carrier is longest in length, while the Nimitz class carrier is the second longest. The total length of these two carriers is 2193 feet; the difference of their lengths is only 9 feet. (*Source: USA Today*)

a. Find the length of each class carrier.

b. If a football field has a length of 100 yards, determine the length of an Enterprise class carrier in terms of number of football fields.

4. Participation in fitness activities for the Millennials (born 1977–1998) and the Gen-Xers (born 1965–1976) has continued to grow in recent years. In 2012, the number of Millennials participating in fitness activities was 11 million more than Gen-Xers. If the total number of Millennials and Gen-Xers participating in fitness activities in 2012 was 93 million, find the number of participants in each age group. (*Source: Topline participation Report, Sporting Goods Manufacturers Association*)

5. A Delta 727 traveled 2520 miles with the wind in 4.5 hours and 2160 miles against the wind in the same amount of time. Find the speed of the plane in still air and the speed of the wind.

6. Terry Watkins can row about 10.6 kilometers in 1 hour downstream and 6.8 kilometers upstream in 1 hour. Find how fast he can row in still water and find the speed of the current.

7. Find how many quarts of 4% butterfat milk and 1% butterfat milk should be mixed to yield 60 quarts of 2% butterfat milk.

8. A pharmacist needs 500 milliliters of a 20% phenobarbital solution but has only 5% and 25% phenobarbital solutions available. Find how many milliliters of each she should mix to get the desired solution.

9. In 2014, the United Kingdom was the most popular host country for U.S. students traveling abroad to study. Italy was the second most popular destination. A total of 66,564

U.S. students studied in one of the two countries. If 8682 more U.S. students studied in the United Kingdom than in Italy, how many students studied abroad in each country? (*Source:* Institute of International Education, Open Doors, 2014)

10. The enrollment at both the University of Texas at El Paso (UTEP) and the University of New Hampshire at Durham (UNH) increased for the 2014–2015 school year. The enrollment at UTEP was 6195 less than twice the enrollment at UNH. Together, these two schools enrolled 37,716 students. Find the number of students enrolled at each school for that school year. (*Source:* UTEP and UNH)

11. Karen Karlin bought some large frames for $15 each and some small frames for $8 each at a closeout sale. If she bought 22 frames for $239, find how many of each type she bought.

12. Hilton University Drama Club sold 311 tickets for a play. Student tickets cost 50 cents each; nonstudent tickets cost $1.50. If total receipts were $385.50, find how many tickets of each type were sold.

13. One number is two less than a second number. Twice the first is 4 more than 3 times the second. Find the numbers.

14. Twice one number plus a second number is 42, and the first number minus the second number is −6. Find the numbers.

15. The annual U.S. consumption of cheddar cheese has been decreasing in recent years, while the consumption of mozzarella cheese has been increasing. For the years 2008 through 2013, the function $y = -0.24x + 10.6$ approximates the annual U.S. per capita consumption of cheddar cheese in pounds, and the function $y = 0.21x + 10.5$ approximates the annual U.S. per capita consumption of mozzarella cheese in pounds. For both functions, x is the number of years after 2008. (*Source:* Based on data from the U.S. Department of Agriculture)

a. Explain how the given function for cheddar cheese verifies that the consumption of cheddar cheese has decreased, while the given function for mozzarella verifies that the consumption of mozzarella cheese has increased.

b. Based on this information, determine the year in which the pounds of cheddar cheese consumed equaled the pounds of mozzarella cheese consumed.

16. Two of the major jobs defined by the U.S. Department of Labor are postal carrier and bill collector. The number of postal carriers is predicted to decline over the next ten years, while the number of bill collectors is predicted to increase. For the years 2012 to 2022, the function $y = -13,910x + 491,600$ approximates the number of postal carriers in the United States, while the function

$y = 5820x + 397,400$ approximates the number of bill collectors. For both functions, x is the number of years after 2012. (*Source:* Based on data from the Bureau of Labor Statistics)

a. Explain how the decrease in postal carrier jobs can be verified by the given function, and the increase in bill collector jobs can be verified by the given function.

b. Based on this information, determine the year in which the number of postal carriers and the number of bill collectors in the United States is the same.

17. An office supply store in San Diego sells 7 writing tablets and 4 pens for $6.40. Also, 2 tablets and 19 pens cost $5.40. Find the price of each.

18. A Candy Barrel shop manager mixes M&M's worth $2.00 per pound with trail mix worth $1.50 per pound. Find how many pounds of each she should use to get 50 pounds of a party mix worth $1.80 per pound.

19. An airplane takes 3 hours to travel a distance of 2160 miles with the wind. The return trip takes 4 hours against the wind. Find the speed of the plane in still air and the speed of the wind.

20. Two cyclists start at the same point and travel in opposite directions. One travels 4 mph faster than the other. In 4 hours, they are 112 miles apart. Find how fast each is traveling.

21. The average American adult is spending ever more time on digital media (online or mobile device) than watching television. From 2010 to 2014, the function $y = 0.04x + 4.27$ can be used to estimate the average number of hours per day that an adult spends watching television, and the function $y = 0.67x + 3.01$ can be used to estimate the average number of hours per day that an adult spends using digital media. For both functions, x is the number of years after 2010. (*Source:* eMarketer)

a. Based on this information, determine the year in which the hours of television viewing is the same as the hours of digital media use.

b. Use these functions to predict how many hours the average American adult spends on television viewing and on digital media for the current year.

22. The rate for fatalities per 100 million vehicle-miles has been slowly decreasing for both automobiles and light trucks (pickups, sport utility vehicles, and minivans). For the years 2007 to 2012, the function $y = -0.08x + 1.08$ can be used to estimate the rate of fatalities per 100 million vehicle-miles for light trucks during this period, and the function $y = -0.03x + 1.01$ can be used to estimate the rate of fatalities per 100 million vehicle-miles for automobiles during this period. For both functions, x is the number of years since 2007. (*Source:* Bureau of Transportation Statistics, U.S. Department of Transportation)

a. Based on this data, estimate the year in which the fatality rate for light trucks equaled the fatality rate for automobiles.

b. Use these equations to predict the fatality rate per 100 million vehicle-miles for light trucks and automobiles in the current year.

△ **23.** The perimeter of a triangle is 93 centimeters. If two sides are equally long and the third side is 9 centimeters longer than the others, find the lengths of the three sides.

24. Jack Reinholt, a car salesman, has a choice of two pay arrangements: a weekly salary of $200 plus 5% commission on sales or a straight 15% commission. Find the amount of weekly sales for which Jack's earnings are the same regardless of the pay arrangement.

25. Hertz car rental agency charges $25 daily plus 10 cents per mile. Budget charges $20 daily plus 25 cents per mile. Find the daily mileage for which the Budget charge for the day is twice that of the Hertz charge for the day.

26. Carroll Blakemore, a drafting student, bought three templates and a mechanical pencil one day for $7.95. Another day, he bought two templates and four mechanical pencils for $12.80. Find the price of each type of item.

△ **27.** In the figure, line *l* and line *m* are parallel lines cut by transversal *t*. Find the values of *x* and *y*.

△ **28.** Find the values of *x* and *y* in the following isosceles triangle.

Given the cost function C(x) and the revenue function R(x), find the number of units x that must be sold to break even. See Example 5.

29. $C(x) = 30x + 10,000 \quad R(x) = 46x$

30. $C(x) = 12x + 15,000 \quad R(x) = 32x$

31. $C(x) = 1.2x + 1500 \quad R(x) = 1.7x$

32. $C(x) = 0.8x + 900 \quad R(x) = 2x$

33. $C(x) = 75x + 160,000 \quad R(x) = 200x$

34. $C(x) = 105x + 70,000 \quad R(x) = 245x$

▶ **35.** The planning department of Abstract Office Supplies has been asked to determine whether the company should introduce a new computer desk next year. The department estimates that $6000 of new manufacturing equipment will need to be purchased and sthat the cost of constructing each desk will be $200. The department also estimates that the revenue from each desk will be $450.

a. Determine the revenue function $R(x)$ from the sale of x desks.

b. Determine the cost function $C(x)$ for manufacturing x desks.

c. Find the break-even point.

36. Baskets, Inc., is planning to introduce a new woven basket. The company estimates that $500 worth of new equipment will be needed to manufacture this new type of basket and that it will cost $15 per basket to manufacture. The company also estimates that the revenue from each basket will be $31.

a. Determine the revenue function $R(x)$ from the sale of x baskets.

b. Determine the cost function $C(x)$ for manufacturing x baskets.

c. Find the break-even point. Round up to the next whole basket.

Solve. See Example 6.

37. Rabbits in a lab are to be kept on a strict daily diet that includes 30 grams of protein, 16 grams of fat, and 24 grams of carbohydrates. The scientist has only three food mixes available with the following grams of nutrients per unit.

	Protein	*Fat*	*Carbohydrate*
Mix A	4	6	3
Mix B	6	1	2
Mix C	4	1	12

Find how many units of each mix are needed daily to meet each rabbit's dietary need.

38. Gerry Gundersen mixes different solutions with concentrations of 25%, 40%, and 50% to get 200 liters of a 32% solution. If he uses twice as much of the 25% solution as of the 40% solution, find how many liters of each kind he uses.

△ **39.** The perimeter of a quadrilateral (four-sided polygon) is 29 inches. The longest side is twice as long as the shortest side. The other two sides are equally long and are 2 inches longer than the shortest side. Find the lengths of all four sides.

△ **40.** The measure of the largest angle of a triangle is 90° more than the measure of the smallest angle, and the measure of the remaining angle is 30° more than the measure of the smallest angle. Find the measure of each angle.

41. The sum of three numbers is 40. The first number is five more than the second number. It is also twice the third. Find the numbers.

42. The sum of the digits of a three-digit number is 15. The tens-place digit is twice the hundreds-place digit, and the ones-place digit is 1 less than the hundreds-place digit. Find the three-digit number.

43. During the 2013–2014 regular NBA season, the top-scoring player was Kevin Durant of the Oklahoma City Thunder. Durant scored a total of 2593 points during the regular season. The number of free throws (each worth one point) he made was 127 more than 3 times the number of three-point field goals he made. The number of two-point field goals he made was 46 less than the number of free throws he made. How many free throws, two-point field goals, and three-point field goals did Kevin Durant make during the 2013–2014 NBA season? (*Source:* National Basketball Association)

44. For 2014, the WNBA's top scorer was Maya Moore of the Minnesota Lynx. She scored a total of 812 points during the regular season. The number of two-point field goals that Moore made was 15 less than 4 times the number of three-point field goals she made. The number of free throws (each worth one point) was 73 fewer than the number of two-point field goals she made. Find how many free throws, two-point field goals, and three-point field goals Maya Moore made during the 2014 regular season. (*Source:* Women's National Basketball Association)

△ **45.** Find the values of x, y, and z in the following triangle.

△ **46.** The sum of the measures of the angles of a quadrilateral is 360°. Find the values of x, y, and z in the following quadrilateral.

REVIEW AND PREVIEW

Multiply both sides of equation (1) by 2 and add the resulting equation to equation (2). See Section 4.2.

47. $3x - y + z = 2$ (1)
$-x + 2y + 3z = 6$ (2)

48. $2x + y + 3z = 7$ (1)
$-4x + y + 2z = 4$ (2)

Multiply both sides of equation (1) by −3 and add the resulting equation to equation (2). See Section 4.2.

49. $x + 2y - z = 0$ (1)
$3x + y - z = 2$ (2)

50. $2x - 3y + 2z = 5$ (1)
$x - 9y + z = -1$ (2)

CONCEPT EXTENSIONS

51. The number of personal bankruptcy petitions filed in the United States varies greatly each year. The number of bankruptcies filed in 2014 was 623,200 less than double the number of bankruptcies filed in 2007. This is equivalent to an increase of 156,800 petitions filed from 2007 to 2014. Find how many personal bankruptcies were filed in each year. (*Source:* Based on data from the Administrative Office of the U.S. Courts)

52. Two major job categories defined by the U.S. Department of Labor are service occupations and sales occupations. In 2014, the median weekly earnings for males in the service occupations were $122 more than the median weekly earnings for females in the service occupations. Also, the median weekly earnings for females in the sales occupations were $146 less than the median weekly earnings for males in the sales occupations. The median weekly earnings for males in the service occupations were $339 less than twice the median weekly earnings for females in the same category. The median weekly earnings for males in the sales occupations were $474 less than twice the median weekly earnings for females in the same category. (*Source:* Based on data from the Bureau of Labor Statistics)

  a. Find the median weekly earnings for females in the service occupations in the United States in 2014.

  b. Find the median weekly earnings for females in the sales occupations in the United States for 2014.

  c. Of the four groups of workers described in the problem, which group makes the greatest weekly earnings? Which group makes the least earnings?

53. Find the values of a, b, and c such that the equation $y = ax^2 + bx + c$ has ordered pair solutions $(1, 6)$, $(-1, -2)$, and $(0, -1)$. To do so, substitute each ordered pair solution into the equation. Each time, the result is an equation in three unknowns: a, b, and c. Then solve the resulting system of three linear equations in three unknowns, a, b, and c.

54. Find the values of a, b, and c such that the equation $y = ax^2 + bx + c$ has ordered pair solutions $(1, 2)$, $(2, 3)$, and $(-1, 6)$. (*Hint:* See Exercise 53.)

55. Data (x, y) for the total number (in thousands) of college-bound students who took the ACT assessment in the year x are approximately $(3, 927)$, $(11, 1179)$, and $(19, 1495)$, where $x = 3$ represents 1993 and $x = 11$ represents 2001. Find the values a, b, and c such that the equation $y = ax^2 + bx + c$ models these data. According to your model, how many students will take the ACT in 2015? (*Source:* ACT, Inc.)

56. Monthly normal rainfall data (x, y) for Portland, Oregon, are $(4, 2.47)$, $(7, 0.58)$, $(8, 1.07)$, where x represents time in months (with $x = 1$ representing January) and y represents rainfall in inches. Find the values of a, b, and c rounded to 2 decimal places such that the equation $y = ax^2 + bx + c$ models this data. According to

your model, how much rain should Portland expect during September? (*Source:* National Climatic Data Center)

The function $f(x) = 0.42x + 8.4$ represents the U.S. annual bottled water consumption (in billions of gallons) and the function $f(x) = -0.17x + 14.2$ represents the U.S. annual soda consumption (in billions of gallons). For both functions, x is the number of years since 2009, and these functions are good for the years 2009–2013.

57. Solve the system formed by these functions. Round each coordinate to the nearest whole number.

58. Use your answer to Exercise 57 to predict the year in which the bottled water and soda consumption will be the same.

Integrated Review   Systems of Linear Equations

Sections 4.1–4.3

The graphs of various systems of equations are shown. Match each graph with the solution of its corresponding system.

A.   **B.**   **C.**   **D.**

1. solution: $(1, 2)$ 2. solution: $(-2, 3)$ 3. no solution   4. infinite number of solutions

Solve each system by elimination or substitution.

5. $\begin{cases} x + y = 4 \\ y = 3x \end{cases}$

6. $\begin{cases} x - y = -4 \\ y = 4x \end{cases}$

7. $\begin{cases} x + y = 1 \\ x - 2y = 4 \end{cases}$

8. $\begin{cases} 2x - y = 8 \\ x + 3y = 11 \end{cases}$

9. $\begin{cases} 2x + 5y = 8 \\ 6x + y = 10 \end{cases}$

10. $\begin{cases} \dfrac{1}{8}x - \dfrac{1}{2}y = -\dfrac{5}{8} \\ -3x - 8y = 0 \end{cases}$

11. $\begin{cases} 4x - 7y = 7 \\ 12x - 21y = 24 \end{cases}$

12. $\begin{cases} 2x - 5y = 3 \\ -4x + 10y = -6 \end{cases}$

13. $\begin{cases} y = \dfrac{1}{3}x \\ 5x - 3y = 4 \end{cases}$

14. $\begin{cases} y = \dfrac{1}{4}x \\ 2x - 4y = 3 \end{cases}$

15. $\begin{cases} x + y = 2 \\ -3y + z = -7 \\ 2x + y - z = -1 \end{cases}$

16. $\begin{cases} y + 2z = -3 \\ x - 2y = 7 \\ 2x - y + z = 5 \end{cases}$

17. $\begin{cases} 2x + 4y - 6z = 3 \\ -x + y - z = 6 \\ x + 2y - 3z = 1 \end{cases}$

18. $\begin{cases} x - y + 3z = 2 \\ -2x + 2y - 6z = -4 \\ 3x - 3y + 9z = 6 \end{cases}$

19. $\begin{cases} x + y - 4z = 5 \\ x - y + 2z = -2 \\ 3x + 2y + 4z = 18 \end{cases}$

20. $\begin{cases} 2x - y + 3z = 2 \\ x + y - 6z = 0 \\ 3x + 4y - 3z = 6 \end{cases}$

21. A first number is 8 less than a second number. Twice the first number is 11 more than the second number. Find the numbers.

△ **22.** The sum of the measures of the angles of a quadrilateral is 360°. The two smallest angles of the quadrilateral have the same measure. The third angle measures 30° more than the measure of one of the smallest angles and the fourth angle measures 50° more than the measure of one of the smallest angles. Find the measure of each angle.

4.4 Solving Systems of Equations by Matrices

OBJECTIVES

1 Use Matrices to Solve a System of Two Equations.

2 Use Matrices to Solve a System of Three Equations.

By now, you may have noticed that the solution of a system of equations depends on the coefficients of the equations in the system and not on the variables. In this section, we introduce solving a system of equations by a **matrix.**

OBJECTIVE

1 Using Matrices to Solve a System of Two Equations

A matrix (plural: **matrices**) is a rectangular array of numbers. The following are examples of matrices.

$$\begin{bmatrix} 1 & 0 \\ 0 & 1 \end{bmatrix} \quad \begin{bmatrix} 2 & 1 & 3 & -1 \\ 0 & -1 & 4 & 5 \\ -6 & 2 & 1 & 0 \end{bmatrix} \quad \begin{bmatrix} a & b & c \\ d & e & f \end{bmatrix}$$

The numbers aligned horizontally in a matrix are in the same **row.** The numbers aligned vertically are in the same **column.**

$$\begin{matrix} \text{row 1} \rightarrow \\ \text{row 2} \rightarrow \end{matrix} \begin{bmatrix} 2 & 1 & 0 \\ -1 & 6 & 2 \end{bmatrix}$$

column 1
column 2
column 3

This matrix has 2 rows and 3 columns. It is called a 2×3 (read "two by three") matrix.

Helpful Hint

Before writing the corresponding matrix associated with a system of equations, make sure that the equations are written in standard form.

To see the relationship between systems of equations and matrices, study the example below.

System of Equations (in standard form)

$$\begin{cases} 2x - 3y = 6 & \text{Equation 1} \\ x + y = 0 & \text{Equation 2} \end{cases}$$

Corresponding Matrix

$$\begin{bmatrix} 2 & -3 & | & 6 \\ 1 & 1 & | & 0 \end{bmatrix} \begin{matrix} \text{Row 1} \\ \text{Row 2} \end{matrix}$$

Notice that the rows of the matrix correspond to the equations in the system. The coefficients of each variable are placed to the left of a vertical dashed line. The constants are placed to the right. Each of the numbers in the matrix is called an **element.**

The method of solving systems by matrices is to write this matrix as an equivalent matrix from which we easily identify the solution. Two matrices are equivalent if they represent systems that have the same solution set. The following **row operations** can be performed on matrices, and the result is an equivalent matrix.

Elementary Row Operations

1. Any two rows in a matrix may be interchanged.

2. The elements of any row may be multiplied (or divided) by the same nonzero number.

3. The elements of any row may be multiplied (or divided) by a nonzero number and added to their corresponding elements in any other row.

Helpful Hint

Notice that these *row* operations are the same operations that we can perform on *equations* in a system.

To solve a system of two equations in x and y by matrices, write the corresponding matrix associated with the system. Then use elementary row operations to write equivalent matrices until you have a matrix of the form

$$\begin{bmatrix} 1 & a & | & b \\ 0 & 1 & | & c \end{bmatrix}$$

where a, b, and c are constants. Why? If a matrix associated with a system of equations is in this form, we can easily solve for x and y. For example,

Matrix		***System of Equations***	
$\begin{bmatrix} 1 & 2 & \mid & -3 \\ 0 & 1 & \mid & 5 \end{bmatrix}$	corresponds to	$\begin{cases} 1x + 2y = -3 \\ 0x + 1y = 5 \end{cases}$ or	$\begin{cases} x + 2y = -3 \\ \quad\quad y = 5 \end{cases}$

In the second equation, we have $y = 5$. Substituting this in the first equation, we have $x + 2(5) = -3$ or $x = -13$. The solution of the system is the ordered pair $(-13, 5)$.

EXAMPLE 1   Use matrices to solve the system.

$$\begin{cases} x + 3y = 5 \\ 2x - y = -4 \end{cases}$$

Solution The corresponding matrix is $\begin{bmatrix} 1 & 3 & \mid & 5 \\ 2 & -1 & \mid & -4 \end{bmatrix}$. We use elementary row operations to write an equivalent matrix that looks like $\begin{bmatrix} 1 & a & \mid & b \\ 0 & 1 & \mid & c \end{bmatrix}$.

For the matrix given, the element in the first row, first column is already 1, as desired. Next we write an equivalent matrix with a 0 below the 1. To do this, we multiply row 1 by -2 and add to row 2. *We will change only row 2.*

$$\begin{bmatrix} 1 & 3 & \mid & 5 \\ -2(1) + 2 & -2(3) + (-1) & \mid & -2(5) + (-4) \end{bmatrix} \text{ simplifies to } \begin{bmatrix} 1 & 3 & \mid & 5 \\ 0 & -7 & \mid & -14 \end{bmatrix}$$

$$\begin{matrix} \uparrow & \uparrow & \uparrow & \uparrow & \uparrow & \uparrow \\ \text{row 1} & \text{row 2} & \text{row 1} & \text{row 2} & \text{row 1} & \text{row 2} \\ \text{element} & \text{element} & \text{element} & \text{element} & \text{element} & \text{element} \end{matrix}$$

Now we change the -7 to a 1 by use of an elementary row operation. We divide row 2 by -7, then

$$\begin{bmatrix} 1 & 3 & \mid & 5 \\ \frac{0}{-7} & \frac{-7}{-7} & \mid & \frac{-14}{-7} \end{bmatrix} \text{ simplifies to } \begin{bmatrix} 1 & 3 & \mid & 5 \\ 0 & 1 & \mid & 2 \end{bmatrix}$$

This last matrix corresponds to the system

$$\begin{cases} x + 3y = 5 \\ \quad\quad y = 2 \end{cases}$$

To find x, we let $y = 2$ in the first equation, $x + 3y = 5$.

$$x + 3y = 5 \quad \text{First equation}$$
$$x + 3(2) = 5 \quad \text{Let } y = 2.$$
$$x = -1$$

The ordered pair solution is $(-1, 2)$. Check to see that this ordered pair satisfies both equations.   □

PRACTICE

1   Use matrices to solve the system.

$$\begin{cases} x + 4y = -2 \\ 3x - y = 7 \end{cases}$$

EXAMPLE 2 Use matrices to solve the system.

$$\begin{cases} 2x - y = 3 \\ 4x - 2y = 5 \end{cases}$$

Solution The corresponding matrix is $\begin{bmatrix} 2 & -1 & | & 3 \\ 4 & -2 & | & 5 \end{bmatrix}$. To get 1 in the row 1, column 1 position, we divide the elements of row 1 by 2.

$$\begin{bmatrix} \dfrac{2}{2} & \dfrac{-1}{2} & | & \dfrac{3}{2} \\ 4 & -2 & | & 5 \end{bmatrix} \quad \text{simplifies to} \quad \begin{bmatrix} 1 & -\dfrac{1}{2} & | & \dfrac{3}{2} \\ 4 & -2 & | & 5 \end{bmatrix}$$

To get 0 under the 1, we multiply the elements of row 1 by -4 and add the new elements to the elements of row 2.

$$\begin{bmatrix} 1 & -\dfrac{1}{2} & | & \dfrac{3}{2} \\ -4(1) + 4 & -4\left(-\dfrac{1}{2}\right) - 2 & | & -4\left(\dfrac{3}{2}\right) + 5 \end{bmatrix} \quad \text{simplifies to} \quad \begin{bmatrix} 1 & -\dfrac{1}{2} & | & \dfrac{3}{2} \\ 0 & 0 & | & -1 \end{bmatrix}$$

The corresponding system is $\begin{cases} x - \dfrac{1}{2}y = \dfrac{3}{2} \\ 0 = -1 \end{cases}$. The equation $0 = -1$ is false for all y or x values; hence, the system is inconsistent and has no solution. □

PRACTICE
2 Use matrices to solve the system.

$$\begin{cases} x - 3y = 3 \\ -2x + 6y = 4 \end{cases}$$

✔ **CONCEPT CHECK**
Consider the system

$$\begin{cases} 2x - 3y = 8 \\ x + 5y = -3 \end{cases}$$

What is wrong with its corresponding matrix shown below?

$$\begin{bmatrix} 2 & -3 & | & 8 \\ 5 & 8 & | & -3 \end{bmatrix}$$

OBJECTIVE
2 Using Matrices to Solve a System of Three Equations

To solve a system of three equations in three variables using matrices, we will write the corresponding matrix in the form

$$\begin{bmatrix} 1 & a & b & | & d \\ 0 & 1 & c & | & e \\ 0 & 0 & 1 & | & f \end{bmatrix}$$

EXAMPLE 3 Use matrices to solve the system.

$$\begin{cases} x + 2y + z = 2 \\ -2x - y + 2z = 5 \\ x + 3y - 2z = -8 \end{cases}$$

(Continued on next page)

Answer to Concept Check:
matrix should be $\begin{bmatrix} 2 & -3 & | & 8 \\ 1 & 5 & | & -3 \end{bmatrix}$

Solution The corresponding matrix is $\begin{bmatrix} 1 & 2 & 1 & 2 \\ -2 & -1 & 2 & 5 \\ 1 & 3 & -2 & -8 \end{bmatrix}$. Our goal is to write an equivalent matrix with 1's along the diagonal (see the numbers in green) and 0's below the 1's. The element in row 1, column 1 is already 1. Next we get 0's for each element in the rest of column 1. To do this, first we multiply the elements of row 1 by 2 and add the new elements to row 2. Also, we multiply the elements of row 1 by -1 and add the new elements to the elements of row 3. We _do not change row 1_. Then

$$\begin{bmatrix} 1 & 2 & 1 & 2 \\ 2(1)-2 & 2(2)-1 & 2(1)+2 & 2(2)+5 \\ -1(1)+1 & -1(2)+3 & -1(1)-2 & -1(2)-8 \end{bmatrix} \text{ simplifies to } \begin{bmatrix} 1 & 2 & 1 & 2 \\ 0 & 3 & 4 & 9 \\ 0 & 1 & -3 & -10 \end{bmatrix}$$

We continue down the diagonal and use elementary row operations to get 1 where the element 3 is now. To do this, we interchange rows 2 and 3.

$$\begin{bmatrix} 1 & 2 & 1 & 2 \\ 0 & 3 & 4 & 9 \\ 0 & 1 & -3 & -10 \end{bmatrix} \text{ is equivalent to } \begin{bmatrix} 1 & 2 & 1 & 2 \\ 0 & 1 & -3 & -10 \\ 0 & 3 & 4 & 9 \end{bmatrix}$$

Next we want the new row 3, column 2 element to be 0. We multiply the elements of row 2 by -3 and add the result to the elements of row 3.

$$\begin{bmatrix} 1 & 2 & 1 & 2 \\ 0 & 1 & -3 & -10 \\ -3(0)+0 & -3(1)+3 & -3(-3)+4 & -3(-10)+9 \end{bmatrix} \text{ simplifies to}$$

$$\begin{bmatrix} 1 & 2 & 1 & 2 \\ 0 & 1 & -3 & -10 \\ 0 & 0 & 13 & 39 \end{bmatrix}$$

Finally, we divide the elements of row 3 by 13 so that the final diagonal element is 1.

$$\begin{bmatrix} 1 & 2 & 1 & 2 \\ 0 & 1 & -3 & -10 \\ \frac{0}{13} & \frac{0}{13} & \frac{13}{13} & \frac{39}{13} \end{bmatrix} \text{ simplifies to } \begin{bmatrix} 1 & 2 & 1 & 2 \\ 0 & 1 & -3 & -10 \\ 0 & 0 & 1 & 3 \end{bmatrix}$$

This matrix corresponds to the system

$$\begin{cases} x + 2y + z = 2 \\ y - 3z = -10 \\ z = 3 \end{cases}$$

We identify the z-coordinate of the solution as 3. Next, we replace z with 3 in the second equation and solve for y.

$$y - 3z = -10 \quad \text{Second equation}$$
$$y - 3(3) = -10 \quad \text{Let } z = 3.$$
$$y = -1$$

To find x, we let $z = 3$ and $y = -1$ in the first equation.

$$x + 2y + z = 2 \quad \text{First equation}$$
$$x + 2(-1) + 3 = 2 \quad \text{Let } z = 3 \text{ and } y = -1.$$
$$x = 1$$

The ordered triple solution is $(1, -1, 3)$. Check to see that it satisfies all three equations in the original system. □

PRACTICE
3 Use matrices to solve the system.

$$\begin{cases} x + 3y - z = 0 \\ 2x + y + 3z = 5 \\ -x - 2y + 4z = 7 \end{cases}$$

✔ Vocabulary, Readiness & Video Check

Use the choices below to fill in each blank.

column	element	row	matrix

1. A(n) _____ is a rectangular array of numbers.

2. Each of the numbers in a matrix is called a(n) _____.

3. The numbers aligned horizontally in a matrix are in the same _____.

4. The numbers aligned vertically in a matrix are in the same _____.

Answer true or false for each statement about operations within a matrix forming an equivalent matrix.

5. Any two columns may be interchanged. _____

6. Any two rows may be interchanged. _____

7. The elements in a row may be added to their corresponding elements in another row. _____

8. The elements of a column may be multiplied by any nonzero number. _____

Martin-Gay Interactive Videos

See Video 4.4

Watch the section lecture video and answer the following questions.

OBJECTIVE
1

9. From the lecture before ▤ Example 1, what elementary row operations can be performed on matrices? Which operation is not performed during Example 1?

OBJECTIVE
2

10. In ▤ Example 2, why do you think the suggestion is made to write neatly when using matrices to solve systems?

4.4 Exercise Set MyMathLab® ▶

Solve each system of linear equations using matrices. See Example 1.

1. $\begin{cases} x + y = 1 \\ x - 2y = 4 \end{cases}$

2. $\begin{cases} 2x - y = 8 \\ x + 3y = 11 \end{cases}$

▶ **3.** $\begin{cases} x + 3y = 2 \\ x + 2y = 0 \end{cases}$

4. $\begin{cases} 4x - y = 5 \\ 3x + 3y = 0 \end{cases}$

Solve each system of linear equations using matrices. See Example 2.

5. $\begin{cases} x - 2y = 4 \\ 2x - 4y = 4 \end{cases}$

6. $\begin{cases} -x + 3y = 6 \\ 3x - 9y = 9 \end{cases}$

7. $\begin{cases} 3x - 3y = 9 \\ 2x - 2y = 6 \end{cases}$

8. $\begin{cases} 9x - 3y = 6 \\ -18x + 6y = -12 \end{cases}$

Solve each system of linear equations using matrices. See Example 3.

9. $\begin{cases} x + y = 3 \\ 2y = 10 \\ 3x + 2y - 4z = 12 \end{cases}$

10. $\begin{cases} 5x = 5 \\ 2x + y = 4 \\ 3x + y - 5z = -15 \end{cases}$

11. $\begin{cases} 2y - z = -7 \\ x + 4y + z = -4 \\ 5x - y + 2z = 13 \end{cases}$

12. $\begin{cases} 4y + 3z = -2 \\ 5x - 4y = 1 \\ -5x + 4y + z = -3 \end{cases}$

MIXED PRACTICE

Solve each system of linear equations using matrices. See Examples 1 through 3.

13. $\begin{cases} x - 4 = 0 \\ x + y = 1 \end{cases}$

14. $\begin{cases} 3y = 6 \\ x + y = 7 \end{cases}$

15. $\begin{cases} x + y + z = 2 \\ 2x \quad - z = 5 \\ \quad 3y + z = 2 \end{cases}$

16. $\begin{cases} x + 2y + z = 5 \\ x - y - z = 3 \\ \quad y + z = 2 \end{cases}$

17. $\begin{cases} 5x - 2y = 27 \\ -3x + 5y = 18 \end{cases}$

18. $\begin{cases} 4x - y = 9 \\ 2x + 3y = -27 \end{cases}$

19. $\begin{cases} 4x - 7y = 7 \\ 12x - 21y = 24 \end{cases}$

20. $\begin{cases} 2x - 5y = 12 \\ -4x + 10y = 20 \end{cases}$

21. $\begin{cases} 4x - y + 2z = 5 \\ 2y + z = 4 \\ 4x + y + 3z = 10 \end{cases}$

22. $\begin{cases} 5y - 7z = 14 \\ 2x + y + 4z = 10 \\ 2x + 6y - 3z = 30 \end{cases}$

▶ 23. $\begin{cases} 4x + y + z = 3 \\ -x + y - 2z = -11 \\ x + 2y + 2z = -1 \end{cases}$

24. $\begin{cases} x + y + z = 9 \\ 3x - y + z = -1 \\ -2x + 2y - 3z = -2 \end{cases}$

REVIEW AND PREVIEW

Determine whether each graph is the graph of a function. See Section 3.2.

25.

26.

27.

28.

Evaluate. See Section 1.3.

29. $(-1)(-5) - (6)(3)$

30. $(2)(-8) - (-4)(1)$

31. $(4)(-10) - (2)(-2)$

32. $(-7)(3) - (-2)(-6)$

33. $(-3)(-3) - (-1)(-9)$

34. $(5)(6) - (10)(10)$

CONCEPT EXTENSIONS

Solve. See the Concept Check in the section.

35. For the system $\begin{cases} x \quad + z = 7 \\ y + 2z = -6, \\ 3x - y = 0 \end{cases}$ which is the correct corresponding matrix in the top of the next column?

a. $\begin{bmatrix} 1 & 1 & | & 7 \\ 1 & 2 & | & -6 \\ 3 & -1 & | & 0 \end{bmatrix}$
b. $\begin{bmatrix} 1 & 0 & 1 & | & 7 \\ 1 & 2 & 0 & | & -6 \\ 3 & -1 & 0 & | & 0 \end{bmatrix}$

c. $\begin{bmatrix} 1 & 0 & 1 & | & 7 \\ 0 & 1 & 2 & | & -6 \\ 3 & -1 & 0 & | & 0 \end{bmatrix}$

36. For the system $\begin{cases} x - 6 = 0 \\ 2x - 3y = 1 \end{cases}$, which is the correct corresponding matrix?

a. $\begin{bmatrix} 1 & -6 & | & 0 \\ 2 & -3 & | & 1 \end{bmatrix}$
b. $\begin{bmatrix} 1 & 0 & | & 6 \\ 2 & -3 & | & 1 \end{bmatrix}$
c. $\begin{bmatrix} 1 & 0 & | & -6 \\ 2 & -3 & | & 1 \end{bmatrix}$

37. The amount of electricity y generated by geothermal sources (in billions of kilowatts) from 2000 to 2014 can be modeled by the linear equation $y = 1.46x + 14.05$, where x represents the number of years since 2000. Similarly, the amount of electricity y generated by wind power (in billions of kilowatts) during the same time period can be modeled by the linear equation $4.24x - y = 0.65$. (*Source:* Based on data from the Energy Administration Office)

a. The data used to form these two models were incomplete. It is impossible to tell from the data the year in which the electricity generated by geothermal sources was the same as the electricity generated by wind power. Use matrix methods to estimate the year in which this occurred.

b. The earliest data for wind power data was 1989, when 2.1 billion kilowatts of electricity was generated. Can this be determined from the given equation? Why do you think that is?

c. According to these models, will the amount of electricity generated by geothermal ever go to zero? Why?

d. Can you think of an explanation why the amount of electricity generated by wind power is increasing so much faster than the amount of electricity generated by geothermal power?

38. The most popular amusement park in the world (according to annual attendance) is Walt Disney World's Magic Kingdom, whose yearly attendance in millions can be approximated by the equation $y = 0.28x + 17.1$, where x is the number of years after 2008. In second place is Walt Disney World's Disneyland, whose yearly attendance in millions can be approximated by the equation $y = 0.36x + 14.7$, where x is the number of years after 2008. Find the year when the attendance in Disneyland is equal to the attendance in the Magic Kingdom. (*Source:* Themed Entertainment Association, Economics Research Associates)

39. For the system $\begin{cases} 2x - 3y = 8 \\ x + 5y = -3 \end{cases}$, explain what is wrong with writing the corresponding matrix as $\begin{bmatrix} 2 & 3 & | & 8 \\ 0 & 5 & | & -3 \end{bmatrix}$.

40. For the system $\begin{cases} 5x + 2y = 0 \\ -y = 2 \end{cases}$, explain what is wrong with writing the corresponding matrix as $\begin{bmatrix} 5 & 2 & | & 0 \\ -1 & 0 & | & 2 \end{bmatrix}$.

4.5 Systems of Linear Inequalities

OBJECTIVE

1 Graph a System of Linear Inequalities.

OBJECTIVE

1 Graphing Systems of Linear Inequalities

In Section 3.7, we solved linear inequalities in two variables as well as their union and intersection. Just as two or more linear equations make a system of linear equations, two or more linear inequalities make a **system of linear inequalities.** Systems of inequalities are very important in a process called linear programming. Many businesses use linear programming to find the most profitable way to use limited resources such as employees, machines, or buildings.

A **solution of a system of linear inequalities** is an ordered pair that satisfies each inequality in the system. The set of all such ordered pairs is the solution set of the system. Graphing this set gives us a picture of the solution set. We can graph a system of inequalities by graphing each inequality in the system and identifying the region of overlap.

Graphing the Solutions of a System of Linear Inequalities

Step 1. Graph each inequality in the system on the same set of axes.

Step 2. The solutions of the system are the points common to the graphs of all the inequalities in the system.

EXAMPLE 1   Graph the solutions of the system: $\begin{cases} 3x \ge y \\ x + 2y \le 8 \end{cases}$

Solution We begin by graphing each inequality on the *same* set of axes. The graph of the solutions of the system is the region contained in the graphs of both inequalities. In other words, it is their intersection.

First let's graph $3x \ge y$. The boundary line is the graph of $3x = y$. We sketch a solid boundary line since the inequality $3x \ge y$ means $3x > y$ or $3x = y$. The test point $(1, 0)$ satisfies the inequality, so we shade the half-plane that includes $(1, 0)$.

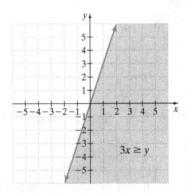

Next we sketch a solid boundary line $x + 2y = 8$ on the same set of axes. The test point $(0, 0)$ satisfies the inequality $x + 2y \le 8$, so we shade the half-plane that includes $(0, 0)$. (For clarity, the graph of $x + 2y \le 8$ is shown here on a separate set of axes.) An ordered pair solution of the system must satisfy both inequalities. These solutions are points that lie in both shaded regions. The solution of the system is the darkest shaded region. This solution includes parts of both boundary lines.

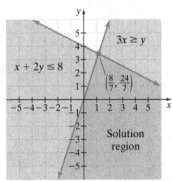

PRACTICE

1   Graph the solutions of the system: $\begin{cases} 4x \ge y \\ x + 3y \ge 6 \end{cases}$

In linear programming, it is sometimes necessary to find the coordinates of the **corner point:** the point at which the two boundary lines intersect. To find the corner point for the system of Example 1, we solve the related linear system

$$\begin{cases} 3x = y \\ x + 2y = 8 \end{cases}$$

using either the substitution or the elimination method. The lines intersect at $\left(\dfrac{8}{7}, \dfrac{24}{7}\right)$, the corner point of the graph.

EXAMPLE 2 Graph the solutions of the system: $\begin{cases} x - y < 2 \\ x + 2y > -1 \\ y < 2 \end{cases}$

Solution First we graph all three inequalities on the same set of axes. All boundary lines are dashed lines since the inequality symbols are $<$ and $>$. The solution of the system is the region shown by the shading. In this example, the boundary lines are *not* part of the solution.

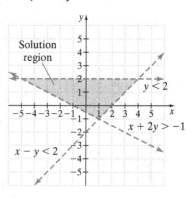

PRACTICE
2   Graph the solutions of the system: $\begin{cases} x - y < 1 \\ y < 4 \\ 3x + y > -3 \end{cases}$

✔ **CONCEPT CHECK**

Describe the solution of the system of inequalities:

$$\begin{cases} x \le 2 \\ x \ge 2 \end{cases}$$

EXAMPLE 3 Graph the solutions of the system: $\begin{cases} -3x + 4y \le 12 \\ x \le 3 \\ x \ge 0 \\ y \ge 0 \end{cases}$

Solution We graph the inequalities on the same set of axes. The intersection of the inequalities is the solution region. It is the only region shaded in this graph and includes the portions of all four boundary lines that border the shaded region.

PRACTICE
3   Graph the solutions of the system: $\begin{cases} -2x + 5y \le 10 \\ x \le 4 \\ x \ge 0 \\ y \ge 0 \end{cases}$

Answer to Concept Check:
the line $x = 2$

✓ **Vocabulary, Readiness & Video Check**

Use the choices below to fill in each blank. Not all choices will be used.

solution   union   system
corner   intersection

1. Two or more linear inequalities form a(n) _____ of linear inequalities.
2. An ordered pair that satisfies each inequality in a system is a(n) _____ of the system.
3. The point where two boundary lines intersect is a(n) _____ point.
4. The solution region of a system of inequalities consists of the _____ of the solution regions of the inequalities in the system.

Martin-Gay Interactive Videos

See Video 4.5

Watch the section lecture video and answer the following question.

OBJECTIVE 1

5. In ▤ Example 1, do the solutions of the first inequality of the system limit where we can choose the test point for the second inequality? Why or why not?

4.5   Exercise Set   MyMathLab®

MIXED PRACTICE

Graph the solutions of each system of linear inequalities. See Examples 1 through 3.

1. $\begin{cases} y \geq x + 1 \\ y \geq 3 - x \end{cases}$

2. $\begin{cases} y \geq x - 3 \\ y \geq -1 - x \end{cases}$

3. $\begin{cases} y < 3x - 4 \\ y \leq x + 2 \end{cases}$

4. $\begin{cases} y \leq 2x + 1 \\ y > x + 2 \end{cases}$

▶ 5. $\begin{cases} y < -2x - 2 \\ y > x + 4 \end{cases}$

6. $\begin{cases} y \leq 2x + 4 \\ y \geq -x - 5 \end{cases}$

7. $\begin{cases} y \geq -x + 2 \\ y \leq 2x + 5 \end{cases}$

8. $\begin{cases} y \geq x - 5 \\ y \geq -3x + 3 \end{cases}$

9. $\begin{cases} x \geq 3y \\ x + 3y \leq 6 \end{cases}$

10. $\begin{cases} -2x > y \\ x + 2y < 3 \end{cases}$

11. $\begin{cases} x \leq 2 \\ y \geq -3 \end{cases}$

12. $\begin{cases} x \geq -3 \\ y \geq -2 \end{cases}$

13. $\begin{cases} y \geq 1 \\ x < -3 \end{cases}$

14. $\begin{cases} y > 2 \\ x \geq -1 \end{cases}$

▶ 15. $\begin{cases} y + 2x \geq 0 \\ 5x - 3y \leq 12 \\ y \leq 2 \end{cases}$

16. $\begin{cases} y + 2x \leq 0 \\ 5x + 3y \geq -2 \\ y \leq 4 \end{cases}$

17. $\begin{cases} 3x - 4y \geq -6 \\ 2x + y \leq 7 \\ y \geq -3 \end{cases}$

18. $\begin{cases} 4x - y \geq -2 \\ 2x + 3y \leq -8 \\ y \geq -5 \end{cases}$

19. $\begin{cases} 2x + y \leq 5 \\ x \leq 3 \\ x \geq 0 \\ y \geq 0 \end{cases}$

20. $\begin{cases} 3x + y \leq 4 \\ x \leq 4 \\ x \geq 0 \\ y \geq 0 \end{cases}$

Match each system of inequalities to the corresponding graph.

21. $\begin{cases} y < 5 \\ x > 3 \end{cases}$

22. $\begin{cases} y > 5 \\ x < 3 \end{cases}$

23. $\begin{cases} y \le 5 \\ x < 3 \end{cases}$

24. $\begin{cases} y > 5 \\ x \ge 3 \end{cases}$

A.

B.

C.

D.

REVIEW

Evaluate each expression. See Section 1.3.

25. $(-3)^2$

26. $(-5)^3$

27. $\left(\dfrac{2}{3}\right)^2$

28. $\left(\dfrac{3}{4}\right)^3$

Perform each indicated operation. See Section 1.3.

29. $(-2)^2 - (-3) + 2(-1)$

30. $5^2 - 11 + 3(-5)$

31. $8^2 + (-13) - 4(-2)$

32. $(-12)^2 + (-1)(2) - 6$

CONCEPT EXTENSIONS

Solve. See the Concept Check in this section.

33. Describe the solution of the system: $\begin{cases} y \le 3 \\ y \ge 3 \end{cases}$.

34. Describe the solution of the system: $\begin{cases} x \le 5 \\ x \le 3 \end{cases}$.

35. Explain how to decide which region to shade to show the solution region of the following system.

$$\begin{cases} x \ge 3 \\ y \ge -2 \end{cases}$$

36. Michael Callac works for a small online catalog company. He budgets his time at work today. Part of the day he will electronically send bills; the rest of the day he can use to send purchase orders. The total time available is at most 8 hours. Less than 3 hours is to be spent sending bills.

a. Write a system of inequalities to describe the situation. (Let x = hours available for sending bills and y = hours available for sending purchase orders.)

b. Graph the solutions of the system.

Chapter 4 **Vocabulary Check**

Fill in each blank with one of the words or phrases listed below.

matrix	consistent	system of equations	triple	row
solution	inconsistent	element	column	

1. Two or more linear equations in two variables form a(n) _____.

2. A(n) _____ of a system of two equations in two variables is an ordered pair that makes both equations true.

3. A(n) _____ system of equations has at least one solution.

4. A solution of a system of three equations in three variables is an ordered _____ that makes all three equations true.

5. A(n) _____ system of equations has no solution.

6. A(n) _____ is a rectangular array of numbers.

7. Each of the numbers in a matrix is called a(n) _____ .

8. The numbers aligned horizontally in a matrix are in the same _____ .

9. The numbers aligned vertically in a matrix are in the same _____ .

Chapter 4 Highlights

DEFINITIONS AND CONCEPTS	EXAMPLES

Section 4.1   Solving Systems of Linear Equations in Two Variables

A **system of linear equations** consists of two or more linear equations.

$$\begin{cases} x - 3y = 6 \\ y = \dfrac{1}{2}x \end{cases} \qquad \begin{cases} x + 2y - z = 1 \\ 3x - y + 4z = 0 \\ 5y + z = 6 \end{cases}$$

A **solution** of a system of two equations in two variables is an ordered pair (x, y) that makes both equations true.

Determine whether $(2, -5)$ is a solution of the system.

$$\begin{cases} x + y = -3 \\ 2x - 3y = 19 \end{cases}$$

Replace x with 2 and y with -5 in both equations.

$$\begin{array}{ll} x + y = -3 & 2x - 3y = 19 \\ 2 + (-5) \stackrel{?}{=} -3 & 2(2) - 3(-5) \stackrel{?}{=} 19 \\ -3 = -3 \quad \text{True} & 4 + 15 \stackrel{?}{=} 19 \\ & 19 = 19 \quad \text{True} \end{array}$$

$(2, -5)$ is a solution of the system.

Geometrically, a solution of a system in two variables is a point of intersection of the graphs of the equations.

Solve by graphing: $\begin{cases} y = 2x - 1 \\ x + 2y = 13 \end{cases}$

(continued)

A system of equations with at least one solution is a **consistent system.** A system that has no solution is an **inconsistent system.**

If the graphs of two linear equations are identical, the equations are **dependent.**

If their graphs are different, the equations are **independent.**

One solution:
Independent equations
Consistent system

No solution:
Independent equations
Inconsistent system

Infinite number of solutions:
Dependent equations
Consistent system

Solving a System of Linear Equations by the Substitution Method

Step 1. Solve one equation for a variable.

Step 2. Substitute the expression for the variable into the other equation.

Step 3. Solve the equation from Step 2 to find the value of one variable.

Step 4. Substitute the value from Step 3 in either original equation to find the value of the other variable.

Step 5. Check the solution in both original equations.

Solve by substitution.

$$\begin{cases} y = x + 2 \\ 3x - 2y = -5 \end{cases}$$

Since the first equation is solved for y, substitute $x + 2$ for y in the second equation.

$$3x - 2y = -5 \quad \text{Second equation}$$
$$3x - 2(x + 2) = -5 \quad \text{Let } y = x + 2.$$
$$3x - 2x - 4 = -5$$
$$x - 4 = -5 \quad \text{Simplify.}$$
$$x = -1 \quad \text{Add 4.}$$

To find y, let $x = -1$ in $y = x + 2$, so $y = -1 + 2 = 1$. The solution $(-1, 1)$ checks.

Solving a System of Linear Equations by the Elimination Method

Step 1. Rewrite each equation in standard form,
$Ax + By = C$.

Step 2. Multiply one or both equations by a nonzero number so that the coefficients of a variable are opposites.

Step 3. Add the equations.

Step 4. Find the value of the remaining variable by solving the resulting equation.

Step 5. Substitute the value from Step 4 into either original equation to find the value of the other variable.

Step 6. Check the solution in both original equations.

Solve by elimination.

$$\begin{cases} x - 3y = -3 \\ -2x + y = 6 \end{cases}$$

Multiply both sides of the first equation by 2.

$$\begin{array}{r} 2x - 6y = -6 \\ -2x + y = 6 \\ \hline -5y = 0 \quad \text{Add.} \\ y = 0 \quad \text{Divide by } -5. \end{array}$$

To find x, let $y = 0$ in an original equation.

$$x - 3y = -3$$
$$x - 3 \cdot 0 = -3$$
$$x = -3$$

The solution $(-3, 0)$ checks.

DEFINITIONS AND CONCEPTS	EXAMPLES

Section 4.2 Solving Systems of Linear Equations in Three Variables

A **solution** of an equation in three variables x, y, and z is an **ordered triple** (x, y, z) that makes the equation a true statement.

Verify that $(-2, 1, 3)$ is a solution of $2x + 3y - 2z = -7$. Replace x with -2, y with 1, and z with 3.

$$2(-2) + 3(1) - 2(3) \stackrel{?}{=} -7$$
$$-4 + 3 - 6 \stackrel{?}{=} -7$$
$$-7 = -7 \quad \text{True}$$

$(-2, 1, 3)$ is a solution.

Solve.

$$\begin{cases} 2x + y - z = 0 & (1) \\ x - y - 2z = -6 & (2) \\ -3x - 2y + 3z = -22 & (3) \end{cases}$$

Solving a System of Three Linear Equations by the Elimination Method

Step 1. Write each equation in standard form,
$Ax + By + Cz = D$.

Step 2. Choose a pair of equations and use them to eliminate a variable.

Step 3. Choose any other pair of equations and eliminate the same variable.

Step 4. Solve the system of two equations in two variables from Steps 2 and 3.

Step 5. Solve for the third variable by substituting the values of the variables from Step 4 into any of the original equations.

Step 6. Check the solution in all three original equations.

1. Each equation is written in standard form.

2.
$$\begin{array}{ll} 2x + y - z = 0 & (1) \\ \underline{x - y - 2z = -6} & (2) \\ 3x \quad\quad - 3z = -6 & (4) \quad \text{Add.} \end{array}$$

3. Eliminate y from equations (1) and (3) also.

$$\begin{array}{ll} 4x + 2y - 2z = 0 & \text{Multiply equation} \\ \underline{-3x - 2y + 3z = -22} \quad (3) & \text{(1) by 2.} \\ x \quad\quad + z = -22 \quad (5) & \text{Add.} \end{array}$$

4. Solve.

$$\begin{cases} 3x - 3z = -6 & (4) \\ x + z = -22 & (5) \end{cases}$$

$$\begin{array}{ll} x - z = -2 & \text{Divide equation (4) by 3.} \\ \underline{x + z = -22} \quad (5) & \\ 2x \quad\quad = -24 & \\ x = -12 & \end{array}$$

To find z, use equation (5).

$$x + z = -22$$
$$-12 + z = -22$$
$$z = -10$$

5. To find y, use equation (1).

$$2x + y - z = 0$$
$$2(-12) + y - (-10) = 0$$
$$-24 + y + 10 = 0$$
$$y = 14$$

6. The solution $(-12, 14, -10)$ checks.

DEFINITIONS AND CONCEPTS	EXAMPLES

Section 4.3 Systems of Linear Equations and Problem Solving

	Two numbers have a sum of 11. Twice one number is 3 less than 3 times the other. Find the numbers.
1. UNDERSTAND the problem.	**1.** Read and reread. $$x = \text{one number}$$ $$y = \text{other number}$$
2. TRANSLATE.	**2.** In words: sum of numbers is 11 Translate: $x + y \quad = \quad 11$ In words: twice one number is 3 less than 3 times the other number Translate: $2x \quad = \quad 3y - 3$
3. SOLVE.	**3.** Solve the system: $\begin{cases} x + y = 11 \\ 2x = 3y - 3 \end{cases}$ In the first equation, $x = 11 - y$. Substitute into the other equation. $$2x = 3y - 3$$ $$2(11 - y) = 3y - 3$$ $$22 - 2y = 3y - 3$$ $$-5y = -25$$ $$y = 5$$ Replace y with 5 in the equation $x = 11 - y$. Then $x = 11 - 5 = 6$. The solution is $(6, 5)$.
4. INTERPRET.	**4.** *Check:* See that $6 + 5 = 11$ is the required sum and that twice 6 is 3 times 5 less 3. *State:* The numbers are 6 and 5.

Section 4.4 Solving Systems of Equations by Matrices

A **matrix** is a rectangular array of numbers.	$$\begin{bmatrix} -7 & 0 & 3 \\ 1 & 2 & 4 \end{bmatrix} \quad \begin{bmatrix} a & b & c \\ d & e & f \\ g & h & i \end{bmatrix}$$
The **matrix** corresponding to a system is composed of the coefficients of the variables and the constants of the system.	The matrix corresponding to the system $$\begin{cases} x - y = 1 \\ 2x + y = 11 \end{cases} \text{ is } \begin{bmatrix} 1 & -1 & \vdots & 1 \\ 2 & 1 & \vdots & 11 \end{bmatrix}$$
The following **row operations** can be performed on matrices, and the result is an equivalent matrix.	Use matrices to solve the system. $\begin{cases} x - y = 1 \\ 2x + y = 11 \end{cases}$
Elementary row operations:	The corresponding matrix is
1. Interchange any two rows.	$$\begin{bmatrix} 1 & -1 & \vdots & 1 \\ 2 & 1 & \vdots & 11 \end{bmatrix}$$
2. Multiply (or divide) the elements of one row by the same nonzero number.	Use row operations to write an equivalent matrix with 1's along the diagonal and 0's below each 1 in the diagonal. Multiply row 1 by -2 and add to row 2. Change row 2 only.
3. Multiply (or divide) the elements of one row by the same nonzero number and add them to their corresponding elements in any other row.	$$\begin{bmatrix} 1 & -1 & \vdots & 1 \\ -2(1) + 2 & -2(-1) + 1 & \vdots & -2(1) + 11 \end{bmatrix}$$ simplifies to $\begin{bmatrix} 1 & -1 & \vdots & 1 \\ 0 & 3 & \vdots & 9 \end{bmatrix}$

DEFINITIONS AND CONCEPTS	EXAMPLES

Section 4.4   Solving Systems of Equations by Matrices (continued)

	Divide row 2 by 3.

$$\begin{bmatrix} 1 & -1 & | & 1 \\ 0 & \dfrac{3}{3} & | & \dfrac{9}{3} \end{bmatrix} \text{ simplifies to } \begin{bmatrix} 1 & -1 & | & 1 \\ 0 & 1 & | & 3 \end{bmatrix}$$

This matrix corresponds to the system

$$\begin{cases} x - y = 1 \\ y = 3 \end{cases}$$

Let $y = 3$ in the first equation.

$$x - 3 = 1$$
$$x = 4$$

The ordered pair solution is $(4, 3)$.

Section 4.5   Systems of Linear Inequalities

A **system of linear inequalities** consists of two or more linear inequalities.

To graph a system of inequalities, graph each inequality in the system. The overlapping region is the solution of the system.

Solve: $\begin{cases} x - y \geq 3 \\ y \leq -2x \end{cases}$

$y \leq -2x$ $x - y \geq 3$

Solution region

Chapter 4 Review

(4.1) *Solve each system of equations in two variables by each method: (a) graphing, (b) substitution, and (c) elimination.*

1. $\begin{cases} 3x + 10y = 1 \\ x + 2y = -1 \end{cases}$

2. $\begin{cases} y = \dfrac{1}{2}x + \dfrac{2}{3} \\ 4x + 6y = 4 \end{cases}$

3. $\begin{cases} 2x - 4y = 22 \\ 5x - 10y = 15 \end{cases}$

4. $\begin{cases} 3x - 6y = 12 \\ 2y = x - 4 \end{cases}$

5. $\begin{cases} \dfrac{1}{2}x - \dfrac{3}{4}y = -\dfrac{1}{2} \\ \dfrac{1}{8}x + \dfrac{3}{4}y = \dfrac{19}{8} \end{cases}$

6. The revenue equation for a certain style of backpack is $y = 32x$, where x is the number of backpacks sold and y is the income in dollars for selling x backpacks. The cost equation for these units is $y = 15x + 25{,}500$, where x is the number of backpacks manufactured and y is the cost in dollars for manufacturing x backpacks. Find the number

of units to be sold for the company to break even. (*Hint*: Solve the system of equations formed by the two given equations.)

(4.2) *Solve each system of equations in three variables.*

7. $\begin{cases} x + z = 4 \\ 2x - y = 4 \\ x + y - z = 0 \end{cases}$

8. $\begin{cases} 2x + 5y = 4 \\ x - 5y + z = -1 \\ 4x - z = 11 \end{cases}$

9. $\begin{cases} 4y + 2z = 5 \\ 2x + 8y = 5 \\ 6x + 4z = 1 \end{cases}$

10. $\begin{cases} 5x + 7y = 9 \\ 14y - z = 28 \\ 4x + 2z = -4 \end{cases}$

11. $\begin{cases} 3x - 2y + 2z = 5 \\ -x + 6y + z = 4 \\ 3x + 14y + 7z = 20 \end{cases}$

12. $\begin{cases} x + 2y + 3z = 11 \\ y + 2z = 3 \\ 2x + 2z = 10 \end{cases}$

13. $\begin{cases} 7x - 3y + 2z = 0 \\ 4x - 4y - z = 2 \\ 5x + 2y + 3z = 1 \end{cases}$

14. $\begin{cases} x - 3y - 5z = -5 \\ 4x - 2y + 3z = 13 \\ 5x + 3y + 4z = 22 \end{cases}$

(4.3) *Use systems of equations to solve.*

15. The sum of three numbers is 98. The sum of the first and second is two more than the third number, and the second is four times the first. Find the numbers.

16. One number is three times a second number, and twice the sum of the numbers is 168. Find the numbers.

17. Two cars leave Chicago, one traveling east and the other west. After 4 hours, they are 492 miles apart. If one car is traveling 7 mph faster than the other, find the speed of each.

18. The foundation for a rectangular Hardware Warehouse has a length three times the width and is 296 feet around. Find the dimensions of the building.

19. James Callahan has available a 10% alcohol solution and a 60% alcohol solution. Find how many liters of each solution he should mix to make 50 liters of a 40% alcohol solution.

20. An employee at See's Candy Store needs a special mixture of candy. She has creme-filled chocolates that sell for $3.00 per pound, chocolate-covered nuts that sell for $2.70 per pound, and chocolate-covered raisins that sell for $2.25 per pound. She wants to have twice as many raisins as nuts in the mixture. Find how many pounds of each she should use to make 45 pounds worth $2.80 per pound.

21. Chris Kringler has $2.77 in her coin jar—all in pennies, nickels, and dimes. If she has 53 coins in all and four more nickels than dimes, find how many of each type of coin she has.

22. If $10,000 and $4000 are invested such that $1250 in interest is earned in one year, and if the rate of interest on the larger investment is 2% more than that on the smaller investment, find the rates of interest.

23. The perimeter of an isosceles (two sides equal) triangle is 73 centimeters. If the unequal side is 7 centimeters longer than the two equal sides, find the lengths of the three sides.

24. The sum of three numbers is 295. One number is five more than the second and twice the third. Find the numbers.

(4.4) *Use matrices to solve each system.*

25. $\begin{cases} 3x + 10y = 1 \\ x + 2y = -1 \end{cases}$

26. $\begin{cases} 3x - 6y = 12 \\ 2y = x - 4 \end{cases}$

27. $\begin{cases} 3x - 2y = -8 \\ 6x + 5y = 11 \end{cases}$

28. $\begin{cases} 6x - 6y = -5 \\ 10x - 2y = 1 \end{cases}$

29. $\begin{cases} 3x - 6y = 0 \\ 2x + 4y = 5 \end{cases}$

30. $\begin{cases} 5x - 3y = 10 \\ -2x + y = -1 \end{cases}$

31. $\begin{cases} 0.2x - 0.3y = -0.7 \\ 0.5x + 0.3y = 1.4 \end{cases}$

32. $\begin{cases} 3x + 2y = 8 \\ 3x - y = 5 \end{cases}$

33. $\begin{cases} x + z = 4 \\ 2x - y = 0 \\ x + y - z = 0 \end{cases}$

34. $\begin{cases} 2x + 5y = 4 \\ x - 5y + z = -1 \\ 4x - z = 11 \end{cases}$

35. $\begin{cases} 3x - y = 11 \\ x + 2z = 13 \\ y - z = -7 \end{cases}$

36. $\begin{cases} 5x + 7y + 3z = 9 \\ 14y - z = 28 \\ 4x + 2z = -4 \end{cases}$

37. $\begin{cases} 7x - 3y + 2z = 0 \\ 4x - 4y - z = 2 \\ 5x + 2y + 3z = 1 \end{cases}$

38. $\begin{cases} x + 2y + 3z = 14 \\ y + 2z = 3 \\ 2x - 2z = 10 \end{cases}$

(4.5) *Graph the solution of each system of linear inequalities.*

39. $\begin{cases} y \geq 2x - 3 \\ y \leq -2x + 1 \end{cases}$

40. $\begin{cases} y \leq -3x - 3 \\ y \leq 2x + 7 \end{cases}$

41. $\begin{cases} x + 2y > 0 \\ x - y \leq 6 \end{cases}$

42. $\begin{cases} x - 2y \geq 7 \\ x + y \leq -5 \end{cases}$

43. $\begin{cases} 3x - 2y \leq 4 \\ 2x + y \geq 5 \\ y \leq 4 \end{cases}$

44. $\begin{cases} 4x - y \leq 0 \\ 3x - 2y \geq -5 \\ y \geq -4 \end{cases}$

45. $\begin{cases} x + 2y \leq 5 \\ x \leq 2 \\ x \geq 0 \\ y \geq 0 \end{cases}$

46. $\begin{cases} x + 3y \leq 7 \\ y \leq 5 \\ x \geq 0 \\ y \geq 0 \end{cases}$

MIXED REVIEW

Solve each system.

47. $\begin{cases} y = x - 5 \\ y = -2x + 2 \end{cases}$

48. $\begin{cases} \dfrac{2}{5}x + \dfrac{3}{4}y = 1 \\ x + 3y = -2 \end{cases}$

49. $\begin{cases} 5x - 2y = 10 \\ x = \dfrac{2}{5}y + 2 \end{cases}$

50. $\begin{cases} x - 4y = 4 \\ \dfrac{1}{8}x - \dfrac{1}{2}y = 3 \end{cases}$

51. $\begin{cases} x - 3y + 2z = 0 \\ 9y - z = 22 \\ 5x + 3z = 10 \end{cases}$

52. One number is five less than three times a second number. If the sum of the numbers is 127, find the numbers.

53. The perimeter of a triangle is 126 units. The length of one side is twice the length of the shortest side. The length of the third side is fourteen more than the length of the shortest side. Find the lengths of the sides of the triangle.

54. Graph the solution of the system: $\begin{cases} y \le 3x - \dfrac{1}{2} \\ 3x + 4y \ge 6 \end{cases}$.

55. The number of newspapers printed as morning editions continues to increase and the number of newspapers printed as evening editions continues to decrease. The number y of daily morning newspapers in existence is approximated by the equation $y = 16.0x + 666$, where x is the number of years since 1995. The number y of daily evening newspapers in existence is approximated by $y = -24.8x + 872$, where x is the number of years since 1995. Use these equations to determine the year in which the number of newspapers printed as morning editions was the same as the number of newspapers printed as evening editions. Round to the nearest whole number. (*Source:* Based on data from Newspaper Association of America)

Chapter 4 Getting Ready for the Test

MULTIPLE CHOICE *All the exercises below are multiple choice. Choose the correct letter.*

1. When solving a system of two linear equations in two variables, all variables subtract out and the resulting equation is $-2 = 0$. What does this mean?

A. the solution is $(-2, 0)$ **B.** the system has an infinite number of solutions   **C.** the system has no solution

2. The ordered triple $(1, 0, -2)$ is a solution to what system?

A. $\begin{cases} 5x - y - z = -7 \\ x + y + z = -1 \\ y + z = -1 \end{cases}$
B. $\begin{cases} 3x - y - 2z = 7 \\ x + y + z = -1 \\ 5x + z = 3 \end{cases}$
C. $\begin{cases} x = -2 \\ x + y + z = -1 \\ x + z = 1 \end{cases}$
D. $\begin{cases} y = 1 \\ x + y + z = -1 \\ x + y = -1 \end{cases}$

3. For the system $\begin{cases} 4x - y = 0 \\ x + z = 1 \\ 3y - z = 12 \end{cases}$ choose the correct corresponding matrix.

A. $\begin{bmatrix} 4 & -1 & | & 0 \\ 1 & 1 & | & 1 \\ 3 & -1 & | & 12 \end{bmatrix}$
B. $\begin{bmatrix} 4 & -1 & 1 & | & 0 \\ 1 & 1 & 1 & | & 1 \\ 1 & 3 & -1 & | & 12 \end{bmatrix}$
C. $\begin{bmatrix} 4 & -1 & 0 & | & 0 \\ 1 & 0 & 1 & | & 1 \\ 0 & 3 & -1 & | & 12 \end{bmatrix}$

MULTIPLE CHOICE *Select the correct choice. The system for Exercises 4–6 is:*

$$\begin{cases} 3x - y + 2z = 3 & \text{Equation (1)} \\ 4x + y - z = 5 & \text{Equation (2)} \\ -x + 5y + 3z = 12 & \text{Equation (3)} \end{cases}$$

The Choices for Exercises 4–6 are:

A. [Equation (1)] + [Equation (2)]

C. [Equation (1)] + 2 · [Equation (2)]

B. [Equation (1)] + 3 · [Equation (3)]

D. [Equation (1)] + [Equation (3)]

4. Which choice eliminates the variable x?

5. Which choice eliminates the variable y?

6. Which choice eliminates the variable z?

MATCHING *Match each system with the graph of its solution region.*

7. $\begin{cases} x \le -3 \\ y \le 3 \end{cases}$

8. $\begin{cases} x \le -3 \\ y \ge 3 \end{cases}$

9. $\begin{cases} x \ge -3 \\ y \ge 3 \end{cases}$

10. $\begin{cases} x \ge -3 \\ y \le 3 \end{cases}$

A.

B.

C.

D.

Chapter 4 Test   MyMathLab® You Tube

Solve each system of equations graphically and then solve by the elimination method or the substitution method.

1. $\begin{cases} 2x - y = -1 \\ 5x + 4y = 17 \end{cases}$

2. $\begin{cases} 7x - 14y = 5 \\ x = 2y \end{cases}$

Solve each system.

3. $\begin{cases} 4x - 7y = 29 \\ 2x + 5y = -11 \end{cases}$

4. $\begin{cases} 15x + 6y = 15 \\ 10x + 4y = 10 \end{cases}$

5. $\begin{cases} 2x - 3y = 4 \\ 3y + 2z = 2 \\ x - z = -5 \end{cases}$

6. $\begin{cases} 3x - 2y - z = -1 \\ 2x - 2y = 4 \\ 2x - 2z = -12 \end{cases}$

7. $\begin{cases} \dfrac{x}{2} + \dfrac{y}{4} = -\dfrac{3}{4} \\ x + \dfrac{3}{4}y = -4 \end{cases}$

Use matrices to solve each system.

8. $\begin{cases} x - y = -2 \\ 3x - 3y = -6 \end{cases}$

9. $\begin{cases} x + 2y = -1 \\ 2x + 5y = -5 \end{cases}$

10. $\begin{cases} x - y - z = 0 \\ 3x - y - 5z = -2 \\ 2x + 3y = -5 \end{cases}$

11. A motel in New Orleans charges \$90 per day for double occupancy and \$80 per day for single occupancy during off-season. If 80 rooms are occupied for a total of \$6930, how many rooms of each kind are occupied?

12. The research department of a company that manufactures children's fruit drinks is experimenting with a new flavor. A 17.5% fructose solution is needed, but only 10% and 20% solutions are available. How many gallons of the 10% fructose solution should be mixed with the 20% fructose solution to obtain 20 gallons of a 17.5% fructose solution?

13. A company that manufactures boxes recently purchased \$2000 worth of new equipment to offer gift boxes to its customers. The cost of producing a package of gift boxes is \$1.50 and it is sold for \$4.00. Find the number of packages that must be sold for the company to break even.

14. The measure of the largest angle of a triangle is 3 less than five times the measure of the smallest angle. The measure of the remaining angle is 1 less than twice the measure of the smallest angle. Find the measure of each angle.

Graph the solutions of the system of linear inequalities.

15. $\begin{cases} 2y - x \ge 1 \\ x + y \ge -4 \\ y \le 2 \end{cases}$

Chapter 4 Cumulative Review

1. Determine whether each statement is true or false.
   a. $3 \in \{x \mid x \text{ is a natural number}\}$
   b. $7 \notin \{1, 2, 3\}$

2. Determine whether each statement is true or false.
   a. $\{0, 7\} \subseteq \{0, 2, 4, 6, 8\}$
   b. $\{1, 3, 5\} \subseteq \{1, 3, 5, 7\}$

3. Simplify the following expressions.
   a. $11 + 2 - 7$
   b. $-5 - 4 + 2$

4. Subtract.
   a. $-7 - (-2)$
   b. $14 - 38$

5. Write the additive inverse, or opposite, of each.
   a. 4
   b. $\dfrac{3}{7}$
   c. -11.2

6. Write the multiplicative inverse, or reciprocal, of each.
   a. 5
   b. $-\dfrac{2}{3}$

7. Use the distributive property to multiply.
   a. $3(2x + y)$
   b. $-(3x - 1)$
   c. $0.7a\,(b - 2)$

8. Use the distributive property to multiply.
   a. $7(3x - 2y + 4)$
   b. $-(-2s - 3t)$

9. Use the distributive property to simplify each expression.
   a. $3x - 5x + 4$
   b. $7yz + yz$
   c. $4z + 6.1$

10. Use the distributive property to simplify each expression.
    a. $5y^2 - 1 + 2(y^2 + 2)$
    b. $(7.8x - 1.2) - (5.6x - 2.4)$

Solve.

11. $-4x - 1 + 5x = 9x + 3 - 7x$

12. $8y - 14 = 6y - 14$

13. $0.3x + 0.1 = 0.27x - 0.02$

14. $2(m - 6) - m = 4(m - 3) - 3m$

15. A pennant in the shape of an isosceles triangle is to be constructed for the Slidell High School Athletic Club and sold at a fund-raiser. The company manufacturing the pennant charges according to perimeter, and the athletic club has determined that a perimeter of 149 centimeters should make a nice profit. If each equal side of the triangle is twice the length of the third side, increased by 12 centimeters, find the lengths of the sides of the triangular pennant.

16. A quadrilateral has four angles whose sum is 360°. In a particular quadrilateral, two angles have the same measure. A third angle is 10° more than the measure of one of the equal angles, and the fourth angle is half the measure of one of the equal angles. Find the measures of the angles.

17. Solve: $3x + 4 \geq 2x - 6$. Graph the solution set and write it in interval notation.

18. Solve: $5(2x - 1) > -5$

19. Solve: $2 < 4 - x < 7$

20. Solve: $-1 < \dfrac{-2x - 1}{3} < 1$

21. Solve: $|2x| + 5 = 7$

22. Solve: $|x - 5| = 4$

23. Solve for m: $|m - 6| < 2$

24. Solve: $|2x + 1| > 5$

25. Plot each ordered pair on a Cartesian coordinate system and name the quadrant or axis in which the point is located.
    a. $(2, -1)$ b. $(0, 5)$
    c. $(-3, 5)$ d. $(-2, 0)$
    e. $\left(-\dfrac{1}{2}, -4\right)$ f. $(1.5, 1.5)$

26. Name the quadrant or axis in which each point is located.
    a. $(-1, -5)$
    b. $(4, -2)$
    c. $(0, 2)$

27. Is the relation $x = y^2$ also a function?

28. Graph: $-2x + \dfrac{1}{2}y = -2$

29. If $f(x) = 7x^2 - 3x + 1$ and $g(x) = 8x - 2$, find the following.
    a. $f(1)$ b. $g(1)$
    c. $f(-2)$ d. $g(0)$

30. If $f(x) = 3x^2$, find the following.
    a. $f(5)$ b. $f(-2)$

31. Graph $g(x) = 2x + 1$. Compare this graph with the graph of $f(x) = 2x$.

32. Find the slope of the line containing $(-2, 6)$ and $(0, 9)$.

33. Find the slope and the y-intercept of the line $3x - 4y = 4$.

34. Find the slope and y-intercept of the line defined by $y = 2$.

35. Are the following pairs of lines parallel, perpendicular, or neither?
    a. $3x + 7y = 4$
       $6x + 14y = 7$

    b. $-x + 3y = 2$
       $2x + 6y = 5$

36. Find an equation of the line through $(0, -9)$ with slope $\dfrac{1}{5}$.

37. Find an equation of the line through points (4, 0) and (−4, −5). Write the equation using function notation.

38. Find an equation of the line through $(-2, 6)$ perpendicular to $f(x) = \dfrac{1}{2}x - \dfrac{1}{3}$. Write the equation in slope-intercept form.

39. Graph: $3x \geq y$

40. Graph: $x \geq 1$

41. Determine whether the given ordered pair is a solution of the system.

   a. $\begin{cases} -x + y = 2 \\ 2x - y = -3 \end{cases}$ $(-1, 1)$

   b. $\begin{cases} 5x + 3y = -1 \\ x - y = 1 \end{cases}$ $(-2, 3)$

42. Solve the system.
$$\begin{cases} 5x + y = -2 \\ 4x - 2y = -10 \end{cases}$$

43. Solve the system.
$$\begin{cases} 3x - y + z = -15 \\ x + 2y - z = 1 \\ 2x + 3y - 2z = 0 \end{cases}$$

44. Solve the system.
$$\begin{cases} x - 2y + z = 0 \\ 3x - y - 2z = -15 \\ 2x - 3y + 3z = 7 \end{cases}$$

45. Use matrices to solve the system.
$$\begin{cases} x + 3y = 5 \\ 2x - y = -4 \end{cases}$$

46. Use matrices to solve the system.
$$\begin{cases} -6x + 8y = 0 \\ 9x - 12y = 2 \end{cases}$$

Exponents, Polynomials, and Polynomial Functions

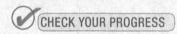
CHECK YOUR PROGRESS

Linear equations are important for solving problems. They are not sufficient, however, to solve all problems. Many real-world phenomena are modeled by polynomials. We begin this chapter by reviewing exponents. We will then study operations on polynomials and how polynomials can be used in problem solving.

A Brief History of Listening to Music (Other than Live)

The phonograph was invented in 1877 by Thomas Edison.

Guglielmo Marconi was awarded one of many patents for radio in 1897.

Walkman is a Sony brand tradename originally used for portable audiocassette players. The prototype was built in 1977.

The first line of iPods was released by Apple, Inc. on October 23, 2001, about 8½ months after iTunes (Macintosh version) was released.

Where Do You Get Your Music?

According to a recent Nielsen Music 360 study, 93% of Americans listen to music and spend more than 25 hours each week doing so. There are many listening options such as radio, CDs, or even streaming to your computer or smartphone. The percent of music heard through streaming is on the rise, as is the number of people who have signed up for music subscription services. The circle graph below shows how we spend money on music.

In Section 5.8, Exercises 103 and 104, we attempt to predict the number of people who have gone digital and use subscription services to stream their music.

How We Spend Our Money on Music

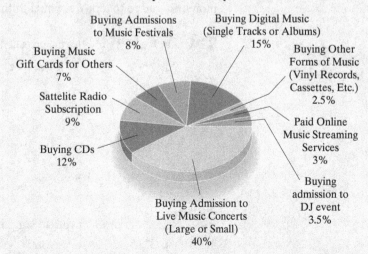

Buying Admissions to Music Festivals 8%

Buying Digital Music (Single Tracks or Albums) 15%

Buying Music Gift Cards for Others 7%

Buying Other Forms of Music (Vinyl Records, Cassettes, Etc.) 2.5%

Sattelite Radio Subscription 9%

Paid Online Music Streaming Services 3%

Buying CDs 12%

Buying admission to DJ event 3.5%

Buying Admission to Live Music Concerts (Large or Small) 40%

Source: Nielsen Music 360 2014

5.1 Exponents and Scientific Notation

OBJECTIVE

1 Using the Product Rule

Recall that exponents may be used to write repeated factors in a more compact form. As we have seen in the previous chapters, exponents can be used when the repeated factor is a number or a variable. For example,

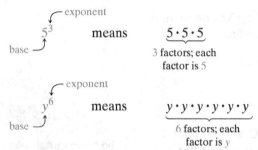

Expressions such as 5^3 and y^6 that contain exponents are called **exponential expressions.**

Exponential expressions can be multiplied, divided, added, subtracted, and themselves raised to powers. In this section, we review operations on exponential expressions.

We review multiplication first. To multiply x^2 by x^3, use the definition of an exponent.

$$x^2 \cdot x^3 = \underbrace{(x \cdot x)(x \cdot x \cdot x)}_{x \text{ is a factor 5 times}}$$

$$= x^5$$

Notice that the result is exactly the same if we add the exponents.

$$x^2 \cdot x^3 = x^{2+3} = x^5$$

This suggests the following.

Product Rule for Exponents

If m and n are positive integers and a is a real number, then

$$a^m \cdot a^n = a^{m+n}$$

In other words, the *product* of exponential expressions with a common base is the common base raised to a power equal to the *sum* of the exponents of the factors.

EXAMPLE 1   Use the product rule to simplify.

    a. $2^2 \cdot 2^5$ **b.** $x^7 x^3$ **c.** $y \cdot y^2 \cdot y^4$

Solution

    a. $2^2 \cdot 2^5 = 2^{2+5} = 2^7$

    b. $x^7 x^3 = x^{7+3} = x^{10}$

    c. $y \cdot y^2 \cdot y^4 = (y^1 \cdot y^2) \cdot y^4$

                $= y^3 \cdot y^4$

                $= y^7$

PRACTICE

1   Use the product rule to simplify.

    a. $3^4 \cdot 3^2$ **b.** $x^5 \cdot x^2$ **c.** $y \cdot y^3 \cdot y^5$

EXAMPLE 2   Use the product rule to simplify.

a. $(3x^6)(5x)$

b. $(-2.4x^3p^2)(4xp^{10})$

Solution   Here, we use properties of multiplication to group together like bases.

a. $(3x^6)(5x) = 3(5)x^6x^1 = 15x^7$

b. $(-2.4x^3p^2)(4xp^{10}) = -2.4(4)x^3x^1p^2p^{10} = -9.6x^4p^{12}$ □

PRACTICE

2   Use the product rule to simplify.

a. $(5z^3)(7z)$

b. $(-4.1t^5q^3)(5tq^5)$ ■

OBJECTIVE

2   Evaluating Expressions Raised to the 0 Power

The definition of a^n does not include the possibility that n might be 0. But if it did, then, by the product rule,

$$\underbrace{a^0 \cdot a^n = a^{0+n} = a^n = 1 \cdot a^n}$$

From this, we reasonably define that $a^0 = 1$ as long as a does not equal 0.

Zero Exponent

If a does not equal 0, then $a^0 = 1$.

EXAMPLE 3   Evaluate the following.

a. 7^0

b. -7^0

c. $(2x + 5)^0$

d. $2x^0$

Solution

a. $7^0 = 1$

b. Without parentheses, only 7 is raised to the 0 power.

$$-7^0 = -(7^0) = -(1) = -1$$

c. $(2x + 5)^0 = 1$

d. $2x^0 = 2(1) = 2$ □

PRACTICE

3   Evaluate the following.

a. 5^0

b. -5^0

c. $(3x - 8)^0$

d. $3x^0$ ■

OBJECTIVE

3   Using the Quotient Rule ▶

To find quotients of exponential expressions, we again begin with the definition of a^n to simplify $\dfrac{x^9}{x^2}$. For example,

$$\frac{x^9}{x^2} = \frac{x \cdot x \cdot x \cdot x \cdot x \cdot x \cdot x \cdot x \cdot x}{x \cdot x} = x^7$$

(Assume for the next two sections that denominators containing variables are not 0.)
Notice that the result is exactly the same if we subtract the exponents.

$$\frac{x^9}{x^2} = x^{9-2} = x^7$$

This suggests the following.

Quotient Rule for Exponents

If a is a nonzero real number and n and m are integers, then

$$\frac{a^m}{a^n} = a^{m-n}$$

In other words, the *quotient* of exponential expressions with a common base is the common base raised to a power equal to the *difference* of the exponents.

EXAMPLE 4   Use the quotient rule to simplify.

a. $\dfrac{x^7}{x^4}$ b. $\dfrac{5^8}{5^2}$ c. $\dfrac{20x^6}{4x^5}$ d. $\dfrac{12y^{10}z^7}{14y^8z^7}$

Solution

a. $\dfrac{x^7}{x^4} = x^{7-4} = x^3$

b. $\dfrac{5^8}{5^2} = 5^{8-2} = 5^6$

c. $\dfrac{20x^6}{4x^5} = 5x^{6-5} = 5x^1$, or $5x$

d. $\dfrac{12y^{10}z^7}{14y^8z^7} = \dfrac{6}{7}y^{10-8} \cdot z^{7-7} = \dfrac{6}{7}y^2z^0 = \dfrac{6}{7}y^2$,   or $\dfrac{6y^2}{7}$

PRACTICE

4   Use the quotient rule to simplify.

a. $\dfrac{z^8}{z^3}$ b. $\dfrac{3^9}{3^3}$ c. $\dfrac{45x^7}{5x^3}$ d. $\dfrac{24a^{14}b^6}{18a^7b^6}$

OBJECTIVE

4   Evaluating Expressions Raised to the Negative nth Power

When the exponent of the denominator is larger than the exponent of the numerator, applying the quotient rule yields a negative exponent. For example,

$$\frac{x^3}{x^5} = x^{3-5} = x^{-2}$$

Using the definition of a^n, though, gives us

$$\frac{x^3}{x^5} = \frac{x \cdot x \cdot x}{x \cdot x \cdot x \cdot x \cdot x} = \frac{1}{x^2}$$

From this, we reasonably define $x^{-2} = \dfrac{1}{x^2}$ or, in general, $a^{-n} = \dfrac{1}{a^n}$.

Negative Exponents

If a is a real number other than 0 and n is a positive integer, then

$$a^{-n} = \frac{1}{a^n}$$

EXAMPLE 5 Simplify and write with positive exponents only.

a. 5^{-2} **b.** $(-4)^{-4}$ **c.** $2x^{-3}$ **d.** $(3x)^{-1}$

e. $\dfrac{m^5}{m^{15}}$ **f.** $\dfrac{3^3}{3^6}$ **g.** $2^{-1} + 3^{-2}$ **h.** $\dfrac{1}{t^{-5}}$

Solution

a. $5^{-2} = \dfrac{1}{5^2} = \dfrac{1}{25}$

> **Helpful Hint**
>
> Study Example 5(c). Make sure you understand that $2x^{-3} = \dfrac{2}{x^3}$

b. $(-4)^{-4} = \dfrac{1}{(-4)^4} = \dfrac{1}{256}$

c. $2x^{-3} = 2 \cdot \dfrac{1}{x^3} = \dfrac{2}{x^3}$ Without parentheses, only x is raised to the -3 power.

d. $(3x)^{-1} = \dfrac{1}{(3x)^1} = \dfrac{1}{3x}$ With parentheses, both 3 and x are raised to the -1 power.

e. $\dfrac{m^5}{m^{15}} = m^{5-15} = m^{-10} = \dfrac{1}{m^{10}}$

f. $\dfrac{3^3}{3^6} = 3^{3-6} = 3^{-3} = \dfrac{1}{3^3} = \dfrac{1}{27}$

g. $2^{-1} + 3^{-2} = \dfrac{1}{2^1} + \dfrac{1}{3^2} = \dfrac{1}{2} + \dfrac{1}{9} = \dfrac{9}{18} + \dfrac{2}{18} = \dfrac{11}{18}$

h. $\dfrac{1}{t^{-5}} = \dfrac{1}{\frac{1}{t^5}} = 1 \div \dfrac{1}{t^5} = 1 \cdot \dfrac{t^5}{1} = t^5$

**PRACTICE
5** Simplify and write with positive exponents only.

a. 6^{-2} **b.** $(-2)^{-6}$ **c.** $3x^{-5}$ **d.** $(5y)^{-1}$ **e.** $\dfrac{k^4}{k^{11}}$

f. $\dfrac{5^3}{5^5}$ **g.** $5^{-1} + 2^{-2}$ **h.** $\dfrac{1}{z^{-8}}$

> **Helpful Hint**
>
> Notice that when a factor containing an exponent is moved from the numerator to the denominator or from the denominator to the numerator, the sign of its exponent changes.
>
> $$x^{-3} = \dfrac{1}{x^3}, \qquad 5^{-2} = \dfrac{1}{5^2} = \dfrac{1}{25}$$
>
> $$\dfrac{1}{y^{-4}} = y^4, \qquad \dfrac{1}{2^{-3}} = 2^3 = 8$$

EXAMPLE 6 Simplify and write with positive exponents only.

a. $\dfrac{x^{-9}}{x^2}$ **b.** $\dfrac{5p^4}{p^{-3}}$ **c.** $\dfrac{2^{-3}}{2^{-1}}$ **d.** $\dfrac{2x^{-7}y^2}{10xy^{-5}}$ **e.** $\dfrac{(3x^{-3})(x^2)}{x^6}$

Solution

a. $\dfrac{x^{-9}}{x^2} = x^{-9-2} = x^{-11} = \dfrac{1}{x^{11}}$

b. $\dfrac{5p^4}{p^{-3}} = 5 \cdot p^{4-(-3)} = 5p^7$

(Continued on next page)

c. $\dfrac{2^{-3}}{2^{-1}} = 2^{-3-(-1)} = 2^{-2} = \dfrac{1}{2^2} = \dfrac{1}{4}$

d. $\dfrac{2x^{-7}y^2}{10xy^{-5}} = \dfrac{x^{-7-1} \cdot y^{2-(-5)}}{5} = \dfrac{x^{-8}y^7}{5} = \dfrac{y^7}{5x^8}$

e. Simplify the numerator first.

$$\dfrac{(3x^{-3})(x^2)}{x^6} = \dfrac{3x^{-3+2}}{x^6} = \dfrac{3x^{-1}}{x^6} = 3x^{-1-6} = 3x^{-7} = \dfrac{3}{x^7}$$ □

PRACTICE

6 Simplify and write with positive exponents only.

a. $\dfrac{z^{-8}}{z^3}$　　b. $\dfrac{7t^3}{t^{-5}}$　　c. $\dfrac{3^{-2}}{3^{-4}}$　　d. $\dfrac{5a^{-5}b^3}{15a^2b^{-4}}$　　e. $\dfrac{(2x^{-5})(x^6)}{x^5}$

✔ **CONCEPT CHECK**

Find and correct the error in the following:

$$\dfrac{y^{-6}}{y^{-2}} = y^{-6-2} = y^{-8} = \dfrac{1}{y^8}$$

EXAMPLE 7 Simplify. Assume that a and t are nonzero integers and that x is not 0.

a. $x^{2a} \cdot x^3$

b. $\dfrac{x^{2t-1}}{x^{t-5}}$

Solution

a. $x^{2a} \cdot x^3 = x^{2a+3}$　　　Use the product rule.

b. $\dfrac{x^{2t-1}}{x^{t-5}} = x^{(2t-1)-(t-5)}$　　　Use the quotient rule.

$= x^{2t-1-t+5} = x^{t+4}$ □

PRACTICE

7 Simplify. Assume that a and t are nonzero integers and that x is not 0.

a. $x^{3a} \cdot x^4$

b. $\dfrac{x^{3t-2}}{x^{t-3}}$

OBJECTIVE

5 Converting Between Scientific Notation and Standard Notation

Very large and very small numbers occur frequently in nature. For example, the distance between the Earth and the Sun is approximately 150,000,000 kilometers. A helium atom has a diameter of 0.000 000 022 centimeter. It can be tedious to write these very large and very small numbers in standard notation like this. **Scientific notation** is a convenient shorthand notation for writing very large and very small numbers.

Helium atom

0.000 000 022
centimeter

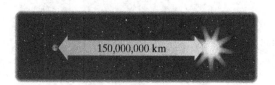

150,000,000 km

> **Scientific Notation**
>
> A positive number is written in **scientific notation** if it is written as the product of a number a, where $1 \le a < 10$, and an integer power r of 10:
>
> $$a \times 10^r$$

The following are examples of numbers written in scientific notation.

diameter of helium atom: 2.2×10^{-8} cm

approximate distance between Earth and the Sun: 1.5×10^8 km

> **Writing a Number in Scientific Notation**
>
> **Step 1.** Move the decimal point in the original number until the new number has a value between 1 and 10, including 1.
>
> **Step 2.** Count the number of decimal places the decimal point was moved in Step 1. If the original number is 10 or greater, the count is positive. If the original number is less than 1, the count is negative.
>
> **Step 3.** Write the product of the new number in Step 1 by 10 raised to an exponent equal to the count found in Step 2.

EXAMPLE 8   Write each number in scientific notation.

    a. 730,000   **b.** 0.00000104

Solution

a. Step 1. Move the decimal point until the number is between 1 and 10.

$$730{,}000.$$

Step 2. The decimal point is moved 5 places and the original number is 10 or greater, so the count is positive 5.

Step 3. $730{,}000 = 7.3 \times 10^5$.

b. Step 1. Move the decimal point until the number is between 1 and 10.

$$0.00000104$$

Step 2. The decimal point is moved 6 places and the original number is less then 1, so the count is -6.

Step 3. $0.00000104 = 1.04 \times 10^{-6}$.

PRACTICE
8   Write each number in scientific notation.

    a. 65,000   **b.** 0.000038

To write a scientific notation number in standard form, we reverse the preceding steps.

> **Writing a Scientific Notation Number in Standard Notation**
>
> Move the decimal point in the number the same number of places as the exponent on 10. If the exponent is positive, move the decimal point to the right. If the exponent is negative, move the decimal point to the left.

EXAMPLE 9 Write each number in standard notation.

a. 7.7×10^8

b. 1.025×10^{-3}

Solution

a. $7.7 \times 10^8 = 770,000,000$ Since the exponent is positive, move the decimal point 8 places to the right. Add zeros as needed.

b. $1.025 \times 10^{-3} = 0.001025$ Since the exponent is negative, move the decimal point 3 places to the left. Add zeros as needed. □

PRACTICE

9 Write each number in standard notation.

a. 6.2×10^5

b. 3.109×10^{-2}

 CONCEPT CHECK

Which of the following numbers have values that are less than 1?

a. 3.5×10^{-5} **b.** 3.5×10^5 **c.** -3.5×10^5 **d.** -3.5×10^{-5}

Scientific Calculator Explorations

Multiply 5,000,000 by 700,000 on your calculator. The display should read $\boxed{3.5 \quad 12}$ or $\boxed{3.5 \text{ E } 12}$, which is the product written in scientific notation. Both these notations mean 3.5×10^{12}.

To enter a number written in scientific notation on a calculator, find the key marked $\boxed{\text{EE}}$. (On some calculators, this key may be marked $\boxed{\text{EXP}}$.)
To enter 7.26×10^{13}, press the keys

$$\boxed{7.26} \quad \boxed{\text{EE}} \quad \boxed{13}$$

The display will read $\boxed{7.26 \quad 13}$ or $\boxed{7.26 \text{ E } 13}$.

Use your calculator to perform each operation indicated.

1. Multiply 3×10^{11} and 2×10^{32}.

2. Divide 6×10^{14} by 3×10^9.

3. Multiply 5.2×10^{23} and 7.3×10^4.

4. Divide 4.38×10^{41} by 3×10^{17}.

Answers to Concept Check:
a, c, d

 ## Vocabulary, Readiness & Video Check

State the base of the exponent 5 in each expression.

1. $9x^5$ **2.** yz^5 **3.** -3^5 **4.** $(-3)^5$ **5.** $(y^7)^5$ **6.** $9 \cdot 2^5$

Martin-Gay Interactive Videos

See Video 5.1

Watch the section lecture video and answer the following questions.

OBJECTIVE 1

7. Why are we reminded that multiplication is commutative and associative during the simplifying of Example 2?

OBJECTIVE 2

8. Example 3 does not contain parentheses yet a discussion of parentheses is an important part of evaluating. Explain.

OBJECTIVE 3

9. When applying the quotient rule in Example 5, how do you know which exponents to subtract?

OBJECTIVE 4

10. What important reminder is made at the beginning of Example 6?

OBJECTIVE 5

11. From Examples 10 and 11, explain how the direction of the movement of the decimal point in Step 1 might suggest another way to determine the sign of the exponent on 10.

5.1 Exercise Set MyMathLab®

Write each expression with positive exponents. See Examples 5 and 6.

1. $5x^{-1}y^{-2}$

2. $7xy^{-4}$

3. $a^2b^{-1}c^{-5}$

4. $a^{-4}b^2c^{-6}$

5. $\dfrac{y^{-2}}{x^{-4}}$

6. $\dfrac{x^{-7}}{z^{-3}}$

Use the product rule to simplify each expression. See Examples 1 and 2.

7. $4^2 \cdot 4^3$

8. $3^3 \cdot 3^5$

9. $x^5 \cdot x^3$

10. $a^2 \cdot a^9$

11. $m \cdot m^7 \cdot m^6$

12. $n \cdot n^{10} \cdot n^{12}$

13. $(4xy)(-5x)$

14. $(-7xy)(7y)$

15. $(-4x^3p^2)(4y^3x^3)$

16. $(-6a^2b^3)(-3ab^3)$

Evaluate each expression. See Example 3.

17. -8^0

18. $(-9)^0$

19. $(4x + 5)^0$

20. $(3x - 1)^0$

21. $-x^0$

22. $-5x^0$

23. $4x^0 + 5$

24. $8x^0 + 1$

Use the quotient rule to simplify. See Example 4.

25. $\dfrac{a^5}{a^2}$

26. $\dfrac{x^9}{x^4}$

27. $-\dfrac{26z^{11}}{2z^7}$

28. $-\dfrac{16x^5}{8x}$

29. $\dfrac{x^9y^6}{x^8y^6}$

30. $\dfrac{a^{12}b^2}{a^9b}$

31. $\dfrac{12x^4y^7}{9xy^5}$

32. $\dfrac{24a^{10}b^{11}}{10ab^3}$

33. $\dfrac{-36a^5b^7c^{10}}{6ab^3c^4}$

34. $\dfrac{49a^3bc^{14}}{-7abc^8}$

Simplify and write using positive exponents only. See Examples 5 and 6.

35. 4^{-2}

36. 2^{-3}

37. $(-3)^{-3}$

38. $(-6)^{-2}$

39. $\dfrac{x^7}{x^{15}}$

40. $\dfrac{z}{z^3}$

41. $5a^{-4}$

42. $10b^{-1}$

43. $\dfrac{x^{-7}}{y^{-2}}$

44. $\dfrac{p^{-13}}{q^{-3}}$

45. $\dfrac{x^{-2}}{x^5}$

46. $\dfrac{z^{-12}}{z^{10}}$

47. $\dfrac{8r^4}{2r^{-4}}$

48. $\dfrac{3s^3}{15s^{-3}}$

49. $\dfrac{x^{-9}x^4}{x^{-5}}$

50. $\dfrac{y^{-7}y}{y^8}$

51. $\dfrac{2a^{-6}b^2}{18ab^{-5}}$

52. $\dfrac{18ab^{-6}}{3a^{-3}b^6}$

53. $\dfrac{(24x^8)(x)}{20x^{-7}}$

54. $\dfrac{(30z^2)(z^5)}{55z^{-4}}$

MIXED PRACTICE

Simplify and write using positive exponents only. See Examples 1 through 6.

55. $-7x^3 \cdot 20x^9$

56. $-3y \cdot -9y^4$

57. $x^7 \cdot x^8 \cdot x$

58. $y^6 \cdot y \cdot y^9$

59. $2x^3 \cdot 5x^7$

60. $-3z^4 \cdot 10z^7$

61. $(5x)^0 + 5x^0$

62. $4y^0 - (4y)^0$

63. $\dfrac{z^{12}}{z^{15}}$

64. $\dfrac{x^{11}}{x^{20}}$

65. $3^0 - 3t^0$

66. $4^0 + 4x^0$

67. $\dfrac{y^{-3}}{y^{-7}}$

68. $\dfrac{y^{-6}}{y^{-9}}$

69. $4^{-1} + 3^{-2}$

70. $1^{-3} - 4^{-2}$

71. $3x^{-1}$

72. $(4x)^{-1}$

73. $\dfrac{r^4}{r^{-4}}$

74. $\dfrac{x^{-5}}{x^3}$

75. $\dfrac{x^{-7}y^{-2}}{x^2y^2}$

76. $\dfrac{a^{-5}b^7}{a^{-2}b^{-3}}$

77. $(-4x^2y)(3x^4)(-2xy^5)$

78. $(-6a^4b)(2b^3)(-3ab^6)$

79. $2^{-4} \cdot x$

80. $5^{-2} \cdot y$

81. $\dfrac{5^{17}}{5^{13}}$

82. $\dfrac{10^{25}}{10^{23}}$

83. $\dfrac{8^{-7}}{8^{-6}}$

84. $\dfrac{13^{-10}}{13^{-9}}$

85. $\dfrac{9^{-5}a^4}{9^{-3}a^{-1}}$

86. $\dfrac{11^{-9}b^3}{11^{-7}b^{-4}}$

87. $\dfrac{14x^{-2}yz^{-4}}{2xyz}$

88. $\dfrac{30x^{-7}yz^{-14}}{3xyz}$

Simplify. Assume that variables in the exponents represent nonzero integers and that x, y, and z are not 0. See Example 7.

89. $x^5 \cdot x^{7a}$

90. $x^{4a} \cdot x^7$

91. $\dfrac{x^{3t-1}}{x^t}$

92. $\dfrac{y^{4p-2}}{y^{3p}}$

93. $y^{2p} \cdot y^{9p}$

94. $x^{9y} \cdot x^{-7y}$

95. $\dfrac{z^{6x}}{z^7}$

96. $\dfrac{y^6}{y^{4z}}$

97. $\dfrac{x^{3t} \cdot x^{4t-1}}{x^t}$

98. $\dfrac{z^{5x} \cdot z^{x-7}}{z^x}$

Write each number in scientific notation. See Example 8.

99. 31,250,000

100. 678,000

101. 0.016

102. 0.007613

103. 67,413

104. 36,800,000

105. 0.0125

106. 0.00084

107. 0.000053

108. 98,700,000,000

Write each number in scientific notation.

109. The approximate distance between Jupiter and the Sun is 778,300,000 kilometers. (*Source:* National Space Data Center)

110. For the 2013–2014 National Football League season, the payroll of the New England Patriots was approximately $143,714,600. (*Source:* NESN.com)

111. The gross domestic product (GDP) of a region is the value of all final goods and services produced within a given year. The GDP of the European Union for 2014 was estimated to be equivalent to U.S. $16,773,000,000,000. (*Source:* International Monetary Fund)

112. By the third quarter of 2014, worldwide sales of the Playstation 4 exceeded 18,500,000 units. (*Source:* Sony)

113. Lake Mead, created from the Colorado River by the Hoover Dam, has a capacity of 124,000,000,000 cubic feet of water. (*Source:* U.S. Bureau of Reclamation)

114. The temperature of the core of the Sun is about 27,000,000°F.

115. A pulsar is a rotating neutron star that gives off sharp, regular pulses of radio waves. For one particular pulsar, the rate of pulses is every 0.001 second.

116. To convert from cubic inches to cubic meters, multiply by 0.0000164.

Write each number in standard notation, without exponents. See Example 9.

117. 3.6×10^{-9}

118. 2.7×10^{-5}

119. 9.3×10^{7}

120. 6.378×10^{8}

121. 1.278×10^{6}

122. 7.6×10^{4}

123. 7.35×10^{12}

124. 1.66×10^{-5}

125. 4.03×10^{-7}

126. 8.007×10^{8}

Write each number in standard notation.

127. The estimated world population in 1 C.E. was 3.0×10^{8}. (*Source:* World Almanac and Book of Facts)

128. There are 3.949×10^{6} miles of highways, roads, and streets in the United States. (*Source:* Bureau of Transportation Statistics)

129. Chiricahua National Monument in Arizona contains 9.5×10^{-3} square kilometers of privately owned land.

130. Hagerman Fossil Beds National Monument in Idaho contains 6.68×10^{-2} square kilometers of privately owned land.

131. In 2014, PepsiCo, Inc. (which includes Frito-Lay and Quaker Foods) had revenue of 6.6683×10^{10}. (*Source:* PepsiCo, Inc.)

132. In 2014, the revenue for Burger King was 1.06×10^{9}. (*Source:* Burger King Corporation)

REVIEW AND PREVIEW

Evaluate. See Sections 1.3 and 5.1.

133. $(5 \cdot 2)^{2}$

134. $5^{2} \cdot 2^{2}$

135. $\left(\dfrac{3}{4}\right)^{3}$

136. $\dfrac{3^{3}}{4^{3}}$

137. $(2^{3})^{2}$

138. $(2^{2})^{3}$

CONCEPT EXTENSIONS

139. Explain how to convert a number from standard notation to scientific notation.

140. Explain how to convert a number from scientific notation to standard notation.

141. Explain why $(-5)^{0}$ simplifies to 1 but -5^{0} simplifies to -1.

142. Explain why both $4x^{0} - 3y^{0}$ and $(4x - 3y)^{0}$ simplify to 1.

143. Simplify where possible.

   a. $x^{a} \cdot x^{a}$ **b.** $x^{a} + x^{a}$

   c. $\dfrac{x^{a}}{x^{b}}$ **d.** $x^{a} \cdot x^{b}$

   e. $x^{a} + x^{b}$

144. Which numbers are equal to 36,000? Of these, which is written in scientific notation?

   a. 36×10^{3} **b.** 360×10^{2}

   c. 0.36×10^{5} **d.** 3.6×10^{4}

Without calculating, determine which number is larger.

145. 7^{11} or 7^{13}

146. 5^{10} or 5^{9}

147. 7^{-11} or 7^{-13}

148. 5^{-10} or 5^{-9}

5.2 More Work with Exponents and Scientific Notation

OBJECTIVE

1   Using the Power Rules

The volume of the cube shown whose side measures x^2 units is $(x^2)^3$ cubic units. To simplify an expression such as $(x^2)^3$, we use the definition of a^n. Then

$$(x^2)^3 = \underbrace{(x^2)(x^2)(x^2)}_{x^2 \text{ is a factor 3 times}} = x^{2+2+2} = x^6$$

x^2 units

Notice that the result is exactly the same if the exponents are multiplied.

$$(x^2)^3 = x^{2\cdot3} = x^6$$

This suggests that the power of an exponential expression raised to a power is the product of the exponents. Two additional rules for exponents are given in the following box.

The Power Rule and Power of a Product or Quotient Rules for Exponents

If a and b are real numbers and m and n are integers, then

$$(a^m)^n = a^{m\cdot n} \qquad \text{Power rule}$$

$$(ab)^m = a^m b^m \qquad \text{Power of a product}$$

$$\left(\frac{a}{b}\right)^n = \frac{a^n}{b^n} \ (b \neq 0) \quad \text{Power of a quotient}$$

EXAMPLE 1   Use the power rule to simplify the following expressions. Use positive exponents to write all results.

a. $(x^5)^7$ **b.** $(2^2)^3$ **c.** $(5^{-1})^2$ **d.** $(y^{-3})^{-4}$

Solution

a. $(x^5)^7 = x^{5\cdot7} = x^{35}$ **b.** $(2^2)^3 = 2^{2\cdot3} = 2^6 = 64$

c. $(5^{-1})^2 = 5^{-1\cdot2} = 5^{-2} = \dfrac{1}{5^2} = \dfrac{1}{25}$ **d.** $(y^{-3})^{-4} = y^{-3(-4)} = y^{12}$ ☐

PRACTICE

1   Use the power rule to simplify the following expressions. Use positive exponents to write all results.

a. $(z^3)^5$ **b.** $(5^2)^2$ **c.** $(3^{-1})^3$ **d.** $(x^{-4})^{-6}$ ■

EXAMPLE 2   Use the power rules to simplify the following. Use positive exponents to write all results.

a. $(5x^2)^3$ **b.** $\left(\dfrac{2}{3}\right)^3$ **c.** $\left(\dfrac{3p^4}{q^5}\right)^2$ **d.** $\left(\dfrac{2^{-3}}{y}\right)^{-2}$ **e.** $(x^{-5}y^2z^{-1})^7$

Solution

a. $(5x^2)^3 = 5^3 \cdot (x^2)^3 = 5^3 \cdot x^{2\cdot3} = 125x^6$

b. $\left(\dfrac{2}{3}\right)^3 = \dfrac{2^3}{3^3} = \dfrac{8}{27}$

c. $\left(\dfrac{3p^4}{q^5}\right)^2 = \dfrac{(3p^4)^2}{(q^5)^2} = \dfrac{3^2 \cdot (p^4)^2}{(q^5)^2} = \dfrac{9p^8}{q^{10}}$

(Continued on next page)

d. $\left(\dfrac{2^{-3}}{y}\right)^{-2} = \dfrac{\left(2^{-3}\right)^{-2}}{y^{-2}}$

$= \dfrac{2^6}{y^{-2}} = 64y^2$ Use the negative exponent rule.

e. $\left(x^{-5}y^2z^{-1}\right)^7 = \left(x^{-5}\right)^7 \cdot \left(y^2\right)^7 \cdot \left(z^{-1}\right)^7$

$= x^{-35}y^{14}z^{-7} = \dfrac{y^{14}}{x^{35}z^7}$ □

PRACTICE
2   Use the power rules to simplify the following. Use positive exponents to write all results.

a. $(2x^3)^5$ **b.** $\left(\dfrac{3}{5}\right)^2$ **c.** $\left(\dfrac{2a^5}{b^7}\right)^4$ **d.** $\left(\dfrac{3^{-2}}{x}\right)^{-1}$ **e.** $(a^{-2}b^{-5}c^4)^{-2}$

OBJECTIVE
2   Using Exponent Rules and Definitions to Simplify Expressions

In the next few examples, we practice the use of several of the rules and definitions for exponents. The following is a summary of these rules and definitions.

Summary of Rules for Exponents

If a and b are real numbers and m and n are integers, then

Product rule	$a^m \cdot a^n = a^{m+n}$	
Zero exponent	$a^0 = 1$	$(a \neq 0)$
Negative exponent	$a^{-n} = \dfrac{1}{a^n}$	$(a \neq 0)$
Quotient rule	$\dfrac{a^m}{a^n} = a^{m-n}$	$(a \neq 0)$
Power rule	$(a^m)^n = a^{m \cdot n}$	
Power of a product	$(ab)^m = a^m \cdot b^m$	
Power of a quotient	$\left(\dfrac{a}{b}\right)^m = \dfrac{a^m}{b^m}$	$(b \neq 0)$

EXAMPLE 3   Simplify each expression. Use positive exponents to write the answers.

a. $(2x^0y^{-3})^{-2}$ **b.** $\left(\dfrac{x^{-5}}{x^{-2}}\right)^{-3}$ **c.** $\left(\dfrac{2}{7}\right)^{-2}$ **d.** $\dfrac{5^{-2}x^{-3}y^{11}}{x^2y^{-5}}$

Solution

a. $(2x^0y^{-3})^{-2} = 2^{-2}(x^0)^{-2}(y^{-3})^{-2}$

$= 2^{-2}x^0y^6$

$= \dfrac{1(y^6)}{2^2}$ Write x^0 as 1.

$= \dfrac{y^6}{4}$

b. $\left(\dfrac{x^{-5}}{x^{-2}}\right)^{-3} = \dfrac{(x^{-5})^{-3}}{(x^{-2})^{-3}} = \dfrac{x^{15}}{x^6} = x^{15-6} = x^9$

c. $\left(\dfrac{2}{7}\right)^{-2} = \dfrac{2^{-2}}{7^{-2}} = \dfrac{7^2}{2^2} = \dfrac{49}{4}$

d. $\dfrac{5^{-2}x^{-3}y^{11}}{x^2y^{-5}} = (5^{-2})\left(\dfrac{x^{-3}}{x^2}\right)\left(\dfrac{y^{11}}{y^{-5}}\right) = 5^{-2}x^{-3-2}y^{11-(-5)} = 5^{-2}x^{-5}y^{16}$

$$= \dfrac{y^{16}}{5^2 x^5} = \dfrac{y^{16}}{25x^5}$$

PRACTICE
3   Simplify each expression. Use positive exponents to write the answers.

a. $(3ab^{-5})^{-3}$ b. $\left(\dfrac{y^{-7}}{y^{-4}}\right)^{-5}$ c. $\left(\dfrac{3}{8}\right)^{-2}$ d. $\dfrac{9^{-2}a^{-4}b^3}{a^2b^{-5}}$

EXAMPLE 4   Simplify each expression. Use positive exponents to write the answers.

a. $\left(\dfrac{3x^2y}{y^{-9}z}\right)^{-2}$ b. $\left(\dfrac{3a^2}{2x^{-1}}\right)^3\left(\dfrac{x^{-3}}{4a^{-2}}\right)^{-1}$

Solution There is often more than one way to simplify exponential expressions. Here, we will simplify inside the parentheses if possible before we apply the power rules for exponents.

a. $\left(\dfrac{3x^2y}{y^{-9}z}\right)^{-2} = \left(\dfrac{3x^2y^{10}}{z}\right)^{-2} = \dfrac{3^{-2}x^{-4}y^{-20}}{z^{-2}} = \dfrac{z^2}{3^2x^4y^{20}} = \dfrac{z^2}{9x^4y^{20}}$

b. $\left(\dfrac{3a^2}{2x^{-1}}\right)^3\left(\dfrac{x^{-3}}{4a^{-2}}\right)^{-1} = \dfrac{27a^6}{8x^{-3}}\cdot\dfrac{x^3}{4^{-1}a^2} = \dfrac{27\cdot4\cdot a^6x^3x^3}{8\cdot a^2} = \dfrac{27a^4x^6}{2}$

PRACTICE
4   Simplify each expression. Use positive exponents to write the answers.

a. $\left(\dfrac{5a^4b}{a^{-8}c}\right)^{-3}$ b. $\left(\dfrac{2x^4}{5y^{-2}}\right)^3\left(\dfrac{x^{-4}}{10y^{-2}}\right)^{-1}$

EXAMPLE 5   Simplify each expression. Assume that *a* and *b* are integers and that *x* and *y* are not 0.

a. $x^{-b}(2x^b)^2$ b. $\dfrac{(y^{3a})^2}{y^{a-6}}$

Solution

a. $x^{-b}(2x^b)^2 = x^{-b}2^2x^{2b} = 4x^{-b+2b} = 4x^b$

b. $\dfrac{(y^{3a})^2}{y^{a-6}} = \dfrac{y^{6a}}{y^{a-6}} = y^{6a-(a-6)} = y^{6a-a+6} = y^{5a+6}$

PRACTICE
5   Simplify each expression. Assume that *a* and *b* are integers and that *x* and *y* are not 0.

a. $x^{-2a}(3x^a)^3$ b. $\dfrac{(y^{3b})^3}{y^{4b-3}}$

OBJECTIVE
3   Computing Using Scientific Notation

To perform operations on numbers written in scientific notation, we use properties of exponents.

EXAMPLE 6 Perform the indicated operations. Write each result in scientific notation.

a. $(8.1 \times 10^5)(5 \times 10^{-7})$

b. $\dfrac{1.2 \times 10^4}{3 \times 10^{-2}}$

Solution

a. $(8.1 \times 10^5)(5 \times 10^{-7}) = 8.1 \times 5 \times 10^5 \times 10^{-7}$ — Not in scientific notation because 40.5 is not between 1 and 10.

$= 40.5 \times 10^{-2}$

$= (4.05 \times 10^1) \times 10^{-2}$

$= 4.05 \times 10^{-1}$

b. $\dfrac{1.2 \times 10^4}{3 \times 10^{-2}} = \left(\dfrac{1.2}{3}\right)\left(\dfrac{10^4}{10^{-2}}\right) = 0.4 \times 10^{4-(-2)}$

$= 0.4 \times 10^6 = (4 \times 10^{-1}) \times 10^6 = 4 \times 10^5$ ☐

PRACTICE

6 Perform the indicated operations. Write each result in scientific notation.

a. $(3.4 \times 10^4)(5 \times 10^{-7})$

b. $\dfrac{1.6 \times 10^8}{4 \times 10^{-2}}$ ◾

EXAMPLE 7 Use scientific notation to simplify $\dfrac{2000 \times 0.000021}{700}$. Write the result in scientific notation.

Solution

$$\dfrac{2000 \times 0.000021}{700} = \dfrac{(2 \times 10^3)(2.1 \times 10^{-5})}{7 \times 10^2} = \dfrac{2(2.1)}{7} \cdot \dfrac{10^3 \cdot 10^{-5}}{10^2}$$

$$= 0.6 \times 10^{-4}$$

$$= (6 \times 10^{-1}) \times 10^{-4}$$

$$= 6 \times 10^{-5}$$ ☐

PRACTICE

7 Use scientific notation to simplify $\dfrac{2400 \times 0.0000014}{800}$. Write the result in scientific notation. ◾

Vocabulary, Readiness & Video Check

Simplify. See Examples 1 through 4.

1. $(x^4)^5$ **2.** $(5^6)^2$ **3.** $x^4 \cdot x^5$ **4.** $x^7 \cdot x^8$ **5.** $(y^6)^7$

6. $(x^3)^4$ **7.** $(z^4)^9$ **8.** $(z^3)^7$ **9.** $(z^{-6})^{-3}$ **10.** $(y^{-4})^{-2}$

Martin-Gay Interactive Videos

See Video 5.2 🔴

Watch the section lecture video and answer the following questions

OBJECTIVE 1

11. Based on ▥ Example 1 and the lecture before, what are the differences between the power rule and product rule for exponents?

OBJECTIVE 2

12. Name all the rules and definitions used to simplify ▥ Example 5.

OBJECTIVE 3

13. In the ▥ Example 6 multiplication problem, why is the first product not the final answer? How can we tell that this first product is not written in scientific notation?

5.2   Exercise Set   MyMathLab® ▶

Simplify. Write each answer using positive exponents only. See Examples 1 and 2.

1. $(3^{-1})^2$

2. $(2^{-2})^2$

▶ **3.** $(x^4)^{-9}$

4. $(y^7)^{-3}$

5. $(3x^2y^3)^2$

6. $(4x^3yz)^2$

7. $\left(\dfrac{2x^5}{y^{-3}}\right)^4$

8. $\left(\dfrac{3a^{-4}}{b^7}\right)^3$

9. $(2a^2bc^{-3})^{-6}$

10. $(6x^{-6}y^7z^0)^{-2}$

▶ **11.** $\left(\dfrac{x^7y^{-3}}{z^{-4}}\right)^{-5}$

12. $\left(\dfrac{a^{-2}b^{-5}}{c^{-11}}\right)^{-6}$

13. $(-2^{-2}y^{-1})^{-3}$

14. $(-4^{-6}y^{-6})^{-4}$

Simplify. Write each answer using positive exponents only. See Examples 3 and 4.

15. $\left(\dfrac{a^{-4}}{a^{-5}}\right)^{-2}$

16. $\left(\dfrac{x^{-9}}{x^{-4}}\right)^{-3}$

17. $\left(\dfrac{6p^6}{p^{12}}\right)^2$

18. $\left(\dfrac{4p^6}{p^9}\right)^3$

19. $(-8y^3xa^{-2})^{-3}$

20. $(-5y^0x^2a^3)^{-3}$

21. $\left(\dfrac{3}{4}\right)^{-3}$

22. $\left(\dfrac{5}{8}\right)^{-2}$

▶ **23.** $\left(\dfrac{2a^{-2}b^5}{4a^2b^7}\right)^{-2}$

24. $\left(\dfrac{5x^7y^4}{10x^3y^{-2}}\right)^{-3}$

25. $\left(\dfrac{x^{-2}y^{-2}}{a^{-3}}\right)^{-7}$

26. $\left(\dfrac{x^{-1}y^{-2}}{z^{-3}}\right)^{-5}$

MIXED PRACTICE

Simplify. Write each answer using positive exponents only. See Examples 1 through 4.

27. $(y^{-5})^2$

28. $(z^{-2})^{13}$

29. $(5^{-1})^3$

30. $(8^2)^{-1}$

31. $(x^7)^{-9}$

32. $(y^{-4})^5$

33. $\left(\dfrac{x^4}{y^{-3}}\right)^{-5}$

34. $\left(\dfrac{a^{-3}}{b^{-6}}\right)^{-4}$

▶ **35.** $(4x^2)^2$

36. $(-8x^3)^2$

37. $\left(\dfrac{4^{-4}}{y^3x}\right)^{-2}$

38. $\left(\dfrac{7^{-3}}{ab^2}\right)^{-2}$

39. $\left(\dfrac{2x^{-3}}{y^{-1}}\right)^{-3}$

40. $\left(\dfrac{n^5}{2m^{-2}}\right)^{-4}$

41. $\dfrac{4^{-1}x^2yz}{x^{-2}yz^3}$

42. $\dfrac{8^{-2}x^{-3}y^{11}}{x^2y^{-5}}$

43. $\left(\dfrac{3x^5}{6x^4}\right)^4$

44. $\left(\dfrac{8^{-3}}{y^2}\right)^{-2}$

▶ **45.** $\dfrac{(y^3)^{-4}}{y^3}$

46. $\dfrac{2(y^3)^{-3}}{y^{-3}}$

47. $\dfrac{3^{-2}a^{-5}b^6}{4^{-2}a^{-7}b^{-3}}$

48. $\dfrac{2^{-3}m^{-4}n^{-5}}{5^{-2}m^{-5}n}$

49. $(4x^6y^5)^{-2}(6x^4y^3)$

50. $(5x^2y^4)^{-2}(3x^9y^4)$

51. $x^6(x^6bc)^{-6}$

52. $y^2(y^2bx)^{-4}$

53. $\dfrac{2^{-3}x^2y^{-5}}{5^{-2}x^7y^{-1}}$

54. $\dfrac{7^{-1}a^{-3}b^5}{a^2b^{-2}}$

55. $\left(\dfrac{2x^2}{y^4}\right)^3\left(\dfrac{2x^5}{y}\right)^{-2}$

56. $\left(\dfrac{3z^{-2}}{y}\right)^2\left(\dfrac{9y^{-4}}{z^{-3}}\right)^{-1}$

Simplify the following. Assume that variables in the exponents represent integers and that all other variables are not 0. See Example 5.

57. $(x^{3a+6})^3$

58. $(x^{2b+7})^2$

59. $\dfrac{x^{4a}(x^{4a})^3}{x^{4a-2}}$

60. $\dfrac{x^{-5y+2}x^{2y}}{x}$

61. $(b^{5x-2})^2$

62. $(c^{2a+3})^3$

63. $\dfrac{(y^{2a})^8}{y^{a-3}}$

64. $\dfrac{(y^{4a})^7}{y^{2a-1}}$

65. $\left(\dfrac{2x^{3t}}{x^{2t-1}}\right)^4$

66. $\left(\dfrac{3y^{5a}}{y^{-a+1}}\right)^2$

67. $\dfrac{25x^{2a+1}y^{a-1}}{5x^{3a+1}y^{2a-3}}$

68. $\dfrac{16x^{-5-3a}y^{-2a-b}}{2x^{-5+3b}y^{-2b-a}}$

Perform each indicated operation. Write each answer in scientific notation. See Examples 6 and 7.

▶ **69.** $(5 \times 10^{11})(2.9 \times 10^{-3})$

70. $(3.6 \times 10^{-12})(6 \times 10^9)$

71. $(2 \times 10^5)^3$

72. $(3 \times 10^{-7})^3$

73. $\dfrac{3.6 \times 10^{-4}}{9 \times 10^2}$

74. $\dfrac{1.2 \times 10^9}{2 \times 10^{-5}}$

75. $\dfrac{0.0069}{0.023}$

76. $\dfrac{0.00048}{0.0016}$

77. $\dfrac{18{,}200 \times 100}{91{,}000}$

78. $\dfrac{0.0003 \times 0.0024}{0.0006 \times 20}$

79. $\dfrac{6000 \times 0.006}{0.009 \times 400}$

80. $\dfrac{0.00016 \times 300}{0.064 \times 100}$

81. $\dfrac{0.00064 \times 2000}{16{,}000}$

82. $\dfrac{0.00072 \times 0.003}{0.00024}$

▶ **83.** $\dfrac{66{,}000 \times 0.001}{0.002 \times 0.003}$

84. $\dfrac{0.0007 \times 11{,}000}{0.001 \times 0.0001}$

85. $\dfrac{9.24 \times 10^{15}}{(2.2 \times 10^{-2})(1.2 \times 10^{-5})}$

86. $\dfrac{(2.6 \times 10^{-3})(4.8 \times 10^{-4})}{1.3 \times 10^{-12}}$

Solve.

87. To convert from square inches to square meters, multiply by 6.452×10^{-4}. The area of the following square is 4×10^{-2} square inches. Convert this area to square meters.

4×10^{-2} sq in.

88. To convert from cubic inches to cubic meters, multiply by 1.64×10^{-5}. A grain of salt is in the shape of a cube. If an average size of a grain of salt is 3.8×10^{-6} cubic inches, convert this volume to cubic meters.

3.8×10^{-6} cu in.

REVIEW AND PREVIEW

Simplify each expression. See Section 1.4.

89. $-5y + 4y - 18 - y$

90. $12m - 14 - 15m - 1$

91. $-3x - (4x - 2)$

92. $-9y - (5 - 6y)$

93. $3(z - 4) - 2(3z + 1)$

94. $5(x - 3) - 4(2x - 5)$

CONCEPT EXTENSIONS

95. Each side of the cube shown is $\dfrac{2x^{-2}}{y}$ meters. Find its volume.

$\dfrac{2x^{-2}}{y}$ m

96. The lot shown is in the shape of a parallelogram with base $\dfrac{3x^{-1}}{y^{-3}}$ feet and height $5x^{-7}$ feet. Find its area.

$5x^{-7}$ ft

$\dfrac{3x^{-1}}{y^{-3}}$ ft

97. The density D of an object is equivalent to the quotient of its mass M and volume V. Thus $D = \dfrac{M}{V}$. Express in scientific notation the density of an object whose mass is 500,000 pounds and whose volume is 250 cubic feet.

98. The density of ordinary water is 3.12×10^{-2} tons per cubic foot. The volume of water in the largest of the Great Lakes, Lake Superior, is 4.269×10^{14} cubic feet. Use the formula $D = \dfrac{M}{V}$ (see Exercise 97) to find the mass (in tons) of the water in Lake Superior. Express your answer in scientific notation. (*Source:* National Ocean Service)

99. Is there a number a such that $a^{-1} = a^1$? If so, give the value of a.

100. Is there a number a such that a^{-2} is a negative number? If so, give the value of a.

101. Explain whether 0.4×10^{-5} is written in scientific notation.

102. In your own words, explain why $a^0 = 1$ (as long as a is not 0).

103. The estimated population of the United States in early 2015 was 3.19×10^8 people. The land area of the United States is 3.536×10^6 square miles. Find the population density (number of people per square mile) for the United States in 2015. Round to the nearest whole. (*Source:* Population Reference Bureau)

104. The estimated population of China at the beginning of 2015 was 1.368×10^9 people. The land area of China is 3.705×10^6 square miles. Find the population density (number of people per square mile) for China at the beginning of 2015. Round to the nearest whole. (*Source:* Population Reference Bureau)

105. In early 2015, the population of the European Union was 5.07×10^8 people. At the same time, the population of the United States was 3.19×10^8 people. How many times greater was the population of the European Union than the population of the United States? Round to the nearest tenth. (*Source:* Population Reference Bureau)

106. In January 2015, the value of goods imported into the United States was $\$2.41 \times 10^{11}$. The estimated population was 3.19×10^8 people. Find the average value of imported goods per person in the United States for January 2015. Round to the nearest dollar. (*Source:* U.S. Bureau of the Census, Bureau of Economic Analysis)

5.3 | Polynomials and Polynomial Functions

OBJECTIVES

1 Identify Term, Constant, Polynomial, Monomial, Binomial, Trinomial, and the Degree of a Term and of a Polynomial.

2 Define Polynomial Functions.

3 Review Combining Like Terms.

4 Add Polynomials.

5 Subtract Polynomials.

6 Recognize the Graph of a Polynomial Function from the Degree of the Polynomial.

OBJECTIVE

1   Identifying Polynomial Terms and Degrees of Terms and Polynomials

A **term** is a number or the product of a number and one or more variables raised to powers. The **numerical coefficient,** or simply the **coefficient,** is the numerical factor of a term.

Term	Numerical Coefficient of Term
$-1.2x^5$	-1.2
x^3y	1
$-z$	-1
2	2
$\dfrac{x^9}{7}\left(\text{or } \dfrac{1}{7}x^9\right)$	$\dfrac{1}{7}$

If a term contains only a number, it is called a **constant term,** or simply a **constant.**

A **polynomial** is a finite sum of terms in which all variables are raised to nonnegative integer powers and no variables appear in any denominator.

Polynomials	Not Polynomials	
$4x^5y + 7xz$	$5x^{-3} + 2x$	Negative integer exponent
$-5x^3 + 2x + \dfrac{2}{3}$	$\dfrac{6}{x^2} - 5x + 1$	Variable in denominator

A polynomial that contains only one variable is called a **polynomial in one variable.** For example, $3x^2 - 2x + 7$ is a **polynomial in x.** This polynomial in x is written in *descending order* since the terms are listed in descending order of the variable's exponents. (The term 7 can be thought of as $7x^0$.) The following examples are polynomials in one variable written in **descending order.**

$$4x^3 - \frac{7}{8}x^2 + 5 \qquad y^2 - 4.7 \qquad \frac{8a^4}{11} - 7a^2 + \frac{4a}{3}$$

A **monomial** is a polynomial consisting of one term. A **binomial** is a polynomial consisting of two terms. A **trinomial** is a polynomial consisting of three terms.

Monomials	Binomials	Trinomials
ax^2	$x + y$	$x^2 + 4xy + y^2$
$-3x$	$6y^2 - 2.9$	$-x^4 + 3x^3 + 0.1$
4	$\dfrac{5}{7}z^3 - 2z$	$8y^2 - 2y - \dfrac{10}{17}$

By definition, all monomials, binomials, and trinomials are also polynomials.

Each term of a polynomial has a **degree.**

> **Helpful Hint**
>
> We usually write answers that are polynomials in one variable in descending order.

Degree of a Term

The **degree of a term** is the sum of the exponents on the *variables* contained in the term.

EXAMPLE 1 Find the degree of each term.

a. $3x^2$ **b.** -2^3x^5 **c.** y **d.** $12x^2yz^3$ **e.** 5.27

Solution

a. The exponent on x is 2, so the degree of the term is 2.

b. The exponent on x is 5, so the degree of the term is 5. (Recall that the degree is the sum of the exponents on only the *variables*.)

c. The degree of y, or y^1, is 1.

d. The degree is the sum of the exponents on the variables, or $2 + 1 + 3 = 6$.

e. The degree of 5.27, which can be written as $5.27x^0$, is 0. ☐

PRACTICE

1 Find the degree of each term.

a. $4x^5$ **b.** -4^3y^3 **c.** z **d.** $65a^3b^7c$ **e.** 36 ■

From the preceding example, we can say that the degree of a constant is 0. Also, the term 0 has no degree.

Each polynomial also has a degree.

> **Degree of a Polynomial**
>
> The **degree of a polynomial** is the largest degree of all its terms.

EXAMPLE 2 Find the degree of each polynomial and indicate whether the polynomial is also a monomial, binomial, or trinomial.

	Polynomial	Degree	Classification
a.	$7x^3 - \dfrac{3}{4}x + 2$	3	Trinomial
b.	$-xyz$	$1 + 1 + 1 = 3$	Monomial
c.	$x^4 - 16.5$	4	Binomial

☐

PRACTICE

2 Find the degree of each polynomial and indicate whether the polynomial is also a monomial, binomial, or trinomial.

	Polynomial	Degree	Classification
a.	$3x^4 + 2x^2 - 3$		
b.	$9abc^3$		
c.	$8x^5 + 5x^3$		

■

EXAMPLE 3 Find the degree of the polynomial:

$$3xy + x^2y^2 - 5x^2 - 6.7$$

Solution The degree of each term is

$$3xy + x^2y^2 - 5x^2 - 6.7$$
$$\downarrow \qquad \downarrow \qquad \downarrow \qquad \downarrow$$
$$\text{Degree:} \quad 2 \qquad 4 \qquad 2 \qquad 0$$

The largest degree of any term is 4, so the degree of this polynomial is 4.   □

PRACTICE
3 Find the degree of the polynomial: $2x^3y - 3x^3y^2 - 9y^5 + 9.6$ ■

OBJECTIVE

2   Defining Polynomial Functions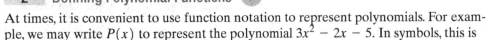

At times, it is convenient to use function notation to represent polynomials. For example, we may write $P(x)$ to represent the polynomial $3x^2 - 2x - 5$. In symbols, this is

$$P(x) = 3x^2 - 2x - 5$$

This function is called a **polynomial function** because the expression $3x^2 - 2x - 5$ is a polynomial.

> **Helpful Hint**
>
> Recall that the symbol $P(x)$ **does not mean** P times x. It is a special symbol used to denote a function.

EXAMPLE 4   If $P(x) = 3x^2 - 2x - 5$, find the following.

  a. $P(1)$ **b.** $P(-2)$

Solution

  a. Substitute 1 for x in $P(x) = 3x^2 - 2x - 5$ and simplify.

$$P(x) = 3x^2 - 2x - 5$$
$$P(1) = 3(1)^2 - 2(1) - 5 = -4$$

  b. Substitute -2 for x in $P(x) = 3x^2 - 2x - 5$ and simplify.

$$P(x) = 3x^2 - 2x - 5$$
$$P(-2) = 3(-2)^2 - 2(-2) - 5 = 11$$ □

PRACTICE
4 If $P(x) = -5x^2 + 2x - 8$, find the following.
  a. $P(-1)$ **b.** $P(3)$ ■

Many real-world phenomena are modeled by polynomial functions. If the polynomial function model is given, we can often find the solution of a problem by evaluating the function at a certain value.

EXAMPLE 5   **Finding the Height of an Object**

The world's highest bridge, the Millau Viaduct in France, is 1125 feet above the River Tarn. An object is dropped from the top of this bridge. Neglecting air resistance, the height of the object at time t seconds is given by the polynomial function $P(t) = -16t^2 + 1125$. Find the height of the object when $t = 1$ second and when $t = 8$ seconds.

Solution To find the height of the object at 1 second, we find $P(1)$.

$$P(t) = -16t^2 + 1125$$
$$P(1) = -16(1)^2 + 1125$$
$$P(1) = 1109$$

When $t = 1$ second, the height of the object is 1109 feet.
To find the height of the object at 8 seconds, we find $P(8)$.

$$P(t) = -16t^2 + 1125$$
$$P(8) = -16(8)^2 + 1125$$
$$P(8) = 101$$

When $t = 8$ seconds, the height of the object is 101 feet. Notice that as time t increases, the height of the object decreases. □

PRACTICE
5   The largest natural bridge is in the canyons at the base of Navajo Mountain, Utah. From the base to the top of the arch, it measures 290 feet. Neglecting air resistance, the height of an object dropped off the bridge is given by the polynomial function $P(t) = -16t^2 + 290$ at time t seconds. Find the height of the object at time $t = 0$ second and $t = 2$ seconds. ■

OBJECTIVE
3   Combining Like Terms Review

Before we add polynomials, recall that terms are considered to be **like terms** if they contain exactly the same variables raised to exactly the same powers.

Like Terms	Unlike Terms
$-5x^2, -x^2$	$4x^2, 3x$
$7xy^3z, -2xzy^3$	$12x^2y^3, -2xy^3$

To simplify a polynomial, we **combine like terms** by using the distributive property. For example, by the distributive property,

$$5x + 7x = (5 + 7)x = 12x$$

EXAMPLE 6   Simplify by combining like terms.

a. $-12x^2 + 7x^2 - 6x$ b. $3xy - 2x + 5xy - x$

Solution By the distributive property,

a. $-12x^2 + 7x^2 - 6x = (-12 + 7)x^2 - 6x = -5x^2 - 6x$

b. Use the associative and commutative properties to group like terms together; then combine.

$$3xy - 2x + 5xy - x = 3xy + 5xy - 2x - x$$
$$= (3 + 5)xy + (-2 - 1)x$$
$$= \underbrace{8xy} - \underbrace{3x}$$ □

Helpful Hint
These two terms are unlike terms.
They cannot be combined.

PRACTICE
6   Simplify by combining like terms.
a. $8x^4 - 5x^4 - 5x$ b. $4ab - 5b + 3ab + 2b$ ■

OBJECTIVE
4   Adding Polynomials

Now we have reviewed the necessary skills to add polynomials.

Adding Polynomials

To add polynomials, combine all like terms.

EXAMPLE 7   Add $11x^3 - 12x^2 + x - 3$ and $x^3 - 10x + 5$.

Solution $(11x^3 - 12x^2 + x - 3) + (x^3 - 10x + 5)$

$\quad = 11x^3 + x^3 - 12x^2 + x - 10x - 3 + 5$ Group like terms.

$\quad = 12x^3 - 12x^2 - 9x + 2$ Combine like terms.   □

PRACTICE
7   Add $5x^3 - 3x^2 - 9x - 8$ and $x^3 + 9x^2 + 2x$.   ■

EXAMPLE 8   Add.

a. $(7x^3y - xy^3 + 11) + (6x^3y - 4)$

b. $(3a^3 - b + 2a - 5) + (a + b + 5)$

Solution

a. To add, remove the parentheses and group like terms.

$\qquad (7x^3y - xy^3 + 11) + (6x^3y - 4)$

$\qquad = 7x^3y - xy^3 + 11 + 6x^3y - 4$

$\qquad = 7x^3y + 6x^3y - xy^3 + 11 - 4$ Group like terms.

$\qquad = 13x^3y - xy^3 + 7$ Combine like terms.

b. $(3a^3 - b + 2a - 5) + (a + b + 5)$

$\qquad = 3a^3 - b + 2a - 5 + a + b + 5$

$\qquad = 3a^3 - b + b + 2a + a - 5 + 5$ Group like terms.

$\qquad = 3a^3 + 3a$ Combine like terms.   □

PRACTICE
8   Add.

a. $(3a^4b - 5ab^2 + 7) + (9ab^2 - 12)$

b. $(2x^5 - 3y + x - 6) + (4y - 2x - 3)$ ■

Sometimes it is more convenient to add polynomials vertically. To do this, line up like terms beneath one another and add like terms. An example is shown later in this section.

OBJECTIVE
5   Subtracting Polynomials

The definition of subtraction of real numbers can be extended to apply to polynomials. To subtract a number, we add its opposite.

$$a - b = a + (-b)$$

Likewise, to subtract a polynomial, we add its opposite. In other words, if P and Q are polynomials, then

$$P - Q = P + (-Q)$$

The polynomial $-Q$ is the **opposite,** or **additive inverse,** of the polynomial Q. We can find $-Q$ by writing the opposite of each term of Q.

✔ **CONCEPT CHECK**

Which polynomial is the opposite of $16x^3 - 5x + 7$?

a. $-16x^3 - 5x + 7$ b. $-16x^3 + 5x - 7$ c. $16x^3 + 5x + 7$ d. $-16x^3 + 5x + 7$

Subtracting Polynomials

To subtract a polynomial, add its opposite.

For example,

To subtract, change the signs; then add.

$$(3x^2 + 4x - 7) - (3x^2 - 2x - 5) = (3x^2 + 4x - 7) + (-3x^2 + 2x + 5)$$
$$= 3x^2 + 4x - 7 - 3x^2 + 2x + 5$$
$$= 6x - 2 \qquad \text{Combine like terms.}$$

EXAMPLE 9   Subtract: $(12z^5 - 12z^3 + z) - (-3z^4 + z^3 + 12z)$

Solution To subtract, add the opposite of the second polynomial to the first polynomial.

$$(12z^5 - 12z^3 + z) - (-3z^4 + z^3 + 12z) \qquad \text{Add the opposite of the}$$
$$= 12z^5 - 12z^3 + z + 3z^4 - z^3 - 12z) \qquad \text{polynomial being subtracted.}$$
$$= 12z^5 + 3z^4 - 12z^3 - z^3 + z - 12z \qquad \text{Group like terms.}$$
$$= 12z^5 + 3z^4 - 13z^3 - 11z \qquad \text{Combine like terms.} \qquad \square$$

PRACTICE
9   Subtract: $(13a^4 - 7a^3 - 9) - (-2a^4 + 8a^3 - 12)$

✔ **CONCEPT CHECK**

Why is the following subtraction incorrect?

$$(7z - 5) - (3z - 4)$$
$$= 7z - 5 - 3z - 4$$
$$= 4z - 9$$

EXAMPLE 10   Subtract $4x^3y^2 - 3x^2y^2 + 2y^2$ from $10x^3y^2 - 7x^2y^2$.

Solution If we subtract 2 from 8, the difference is $8 - 2 = 6$. Notice the order of the numbers and then write "Subtract $4x^3y^2 - 3x^2y^2 + 2y^2$ from $10x^3y^2 - 7x^2y^2$" as a mathematical expression.

$$(10x^3y^2 - 7x^2y^2) - (4x^3y^2 - 3x^2y^2 + 2y^2)$$
$$= 10x^3y^2 - 7x^2y^2 - 4x^3y^2 + 3x^2y^2 - 2y^2 \qquad \text{Remove parentheses.}$$
$$= 6x^3y^2 - 4x^2y^2 - 2y^2 \qquad \text{Combine like terms.} \qquad \square$$

Answers to Concept Checks:
b;
With parentheses removed, the expression should be
$7z - 5 - 3z + 4 = 4z - 1$

PRACTICE
10   Subtract $5x^2y^2 - 3xy^2 + 5y^3$ from $11x^2y^2 - 7xy^2$.

To add or subtract polynomials vertically, just remember to line up like terms. For example, perform the subtraction, from Example 10,

$$(10x^3y^2 - 7x^2y^2) - (4x^3y^2 - 3x^2y^2 + 2y^2)$$

vertically.

Add the opposite of the second polynomial.

$$
\begin{array}{l}
10x^3y^2 - 7x^2y^2 \\
\underline{-(4x^3y^2 - 3x^2y^2 + 2y^2)}
\end{array}
\quad \text{is equivalent to} \quad
\begin{array}{l}
10x^3y^2 - 7x^2y^2 \\
\underline{-4x^3y^2 + 3x^2y^2 - 2y^2} \\
6x^3y^2 - 4x^2y^2 - 2y^2
\end{array}
$$

Polynomial functions, like polynomials, can be added, subtracted, multiplied, and divided. For example, if

$$P(x) = x^2 + x + 1$$

then

$$2P(x) = 2(x^2 + x + 1) = 2x^2 + 2x + 2 \quad \text{Use the distributive property.}$$

Also, if $Q(x) = 5x^2 - 1$, then

$$P(x) + Q(x) = (x^2 + x + 1) + (5x^2 - 1) = 6x^2 + x.$$

A useful business and economics application of subtracting polynomial functions is finding the profit function $P(x)$ when given a revenue function $R(x)$ and a cost function $C(x)$. In business, it is true that

$$\text{profit} = \text{revenue} - \text{cost, or}$$
$$P(x) = R(x) - C(x)$$

For example, if the revenue function is $R(x) = 7x$ and the cost function is $C(x) = 2x + 5000$, then the profit function is

$$P(x) = R(x) - C(x)$$

or

$$P(x) = 7x - (2x + 5000) \quad \text{Substitute } R(x) = 7x$$
$$P(x) = 5x - 5000 \quad \text{and } C(x) = 2x + 5000.$$

Problem-solving exercises involving profit are in the exercise set.

OBJECTIVE

6 Recognizing Graphs of Polynomial Functions from Their Degree

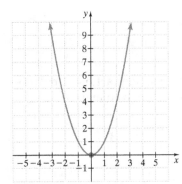

In this section, we reviewed how to find the degree of a polynomial. Knowing the degree of a polynomial can help us recognize the graph of the related polynomial function. For example, we know from Section 3.1 that the graph of the polynomial function $f(x) = x^2$ is a parabola as shown to the left.

The polynomial x^2 has degree 2. The graphs of all polynomial functions of degree 2 will have this same general shape—opening upward, as shown, or downward. Graphs of polynomial functions of degree 2 or 3 will, in general, resemble one of the graphs shown next.

General Shapes of Graphs of Polynomial Functions
Degree 2

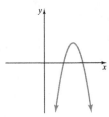

Coefficient of x^2
is a positive number.

Coefficient of x^2
is a negative number.

Degree 3

Coefficient of x^3
is a positive number.

Coefficient of x^3
is a negative number.

EXAMPLE 11 Determine which of the following graphs most closely resembles the graph of $f(x) = 5x^3 - 6x^2 + 2x + 3$.

A   B   C   D

<u>Solution</u> The degree of $f(x)$ is 3, which means that its graph has the shape of B or D. The coefficient of x^3 is 5, a positive number, so the graph has the shape of B. □

PRACTICE
11 Determine which of the following graphs most closely resembles the graph of $f(x) = x^3 - 3$.

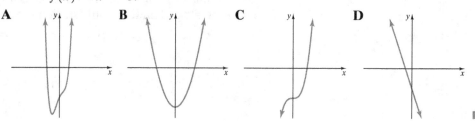

A   B   C   D

Graphing Calculator Explorations

A graphing calculator may be used to visualize addition and subtraction of polynomials in one variable. For example, to visualize the following polynomial subtraction statement

$$(3x^2 - 6x + 9) - (x^2 - 5x + 6) = 2x^2 - x + 3$$

graph both

$$Y_1 = (3x^2 - 6x + 9) - (x^2 - 5x + 6) \quad \text{Left side of equation}$$

and

$$Y_2 = 2x^2 - x + 3 \quad \text{Right side of equation}$$

on the same screen and see that their graphs coincide. (*Note:* If the graphs do not coincide, we can be sure that a mistake has been made in combining polynomials or in calculator keystrokes. If the graphs appear to coincide, we cannot be sure that our work is correct. This is because it is possible for the graphs to differ so slightly that we do not notice it.)

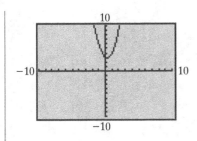

The graphs of Y_1 and Y_2 are shown. The graphs appear to coincide, so the subtraction statement

$$(3x^2 - 6x + 9) - (x^2 - 5x + 6) = 2x^2 - x + 3$$

appears to be correct.

Perform the indicated operations. Then visualize by using the procedure described above.

1. $(2x^2 + 7x + 6) + (x^3 - 6x^2 - 14)$

2. $(-14x^3 - x + 2) + (-x^3 + 3x^2 + 4x)$

3. $(1.8x^2 - 6.8x - 1.7) - (3.9x^2 - 3.6x)$

4. $(-4.8x^2 + 12.5x - 7.8) - (3.1x^2 - 7.8x)$

5. $(1.29x - 5.68) + (7.69x^2 - 2.55x + 10.98)$

6. $(-0.98x^2 - 1.56x + 5.57) + (4.36x - 3.71)$

✔ Vocabulary, Readiness & Video Check

Use the choices below to fill in each blank. Not all choices will be used.

monomial	trinomial	like	degree	coefficient
binomial	polynomial	unlike	variables	term

1. The numerical factor of a term is the _____.

2. A(n) _____ is a finite sum of terms in which all variables are raised to nonnegative integer powers and no variables appear in any denominator.

3. A(n) _____ is a polynomial with 2 terms.

4. A(n) _____ is a polynomial with 1 term.

5. A(n) _____ is a polynomial with 3 terms.

6. The degree of a term is the sum of the exponents on the _____ in the term.

7. The _____ of a polynomial is the largest degree of all its terms.

8. _____ terms contain the same variables raised to the same powers.

Martin-Gay Interactive Videos

See Video 5.3

Watch the section lecture video and answer the following questions.

OBJECTIVE 1

9. In ▦ Example 3, why is the degree of each term found when this is not asked for?

OBJECTIVE 2

10. From ▦ Example 4, finding the value of a polynomial function at a given replacement value is similar to what?

OBJECTIVE 3

11. How is the polynomial in ▦ Example 5 simplified?

OBJECTIVE 4

12. From ▦ Example 6, how do you add polynomials?

OBJECTIVE 5

13. From ▦ Examples 7 and 8, how do you change a polynomial subtraction problem into an equivalent addition problem?

OBJECTIVE 6

14. Which of the basic graph shapes, A, B, C, or D, in ▦ Examples 9 and 10 most closely resembles the graph of $f(x) = -2x^2 - 4x + 5$? Explain.

5.3 Exercise Set MyMathLab▶

Find the degree of each term. See Example 1.

1. 4

2. 7

▶ **3.** $5x^2$

4. $-z^3$

▶ **5.** $-3xy^2$

6. $12x^3z$

7. -8^7y^3

8. $-9^{11}y^5$

9. $3.78ab^3c^5$

10. $9.11r^2st^{12}$

Find the degree of each polynomial and indicate whether the polynomial is a monomial, binomial, trinomial, or none of these. See Examples 2 and 3.

11. $6x + 0.3$

12. $7x - 0.8$

13. $3x^2 - 2x + 5$

14. $5x^2 - 3x - 2$

15. -3^4xy^2

16. -7^5abc

▶ **17.** $x^2y - 4xy^2 + 5x + y^4$

18. $-2x^2y - 3y^2 + 4x + y^5$

If $P(x) = x^2 + x + 1$ and $Q(x) = 5x^2 - 1$, find the following. See Example 4.

19. $P(7)$

20. $Q(4)$

▶ **21.** $Q(-10)$

22. $P(-4)$

23. $Q\left(\dfrac{1}{4}\right)$

24. $P\left(\dfrac{1}{2}\right)$

Refer to Example 5 for Exercises 25 through 28.

25. Find the height of the object at $t = 2$ seconds.

26. Find the height of the object at $t = 4$ seconds.

27. Find the height of the object at $t = 6$ seconds.

28. Approximate (to the nearest second) how long it takes before the object hits the ground. (*Hint:* The object hits the ground when $P(x) = 0$.)

Simplify each polynomial by combining like terms. See Example 6.

29. $5y + y - 6y^2 - y^2$

30. $-x + 3x - 4x^2 - 9x^2$

31. $4x^2y + 2x - 3x^2y - \dfrac{1}{2} - 7x$

32. $-8xy^2 + 4x - x + 2xy^2 - \dfrac{11}{15}$

▶ **33.** $7x^2 - 2xy + 5y^2 - x^2 + xy + 11y^2$

34. $-a^2 + 18ab - 2b^2 + 14a^2 - 12ab - b^2$

Add. See Examples 7 and 8.

35. $(9y^2 + y - 8) + (9y^2 - y - 9)$

36. $(x^2 + 4x - 7) + (8x^2 + 9x - 7)$

▶ **37.** $(x^2 + xy - y^2)$ and $(2x^2 - 4xy + 7y^2)$

38. $(6x^2 + 5x + 7)$ and $(x^2 + 6x - 3)$

39. $\begin{array}{r} x^2 - 6x + 3 \\ + \quad (2x + 5) \\ \hline \end{array}$

40. $\begin{array}{r} -2x^2 + 3x - 9 \\ + \quad (2x - 3) \\ \hline \end{array}$

41. $(7x^3y - 4xy + 8) + (5x^3y + 4xy + 8x)$

42. $(9xyz + 4x - y) + (-9xyz - 3x + y + 2)$

43. $(0.6x^3 + 1.2x^2 - 4.5x + 9.1) + (3.9x^3 - x^2 + 0.7x)$

44. $(9.3y^2 - y + 12.8) + (2.6y^2 + 4.4y - 8.9)$

Subtract. See Examples 9 and 10.

45. $(9y^2 - 7y + 5) - (8y^2 - 7y + 2)$

46. $(2x^2 + 3x + 12) - (20x^2 - 5x - 7)$

47. Subtract $(6x^2 - 3x)$ from $(4x^2 + 2x)$.

48. Subtract $(8y^2 + 4x)$ from $(y^2 + x)$.

▶ **49.** $\begin{array}{r} 6y^2 - 6y + 4 \\ -(-y^2 + 6y + 7) \\ \hline \end{array}$

50. $\begin{array}{r} -4x^3 + 4x^2 - 4x \\ -(2x^3 - 2x^2 + 3x) \\ \hline \end{array}$

▶ **51.** $(9x^3 - 2x^2 + 4x - 7) - (2x^3 - 6x^2 - 4x + 3)$

52. $(3x^2 + 6xy + 3y^2) - (8x^2 - 6xy - y^2)$

53. Subtract $\left(y^2 + 4yx + \dfrac{1}{7}\right)$ from $\left(-19y^2 + 7yx + \dfrac{1}{7}\right)$.

54. Subtract $\left(13x^2 + x^2y - \dfrac{1}{4}\right)$ from $\left(3x^2 - 4x^2y - \dfrac{1}{4}\right)$.

MIXED PRACTICE

Perform the indicated operations and simplify. See Examples 6 through 10.

55. $(-3x + 8) + (-3x^2 + 3x - 5)$

56. $(-5y^2 - 2y + 4) + (3y + 7)$

57. $(5y^4 - 7y^2 + x^2 - 3) + (-3y^4 + 2y^2 + 4)$

58. $(8x^4 - 14x^2 + x + 6) + (-12x^6 - 21x^4 - 9x^2)$

59. $(4x^2 - 6x + 2) - (-x^2 + 3x + 5)$

60. $(7x^2 + x + 1) - (6x^2 + x - 1)$

61. $(5x^2 + x + 9) - (2x^2 - 9)$

62. $(4x - 4) - (-x - 4)$

63. $(5x - 11) + (-x - 2)$

64. $(3x^2 - 2x) + (-5x^2 - 9x)$

65. $(3x^3 - b + 2a - 6) + (-4x^3 + b + 6a - 6)$

66. $(9y^3 - a + 7b - 3) + (-2y^3 + a + 6b - 8)$

67. $(14ab - 10a^2b + 6b^2) - (18a^2 - 20a^2b - 6b^2)$

68. $(13x^2 - 26x^2y^2 + 4) - (19x^2 + x^2y^2 - 11)$

69. $3x^2 + 15x + 8$
$+(2x^2 + 7x + 8)$

70. $9x^2 + 9x - 4$
$+(7x^2 - 3x - 4)$

71. $(7x^2 - 5) + (-3x^2 - 2) - (4x^2 - 7)$

72. $(9y^2 - 3) + (-4y^2 + 1) - (5y^2 - 2)$

73. $(-3 + 4x^2 + 7xy^2) + (2x^3 - x^2 + xy^2)$

74. $(-3x^2y + 4) + (-7x^2y - 8y)$

75. $3x^2 - 4x + 8$
$- \quad (5x - 7)$

76. $-3x^2 - 5x + 1$
$- \quad (3x + 12)$

77. Subtract $(3x + 7)$ from the sum of $(7x^2 + 4x + 9)$ and $(8x^2 + 7x - 8)$.

78. Subtract $(9x + 8)$ from the sum of $(3x^2 - 2x - x^3 + 2)$ and $(5x^2 - 8x - x^3 + 4)$.

79. $\left(\dfrac{2}{3}x^2 - \dfrac{1}{6}x + \dfrac{5}{6}\right) - \left(\dfrac{1}{3}x^2 + \dfrac{5}{6}x - \dfrac{1}{6}\right)$

80. $\left(\dfrac{3}{16}x^2 + \dfrac{5}{8}x - \dfrac{1}{4}\right) - \left(\dfrac{5}{16}x^2 - \dfrac{3}{8}x + \dfrac{3}{4}\right)$

Use the information below to solve Exercises 81 and 82. The surface area of a rectangular box is given by the polynomial function

$$SA = 2HL + 2LW + 2HW$$

and is measured in square units. In business, surface area is often calculated to help determine cost of materials.

△ 81. A rectangular box is to be constructed to hold a new camcorder. The box is to have dimensions 5 inches by 4 inches by 9 inches. Find the surface area of the box.

△ 82. Suppose it has been determined that a box of dimensions 4 inches by 4 inches by 8.5 inches can be used to contain the camcorder in Exercise 81. Find the surface area of this box and calculate the square inches of material saved by using this box instead of the box in Exercise 81.

83. A projectile is fired upward from the ground with an initial velocity of 300 feet per second. Neglecting air resistance, the height of the projectile at any time t can be described by the polynomial function $P(t) = -16t^2 + 300t$. Find the height of the projectile at each given time.

a. $t = 1$ second

b. $t = 2$ seconds

c. $t = 10$ seconds

d. $t = 14$ seconds

e. Explain why the height increases and then decreases as time passes.

f. Approximate (to the nearest second) how long before the object hits the ground.

84. A worker at the Hoover Dam bypass bridge was spending his lunch break tossing a football. He threw the ball upward with an initial velocity of 10 feet per second but missed the ball, and it went over his head and down toward the river. The height of the football above the Colorado River at any time t can be described by the polynomial function $P(t) = -16t^2 + 10t + 910$. Find the height of the football at each given time.

a. $t = 0$ seconds

b. $t = \dfrac{1}{2}$ second

c. $t = 3$ seconds

d. $t = 5$ seconds

e. Explain why the height increases and then decreases as time passes.

f. Approximate (to the nearest second) how long before the football lands in the river.

85. The polynomial function $P(x) = 45x - 100,000$ models the relationship between the number of computer travelcases x that a company sells and the profit the company makes, $P(x)$. Find $P(4000)$, the profit from selling 4000 computer travelcases.

86. The total cost (in dollars) for MCD, Inc., Manufacturing Company to produce x blank CDs per week is given by the polynomial function $C(x) = 0.2x + 5000$. Find the total cost of producing 20,000 CDs per week.

87. The total revenues (in dollars) for an art supply company to sell x boxes of colored pencils per week over the Internet is given by the polynomial function $R(x) = 11x$. Find the total revenue from selling 1500 boxes of colored pencils.

88. The total revenues (in dollars) for MCD, Inc., Manufacturing Company to sell x blank CDs per week is given by the polynomial function $R(x) = 0.9x$. Find the total revenue from selling 20,000 CDs per week.

Match each equation with its graph. See Example 11.

89. $f(x) = 3x^2 - 2$

90. $h(x) = 5x^3 - 6x + 2$

91. $g(x) = -2x^3 - 3x^2 + 3x - 2$

92. $F(x) = -2x^2 - 6x + 2$

A.

B.

C.

D.

REVIEW AND PREVIEW

Multiply. See Section 1.4.

93. $5(3x - 2)$

94. $-7(2z - 6y)$

95. $-2(x^2 - 5x + 6)$

96. $5(-3y^2 - 2y + 7)$

CONCEPT EXTENSIONS

Solve. See the Concept Checks in this section.

97. Which polynomial(s) is the opposite of $8x - 6$?

   a. $-(8x - 6)$ **b.** $8x + 6$

   c. $-8x + 6$ **d.** $-8x - 6$

98. Which polynomial(s) is the opposite of $-y^5 + 10y^3 - 2.3$?

   a. $y^5 + 10y^3 + 2.3$ **b.** $-y^5 - 10y^3 - 2.3$

   c. $y^5 + 10y^3 - 2.3$ **d.** $y^5 - 10y^3 + 2.3$

99. Correct the subtraction.

$$(12x - 1.7) - (15x + 6.2) = 12x - 1.7 - 15x + 6.2$$
$$= -3x + 4.5$$

100. Correct the addition.

$$(12x - 1.7) + (15x + 6.2) = 12x - 1.7 + 15x + 6.2$$
$$= 27x + 7.9$$

101. Write a function, $P(x)$, so that $P(0) = 7$.

102. Write a function, $R(x)$, so that $R(1) = 2$.

103. In your own words, describe how to find the degree of a term.

104. In your own words, describe how to find the degree of a polynomial.

Perform the indicated operations.

105. $(4x^{2a} - 3x^a + 0.5) - (x^{2a} - 5x^a - 0.2)$

106. $(9y^{5a} - 4y^{3a} + 1.5y) - (6y^{5a} - y^{3a} + 4.7y)$

107. $(8x^{2y} - 7x^y + 3) + (-4x^{2y} + 9x^y - 14)$

108. $(14z^{5x} + 3z^{2x} + z) - (2z^{5x} - 10z^{2x} + 3z)$

Find each perimeter.

△ **109.**

△ **110.**

If $P(x) = 3x + 3$, $Q(x) = 4x^2 - 6x + 3$, and $R(x) = 5x^2 - 7$, find the following.

111. $P(x) + Q(x)$

112. $R(x) + P(x)$

113. $Q(x) - R(x)$

114. $P(x) - Q(x)$

115. $2[Q(x)] - R(x)$

116. $-5[P(x)] - Q(x)$

117. $3[R(x)] + 4[P(x)]$

118. $2[Q(x)] + 7[R(x)]$

If $P(x)$ is the polynomial given, find **a.** $P(a)$, **b.** $P(-x)$, *and* **c.** $P(x + h)$.

119. $P(x) = 2x - 3$

120. $P(x) = 8x + 3$

121. $P(x) = 4x$

122. $P(x) = -4x$

123. $P(x) = 4x - 1$

124. $P(x) = 3x - 2$

125. The function $f(x) = 0.24x^2 + 8.41x + 122.8$ can be used to approximate the amount of restaurant food-and-drink sales, where x is the number of years since 1980 and $f(x)$ or y is the sales (in billions of dollars.)

   a. Approximate the restaurant food-and-drink sales in 2005.

   b. Approximate the restaurant food-and-drink sales in 2010.

   c. Use this function to estimate the restaurant food-and-drink sales in 2020.

   d. From parts **a**, **b**, and **c**, determine whether the restaurant food-and-drink sales is increasing at a steady rate. Explain why or why not.

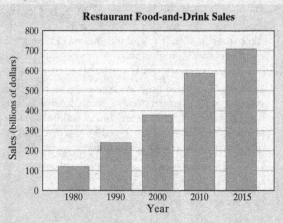

Source: National Restaurant Association

126. The function $f(x) = 0.0003x^2 + 0.24x + 9.2$ can be used to approximate the total cheese production in the United States from 2005 to 2014, where x is the number of years after 2005 and y is pounds of cheese (in billions). Round answers to the nearest tenth of a billion. (*Source:* National Agricultural Statistics Service, USDA)

   a. Approximate the number of pounds of cheese produced in the United States in 2005.

   b. Approximate the number of pounds of cheese produced in the United States in 2010.

   c. Use this function to estimate the pounds of cheese produced in the United States in 2020.

   d. From parts **a**, **b**, and **c**, determine whether the number of pounds of cheese produced in the United States is increasing at a steady rate. Explain why or why not.

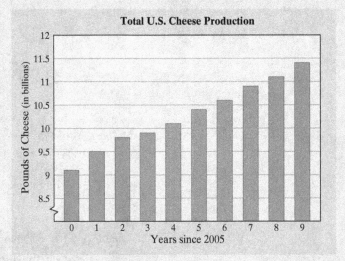

5.4 | Multiplying Polynomials

OBJECTIVES

1 Multiply Two Polynomials.

2 Multiply Binomials.

3 Square Binomials.

4 Multiply the Sum and Difference of Two Terms.

5 Multiply Three or More Polynomials.

6 Evaluate Polynomial Functions.

OBJECTIVE

1   Multiplying Two Polynomials

Properties of real numbers and exponents are used continually in the process of multiplying polynomials. To multiply monomials, for example, we apply the commutative and associative properties of real numbers and the product rule for *exponents*.

EXAMPLE 1   Multiply.

   a. $(2x^3)(5x^6)$ **b.** $(7y^4z^4)(-xy^{11}z^5)$

Solution   Group like bases and apply the product rule for exponents.

   a. $(2x^3)(5x^6) = 2(5)(x^3)(x^6) = 10x^9$

   b. $(7y^4z^4)(-xy^{11}z^5) = 7(-1)x(y^4y^{11})(z^4z^5) = -7xy^{15}z^9$ ☐

PRACTICE

1   Multiply.

   a. $(3x^4)(2x^2)$

   b. $(-5m^4np^3)(-8mnp^5)$ ■

To multiply a monomial by a polynomial other than a monomial, we use an expanded form of the distributive property.

$$a(b + c + d + \cdots + z) = ab + ac + ad + \cdots + az$$

Notice that the monomial a is multiplied by each term of the polynomial.

> **Helpful Hint**
>
> See Sections 5.1 and 5.2 to review exponential expressions further.

EXAMPLE 2   Multiply.

   a. $2x(5x - 4)$ **b.** $-3x^2(4x^2 - 6x + 1)$ **c.** $-xy(7x^2y + 3xy - 11)$

Solution   Apply the distributive property.

   a. $2x(5x - 4) = 2x(5x) + 2x(-4)$ Use the distributive property.

                  $= 10x^2 - 8x$ Multiply.

(Continued on next page)

b. $-3x^2(4x^2 - 6x + 1) = -3x^2(4x^2) + (-3x^2)(-6x) + (-3x^2)(1)$
$$= -12x^4 + 18x^3 - 3x^2$$

c. $-xy(7x^2y + 3xy - 11) = -xy(7x^2y) + (-xy)(3xy) + (-xy)(-11)$
$$= -7x^3y^2 - 3x^2y^2 + 11xy \qquad \square$$

PRACTICE

2 Multiply.

    a. $3x(7x - 1)$ **b.** $-5a^2(3a^2 - 6a + 5)$ **c.** $-mn^3(5m^2n^2 + 2mn - 5m)$ ■

To multiply any two polynomials, we can use the following.

> **Multiplying Two Polynomials**
>
> To multiply any two polynomials, use the distributive property and multiply each term of one polynomial by each term of the other polynomial. Then combine any like terms.

✔ **CONCEPT CHECK**
Find the error:

$4x(x - 5) + 2x$
$$= 4x(x) + 4x(-5) + 4x(2x)$$
$$= 4x^2 - 20x + 8x^2$$
$$= 12x^2 - 20x$$

EXAMPLE 3   Multiply and simplify the product if possible.

    a. $(x + 3)(2x + 5)$ **b.** $(2x - 3)(5x^2 - 6x + 7)$

Solution

    a. Multiply each term of $(x + 3)$ by $(2x + 5)$.

$(x + 3)(2x + 5) = x(2x + 5) + 3(2x + 5)$ Apply the distributive property.
$$= 2x^2 + 5x + 6x + 15 \qquad \text{Apply the distributive property again.}$$
$$= 2x^2 + 11x + 15 \qquad\qquad \text{Combine like terms.}$$

    b. Multiply each term of $(2x - 3)$ by each term of $(5x^2 - 6x + 7)$.

$(2x - 3)(5x^2 - 6x + 7) = 2x(5x^2 - 6x + 7) + (-3)(5x^2 - 6x + 7)$
$$= 10x^3 - 12x^2 + 14x - 15x^2 + 18x - 21$$
$$= 10x^3 - 27x^2 + 32x - 21 \quad \text{Combine like terms.}$$
$$\square$$

PRACTICE

3 Multiply and simplify the product if possible.

    a. $(x + 5)(2x + 3)$ **b.** $(3x - 1)(x^2 - 6x + 2)$ ■

Answer to Concept Check:
$4x(x - 5) + 2x$
$$= 4x(x) + 4x(-5) + 2x$$
$$= 4x^2 - 20x + 2x$$
$$= 4x^2 - 18x$$

Sometimes polynomials are easier to multiply vertically, in the same way we multiply real numbers. When multiplying vertically, we line up like terms in the **partial products** vertically. This makes combining like terms easier.

EXAMPLE 4   Multiply vertically: $(4x^2 + 7)(x^2 + 2x + 8)$

Solution

$$
\begin{array}{r}
x^2 + 2x + 8 \\
\times \qquad 4x^2 + 7 \\
\hline
7x^2 + 14x + 56 \\
4x^4 + 8x^3 + 32x^2 \qquad\quad \\
\hline
4x^4 + 8x^3 + 39x^2 + 14x + 56
\end{array}
$$

$7(x^2 + 2x + 8)$
$4x^2(x^2 + 2x + 8)$
Combine like terms.   ☐

PRACTICE
4   Multiply vertically: $(3x^2 + 2)(x^2 - 4x - 5)$ ◼

OBJECTIVE
2   Multiplying Binomials

When multiplying a binomial by a binomial, we can use a special order of multiplying terms, called the **FOIL** order. The letters of FOIL stand for "**First-Outer-Inner-Last**." To illustrate this method, let's multiply $(2x - 3)$ by $(3x + 1)$.

Multiply the **First** terms of each binomial. $(2x - 3)(3x + 1)$ **F** $2x(3x) = 6x^2$

Multiply the **Outer** terms of each binomial. $(2x - 3)(3x + 1)$ **O** $2x(1) = 2x$

Multiply the **Inner** terms of each binomial. $(2x - 3)(3x + 1)$ **I** $-3(3x) = -9x$

Multiply the **Last** terms of each binomial. $(2x - 3)(3x + 1)$ **L** $-3(1) = -3$
   Combine like terms.

$$6x^2 + 2x - 9x - 3 = 6x^2 - 7x - 3$$

EXAMPLE 5   Use the FOIL order to multiply: $(x - 1)(x + 2)$

Solution

$$
\begin{array}{l}
\overset{\text{First}}{} \quad \overset{\text{Outer}}{} \quad \overset{\text{Inner}}{} \quad \overset{\text{Last}}{} \\
(x - 1)(x + 2) = x \cdot x \; + \; 2 \cdot x \; + \; (-1)x \; + \; (-1)(2) \\
\qquad\qquad\quad = x^2 + 2x - x - 2 \\
\qquad\qquad\quad = x^2 + x - 2 \quad \text{Combine like terms.} \quad ☐
\end{array}
$$

PRACTICE
5   Use the FOIL order to multiply: $(x - 5)(x + 3)$ ◼

EXAMPLE 6   Multiply.

    a. $(2x - 7)(3x - 4)$ **b.** $(3x^2 + y)(5x^2 - 2y)$

Solution

$$
\begin{array}{l}
\qquad\qquad\qquad\;\; \overset{\text{First}}{} \quad\;\; \overset{\text{Outer}}{} \quad\;\;\; \overset{\text{Inner}}{} \quad\;\; \overset{\text{Last}}{} \\
\textbf{a.}\; (2x - 7)(3x - 4) = 2x(3x) + 2x(-4) + (-7)(3x) + (-7)(-4) \\
\qquad\qquad\qquad\quad = 6x^2 - 8x - 21x + 28 \\
\qquad\qquad\qquad\quad = 6x^2 - 29x + 28
\end{array}
$$

$$
\begin{array}{l}
\qquad\qquad\qquad\qquad\quad \overset{\text{F}}{} \quad\;\; \overset{\text{O}}{} \quad\;\; \overset{\text{I}}{} \quad\;\; \overset{\text{L}}{} \\
\textbf{b.}\; (3x^2 + y)(5x^2 - 2y) = 15x^4 - 6x^2y + 5x^2y - 2y^2 \\
\qquad\qquad\qquad\qquad\quad = 15x^4 - x^2y - 2y^2 \qquad ☐
\end{array}
$$

(_Continued on next page_)

PRACTICE
6 Multiply.

a. $(3x - 5)(2x - 7)$

b. $(2x^2 - 3y)(4x^2 + y)$

OBJECTIVE
3 Squaring Binomials

The **square of a binomial** is a special case of the product of two binomials. By the FOIL order for multiplying two binomials, we have

$$(a + b)^2 = (a + b)(a + b)$$

F O I L

$$= a^2 + ab + ba + b^2$$
$$= a^2 + 2ab + b^2$$

This product can be visualized geometrically by analyzing areas.

Area of larger square: $(a + b)^2$

Sum of areas of smaller rectangles: $a^2 + 2ab + b^2$

Thus, $(a + b)^2 = a^2 + 2ab + b^2$

The same pattern occurs for the square of a difference. In general,

---

Square of a Binomial

$$(a + b)^2 = a^2 + 2ab + b^2 \qquad (a - b)^2 = a^2 - 2ab + b^2$$

In other words, a binomial squared is the sum of the first term squared, twice the product of both terms, and the second term squared.

EXAMPLE 7 Multiply.

a. $(x + 5)^2$ b. $(x - 9)^2$ c. $(3x + 2z)^2$ d. $(4m^2 - 3n)^2$

Solution

a. $(a + b)^2 = a^2 + 2 \cdot a \cdot b + b^2$

$(x + 5)^2 = x^2 + 2 \cdot x \cdot 5 + 5^2 = x^2 + 10x + 25$

b. $(x - 9)^2 = x^2 - 2 \cdot x \cdot 9 + 9^2 = x^2 - 18x + 81$

c. $(3x + 2z)^2 = (3x)^2 + 2(3x)(2z) + (2z)^2 = 9x^2 + 12xz + 4z^2$

d. $(4m^2 - 3n)^2 = (4m^2)^2 - 2(4m^2)(3n) + (3n)^2 = 16m^4 - 24m^2n + 9n^2$

PRACTICE
7 Multiply.

a. $(x + 6)^2$ b. $(x - 2)^2$ c. $(3x + 5y)^2$ d. $(3x^2 - 8b)^2$

Helpful Hint

Note that $(a + b)^2 = a^2 + 2ab + b^2$, **not** $a^2 + b^2$. Also,

$(a - b)^2 = a^2 - 2ab + b^2$, **not** $a^2 - b^2$.

The figure on the left margin shows a square divided into four regions: the top-left is a^2 with side a, top-right is ab, bottom-left is ab with side b, bottom-right is b^2. The left side is labeled $a + b$, the bottom is labeled $a + b$.

OBJECTIVE

4 Multiplying the Sum and Difference of Two Terms

Another special product applies to the sum and difference of the same two terms. Multiply $(a + b)(a - b)$ to see a pattern.

$$(a + b)(a - b) = a^2 - ab + ba - b^2$$
$$= a^2 - b^2$$

Product of the Sum and Difference of Two Terms

$$(a + b)(a - b) = a^2 - b^2$$

The product of the sum and difference of the same two terms is the difference of the first term squared and the second term squared.

EXAMPLE 8   Multiply.

  a. $(x - 3)(x + 3)$

  c. $(x^2 + 2y)(x^2 - 2y)$

  b. $(4y + 1)(4y - 1)$

  d. $\left(3m^2 - \dfrac{1}{2} \right)\left(3m^2 + \dfrac{1}{2} \right)$

Solution

  a. $(a + b)(a - b) = a^2 - b^2$
  $\quad \downarrow \quad \downarrow \quad \downarrow \quad \downarrow \qquad \downarrow \quad \downarrow$
  $\quad (x + 3)(x - 3) = x^2 - 3^2 = x^2 - 9$

  b. $(4y + 1)(4y - 1) = (4y)^2 - 1^2 = 16y^2 - 1$

  c. $(x^2 + 2y)(x^2 - 2y) = (x^2)^2 - (2y)^2 = x^4 - 4y^2$

  d. $\left(3m^2 - \dfrac{1}{2} \right)\left(3m^2 + \dfrac{1}{2} \right) = (3m^2)^2 - \left(\dfrac{1}{2} \right)^2 = 9m^4 - \dfrac{1}{4}$ ▢

PRACTICE

8   Multiply.

  a. $(x - 7)(x + 7)$

  c. $\left(5x^2 + \dfrac{1}{4} \right)\left(5x^2 - \dfrac{1}{4} \right)$

  b. $(2a + 5)(2a - 5)$

  d. $(a^3 - 4b^2)(a^3 + 4b^2)$ ■

EXAMPLE 9   Multiply: $[3 + (2a + b)]^2$

Solution Think of 3 as the first term and $(2a + b)$ as the second term, and apply the method for squaring a binomial.

$$[a \quad + b \quad]^2 = a^2 + 2(a) \cdot \ b \ + \ b^2$$
$$[3 + \overbrace{(2a + b)}]^2 = 3^2 + 2(3)\overbrace{(2a + b)} + \overbrace{(2a + b)^2}$$
$$= 9 + 6(2a + b) + (2a + b)^2$$
$$= 9 + 12a + 6b + (2a)^2 + 2(2a)(b) + b^2 \quad \text{Square } (2a + b).$$
$$= 9 + 12a + 6b + 4a^2 + 4ab + b^2 \qquad ▢$$

PRACTICE

9   Multiply: $[2 + (3x - y)]^2$ ■

EXAMPLE 10 Multiply: $[(5x - 2y) - 1][(5x - 2y) + 1]$

Solution Think of $(5x - 2y)$ as the first term and 1 as the second term and apply the method for the product of the sum and difference of two terms.

$$
\begin{array}{ccccc}
(a & -b) & (a & + b) = & a^2 & - b^2 \\
\end{array}
$$
$$
\begin{aligned}
[(5x - 2y) - 1][(5x - 2y) + 1] &= (5x - 2y)^2 - 1^2 \\
&= (5x)^2 - 2(5x)(2y) + (2y)^2 - 1 \quad \text{Square} \\
&= 25x^2 - 20xy + 4y^2 - 1 \qquad (5x - 2y).
\end{aligned}
$$

PRACTICE
10 Multiply: $[(3x - y) - 5][(3x - y) + 5]$

OBJECTIVE
5 Multiplying Three or More Polynomials ▶

To multiply three or more polynomials, more than one method may be needed.

EXAMPLE 11 Multiply: $(x - 3)(x + 3)(x^2 - 9)$

Solution We multiply the first two binomials, the sum and difference of two terms. Then we multiply the resulting two binomials, the square of a binomial.

$$
\begin{aligned}
(x - 3)(x + 3)(x^2 - 9) &= (x^2 - 9)(x^2 - 9) \quad \text{Multiply } (x - 3)(x + 3). \\
&= (x^2 - 9)^2 \\
&= x^4 - 18x^2 + 81 \qquad \text{Square } (x^2 - 9).
\end{aligned}
$$

PRACTICE
11 Multiply: $(x + 4)(x - 4)(x^2 - 16)$

OBJECTIVE
6 Evaluating Polynomial Functions ▶

Our work in multiplying polynomials is often useful in evaluating polynomial functions.

EXAMPLE 12 If $f(x) = x^2 + 5x - 2$, find $f(a + 1)$.

Solution To find $f(a + 1)$, replace x with the expression $a + 1$ in the polynomial function $f(x)$.

$$
\begin{aligned}
f(x) &= x^2 + 5x - 2 \\
f(a + 1) &= (a + 1)^2 + 5(a + 1) - 2 \\
&= a^2 + 2a + 1 + 5a + 5 - 2 \\
&= a^2 + 7a + 4
\end{aligned}
$$

PRACTICE
12 If $f(x) = x^2 - 3x + 5$, find $f(h + 1)$.

Graphing Calculator Explorations

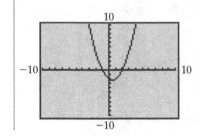

In the previous section, we used a graphing calculator to visualize addition and subtraction of polynomials in one variable. In this section, the same method is used to visualize multiplication of polynomials in one variable. For example, to see that

$$(x - 2)(x + 1) = x^2 - x - 2,$$

graph both $Y_1 = (x - 2)(x + 1)$ and $Y_2 = x^2 - x - 2$ on the same screen and see whether their graphs coincide.

By tracing along both graphs, we see that the graphs of Y_1 and Y_2 appear to coincide, and thus $(x - 2)(x + 1) = x^2 - x - 2$ appears to be correct.

Multiply. Then use a graphing calculator to visualize the results.

1. $(x + 4)(x - 4)$ **2.** $(x + 3)(x + 3)$

3. $(3x - 7)^2$ **4.** $(5x - 2)^2$

5. $(5x + 1)(x^2 - 3x - 2)$ **6.** $(7x + 4)(2x^2 + 3x - 5)$

✔ Vocabulary, Readiness & Video Check

Use the choices to fill in each blank.

1. $(6x^3)\left(\dfrac{1}{2}x^3\right) = $ _____

   a. $3x^3$ **b.** $3x^6$ **c.** $10x^6$ **d.** $\dfrac{13}{2}x^6$

2. $(x + 7)^2 = $ _____

   a. $x^2 + 49$ **b.** $x^2 - 49$ **c.** $x^2 + 14x + 49$ **d.** $x^2 + 7x + 49$

3. $(x + 7)(x - 7) = $ _____

   a. $x^2 + 49$ **b.** $x^2 - 49$ **c.** $x^2 + 14x - 49$ **d.** $x^2 + 7x - 49$

4. The product of $(3x - 1)(4x^2 - 2x + 1)$ is a polynomial of degree _____.

   a. 3   **b.** 12   **c.** $12x^3$ **d.** 2

5. If $f(x) = x^2 + 1$ then $f(a + 1) = $ _____

   a. $(a + 1)^2$ **b.** $a + 1$ **c.** $(a + 1)^2 + (a + 1)$ **d.** $(a + 1)^2 + 1$

6. $[x + (2y + 1)]^2 = $ _____

   a. $[x + (2y + 1)][x - (2y + 1)]$ **b.** $[x + (2y + 1)][x + (2y + 1)]$ **c.** $[x + (2y + 1)][x + (2y - 1)]$

Martin-Gay Interactive Videos

See Video 5.4

Watch the section lecture video and answer the following questions.

OBJECTIVE 1

7. From ▦ Examples 1 and 2, what property is key when multiplying polynomials? What exponent rule is often used when applying this property?

OBJECTIVE 2

8. From ▦ Examples 3 and 4, for what type of multiplication of polynomials is the FOIL method used?

OBJECTIVE 3

9. Name at least one other method you can use to multiply ▦ Example 5.

OBJECTIVE 4

10. From ▦ Example 6, why does multiplying the sum and difference of the same two terms always give you a binomial answer?

OBJECTIVE 5

11. From ▦ Example 9, how do you multiply three or more polynomials?

OBJECTIVE 6

12. From ▦ Example 10, can a polynomial function be evaluated only for a numerical value?

5.4 Exercise Set MyMathLab®

Multiply. See Examples 1 through 4.

1. $(-4x^3)(3x^2)$ **2.** $(-6a)(4a)$

3. $(8.6a^4b^5c)(10ab^3c^2)$ **4.** $(7.1xy^2z^{11})(10xy^7z)$

▶ **5.** $3x(4x + 7)$ **6.** $5x(6x - 4)$

7. $-6xy(4x + y)$ **8.** $-8y(6xy + 4x)$

9. $-4ab(xa^2 + ya^2 - 3)$ **10.** $-6b^2z(z^2a + baz - 3b)$

11. $(x - 3)(2x + 4)$

12. $(y + 5)(3y - 2)$

13. $(2x + 3)(x^3 - x + 2)$

14. $(a + 2)(3a^2 - a + 5)$

15. $\begin{array}{r} 3x - 2 \\ \times\ 5x + 1 \\ \hline \end{array}$

16. $\begin{array}{r} 2z - 4 \\ \times\ 6z - 2 \\ \hline \end{array}$

17. $\begin{array}{r} 3m^2 + 2m - 1 \\ \times\ \qquad 5m + 2 \\ \hline \end{array}$

18. $\begin{array}{r} 2x^2 - 3x - 4 \\ \times\ \qquad 4x + 5 \\ \hline \end{array}$

19. $-6a^2b^2(5a^2b^2 - 6a - 6b)$ **20.** $7x^2y^3(-3ax - 4xy + z)$

Multiply the binomials. See Examples 5 and 6.

21. $(x - 3)(x + 4)$

22. $(c - 3)(c + 1)$

23. $(5x - 8y)(2x - y)$

24. $(2n - 9m)(n - 7m)$

25. $\left(4x + \dfrac{1}{3}\right)\left(4x - \dfrac{1}{2}\right)$

26. $\left(4y - \dfrac{1}{3}\right)\left(3y - \dfrac{1}{8}\right)$

27. $(5x^2 - 2y^2)(x^2 - 3y^2)$

28. $(4x^2 - 5y^2)(x^2 - 2y^2)$

Use special products to multiply. See Examples 7 and 8.

29. $(x + 4)^2$

30. $(x - 5)^2$

31. $(6y - 1)(6y + 1)$

32. $(7x - 9)(7x + 9)$

33. $(3x - y)^2$

34. $(4x + z)^2$

35. $(7ab + 3c)(7ab - 3c)$

36. $(3xy - 2b)(3xy + 2b)$

37. $\left(3x + \dfrac{1}{2}\right)\left(3x - \dfrac{1}{2}\right)$

38. $\left(2x - \dfrac{1}{3}\right)\left(2x + \dfrac{1}{3}\right)$

Use special products to multiply. See Examples 9 and 10.

39. $[3 + (4b + a)]^2$

40. $[5 - (3b - a)]^2$

41. $[(2s - 3) - 1][(2s - 3) + 1]$

42. $[(2y + 5) + 6][(2y + 5) - 6]$

43. $[(x^2 + 4x) - 6]^2$

44. $[(2a^2 + 4a) + 1]^2$

Multiply. See Example 11.

45. $(x + y)(x - y)(x^2 - y^2)$ **46.** $(z - y)(z + y)(z^2 - y^2)$

47. $(x - 2)^4$

48. $(x - 1)^4$

49. $(x - 5)(x + 5)(x^2 + 25)$ **50.** $(x + 3)(x - 3)(x^2 + 9)$

MIXED PRACTICE

Multiply. See Examples 1 through 11.

51. $-8a^2b(3b^2 - 5b + 20)$

52. $-9xy^2(3x^2 - 2x + 10)$

53. $(6x + 1)^2$

54. $(4x + 7)^2$

55. $(5x^3 + 2y)(5x^3 - 2y)$

56. $(3x^4 + 2y)(3x^4 - 2y)$

57. $(2x^3 + 5)(5x^2 + 4x + 1)$ **58.** $(3y^3 - 1)(3y^3 - 6y + 1)$

59. $(3x^2 + 2x - 1)^2$

60. $(4x^2 + 4x - 4)^2$

61. $(3x - 1)(x + 3)$

62. $(5d - 3)(d + 6)$

63. $(3x^4 + 1)(3x^2 + 5)$

64. $(4x^3 - 5)(5x^2 + 6)$

65. $(3x + 1)^2$

66. $(4x + 6)^2$

67. $(3b - 6y)(3b + 6y)$

68. $(2x - 4y)(2x + 4y)$

69. $(7x - 3)(7x + 3)$

70. $(4x + 1)(4x - 1)$

71. $\begin{array}{r} 3x^2 + 4x - 4 \\ \times\ \qquad 3x + 6 \\ \hline \end{array}$

72. $\begin{array}{r} 6x^2 + 2x - 1 \\ \times\ \qquad 3x - 6 \\ \hline \end{array}$

73. $(4x^2 - 2x + 5)(3x + 1)$ **74.** $(5x^2 - x - 2)(2x - 1)$

75. $[(x + y) - 7]^2$

76. $[(a + b) - 8]^2$

77. $(11a^2 + 1)(2a + 1)$

78. $(13x^2 + 1)(3x + 1)$

79. $\left(\dfrac{2}{3}n - 2\right)\left(\dfrac{1}{2}n - 9\right)$ **80.** $\left(\dfrac{3}{5}y - 6\right)\left(\dfrac{1}{3}y - 10\right)$

81. $(3x + 1)(3x - 1)(2y + 5x)$

82. $(2a + 1)(2a - 1)(6a + 7b)$

If $f(x) = x^2 - 3x$, find the following. See Example 12.

83. $f(a)$

84. $f(c)$

85. $f(a + h)$

86. $f(a + 5)$

87. $f(b - 2)$

88. $f(a - b)$

REVIEW AND PREVIEW

Use the slope-intercept form of a line, $y = mx + b$, to find the slope of each line. See Section 3.4.

89. $y = -2x + 7$

90. $y = \dfrac{3}{2}x - 1$

91. $3x - 5y = 14$

92. $x + 7y = 2$

Use the vertical line test to determine whether the following are graphs of functions. See Section 3.2.

93.

94.

CONCEPT EXTENSIONS

Solve. See the Concept Check in this section.

95. Find the error: $7y(3z - 2) + 1$

$$= 21yz - 14y + 7y$$
$$= 21yz - 7y$$

96. Find the error: $2x + 3x(12 - x)$

$$= 5x(12 - x)$$
$$= 60x - 5x^2$$

97. Explain how to multiply a polynomial by a polynomial.

98. Explain why $(3x + 2)^2$ does not equal $9x^2 + 4$.

99. If $F(x) = x^2 + 3x + 2$, find
  a. $F(a + h)$
  b. $F(a)$
  c. $F(a + h) - F(a)$

100. If $g(x) = x^2 + 2x + 1$, find
  a. $g(a + h)$
  b. $g(a)$
  c. $g(a + h) - g(a)$

Multiply. Assume that variables represent positive integers.

101. $5x^2y^n(6y^{n+1} - 2)$

102. $-3yz^n(2y^3z^{2n} - 1)$

103. $(x^a + 5)(x^{2a} - 3)$

104. $(x^a + y^{2b})(x^a - y^{2b})$

For Exercises 105 through 108, write the result as a simplified polynomial.

105. Find the area of the circle. Do not approximate π.

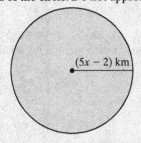

(5x − 2) km

106. Find the volume of the cylinder. Do not approximate π.

(y − 3) cm

7y cm

Find the area of each shaded region.

107.

(3x − 2) in.

(3x − 2) in.

x

x

108.

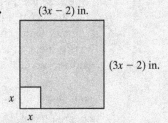

x − 7

2x

x

109. Perform each indicated operation. Explain the difference between the two problems.
  a. $(3x + 5) + (3x + 7)$
  b. $(3x + 5)(3x + 7)$

110. Explain when the FOIL method can be used to multiply polynomials.

If $R(x) = x + 5$, $Q(x) = x^2 - 2$, and $P(x) = 5x$, find the following.

111. $P(x) \cdot R(x)$

112. $P(x) \cdot Q(x)$

113. $[Q(x)]^2$

114. $[R(x)]^2$

115. $R(x) \cdot Q(x)$

116. $P(x) \cdot R(x) \cdot Q(x)$

5.5 The Greatest Common Factor and Factoring by Grouping

OBJECTIVE

1 Identifying the GCF

Factoring is the reverse process of multiplying. It is the process of writing a polynomial as a product.

$$\overset{\text{factoring}}{\overbrace{6x^2 + 13x - 5 = (3x - 1)(2x + 5)}_{\text{multiplying}}}$$

In the next few sections, we review techniques for factoring polynomials. These techniques are used at the end of this chapter to solve polynomial equations.

To factor a polynomial, we first factor out the **greatest common factor** (GCF) of its terms, using the distributive property. The GCF of a list of terms or monomials is the product of the GCF of the numerical coefficients and each GCF of the powers of a common variable.

> **Finding the GCF of a List of Monomials**
>
> **Step 1.** Find the GCF of the numerical coefficients.
>
> **Step 2.** Find the GCF of the variable factors.
>
> **Step 3.** The product of the factors found in Steps 1 and 2 is the GCF of the monomials.

EXAMPLE 1 Find the GCF of $20x^3y$, $10x^2y^2$, and $35x^3$.

Solution The GCF of the numerical coefficients 20, 10, and 35 is 5, the largest integer that is a factor of each coefficient. The GCF of the variable factors x^3, x^2, and x^3 is x^2 because x^2 is the largest factor common to all three powers of x. The variable y is not a common factor because it does not appear in all three monomials. The GCF is thus

$$5 \cdot x^2, \quad \text{or} \quad 5x^2$$

To see this in factored form,

$$20x^3y = 2 \cdot 2 \cdot 5 \cdot x^2 \cdot x \cdot y$$
$$10x^2y^2 = 2 \cdot 5 \cdot x^2 \cdot y^2$$
$$35x^3 = 7 \cdot 5 \cdot x^2 \cdot x$$
$$\mathbf{GCF} = 5 \cdot x^2$$

PRACTICE

1 Find the GCF of $32x^4y^2$, $48x^3y$, and $24y^2$.

OBJECTIVE

2 Factoring Out the GCF of a Polynomial's Terms

A first step in factoring polynomials is to use the distributive property and write the polynomial as a product of the GCF of its monomial terms and a simpler polynomial. This is called **factoring out** the GCF.

EXAMPLE 2 Factor.

    a. $8x^2 + 4$ **b.** $5y - 2z^4$ **c.** $6x^2 - 3x^3 + 12x^4$

Solution

    a. The GCF of terms $8x^2$ and 4 is 4.

$$8x^2 + 4 = 4 \cdot 2x^2 + 4 \cdot 1 \quad \text{Factor out 4 from each term.}$$
$$= 4(2x^2 + 1) \quad \text{Apply the distributive property.}$$

The factored form of $8x^2 + 4$ is $4(2x^2 + 1)$. To check, multiply $4(2x^2 + 1)$ to see that the product is $8x^2 + 4$.

b. There is no common factor of the terms $5y$ and $-2z^4$ other than 1 (or -1).

c. The greatest common factor of $6x^2, -3x^3$, and $12x^4$ is $3x^2$. Thus,

$$6x^2 - 3x^3 + 12x^4 = 3x^2 \cdot 2 - 3x^2 \cdot x + 3x^2 \cdot 4x^2$$
$$= 3x^2(2 - x + 4x^2) \qquad \square$$

PRACTICE

2 Factor.

a. $12x^2 + 9 + 15x$ **b.** $3x - 8y^3$ **c.** $8a^4 - 2a^3$ ∎

> **Helpful Hint**
>
> To verify that the GCF has been factored out correctly, multiply the factors together and see that their product is the original polynomial.

EXAMPLE 3   Factor: $17x^3y^2 - 34x^4y^2$

Solution The GCF of the two terms is $17x^3y^2$, which we factor out of each term.

$$17x^3y^2 - 34x^4y^2 = 17x^3y^2 \cdot 1 - 17x^3y^2 \cdot 2x$$
$$= 17x^3y^2(1 - 2x) \qquad \square$$

PRACTICE

3   Factor: $64x^5y^2 - 8x^3y^2$ ∎

> **Helpful Hint**
>
> If the GCF happens to be one of the terms in the polynomial, a factor of 1 will remain for this term when the GCF is factored out.
>   For example, in the polynomial $21x^2 + 7x$, the GCF of $21x^2$ and $7x$ is $7x$, so
>
> $$21x^2 + 7x = 7x \cdot 3x + 7x \cdot 1 = 7x(3x + 1)$$

✔ **CONCEPT CHECK**

Which factorization of $15x^2 + 9x - 3$ is correct?

a. $3(5x^2 + 3x + 1)$ **b.** $3(5x^2 + 3x - 1)$ **c.** $3(5x^2 + 3x - 3)$ **d.** $3(5x^2 + 3x)$

EXAMPLE 4   Factor: $-3x^3y + 2x^2y - 5xy$

Solution Two possibilities are shown for factoring this polynomial. First, the common factor xy is factored out.

$$-3x^3y + 2x^2y - 5xy = xy(-3x^2 + 2x - 5)$$

Also, the common factor $-xy$ can be factored out as shown.

$$-3x^3y + 2x^2y - 5xy = -xy(3x^2) + (-xy)(-2x) + (-xy)(5)$$
$$= -xy(3x^2 - 2x + 5)$$

Both of these alternatives are correct. $\square$

PRACTICE

4   Factor: $-9x^4y^2 + 5x^2y^2 + 7xy^2$ ∎

EXAMPLE 5 Factor: $2(x - 5) + 3a(x - 5)$

Solution The greatest common factor is the binomial factor $(x - 5)$.

$$2(x - 5) + 3a(x - 5) = (x - 5)(2 + 3a) \qquad \square$$

PRACTICE
5 Factor: $3(x + 4) + 5b(x + 4)$ ■

EXAMPLE 6 Factor: $7x(x^2 + 5y) - (x^2 + 5y)$

Solution $\qquad 7x(x^2 + 5y) - (x^2 + 5y) = 7x(x^2 + 5y) - 1(x^2 + 5y)$

$$= (x^2 + 5y)(7x - 1) \qquad \square$$

> **Helpful Hint**
> Notice that we wrote $-(x^2 + 5y)$ as $-1(x^2 + 5y)$ to aid in factoring.

PRACTICE
6 Factor: $8b(a^3 + 2y) - (a^3 + 2y)$ ■

OBJECTIVE

3 Factoring Polynomials by Grouping ▶

Sometimes it is possible to factor a polynomial by grouping the terms of the polynomial and looking for common factors in each group. This method of factoring is called **factoring by grouping.**

EXAMPLE 7 Factor: $ab - 6a + 2b - 12$

Solution First look for the GCF of all four terms. The GCF of all four terms is 1. Next, group the first two terms and the last two terms and factor out common factors from each group.

$$ab - 6a + 2b - 12 = (ab - 6a) + (2b - 12)$$

Factor a from the first group and 2 from the second group.

$$= a(b - 6) + 2(b - 6)$$

Now we see a GCF of $(b - 6)$. Factor out $(b - 6)$ to get

$$a(b - 6) + 2(b - 6) = (b - 6)(a + 2)$$

Check: To check, multiply $(b - 6)$ and $(a + 2)$ to see that the product is $ab - 6a + 2b - 12$. $\qquad \square$

PRACTICE
7 Factor: $xy - 5x - 10 + 2y$ ■

> **Helpful Hint**
> Notice that the polynomial $a(b - 6) + 2(b - 6)$ is *not* in factored form. It is a *sum*, not a *product*. The factored form is $(b - 6)(a + 2)$.

EXAMPLE 8 Factor: $x^3 + 5x^2 + 3x + 15$

Solution

$$\begin{aligned} x^3 + 5x^2 + 3x + 15 &= (x^3 + 5x^2) + (3x + 15) && \text{Group pairs of terms.} \\ &= x^2(x + 5) + 3(x + 5) && \text{Factor each binomial.} \\ &= (x + 5)(x^2 + 3) && \text{Factor out the common factor, } (x + 5). \quad \square \end{aligned}$$

PRACTICE
8 Factor: $a^3 + 2a^2 + 5a + 10$ ■

EXAMPLE 9   Factor: $m^2n^2 + m^2 - 2n^2 - 2$

Solution $m^2n^2 + m^2 - 2n^2 - 2 = (m^2n^2 + m^2) + (-2n^2 - 2)$ Group pairs of terms.
$= m^2(n^2 + 1) - 2(n^2 + 1)$ Factor each binomial.
$= (n^2 + 1)(m^2 - 2)$ Factor out the common factor, $(n^2 + 1)$.   □

PRACTICE
9   Factor: $x^2y^2 + 3y^2 - 5x^2 - 15$ ▪

EXAMPLE 10   Factor: $xy + 2x - y - 2$

Solution $xy + 2x - y - 2 = (xy + 2x) + (-y - 2)$ Group pairs of terms.
$= x(y + 2) - 1(y + 2)$ Factor each binomial.
$= (y + 2)(x - 1)$ Factor out the common factor, $(y + 2)$.   □

PRACTICE
10   Factor: $pq + 3p - q - 3$ ▪

✔ **Vocabulary, Readiness & Video Check**

Use the choices below to fill in each blank. Some choices will be used more than once and some not at all.

least   greatest   sum   product   factoring x^3 x^7 true   false

1. The reverse process of multiplying is _____.
2. The greatest common factor (GCF) of x^7, x^3, x^5 is _____.
3. In general, the GCF of a list of common variables raised to powers is the _____ exponent in the list.
4. Factoring means writing as a _____.
5. True or false: A factored form of $2xy^3 + 10xy$ is $2xy \cdot y^2 + 2xy \cdot 5$. _____
6. True or false: A factored form of $x^3 - 6x^2 + x$ is $x(x^2 - 6x)$. _____
7. True or false: A factored form of $5x - 5y + x^3 - x^2y$ is $5(x - y) + x^2(x - y)$. _____
8. True or false: A factored form of $5x - 5y + x^3 - x^2y$ is $(x - y)(5 + x^2)$. _____

Martin-Gay Interactive Videos

See Video 5.5 🌐

Watch the section lecture video and answer the following questions.

OBJECTIVE 1
9. From ▦ Example 1, how do you find the GCF of a list of common variables raised to powers?

OBJECTIVE 2
10. From ▦ Example 2, when factoring out a GCF from a polynomial, what two operations may help? How?

OBJECTIVE 3
11. In ▦ Examples 4 and 5, what are you reminded to do first when factoring a polynomial? How do you know to check to see if factoring by grouping might work?

5.5   Exercise Set MyMathLab® ▶

Find the GCF of each list of monomials. See Example 1.

1. a^8, a^5, a^3
2. b^9, b^2, b^5
3. $x^2y^3z^3, y^2z^3, xy^2z^2$
4. $xy^2z^3, x^2y^2z^2, x^2y^3$
5. $6x^3y, 9x^2y^2, 12x^2y$
6. $4xy^2, 16xy^3, 8x^2y^2$

▶ 7. $10x^3yz^3, 20x^2z^5, 45xz^3$
8. $12y^2z^4, 9xy^3z^4, 15x^2y^2z^3$

Factor out the GCF in each polynomial. See Examples 2 through 6.

9. $18x - 12$
10. $21x + 14$
11. $4y^2 - 16xy^3$
12. $3z - 21xz^4$

▶ **13.** $6x^5 - 8x^4 + 2x^3$

14. $9x + 3x^2 - 6x^3$

15. $8a^3b^3 - 4a^2b^2 + 4ab + 16ab^2$

16. $12a^3b - 6ab + 18ab^2 - 18a^2b$

17. $6(x + 3) + 5a(x + 3)$

18. $2(x - 4) + 3y(x - 4)$

▶ **19.** $2x(z + 7) + (z + 7)$

20. $9x(y - 2) + (y - 2)$

21. $3x(6x^2 + 5) - 2(6x^2 + 5)$

22. $4x(2y^2 + 3) - 5(2y^2 + 3)$

23. $20a^3 + 5a^2 + 1$

24. $12b^4 - 3b^2 + 1$

25. $39x^3y^3 - 26x^2y^3$

26. $38x^2y^4 - 57xy^4$

Factor each polynomial by grouping. See Examples 7 through 10.

▶ **27.** $ab + 3a + 2b + 6$

28. $ab + 2a + 5b + 10$

29. $ac + 4a - 2c - 8$

30. $bc + 8b - 3c - 24$

31. $2xy - 3x - 4y + 6$

32. $12xy - 18x - 10y + 15$

▶ **33.** $12xy - 8x - 3y + 2$

34. $20xy - 15x - 4y + 3$

MIXED PRACTICE

Factor each polynomial. See Examples 1 through 10.

35. $6x^3 + 9$

36. $6x^2 - 8$

37. $x^3 + 3x^2$

38. $x^4 - 4x^3$

39. $8a^3 - 4a$

40. $12b^4 + 3b^2$

41. $8m^3 + 4m^2 + 1$

42. $30n^4 + 15n^2 + 1$

43. $-20x^2y + 16xy^3$

44. $-18xy^3 + 27x^4y$

45. $10a^2b^3 + 5ab^2 - 15ab^3$

46. $10ef - 20e^2f^3 + 30e^3f$

47. $9abc^2 + 6a^2bc - 6ab + 3bc$

48. $4a^2b^2c - 6ab^2c - 4ac + 8a$

49. $4x(y - 2) - 3(y - 2)$

50. $8y(z + 8) - 3(z + 8)$

51. $6xy + 10x + 9y + 15$

52. $15xy + 20x + 6y + 8$

53. $xy + 3y - 5x - 15$

54. $xy + 4y - 3x - 12$

55. $6ab - 2a - 9b + 3$

56. $16ab - 8a - 6b + 3$

57. $12xy + 18x + 2y + 3$

58. $20xy + 8x + 5y + 2$

59. $2m(n - 8) - (n - 8)$

60. $3a(b - 4) - (b - 4)$

61. $15x^3y^2 - 18x^2y^2$

62. $12x^4y^2 - 16x^3y^3$

63. $2x^2 + 3xy + 4x + 6y$

64. $3x^2 + 12x + 4xy + 16y$

65. $5x^2 + 5xy - 3x - 3y$

66. $4x^2 + 2xy - 10x - 5y$

67. $x^3 + 3x^2 + 4x + 12$

68. $x^3 + 4x^2 + 3x + 12$

69. $x^3 - x^2 - 2x + 2$

70. $x^3 - 2x^2 - 3x + 6$

REVIEW AND PREVIEW

Simplify the following. See Section 5.1.

71. $(5x^2)(11x^5)$ **72.** $(7y)(-2y^3)$

73. $(5x^2)^3$ **74.** $(-2y^3)^4$

Find each product by using the FOIL order of multiplying binomials. See Section 5.4.

75. $(x + 2)(x - 5)$

76. $(x - 7)(x - 1)$

77. $(x + 3)(x + 2)$

78. $(x - 4)(x + 2)$

79. $(y - 3)(y - 1)$

80. $(s + 8)(s + 10)$

CONCEPT EXTENSIONS

Solve. See the Concept Check in this section.

81. Which factorization of $10x^2 - 2x - 2$ is correct?

   a. $2(5x^2 - x + 1)$

   b. $2(5x^2 - x)$

   c. $2(5x^2 - x - 2)$

   d. $2(5x^2 - x - 1)$

82. Which factorization of $x^4 + 5x^3 - x^2$ is correct?

   a. $-1(x^4 + 5x^3 + x^2)$

   b. $x^2(x^2 + 5x^3 - x^2)$

   c. $x^2(x^2 + 5x - 1)$

   d. $5x^2(x^2 + 5x - 5)$

Solve.

△ **83.** The area of the material needed to manufacture a tin can is given by the polynomial $2\pi r^2 + 2\pi rh$, where the radius is r and height is h. Factor this expression.

84. To estimate the cost of a new product, one expression used by the production department is $4\pi r^2 + \frac{4}{3}\pi r^3$. Write an equivalent expression by factoring $4\pi r^2$ from both terms.

85. At the end of T years, the amount of money A in a savings account earning simple interest from an initial investment of \$5600 at rate R is given by the formula $A = 5600 + 5600RT$. Write an equivalent equation by factoring the expression $5600 + 5600RT$.

△ **86.** An open-topped box has a square base and a height of 10 inches. If each of the bottom edges of the box has length x inches, find the amount of material needed to construct the box. Write the answer in factored form.

10 in.

x x

87. When $3x^2 - 9x + 3$ is factored, the result is $3(x^2 - 3x + 1)$. Explain why it is necessary to include the term 1 in this factored form.

88. Construct a trinomial whose greatest common factor is $5x^2y^3$.

89. A factored polynomial can be in many forms. For example, a factored form of $xy - 3x - 2y + 6$ is $(x - 2)(y - 3)$. Which of the following is not a factored form of $xy - 3x - 2y + 6$?

a. $(2 - x)(3 - y)$ **b.** $(-2 + x)(-3 + y)$
c. $(y - 3)(x - 2)$ **d.** $(-x + 2)(-y + 3)$

90. Which factorization of $12x^2 + 9x + 3$ is correct?

a. $3(4x^2 + 3x + 1)$ **b.** $3(4x^2 + 3x - 1)$
c. $3(4x^2 + 3x - 3)$ **d.** $3(4x^2 + 3x)$

91. Explain why $9(5 - x) + y(5 - x)$ is not a factored form of $45 - 9x + 5y - xy$.

92. Consider the following sequence of algebraic steps:

$$x^3 - 6x^2 + 2x - 10 = (x^3 - 6x^2) + (2x - 10)$$
$$= x^2(x - 6) + 2(x - 5)$$

Explain whether the final result is the factored form of the original polynomial.

93. The amount E of voltage in an electrical circuit is given by the formula

$$IR_1 + IR_2 = E$$

Write an equivalent equation by factoring the expression $IR_1 + IR_2$.

94. At the end of T years, the amount of money A in a savings account earning simple interest from an initial investment of P dollars at rate R is given by the formula

$$A = P + PRT$$

Write an equivalent equation by factoring the expression $P + PRT$.

Factor out the greatest common factor. Assume that variables used as exponents represent positive integers.

95. $x^{3n} - 2x^{2n} + 5x^n$

96. $3y^n + 3y^{2n} + 5y^{8n}$

97. $6x^{8a} - 2x^{5a} - 4x^{3a}$

98. $3x^{5a} - 6x^{3a} + 9x^{2a}$

99. An object is thrown upward from the ground with an initial velocity of 64 feet per second. The height $h(t)$ in feet of the object after t seconds is given by the polynomial function

$$h(t) = -16t^2 + 64t$$

a. Write an equivalent factored expression for the function $h(t)$ by factoring $-16t^2 + 64t$.

b. Find $h(1)$ by using

$$h(t) = -16t^2 + 64t$$

and then by using the factored form of $h(t)$.

c. Explain why the values found in part **b** are the same.

100. An object is dropped from the gondola of a hot-air balloon at a height of 224 feet. The height $h(t)$ of the object after t seconds is given by the polynomial function

$$h(t) = -16t^2 + 224$$

224 ft

a. Write an equivalent factored expression for the function $h(t)$ by factoring $-16t^2 + 224$.

b. Find $h(2)$ by using $h(t) = -16t^2 + 224$ and then by using the factored form of the function.

c. Explain why the values found in part **b** are the same.

101. The polynomial function $f(x) = 64x^3 - 744x^2 + 13{,}452x + 75{,}784$ models the number of patents granted to United States citizens by the U.S. Patent Office for the years 2008 to 2014, where x represents the number of years since 2008 and $f(x)$ is the number of patents granted to U.S. citizens. Write an equivalent expression for $f(x)$ by factoring the greatest common factor from the terms of $f(x)$. (*Source:* U.S. Patent Office)

102. The number of users of social media worldwide is increasing. The polynomial function $f(x) = -0.25x^2 + 1.25x + 0.50$ models the number of social media users worldwide (in billions) for the years 2012 to 2015, where x is the number of years after 2012 and $f(x)$ is the number of social media users worldwide (in billions). Write an equivalent expression for $f(x)$ by factoring out a factor of -0.25 from the terms of $f(x)$. (*Source:* Based on data from Techcrunch.com)

5.6 Factoring Trinomials ▶

OBJECTIVE

1 Factoring Trinomials of the Form $x^2 + bx + c$ ▶

In the previous section, we used factoring by grouping to factor four-term polynomials. In this section, we present techniques for factoring trinomials. Since $(x - 2)(x + 5) = x^2 + 3x - 10$, we say that $(x - 2)(x + 5)$ is a factored form of $x^2 + 3x - 10$. Taking a close look at how $(x - 2)$ and $(x + 5)$ are multiplied suggests a pattern for factoring trinomials of the form

$$x^2 + bx + c$$

$$(x - 2)(x + 5) = x^2 + 3x - 10$$

The pattern for factoring is summarized next.

Factoring a Trinomial of the Form $x^2 + bx + c$

Find two numbers whose product is c and whose sum is b. The factored form of $x^2 + bx + c$ is

$$(x + \text{one number})(x + \text{other number})$$

EXAMPLE 1 Factor: $x^2 + 10x + 16$

Solution We look for two integers whose product is 16 and whose sum is 10. Since our integers must have a positive product and a positive sum, we look at only positive factors of 16.

Positive Factors of 16	Sum of Factors
1, 16	$1 + 16 = 17$
4, 4	$4 + 4 = 8$
2, 8	$2 + 8 = 10$ Correct pair

The correct pair of numbers is 2 and 8 because their product is 16 and their sum is 10. Thus,

$$x^2 + 10x + 16 = (x + 2)(x + 8)$$

Check: To check, see that $(x + 2)(x + 8) = x^2 + 10x + 16$. ☐

PRACTICE

1 Factor: $x^2 + 5x + 6$ ∎

EXAMPLE 2 Factor: $x^2 - 12x + 35$

Solution We need to find two integers whose product is 35 and whose sum is -12. Since our integers must have a positive product and a negative sum, we consider only negative factors of 35.

Negative Factors of 35	Sum of Factors
$-1, -35$	$-1 + (-35) = -36$
$-5, -7$	$-5 + (-7) = -12$ Correct pair

The numbers are -5 and -7.

$$x^2 - 12x + 35 = [x + (-5)][x + (-7)]$$
$$= (x - 5)(x - 7)$$

Check: To check, see that $(x - 5)(x - 7) = x^2 - 12x + 35$. □

PRACTICE
2 Factor: $x^2 - 11x + 24$ ■

EXAMPLE 3 Factor: $5x^3 - 30x^2 - 35x$

Solution First we factor out the greatest common factor, $5x$.

$$5x^3 - 30x^2 - 35x = 5x(x^2 - 6x - 7)$$

Next we try to factor $x^2 - 6x - 7$ by finding two numbers whose product is -7 and whose sum is -6. The numbers are 1 and -7.

$$5x^3 - 30x^2 - 35x = 5x(x^2 - 6x - 7)$$
$$= 5x(x + 1)(x - 7) □$$

PRACTICE
3 Factor: $3x^3 - 9x^2 - 30x$ ■

> **Helpful Hint**
> If the polynomial to be factored contains a common factor that is factored out, don't forget to include that common factor in the final factored form of the original polynomial.

EXAMPLE 4 Factor: $2n^2 - 38n + 80$

Solution The terms of this polynomial have a greatest common factor, 2, which we factor out first.

$$2n^2 - 38n + 80 = 2(n^2 - 19n + 40)$$

Next we factor $n^2 - 19n + 40$ by finding two numbers whose product is 40 and whose sum is -19. Both numbers must be negative since their sum is -19. Possibilities are

$$-1 \text{ and } -40, \quad -2 \text{ and } -20, \quad -4 \text{ and } -10, \quad -5 \text{ and } -8$$

None of the pairs has a sum of -19, so no further factoring with integers is possible. The factored form of $2n^2 - 38n + 80$ is

$$2n^2 - 38n + 80 = 2(n^2 - 19n + 40) □$$

PRACTICE
4 Factor: $2b^2 - 18b - 22$ ■

We call a polynomial such as $n^2 - 19n + 40$, which cannot be factored further, a **prime polynomial.**

OBJECTIVE
2 Factoring Trinomials of the Form $ax^2 + bx + c$ ▶

Next, we factor trinomials of the form $ax^2 + bx + c$, where the coefficient a of x^2 is not 1. Don't forget that the first step in factoring any polynomial is to factor out the greatest common factor of its terms. We will review two methods here. The first method we'll call trial and check.

OBJECTIVE
2a Method 1—Factoring $ax^2 + bx + c$ by Trial and Check ▶

EXAMPLE 5 Factor: $2x^2 + 11x + 15$

Solution Factors of $2x^2$ are $2x$ and x. Let's try these factors as first terms of the binomials.

$$2x^2 + 11x + 15 = (2x +)(x +)$$

Next we try combinations of factors of 15 until the correct middle term, $11x$, is obtained. We will try only positive factors of 15 since the coefficient of the middle term, 11, is positive. Positive factors of 15 are 1 and 15 and 3 and 5.

$(2x + 1)(x + 15)$
$1x$
$\dfrac{30x}{31x}$ Incorrect middle term

$(2x + 15)(x + 1)$
$15x$
$\dfrac{2x}{17x}$ Incorrect middle term

$(2x + 3)(x + 5)$
$3x$
$\dfrac{10x}{13x}$ Incorrect middle term

$(2x + 5)(x + 3)$
$5x$
$\dfrac{6x}{11x}$ Correct middle term

Thus, the factored form of $2x^2 + 11x + 15$ is $(2x + 5)(x + 3)$.

PRACTICE
5   Factor: $2x^2 + 13x + 6$

Factoring a Trinomial of the Form $ax^2 + bx + c$

Step 1. Write all pairs of factors of ax^2.

Step 2. Write all pairs of factors of c, the constant term.

Step 3. Try various combinations of these factors until the correct middle term bx is found.

Step 4. If no combination exists, the polynomial is **prime.**

EXAMPLE 6   Factor: $3x^2 - x - 4$

Solution   Factors of $3x^2$: $3x \cdot x$

Factors of -4: $-1 \cdot 4$, $1 \cdot -4$, $-2 \cdot 2$, $2 \cdot -2$

Let's try possible combinations of these factors.

$(3x - 1)(x + 4)$
$-1x$
$\dfrac{12x}{11x}$ Incorrect middle term

$(3x + 4)(x - 1)$
$4x$
$\dfrac{-3x}{1x}$ Incorrect middle term

$(3x - 4)(x + 1)$
$-4x$
$\dfrac{3x}{-1x}$ Correct middle term

Thus, $3x^2 - x - 4 = (3x - 4)(x + 1)$.

PRACTICE
6   Factor: $4x^2 + 5x - 6$

Helpful Hint—Sign Patterns

A positive constant in a trinomial tells us to look for two numbers with the same sign. The sign of the coefficient of the middle term tells us whether the signs are both positive or both negative.

both same   both same
positive sign   negative sign

$$2x^2 + 7x + 3 = (2x + 1)(x + 3) \qquad 2x^2 - 7x + 3 = (2x - 1)(x - 3)$$

A negative constant in a trinomial tells us to look for two numbers with opposite signs.

opposite signs   opposite signs

$$2x^2 - 5x - 3 = (2x + 1)(x - 3) \qquad 2x^2 + 5x - 3 = (2x - 1)(x + 3)$$

EXAMPLE 7   Factor: $12x^3y - 22x^2y + 8xy$

Solution First we factor out the greatest common factor of the terms of this trinomial, $2xy$.

$$12x^3y - 22x^2y + 8xy = 2xy(6x^2 - 11x + 4)$$

Now we try to factor the trinomial $6x^2 - 11x + 4$.
Factors of $6x^2$: $2x \cdot 3x, \quad 6x \cdot x$

Let's try $2x$ and $3x$.

$$2xy(6x^2 - 11x + 4) = 2xy(2x + \quad)(3x + \quad)$$

The constant term, 4, is positive and the coefficient of the middle term, -11, is negative, so we factor 4 into negative factors only.
Negative factors of 4: $-4(-1), \quad -2(-2)$

Let's try -4 and -1.

$$2xy(2x - 4)(3x - 1)$$

$-12x$

$\dfrac{-2x}{-14x}$ Incorrect middle term

This combination cannot be correct because one of the factors, $(2x - 4)$, has a common factor of 2. This cannot happen if the polynomial $6x^2 - 11x + 4$ has no common factors.

Now let's try -1 and -4.

$$2xy(2x - 1)(3x - 4)$$

$-3x$

$\dfrac{-8x}{-11x}$ Correct middle term

Thus,

$$12x^3y - 22x^2y + 8xy = 2xy(2x - 1)(3x - 4)$$

If this combination had not worked, we would have tried -2 and -2 as factors of 4 and then $6x$ and x as factors of $6x^2$.   □

PRACTICE

7   Factor: $18b^4 - 57b^3 + 30b^2$

> Helpful Hint
> If a trinomial has no common factor (other than 1), then none of its binomial factors will contain a common factor (other than 1).

EXAMPLE 8 Factor: $16x^2 + 24xy + 9y^2$

Solution No greatest common factor can be factored out of this trinomial.

Factors of $16x^2$: $16x \cdot x$, $8x \cdot 2x$, $4x \cdot 4x$

Factors of $9y^2$: $y \cdot 9y$, $3y \cdot 3y$

We try possible combinations until the correct factorization is found.

$$16x^2 + 24xy + 9y^2 = (4x + 3y)(4x + 3y) \quad \text{or} \quad (4x + 3y)^2 \qquad \square$$

PRACTICE
8 Factor: $25x^2 + 20xy + 4y^2$ ∎

The trinomial $16x^2 + 24xy + 9y^2$ in Example 8 is an example of a **perfect square trinomial** since its factors are two identical binomials. In the next section, we examine a special method for factoring perfect square trinomials.

OBJECTIVE
2b Method 2—Factoring $ax^2 + bx + c$ by Grouping

There is another method we can use when factoring trinomials of the form $ax^2 + bx + c$: Write the trinomial as a four-term polynomial and then factor by grouping.

> **Factoring a Trinomial of the Form $ax^2 + bx + c$ by Grouping**
>
> **Step 1.** Find two numbers whose product is $a \cdot c$ and whose sum is b.
> **Step 2.** Write the term bx as a sum by using the factors found in Step 1.
> **Step 3.** Factor by grouping.

EXAMPLE 9 Factor: $6x^2 + 13x + 6$

Solution In this trinomial, $a = 6$, $b = 13$, and $c = 6$.

Step 1. Find two numbers whose product is $a \cdot c$, or $6 \cdot 6 = 36$, and whose sum is b, 13. The two numbers are 4 and 9.

Step 2. Write the middle term, $13x$, as the sum $4x + 9x$.

$$6x^2 + 13x + 6 = 6x^2 + 4x + 9x + 6$$

Step 3. Factor $6x^2 + 4x + 9x + 6$ by grouping.

$$(6x^2 + 4x) + (9x + 6) = 2x(3x + 2) + 3(3x + 2)$$
$$= (3x + 2)(2x + 3) \qquad \square$$

PRACTICE
9 Factor: $20x^2 + 23x + 6$ ∎

✔ CONCEPT CHECK
Name one way that a factorization can be checked.

EXAMPLE 10 Factor: $18x^2 - 9x - 2$

Solution In this trinomial, $a = 18$, $b = -9$, and $c = -2$.

Step 1. Find two numbers whose product is $a \cdot c$ or $18(-2) = -36$ and whose sum is b, -9. The two numbers are -12 and 3.

Step 2. Write the middle term, $-9x$, as the sum $-12x + 3x$.

$$18x^2 - 9x - 2 = 18x^2 - 12x + 3x - 2$$

Step 3. Factor by grouping.

$$(18x^2 - 12x) + (3x - 2) = 6x(3x - 2) + 1(3x - 2)$$
$$= (3x - 2)(6x + 1). \qquad \square$$

PRACTICE
10 Factor: $15x^2 + 4x - 3$ ■

OBJECTIVE
3 Factoring by Substitution

A complicated-looking polynomial may be a simpler trinomial in disguise. Revealing the simpler trinomial is possible by substitution.

EXAMPLE 11 Factor: $2(a + 3)^2 - 5(a + 3) - 7$

Solution The quantity $(a + 3)$ is in two of the terms of this polynomial. **Substitute x** for $(a + 3)$, and the result is the following simpler trinomial.

$$2(a + 3)^2 - 5(a + 3) - 7 \quad \text{Original trinomial}$$
$$\downarrow \qquad\qquad \downarrow$$
$$= 2(x)^2 \quad - \quad 5(x) - 7 \qquad \text{Substitute } x \text{ for } (a + 3).$$

Now factor $2x^2 - 5x - 7$.

$$2x^2 - 5x - 7 = (2x - 7)(x + 1)$$

But the quantity in the original polynomial was $(a + 3)$, not x. Thus, we need to reverse the substitution and replace x with $(a + 3)$.

$$(2x - 7)(x + 1) \qquad \text{Factored expression}$$
$$= [2(a + 3) - 7][(a + 3) + 1] \quad \text{Substitute } (a + 3) \text{ for } x.$$
$$= (2a + 6 - 7)(a + 3 + 1) \qquad \text{Remove inside parentheses.}$$
$$= (2a - 1)(a + 4) \qquad\qquad \text{Simplify.}$$

Thus, $2(a + 3)^2 - 5(a + 3) - 7 = (2a - 1)(a + 4)$. $\qquad \square$

PRACTICE
11 Factor: $3(x + 1)^2 - 7(x + 1) - 20$ ■

EXAMPLE 12 Factor: $5x^4 + 29x^2 - 42$

Solution Again, substitution may help us factor this polynomial more easily. Since this polynomial contains the variable x, we will choose a different substitution variable. Let $y = x^2$, so $y^2 = (x^2)^2$, or x^4. Then

$$5x^4 + 29x^2 - 42$$
$$\downarrow \qquad \downarrow$$

becomes

$$5y^2 + 29y - 42$$

which factors as

$$5y^2 + 29y - 42 = (5y - 6)(y + 7)$$

Next, replace y with x^2 to get

$$(5x^2 - 6)(x^2 + 7) \qquad \square$$

PRACTICE
12 Factor: $6x^4 - 11x^2 - 10$ ■

✔ **Vocabulary, Readiness & Video Check**

1. Find two numbers whose product is 10 and whose sum is 7.
2. Find two numbers whose product is 12 and whose sum is 8.
3. Find two numbers whose product is 24 and whose sum is 11.
4. Find two numbers whose product is 30 and whose sum is 13.

Martin-Gay Interactive Videos

See Video 5.6 💧

Watch the section lecture video and answer the following questions.

OBJECTIVE
1
5. In ▦ Example 2, we know one of the factors of −24 is negative. How do we determine which one?

OBJECTIVE
1
6. In ▦ Example 3, once the GCF is factored out how do we know both factors of +8 are negative?

OBJECTIVE
2a
7. From ▦ Example 4, explain in your own words how to factor a trinomial with a first-term coefficient ≠ 1 by trial and error.

OBJECTIVE
2b
8. From ▦ Example 6 and the lecture before, why does writing the middle term of your trinomial as the sum of two terms suggest we'd need to factor by grouping?

OBJECTIVE
3
9. In ▦ Example 8, the goal is to factor the polynomial, so why are we not done once we have substituted, then factored?

5.6 Exercise Set MyMathLab®

Factor each trinomial. See Examples 1 through 4.

▶ 1. $x^2 + 9x + 18$ 2. $x^2 + 9x + 20$

3. $x^2 - 12x + 32$ 4. $x^2 - 12x + 27$

5. $x^2 + 10x - 24$ 6. $x^2 + 3x - 54$

▶ 7. $x^2 - 2x - 24$ 8. $x^2 - 9x - 36$

▶ 9. $3x^2 - 18x + 24$ 10. $5x^2 - 45x + 70$

11. $4x^2z + 28xz + 40z$ 12. $x^2y^2 + 4xy^2 + 3y^2$

13. $2x^2 - 24x - 64$ 14. $3n^2 - 6n - 51$

Factor each trinomial. See Examples 5 through 10.

15. $5x^2 + 16x + 3$ 16. $3x^2 + 8x + 4$

17. $2x^2 - 11x + 12$ 18. $3x^2 - 19x + 20$

19. $2x^2 + 25x - 20$ 20. $6x^2 + 13x + 8$

21. $4x^2 - 12x + 9$ 22. $25x^2 - 30x + 9$

23. $12x^2 + 10x - 50$ 24. $12y^2 - 48y + 45$

25. $3y^4 - y^3 - 10y^2$ 26. $2x^2z + 5xz - 12z$

27. $6x^3 + 8x^2 + 24x$ 28. $18y^3 + 6y^2 + 2y$

29. $2x^2 - 5xy - 3y^2$ 30. $6x^2 + 11xy + 4y^2$

31. $28y^2 + 22y + 4$ 32. $24y^3 - 2y^2 - y$

33. $2x^2 + 15x - 27$ 34. $3x^2 + 14x + 15$

Use substitution to factor each polynomial completely. See Examples 11 and 12.

35. $x^4 + x^2 - 6$ 36. $x^4 - x^2 - 20$

37. $(5x + 1)^2 + 8(5x + 1) + 7$ 38. $(3x - 1)^2 + 5(3x - 1) + 6$

39. $x^6 - 7x^3 + 12$ 40. $x^6 - 4x^3 - 12$

41. $(a + 5)^2 - 5(a + 5) - 24$

42. $(3c + 6)^2 + 12(3c + 6) - 28$

MIXED PRACTICE

Factor each polynomial completely. See Examples 1 through 12.

43. $x^2 - 24x - 81$ 44. $x^2 - 48x - 100$

45. $x^2 - 15x - 54$ 46. $x^2 - 15x + 54$

47. $3x^2 - 6x + 3$ 48. $8x^2 - 8x + 2$

▶ 49. $3x^2 - 5x - 2$ 50. $5x^2 - 14x - 3$

51. $8x^2 - 26x + 15$ 52. $12x^2 - 17x + 6$

▶ 53. $18x^4 + 21x^3 + 6x^2$ 54. $20x^5 + 54x^4 + 10x^3$

55. $x^2 + 8xz + 7z^2$ 56. $a^2 - 2ab - 15b^2$

57. $x^2 - x - 12$ 58. $x^2 + 4x - 5$

59. $3a^2 + 12ab + 12b^2$ 60. $2x^2 + 16xy + 32y^2$

61. $x^2 + 4x + 5$ 62. $x^2 + 5x + 8$

63. $2(x + 4)^2 + 3(x + 4) - 5$ 64. $3(x + 3)^2 + 2(x + 3) - 5$

65. $6x^2 - 49x + 30$

66. $4x^2 - 39x + 27$

67. $x^4 - 5x^2 - 6$

68. $x^4 - 5x^2 + 6$

69. $6x^3 - x^2 - x$

70. $12x^3 + x^2 - x$

71. $12a^2 - 29ab + 15b^2$

72. $16y^2 + 6yx - 27x^2$

73. $9x^2 + 30x + 25$

74. $4x^2 + 12x + 9$

75. $3x^2y - 11xy + 8y$

76. $5xy^2 - 9xy + 4x$

77. $2x^2 + 2x - 12$

78. $3x^2 + 6x - 45$

79. $(x - 4)^2 + 3(x - 4) - 18$

80. $(x - 3)^2 - 2(x - 3) - 8$

81. $2x^6 + 3x^3 - 9$

82. $3x^6 - 14x^3 + 8$

83. $72xy^4 - 24xy^2z + 2xz^2$

84. $36xy^2 - 48xyz^2 + 16xz^4$

85. $2x^3y + 2x^2y - 12xy$

86. $3x^2y^3 + 6x^2y^2 - 45x^2y$

87. $x^2 + 6xy + 5y^2$

88. $x^2 + 6xy + 8y^2$

REVIEW AND PREVIEW

Multiply. See Section 5.4.

89. $(x - 3)(x + 3)$

90. $(x - 4)(x + 4)$

91. $(2x + 1)^2$

92. $(3x + 5)^2$

93. $(x - 2)(x^2 + 2x + 4)$

94. $(y + 1)(y^2 - y + 1)$

CONCEPT EXTENSIONS

95. Find all positive and negative integers b such that $x^2 + bx + 6$ is factorable.

96. Find all positive and negative integers b such that $x^2 + bx - 10$ is factorable.

△ **97.** The volume $V(x)$ of a box in terms of its height x is given by the function $V(x) = x^3 + 2x^2 - 8x$. Factor this expression for $V(x)$.

△ **98.** Based on your results from Exercise 97, find the length and width of the box if the height is 5 inches and the dimensions of the box are whole numbers.

99. Suppose that a movie is being filmed in New York City. An action shot requires an object to be thrown upward with an initial velocity of 80 feet per second off the top of 1 Madison Square Plaza, a height of 576 feet. The height $h(t)$

in feet of the object after t seconds is given by the function $h(t) = -16t^2 + 80t + 576$. (*Source: The World Almanac*)

a. Find the height of the object at $t = 0$ seconds, $t = 2$ seconds, $t = 4$ seconds, and $t = 6$ seconds.

b. Explain why the height of the object increases and then decreases as time passes.

c. Factor the polynomial $-16t^2 + 80t + 576$.

576 ft

100. Suppose that an object is thrown upward with an initial velocity of 64 feet per second off the edge of a 960-foot cliff. The height $h(t)$ in feet of the object after t seconds is given by the function

$$h(t) = -16t^2 + 64t + 960$$

a. Find the height of the object at $t = 0$ seconds, $t = 3$ seconds, $t = 6$ seconds, and $t = 9$ seconds.

b. Explain why the height of the object increases and then decreases as time passes.

c. Factor the polynomial $-16t^2 + 64t + 960$.

Factor. Assume that variables used as exponents represent positive integers.

101. $x^{2n} + 10x^n + 16$

102. $x^{2n} - 7x^n + 12$

103. $x^{2n} - 3x^n - 18$

104. $x^{2n} + 7x^n - 18$

105. $2x^{2n} + 11x^n + 5$

106. $3x^{2n} - 8x^n + 4$

107. $4x^{2n} - 12x^n + 9$

108. $9x^{2n} + 24x^n + 16$

Recall that a graphing calculator may be used to check addition, subtraction, and multiplication of polynomials. In the same manner, a graphing calculator may be used to check factoring of polynomials in one variable. For example, to see that

$$2x^3 - 9x^2 - 5x = x(2x + 1)(x - 5)$$

graph $Y_1 = 2x^3 - 9x^2 - 5x$ *and* $Y_2 = x(2x + 1)(x - 5)$. *Then trace along both graphs to see that they coincide. Factor the following and use this method to check your results.*

109. $x^4 + 6x^3 + 5x^2$

110. $x^3 + 6x^2 + 8x$

111. $30x^3 + 9x^2 - 3x$

112. $-6x^4 + 10x^3 - 4x^2$

5.7 | Factoring by Special Products

OBJECTIVES

1 Factor a Perfect Square Trinomial.

2 Factor the Difference of Two Squares.

3 Factor the Sum or Difference of Two Cubes.

OBJECTIVE

1   Factoring a Perfect Square Trinomial

In the previous section, we considered a variety of ways to factor trinomials of the form $ax^2 + bx + c$. In Example 8, we factored $16x^2 + 24xy + 9y^2$ as

$$16x^2 + 24xy + 9y^2 = (4x + 3y)^2$$

Recall that $16x^2 + 24xy + 9y^2$ is a perfect square trinomial because its factors are two identical binomials. A perfect square trinomial can be factored quickly if you recognize the trinomial as a perfect square.

A trinomial is a perfect square trinomial if it can be written so that its first term is the square of some quantity a, its last term is the square of some quantity b, and its middle term is twice the product of the quantities a and b.

The following special formulas can be used to factor perfect square trinomials.

Perfect Square Trinomials

$$a^2 + 2ab + b^2 = (a + b)^2$$
$$a^2 - 2ab + b^2 = (a - b)^2$$

Notice that these formulas above are the same special products from Section 5.4 for the square of a binomial.

From

$$a^2 + 2ab + b^2 = (a + b)^2,$$

we see that

$$16x^2 + 24xy + 9y^2 = (4x)^2 + 2(4x)(3y) + (3y)^2 = (4x + 3y)^2$$

EXAMPLE 1   Factor: $m^2 + 10m + 25$

Solution Notice that the first term is a square: $m^2 = (m)^2$, the last term is a square: $25 = 5^2$; and $10m = 2 \cdot 5 \cdot m$.

Thus,

$$m^2 + 10m + 25 = m^2 + 2(m)(5) + 5^2 = (m + 5)^2 \qquad \square$$

PRACTICE
1   Factor: $b^2 + 16b + 64$

EXAMPLE 2   Factor: $12a^2x - 12abx + 3b^2x$

Solution The terms of this trinomial have a GCF, $3x$, which we factor out first.

$$12a^2x - 12abx + 3b^2x = 3x(4a^2 - 4ab + b^2)$$

Now, the polynomial $4a^2 - 4ab + b^2$ is a perfect square trinomial. Notice that the first term is a square: $4a^2 = (2a)^2$; the last term is a square: $b^2 = (b)^2$; and $4ab = 2(2a)(b)$. The factoring can now be completed as

$$3x(4a^2 - 4ab + b^2) = 3x(2a - b)^2 \qquad \square$$

PRACTICE
2   Factor: $45x^2b - 30xb + 5b$

Helpful Hint

If you recognize a trinomial as a perfect square trinomial, use the special formulas to factor. However, methods for factoring trinomials in general from Section 5.6 will also result in the correct factored form.

OBJECTIVE

2   Factoring the Difference of Two Squares

We now factor special types of binomials, beginning with the **difference of two squares.** The special product pattern presented in Section 5.4 for the product of a sum and a difference of two terms is used again here. However, the emphasis is now on factoring rather than on multiplying.

Difference of Two Squares

$$a^2 - b^2 = (a + b)(a - b)$$

Notice that a binomial is a difference of two squares when it is the difference of the square of some quantity a and the square of some quantity b.

EXAMPLE 3   Factor the following.

    a. $x^2 - 9$ **b.** $16y^2 - 9$ **c.** $50 - 8y^2$ **d.** $x^2 - \dfrac{1}{4}$

Solution

    a. $x^2 - 9 = x^2 - 3^2$ **b.** $16y^2 - 9 = (4y)^2 - 3^2$

              $= (x + 3)(x - 3)$ $= (4y + 3)(4y - 3)$

    c. First factor out the common factor 2.

         $50 - 8y^2 = 2(25 - 4y^2)$

                 $= 2(5 + 2y)(5 - 2y)$

    d. $x^2 - \dfrac{1}{4} = x^2 - \left(\dfrac{1}{2}\right)^2 = \left(x + \dfrac{1}{2}\right)\left(x - \dfrac{1}{2}\right)$

PRACTICE

3   Factor the following.

    a. $x^2 - 16$

    b. $25b^2 - 49$

    c. $45 - 20x^2$

    d. $y^2 - \dfrac{1}{81}$

The binomial $x^2 + 9$ is a **sum of two squares** and cannot be factored by using real numbers. **In general, except for factoring out a GCF, the sum of two squares usually cannot be factored by using real numbers.**

Helpful Hint

The sum of two squares whose GCF is 1 usually cannot be factored by using real numbers. For example, $x^2 + 9$ is a prime polynomial.

EXAMPLE 4   Factor the following.

    a. $p^4 - 16$ **b.** $(x + 3)^2 - 36$

Solution

    a. $p^4 - 16 = (p^2)^2 - 4^2$

                 $= (p^2 + 4)(p^2 - 4)$

The binomial factor $p^2 + 4$ cannot be factored by using real numbers, but the binomial factor $p^2 - 4$ is a difference of squares.

$$(p^2 + 4)\overbrace{(p^2 - 4)} = (p^2 + 4)(p + 2)(p - 2)$$

b. Factor $(x + 3)^2 - 36$ as the difference of squares.

$$(x + 3)^2 - 36 = (x + 3)^2 - 6^2$$
$$= [(x + 3) + 6][(x + 3) - 6] \quad \text{Factor.}$$
$$= [x + 3 + 6][x + 3 - 6] \quad \text{Remove parentheses.}$$
$$= (x + 9)(x - 3) \quad \text{Simplify.} \qquad \square$$

PRACTICE
4 Factor the following.
    a. $x^4 - 10,000$
    b. $(x + 2)^2 - 49$ ∎

✔ **CONCEPT CHECK**
Is $(x - 4)(y^2 - 9)$ completely factored? Why or why not?

EXAMPLE 5 Factor: $x^2 + 4x + 4 - y^2$

Solution Factoring by grouping comes to mind since the sum of the first three terms of this polynomial is a perfect square trinomial.

$$x^2 + 4x + 4 - y^2 = (x^2 + 4x + 4) - y^2 \quad \text{Group the first three terms.}$$
$$= (x + 2)^2 - y^2 \quad \text{Factor the perfect square trinomial.}$$

This is not factored yet since we have a *difference*, not a *product*. Since $(x + 2)^2 - y^2$ is a difference of squares, we have

$$(x + 2)^2 - y^2 = [(x + 2) + y][(x + 2) - y]$$
$$= (x + 2 + y)(x + 2 - y) \qquad \square$$

PRACTICE
5 Factor: $m^2 + 6m + 9 - n^2$ ∎

OBJECTIVE
3 Factoring the Sum or Difference of Two Cubes ▶

Although the sum of two squares usually cannot be factored, the sum of two cubes, as well as the difference of two cubes, can be factored as follows.

> **Sum and Difference of Two Cubes**
> $$a^3 + b^3 = (a + b)(a^2 - ab + b^2)$$
> $$a^3 - b^3 = (a - b)(a^2 + ab + b^2)$$

To check the first pattern, let's find the product of $(a + b)$ and $(a^2 - ab + b^2)$.

$$(a + b)(a^2 - ab + b^2) = a(a^2 - ab + b^2) + b(a^2 - ab + b^2)$$
$$= a^3 - a^2b + ab^2 + a^2b - ab^2 + b^3$$
$$= a^3 + b^3$$

EXAMPLE 6 Factor: $x^3 + 8$

Solution First we write the binomial in the form $a^3 + b^3$. Then we use the formula

$$a^3 + b^3 = (a + b)(a^2 - a \cdot b + b^2), \quad \text{where } a \text{ is } x \text{ and } b \text{ is } 2.$$
$$\downarrow \quad \downarrow \quad \quad \downarrow \quad \downarrow \quad \downarrow \quad \quad \downarrow \downarrow \quad \downarrow$$
$$x^3 + 8 = x^3 + 2^3 = (x + 2)(x^2 - x \cdot 2 + 2^2)$$

Thus, $x^3 + 8 = (x + 2)(x^2 - 2x + 4)$ $\qquad \square$

Answer to Concept Check:
no; $(y^2 - 9)$ can be factored

PRACTICE
6 Factor: $x^3 + 64$ ∎

EXAMPLE 7   Factor: $p^3 + 27q^3$

Solution
$$\begin{aligned}
p^3 + 27q^3 &= p^3 + (3q)^3 \\
&= (p + 3q)[p^2 - (p)(3q) + (3q)^2] \\
&= (p + 3q)(p^2 - 3pq + 9q^2)
\end{aligned}$$

PRACTICE
7   Factor: $a^3 + 8b^3$

EXAMPLE 8   Factor: $y^3 - 64$

Solution This is a difference of cubes since $y^3 - 64 = y^3 - 4^3$.

Use the formula for factoring the difference of two cubes.

$$a^3 - b^3 = (a - b)(a^2 + a \cdot b + b^2)$$
$$\downarrow \quad \downarrow \qquad \downarrow \quad \downarrow \quad \downarrow \quad \downarrow \quad \downarrow \quad \downarrow$$
$$y^3 - 4^3 = (y - 4)(y^2 + y \cdot 4 + 4^2)$$
$$= (y - 4)(y^2 + 4y + 16)$$

PRACTICE
8   Factor: $27 - y^3$

Helpful Hint

When factoring sums or differences of cubes, be sure to notice the sign patterns.

Same sign
$$x^3 + y^3 = (x + y)(x^2 - xy + y^2)$$
Opposite sign
Always positive

Same sign
$$x^3 - y^3 = (x - y)(x^2 + xy + y^2)$$
Opposite sign

EXAMPLE 9   Factor: $125q^2 - n^3q^2$

Solution First we factor out a common factor of q^2.

$$\begin{aligned}
125q^2 - n^3q^2 &= q^2(125 - n^3) \\
&= q^2(5^3 - n^3)
\end{aligned}$$

Opposite sign   Positive
$$= q^2(5 - n)[5^2 + (5)(n) + (n^2)]$$
$$= q^2(5 - n)(25 + 5n + n^2)$$

Thus, $125q^2 - n^3q^2 = q^2(5 - n)(25 + 5n + n^2)$. The trinomial $25 + 5n + n^2$ cannot be factored further.

PRACTICE
9   Factor: $b^3x^2 - 8x^2$

Vocabulary, Readiness & Video Check

Write each term as a square. For example, $25x^2$ as a square is $(5x)^2$.

1. $81y^2$ **2.** $4z^2$ **3.** $64x^6$ **4.** $49y^6$

Write each term as a cube.

5. $8x^3$ **6.** $27y^3$ **7.** $64x^6$ **8.** x^3y^6

Martin-Gay Interactive Videos

See Video 5.7

Watch the section lecture video and answer the following questions.

OBJECTIVE 1
9. From Example 1, what is the first step to see if you have a perfect square trinomial? How do you then finish determining that you do indeed have a perfect square trinomial?

OBJECTIVE 2
10. In Example 2, the original binomial is rewritten to write each term as a square. Give two reasons why this is helpful.

OBJECTIVE 3
11. In Examples 4 and 5, what tips are given to remember how to factor the sum or difference of two cubes rather than memorizing the formulas?

5.7 Exercise Set MyMathLab®

Factor. See Examples 1 and 2.

1. $x^2 + 6x + 9$ **2.** $x^2 - 10x + 25$

3. $4x^2 - 12x + 9$ **4.** $9a^2 - 30a + 25$

5. $25x^2 + 10x + 1$ **6.** $4a^2 + 12a + 9$

7. $3x^2 - 24x + 48$ **8.** $2x^2 + 28x + 98$

9. $9y^2x^2 + 12yx^2 + 4x^2$

10. $4x^2y^3 - 4xy^3 + y^3$

11. $16x^2 - 56xy + 49y^2$

12. $81x^2 + 36xy + 4y^2$

Factor. See Examples 3 through 5.

13. $x^2 - 25$ **14.** $y^2 - 100$

15. $\frac{1}{9} - 4z^2$ **16.** $\frac{1}{16} - y^2$

17. $(y + 2)^2 - 49$ **18.** $(x - 1)^2 - 64$

19. $64x^2 - 100$ **20.** $4x^2 - 36$

21. $(x + 2y)^2 - 9$ **22.** $(3x + y)^2 - 25$

23. $x^2 + 6x + 9 - y^2$ **24.** $x^2 + 12x + 36 - y^2$

25. $x^2 + 16x + 64 - x^4$ **26.** $x^2 + 20x + 100 - x^4$

Factor. See Examples 6 through 9.

27. $x^3 + 27$ **28.** $y^3 + 1$

29. $z^3 - 1$ **30.** $x^3 - 8$

31. $m^3 + n^3$ **32.** $p^3 + 125q^3$

33. $27y^2 - x^3y^2$ **34.** $64q^2 - q^2p^3$

35. $8ab^3 + 27a^4$ **36.** $a^3b + 8b^4$

37. $250y^3 - 16x^3$ **38.** $54y^3 - 128$

MIXED PRACTICE

Factor completely. See Examples 1 through 9.

39. $x^2 - 12x + 36$ **40.** $x^2 - 18x + 81$

41. $18x^2y - 2y$ **42.** $12xy^2 - 108x$

43. $9x^2 - 49$ **44.** $25x^2 - 4$

45. $x^4 - 1$ **46.** $x^4 - 256$

47. $x^6 - y^3$ **48.** $x^3 - y^6$

49. $8x^3 + 27y^3$ **50.** $125x^3 + 8y^3$

51. $4x^2 + 4x + 1 - z^2$ **52.** $9y^2 + 12y + 4 - x^2$

53. $3x^6y^2 + 81y^2$ **54.** $x^2y^9 + x^2y^3$

55. $n^3 - \frac{1}{27}$ **56.** $p^3 + \frac{1}{125}$

57. $-16y^2 + 64$ **58.** $-12y^2 + 108$

59. $x^2 - 10x + 25 - y^2$

60. $x^2 - 18x + 81 - y^2$

61. $a^3b^3 + 125$

62. $x^3y^3 + 216$

63. $\dfrac{x^2}{25} - \dfrac{y^2}{9}$

64. $\dfrac{a^2}{4} - \dfrac{b^2}{49}$

65. $(x + y)^3 + 125$

66. $(r + s)^3 + 27$

REVIEW AND PREVIEW

Solve the following equations. See Section 2.1.

67. $x - 5 = 0$

68. $x + 7 = 0$

69. $3x + 1 = 0$

70. $5x - 15 = 0$

71. $-2x = 0$

72. $3x = 0$

73. $-5x + 25 = 0$

74. $-4x - 16 = 0$

CONCEPT EXTENSIONS

Determine whether each polynomial is factored completely. See the Concept Check in this section.

75. $5x(x^2 - 4)$

76. $x^2y^2(x^3 - y^3)$

77. $7y(a^2 + a + 1)$

78. $9z(x^2 + 4)$

△ **79.** A manufacturer of metal washers needs to determine the cross-sectional area of each washer. If the outer radius of the washer is R and the radius of the hole is r, express the area of the washer as a polynomial. Factor this polynomial completely.

△ **80.** Express the area of the shaded region as a polynomial. Factor the polynomial completely.

Express the volume of each solid as a polynomial. To do so, subtract the volume of the "hole" from the volume of the larger solid. Then factor the resulting polynomial.

△ **81.**   △ **82.**

Find the values of c that makes each trinomial a perfect square trinomial.

83. $x^2 + 6x + c$

84. $y^2 + 10y + c$

85. $m^2 - 14m + c$

86. $n^2 - 2n + c$

87. $x^2 + cx + 16$

88. $x^2 + cx + 36$

89. Factor $x^6 - 1$ completely, using the following methods from this chapter.

    a. Factor the expression by treating it as the difference of two squares, $(x^3)^2 - 1^2$.

    b. Factor the expression, treating it as the difference of two cubes, $(x^2)^3 - 1^3$.

    c. Are the answers to parts **a** and **b** the same? Why or why not?

90. Factor $x^{12} - 1$ completely, using the following methods from this chapter:

    a. Factor the expression by treating it as the difference of two squares, $(x^3)^4 - 1^4$.

    b. Factor the expression by treating it as the difference of two cubes, $(x^4)^3 - 1^3$.

    c. Are the answers to parts **a** and **b** the same? Why or why not?

Factor. Assume that variables used as exponents represent positive integers.

91. $x^{2n} - 25$

92. $x^{2n} - 36$

93. $36x^{2n} - 49$

94. $25x^{2n} - 81$

95. $x^{4n} - 16$

96. $x^{4n} - 625$

Integrated Review — Operations on Polynomials and Factoring Strategies

Sections 5.1–5.7

Operations on Polynomials

Perform each indicated operation.

1. $(-y^2 + 6y - 1) + (3y^2 - 4y - 10)$

2. $(5z^4 - 6z^2 + z + 1) - (7z^4 - 2z + 1)$

3. Subtract $(x - 5)$ from $(x^2 - 6x + 2)$.

4. $(2x^2 + 6x - 5) + (5x^2 - 10x)$

5. $(5x - 3)^2$

6. $(5x^2 - 14x - 3) - (5x + 1)$

7. $\dfrac{2x^4}{x} - \dfrac{3x^2}{x} + \dfrac{5x}{x} - \dfrac{2}{2}$

8. $(4x - 1)(x^2 - 3x - 2)$

Factoring Strategies

The key to proficiency in factoring polynomials is to practice until you are comfortable with each technique. A strategy for factoring polynomials completely is given next.

Factoring a Polynomial

Step 1. Are there any common factors? If so, factor out the greatest common factor.

Step 2. How many terms are in the polynomial?

    a. If there are *two* terms, decide if one of the following formulas may be applied:

        i. Difference of two squares: $a^2 - b^2 = (a - b)(a + b)$

        ii. Difference of two cubes: $a^3 - b^3 = (a - b)(a^2 + ab + b^2)$

        iii. Sum of two cubes: $a^3 + b^3 = (a + b)(a^2 - ab + b^2)$

    b. If there are *three* terms, try one of the following:

        i. Perfect square trinomial: $a^2 + 2ab + b^2 = (a + b)^2$

$$a^2 - 2ab + b^2 = (a - b)^2$$

        ii. If not a perfect square trinomial, factor by using the methods presented in Sections 5.5 and 5.6.

    c. If there are *four* or more terms, try factoring by grouping.

Step 3. See whether any factors in the factored polynomial can be factored further.

A few examples are worked for you below.

EXAMPLE I   Factor each polynomial completely.

    a. $8a^2b - 4ab$ **b.** $36x^2 - 9$ **c.** $2x^2 - 5x - 7$

    d. $5p^2 + 5 + qp^2 + q$ **e.** $9x^2 + 24x + 16$ **f.** $y^2 + 25$

Solution

a. Step 1. The terms have a common factor of $4ab$, which we factor out.

$$8a^2b - 4ab = 4ab(2a - 1)$$

    Step 2. There are two terms, but the binomial $2a - 1$ is not the difference of two squares or the sum or difference of two cubes.

    Step 3. The factor $2a - 1$ cannot be factored further.

b. Step 1. Factor out a common factor of 9.

$$36x^2 - 9 = 9(4x^2 - 1)$$

    Step 2. The factor $4x^2 - 1$ has two terms, and it is the difference of two squares.

$$9(4x^2 - 1) = 9(2x + 1)(2x - 1)$$

    Step 3. No factor with more than one term can be factored further.

c. Step 1. The terms of $2x^2 - 5x - 7$ contain no common factor other than 1 or -1.

    Step 2. There are three terms. The trinomial is not a perfect square, so we factor by methods from Section 5.6.

$$2x^2 - 5x - 7 = (2x - 7)(x + 1)$$

    Step 3. No factor with more than one term can be factored further.

d. Step 1. There is no common factor of all terms of $5p^2 + 5 + qp^2 + q$.

    Step 2. The polynomial has four terms, so try factoring by grouping.

$$5p^2 + 5 + qp^2 + q = (5p^2 + 5) + (qp^2 + q) \quad \text{Group the terms.}$$
$$= 5(p^2 + 1) + q(p^2 + 1)$$
$$= (p^2 + 1)(5 + q)$$

    Step 3. No factor can be factored further.

e. Step 1. The terms of $9x^2 + 24x + 16$ contain no common factor other than 1 or -1.

Step 2. The trinomial $9x^2 + 24x + 16$ is a perfect square trinomial, and $9x^2 + 24x + 16 = (3x + 4)^2$.

Step 3. No factor can be factored further.

f. Step 1. There is no common factor of $y^2 + 25$ other than 1.

Step 2. This binomial is the sum of two squares and is prime.

Step 3. The binomial $y^2 + 25$ cannot be factored further. ☐

PRACTICE

1 Factor each polynomial completely.

   a. $12x^2y - 3xy$ **b.** $49x^2 - 4$

   c. $5x^2 + 2x - 3$ **d.** $3x^2 + 6 + x^3 + 2x$

   e. $4x^2 + 20x + 25$ **f.** $b^2 + 100$

EXAMPLE 2   Factor each polynomial completely.

   a. $27a^3 - b^3$ **b.** $3n^2m^4 - 48m^6$ **c.** $2x^2 - 12x + 18 - 2z^2$

   d. $8x^4y^2 + 125xy^2$ **e.** $(x - 5)^2 - 49y^2$

Solution

a. This binomial is the difference of two cubes.

$$27a^3 - b^3 = (3a)^3 - b^3$$
$$= (3a - b)[(3a)^2 + (3a)(b) + b^2]$$
$$= (3a - b)(9a^2 + 3ab + b^2)$$

b. $3n^2m^4 - 48m^6 = 3m^4(n^2 - 16m^2)$ Factor out the GCF, $3m^4$.

$$= 3m^4(n + 4m)(n - 4m)$$ Factor the difference of squares.

c. $2x^2 - 12x + 18 - 2z^2 = 2(x^2 - 6x + 9 - z^2)$ The GCF is 2.

$$= 2[(x^2 - 6x + 9) - z^2]$$ Group the first three terms together.

$$= 2[(x - 3)^2 - z^2]$$ Factor the perfect square trinomial.

$$= 2[(x - 3) + z][(x - 3) - z]$$ Factor the difference of squares.

$$= 2(x - 3 + z)(x - 3 - z)$$

d. $8x^4y^2 + 125xy^2 = xy^2(8x^3 + 125)$ The GCF is xy^2.

$$= xy^2[(2x)^3 + 5^3]$$

$$= xy^2(2x + 5)[(2x)^2 - (2x)(5) + 5^2]$$ Factor the sum of cubes.

$$= xy^2(2x + 5)(4x^2 - 10x + 25)$$

e. This binomial is the difference of squares.

$$(x - 5)^2 - 49y^2 = (x - 5)^2 - (7y)^2$$
$$= [(x - 5) + 7y][(x - 5) - 7y]$$
$$= (x - 5 + 7y)(x - 5 - 7y)$$ ☐

PRACTICE
2

Factor each polynomial completely.

a. $64x^3 + y^3$

b. $7x^2y^2 - 63y^4$

c. $3x^2 + 12x + 12 - 3b^2$

d. $x^5y^4 + 27x^2y$

e. $(x + 7)^2 - 81y^2$ ■

Factor completely.

9. $x^2 - 8x + 16 - y^2$

10. $12x^2 - 22x - 20$

11. $x^4 - x$

12. $(2x + 1)^2 - 3(2x + 1) + 2$

13. $14x^2y - 2xy$

14. $24ab^2 - 6ab$

15. $4x^2 - 16$

16. $9x^2 - 81$

17. $3x^2 - 8x - 11$

18. $5x^2 - 2x - 3$

19. $4x^2 + 8x - 12$

20. $6x^2 - 6x - 12$

21. $4x^2 + 36x + 81$

22. $25x^2 + 40x + 16$

23. $8x^3 + 125y^3$

24. $27x^3 - 64y^3$

25. $64x^2y^3 - 8x^2$

26. $27x^5y^4 - 216x^2y$

27. $(x + 5)^3 + y^3$

28. $(y - 1)^3 + 27x^3$

29. $(5a - 3)^2 - 6(5a - 3) + 9$

30. $(4r + 1)^2 + 8(4r + 1) + 16$

31. $7x^2 - 63x$

32. $20x^2 + 23x + 6$

33. $ab - 6a + 7b - 42$

34. $20x^2 - 220x + 600$

35. $x^4 - 1$

36. $15x^2 - 20x$

37. $10x^2 - 7x - 33$

38. $45m^3n^3 - 27m^2n^2$

39. $5a^3b^3 - 50a^3b$

40. $x^4 + x$

41. $16x^2 + 25$

42. $20x^3 + 20y^3$

43. $10x^3 - 210x^2 + 1100x$

44. $9y^2 - 42y + 49$

45. $64a^3b^4 - 27a^3b$

46. $y^4 - 16$

47. $2x^3 - 54$

48. $2sr + 10s - r - 5$

49. $3y^5 - 5y^4 + 6y - 10$

50. $64a^2 + b^2$

51. $100z^3 + 100$

52. $250x^4 - 16x$

53. $4b^2 - 36b + 81$

54. $2a^5 - a^4 + 6a - 3$

55. $(y - 6)^2 + 3(y - 6) + 2$

56. $(c + 2)^2 - 6(c + 2) + 5$

△ **57.** Express the area of the shaded region as a polynomial. Factor the polynomial completely.

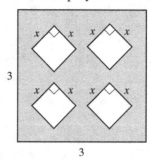

5.8 Solving Equations by Factoring and Problem Solving

OBJECTIVES

1 Solve Polynomial Equations by Factoring.

2 Solve Problems That Can Be Modeled by Polynomial Equations.

3 Find the *x*-Intercepts of a Polynomial Function.

OBJECTIVE

1 Solving Polynomial Equations by Factoring

In this section, your efforts to learn factoring start to pay off. We use factoring to solve polynomial equations, which in turn helps us solve problems that can be modeled by polynomial equations and helps us sketch the graphs of polynomial functions.

A **polynomial equation** is the result of setting two polynomials equal to each other. Examples of polynomial equations are

$$3x^3 - 2x^2 = x^2 + 2x - 1 \qquad 2.6x + 7 = -1.3 \qquad -5x^2 - 5 = -9x^2 - 2x + 1$$

A polynomial equation is in **standard form** if one side of the equation is 0. In standard form, the polynomial equations above are

$$3x^3 - 3x^2 - 2x + 1 = 0 \qquad 2.6x + 8.3 = 0 \qquad 4x^2 + 2x - 6 = 0$$

The degree of a simplified polynomial equation in standard form is the same as the highest degree of any of its terms. A polynomial equation of degree 2 is also called a **quadratic equation.**

A solution of a polynomial equation in one variable is a value of the variable that makes the equation true. The method presented in this section for solving polynomial equations is called the **factoring method.** This method is based on the **zero factor property.**

Zero Factor Property

If a and b are real numbers and $a \cdot b = 0$, then $a = 0$ or $b = 0$. This property is true for three or more factors also.

In other words, if the product of two or more real numbers is zero, then at least one number must be zero.

EXAMPLE 1 Solve: $(x + 2)(x - 6) = 0$

Solution By the zero factor property, $(x + 2)(x - 6) = 0$ only if $x + 2 = 0$ or $x - 6 = 0$.

$$x + 2 = 0 \quad \text{or} \quad x - 6 = 0 \quad \text{Apply the zero factor property.}$$
$$x = -2 \quad \text{or} \quad x = 6 \quad \text{Solve each linear equation.}$$

To check, let $x = -2$ and then let $x = 6$ in the original equation.

Let $x = -2$.	Let $x = 6$.
Then $(x + 2)(x - 6) = 0$	Then $(x + 2)(x - 6) = 0$
becomes $(-2 + 2)(-2 - 6) \stackrel{?}{=} 0$	becomes $(6 + 2)(6 - 6) \stackrel{?}{=} 0$
$(0)(-8) \stackrel{?}{=} 0$	$(8)(0) \stackrel{?}{=} 0$
$0 = 0$ True	$0 = 0$ True

Both -2 and 6 check, so they are both solutions. The solution set is $\{-2, 6\}$. ☐

PRACTICE

1 Solve: $(x + 8)(x - 5) = 0$ ■

EXAMPLE 2 Solve: $2x^2 + 9x - 5 = 0$

Solution To use the zero factor property, one side of the equation must be 0, and the other side must be in factored form.

$$2x^2 + 9x - 5 = 0$$
$$(2x - 1)(x + 5) = 0 \qquad \text{Factor.}$$
$$2x - 1 = 0 \quad \text{or} \quad x + 5 = 0 \qquad \text{Set each factor equal to zero.}$$
$$2x = 1$$
$$x = \frac{1}{2} \quad \text{or} \quad x = -5 \qquad \text{Solve each linear equation.}$$

The solutions are -5 and $\frac{1}{2}$. To check, let $x = \frac{1}{2}$ in the original equation; then let $x = -5$ in the original equation. The solution set is $\left\{-5, \frac{1}{2}\right\}$. □

PRACTICE
2 Solve: $3x^2 + 10x - 8 = 0$ ■

Solving Polynomial Equations by Factoring

Step 1. Write the equation in standard form so that one side of the equation is 0.

Step 2. Factor the polynomial completely.

Step 3. Set each factor containing a variable equal to 0.

Step 4. Solve the resulting equations.

Step 5. Check each solution in the original equation.

Since it is not always possible to factor a polynomial, not all polynomial equations can be solved by factoring. Other methods of solving polynomial equations are presented in Chapter 8.

EXAMPLE 3 Solve: $x(2x - 7) = 4$

Solution First, write the equation in standard form; then, factor.

$$x(2x - 7) = 4$$
$$2x^2 - 7x = 4 \qquad \text{Multiply.}$$
$$2x^2 - 7x - 4 = 0 \qquad \text{Write in standard form.}$$
$$(2x + 1)(x - 4) = 0 \qquad \text{Factor.}$$
$$2x + 1 = 0 \quad \text{or} \quad x - 4 = 0 \qquad \text{Set each factor equal to zero.}$$
$$2x = -1 \qquad \qquad \text{Solve.}$$
$$x = -\frac{1}{2} \quad \text{or} \quad x = 4$$

The solutions are $-\frac{1}{2}$ and 4. Check both solutions in the original equation. □

PRACTICE
3 Solve: $x(3x + 14) = -8$ ■

Helpful Hint

To apply the zero factor property, one side of the equation must be 0, and the other side of the equation must be factored. To solve the equation $x(2x - 7) = 4$, for example, you may **not** set each factor equal to 4.

EXAMPLE 4   Solve: $3(x^2 + 4) + 5 = -6(x^2 + 2x) + 13$

Solution Rewrite the equation so that one side is 0.

$$3(x^2 + 4) + 5 = -6(x^2 + 2x) + 13.$$

$\quad\quad 3x^2 + 12 + 5 = -6x^2 - 12x + 13$ Apply the distributive property.

$\quad\quad\quad 9x^2 + 12x + 4 = 0$ Rewrite the equation so that one side is 0.

$\quad (3x + 2)(3x + 2) = 0$ Factor.

$\quad\quad\quad 3x + 2 = 0 \quad$ or $\quad 3x + 2 = 0$ Set each factor equal to 0.

$\quad\quad\quad\quad\quad 3x = -2 \quad$ or $\quad\quad 3x = -2$

$\quad\quad\quad\quad\quad\quad x = -\dfrac{2}{3} \quad$ or $\quad\quad x = -\dfrac{2}{3}$ Solve each equation.

The solution is $-\dfrac{2}{3}$. Check by substituting $-\dfrac{2}{3}$ into the original equation.   ☐

PRACTICE
4   Solve: $8(x^2 + 3) + 4 = -8x(x + 3) + 19$ ■

If the equation contains fractions, we clear the equation of fractions as a first step.

EXAMPLE 5   Solve: $2x^2 = \dfrac{17}{3}x + 1$

Solution $\quad\quad\quad 2x^2 = \dfrac{17}{3}x + 1$

$\quad\quad 3(2x^2) = 3\left(\dfrac{17}{3}x + 1\right)$ Clear the equation of fractions.

$\quad\quad\quad\quad 6x^2 = 17x + 3$ Apply the distributive property.

$\quad 6x^2 - 17x - 3 = 0$ Rewrite the equation in standard form.

$\quad (6x + 1)(x - 3) = 0$ Factor.

$\quad\quad\quad 6x + 1 = 0 \quad$ or $\quad x - 3 = 0$ Set each factor equal to zero.

$\quad\quad\quad\quad\quad 6x = -1$

$\quad\quad\quad\quad\quad\quad x = -\dfrac{1}{6} \quad$ or $\quad\quad x = 3$ Solve each equation.

The solutions are $-\dfrac{1}{6}$ and 3.   ☐

PRACTICE
5   Solve: $4x^2 = \dfrac{15}{2}x + 1$ ■

EXAMPLE 6   Solve: $x^3 = 4x$

Solution $\quad\quad\quad x^3 = 4x$

$\quad\quad\quad x^3 - 4x = 0$ Rewrite the equation so that one side is 0.

$\quad\quad x(x^2 - 4) = 0$ Factor out the GCF, x.

$x(x + 2)(x - 2) = 0$ Factor the difference of squares.

$x = 0 \quad$ or $\quad x + 2 = 0 \quad$ or $\quad x - 2 = 0$ Set each factor equal to 0.

$x = 0 \quad$ or $\quad\quad x = -2 \quad$ or $\quad\quad x = 2$ Solve each equation.

The solutions are $-2, 0$, and 2. Check by substituting into the original equation.   ☐

PRACTICE
6   Solve: $x^3 = 2x^2 + 3x$ ■

Notice that the *third*-degree equation of Example 6 yielded *three* solutions.

EXAMPLE 7 Solve: $x^3 + 5x^2 = x + 5$

Solution First, write the equation so that one side is 0.

$$x^3 + 5x^2 - x - 5 = 0$$
$$(x^3 - x) + (5x^2 - 5) = 0 \qquad \text{Factor by grouping.}$$
$$x(x^2 - 1) + 5(x^2 - 1) = 0$$
$$(x^2 - 1)(x + 5) = 0$$
$$(x + 1)(x - 1)(x + 5) = 0 \qquad \text{Factor the difference of squares.}$$
$$x + 1 = 0 \quad \text{or} \quad x - 1 = 0 \quad \text{or} \quad x + 5 = 0 \qquad \text{Set each factor equal to 0.}$$
$$x = -1 \quad \text{or} \qquad x = 1 \quad \text{or} \qquad x = -5 \qquad \text{Solve each equation.}$$

The solutions are -5, -1, and 1. Check in the original equation. ☐

PRACTICE
7 Solve: $x^3 - 9x = 18 - 2x^2$ ■

✔ **CONCEPT CHECK**

Which solution strategies are incorrect? Why?

a. Solve $(y - 2)(y + 2) = 4$ by setting each factor equal to 4.
b. Solve $(x + 1)(x + 3) = 0$ by setting each factor equal to 0.
c. Solve $z^2 + 5z + 6 = 0$ by factoring $z^2 + 5z + 6$ and setting each factor equal to 0.
d. Solve $x^2 + 6x + 8 = 10$ by factoring $x^2 + 6x + 8$ and setting each factor equal to 0.

OBJECTIVE

2 Solving Problems Modeled by Polynomial Equations

Some problems may be modeled by polynomial equations. To solve these problems, we use the same problem-solving steps that were introduced in Section 2.2. When solving these problems, keep in mind that a solution of an equation that models a problem is not always a solution of the problem. For example, a person's weight or the length of a side of a geometric figure is always a positive number. Discard solutions that do not make sense as solutions of the problem.

EXAMPLE 8 **Finding the Return Time of a Rocket**

An Alpha III model rocket is launched from the ground with an A8–3 engine. Without a parachute, the height of the rocket h at time t seconds is approximated by the equation

$$h = -16t^2 + 144t$$

Find how long it takes the rocket to return to the ground.

Solution

1. UNDERSTAND. Read and reread the problem. The equation $h = -16t^2 + 144t$ models the height of the rocket. Familiarize yourself with this equation by finding a few values.

   When $t = 1$ second, the height of the rocket is

   $$h = -16(1)^2 + 144(1) = 128 \text{ feet}$$

   When $t = 2$ seconds, the height of the rocket is

   $$h = -16(2)^2 + 144(2) = 224 \text{ feet}$$

2. TRANSLATE. To find how long it takes the rocket to return to the ground, we want to know what value of t makes the height h equal to 0. That is, we want to solve $h = 0$.

   $$-16t^2 + 144t = 0$$

Answer to Concept Check:
a and d; the zero factor property works
only if one side of the equation is 0

3. SOLVE the quadratic equation by factoring.

$$-16t^2 + 144t = 0$$
$$-16t(t - 9) = 0$$
$$-16t = 0 \quad \text{or} \quad t - 9 = 0$$
$$t = 0 \quad \text{or} \quad t = 9$$

4. INTERPRET. The height h is 0 feet at time 0 seconds (when the rocket is launched) and at time 9 seconds.

Check: See that the height of the rocket at 9 seconds equals 0.

$$h = -16(9)^2 + 144(9) = -1296 + 1296 = 0$$

State: The rocket returns to the ground 9 seconds after it is launched.   ☐

PRACTICE
8 A model rocket is launched from the ground. Its height h in feet at time t seconds is approximated by the equation $h = -16t^2 + 96t$. Find how long it takes the rocket to return to the ground.   ▪

Some of the exercises at the end of this section use the **Pythagorean theorem.** Before we review this theorem, recall that a **right triangle** is a triangle that contains a 90° angle, or right angle. The **hypotenuse** of a right triangle is the side opposite the right angle and is the longest side of the triangle. The **legs** of a right triangle are the other sides of the triangle.

Leg b
Hypotenuse
c
Leg a

Pythagorean Theorem

In a right triangle, the sum of the squares of the lengths of the two legs is equal to the square of the length of the hypotenuse.

$$(\text{leg})^2 + (\text{leg})^2 = (\text{hypotenuse})^2 \quad \text{or} \quad a^2 + b^2 = c^2$$

△ **EXAMPLE 9**   **Using the Pythagorean Theorem**

While framing an addition to an existing home, a carpenter used the Pythagorean theorem to determine whether a wall was "square"—that is, whether the wall formed a right angle with the floor. He used a triangle whose sides are three consecutive integers. Find a right triangle whose sides are three consecutive integers.

Solution

1. **UNDERSTAND.** Read and reread the problem.

   Let $x, x + 1$, and $x + 2$ be three consecutive integers. Since these integers represent lengths of the sides of a right triangle, we have

   $$x = \text{one leg}$$
   $$x + 1 = \text{other leg}$$
   $$x + 2 = \text{hypotenuse (longest side)}$$

2. **TRANSLATE.** By the Pythagorean theorem, we have

In words:	$(\text{leg})^2$	$+$	$(\text{leg})^2$	$=$	$(\text{hypotenuse})^2$
	$\downarrow$		$\downarrow$		$\downarrow$
Traslate:	$(x)^2$	$+$	$(x + 1)^2$	$=$	$(x + 2)^2$

3. **SOLVE** the equation.

   $$x^2 + (x + 1)^2 = (x + 2)^2$$
   $$x^2 + x^2 + 2x + 1 = x^2 + 4x + 4 \qquad \text{Multiply.}$$
   $$2x^2 + 2x + 1 = x^2 + 4x + 4$$
   $$x^2 - 2x - 3 = 0 \qquad \text{Write in standard form.}$$
   $$(x - 3)(x + 1) = 0$$
   $$x - 3 = 0 \quad \text{or} \quad x + 1 = 0$$
   $$x = 3 \qquad\qquad x = -1$$

4. **INTERPRET.** Discard $x = -1$ since length cannot be negative. If $x = 3$, then $x + 1 = 4$ and $x + 2 = 5$.

   Check: To check, see that $(\text{leg})^2 + (\text{leg})^2 = (\text{hypotenuse})^2$
   $$3^2 + 4^2 = 5^2$$
   $$9 + 16 = 25 \quad \text{True}$$

   State: The lengths of the sides of the right triangle are 3, 4, and 5 units. The carpenter used this information, for example, by marking off lengths of 3 and 4 feet on the floor and framing respectively. If the diagonal length between these marks was 5 feet, the wall was "square." If not, adjustments were made.

PRACTICE

9 Find a right triangle whose sides are consecutive even integers.

OBJECTIVE

3 Finding the *x*-Intercepts of Polynomial Functions

Recall that to find the *x*-intercepts of the graph of a function, let $f(x) = 0$ or $y = 0$ and solve for *x*. This fact gives us a visual interpretation of the results of this section.

From Example 1, we know that the solutions of the equation $(x + 2)(x - 6) = 0$ are -2 and 6. These solutions give us important information about the related polynomial function $p(x) = (x + 2)(x - 6)$. We know that when *x* is -2 or when *x* is 6, the value of $p(x)$ is 0.

$$p(x) = (x + 2)(x - 6)$$
$$p(-2) = (-2 + 2)(-2 - 6) = (0)(-8) = 0$$
$$p(6) = (6 + 2)(6 - 6) = (8)(0) = 0$$

Thus, we know that $(-2, 0)$ and $(6, 0)$ are the *x*-intercepts of the graph of $p(x)$.

We also know that the graph of $p(x)$ does not cross the *x*-axis at any other point. For this reason, and the fact that $p(x) = (x + 2)(x - 6) = x^2 - 4x - 12$ has degree 2, we conclude that the graph of *p* must look something like one of these two graphs:

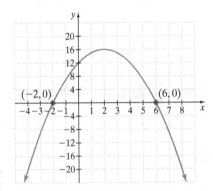

> **Helpful Hint**
>
> From our discussion on the bottom of page 261, the graph of $p(x) = (x + 2)(x - 6) = x^2 - 4x - 12$ must look like the graph on the left since the coefficient of x^2 is positive.

In a later chapter, we explore these graphs more fully. For the moment, know that the solutions of a polynomial equation are the *x*-intercepts of the graph of the related function and that the *x*-intercepts of the graph of a polynomial function are the solutions of the related polynomial equation. These values are also called **roots,** or **zeros,** of a polynomial function.

EXAMPLE 10 **Match Each Function with Its Graph**

$$f(x) = (x - 3)(x + 2) \quad g(x) = x(x + 2)(x - 2) \quad h(x) = (x - 2)(x + 2)(x - 1)$$

A.

B.

C.
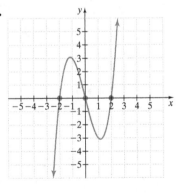

Solution The graph of the function $f(x) = (x - 3)(x + 2)$ has two *x*-intercepts, $(3, 0)$ and $(-2, 0)$, because the equation $0 = (x - 3)(x + 2)$ has two solutions, 3 and -2.

The graph of $f(x)$ is graph B.

The graph of the function $g(x) = x(x + 2)(x - 2)$ has three *x*-intercepts, $(0, 0)$, $(-2, 0)$, and $(2, 0)$, because the equation $0 = x(x + 2)(x - 2)$ has three solutions, $0, -2$, and 2.

The graph of $g(x)$ is graph C.

The graph of the function $h(x) = (x - 2)(x + 2)(x - 1)$ has three x-intercepts, $(2, 0)$, $(-2, 0)$, and $(1, 0)$, because the equation $0 = (x - 2)(x + 2)(x - 1)$ has three solutions, 2, -2, and 1.

The graph of $h(x)$ is graph A. □

PRACTICE

10 Match each function with its graph.

$$f(x) = (x - 1)(x + 3) \quad g(x) = x(x + 3)(x - 2) \quad h(x) = (x - 3)(x + 2)(x - 2)$$

A.

B.

C.

Graphing Calculator Explorations

We can use a graphing calculator to approximate real-number solutions of any quadratic equation in standard form, whether the associated polynomial is factorable or not. For example, let's solve the quadratic equation $x^2 - 2x - 4 = 0$. The solutions of this equation will be the x-intercepts of the graph of the function $f(x) = x^2 - 2x - 4$. (Recall that to find x-intercepts, we let $f(x) = 0$ or $y = 0$.) When we use a standard window, the graph of this function looks like this.

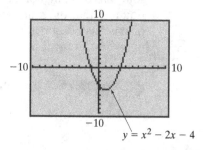

The graph appears to have one x-intercept between -2 and -1 and one between 3 and 4. To find the x-intercept between 3 and 4 to the nearest hundredth, we can use a zero feature, a Zoom feature, which magnifies a portion of the graph around the cursor, or we can redefine our window. If we redefine our window to

$$\text{Xmin} = 2 \qquad \text{Ymin} = -1$$
$$\text{Xmax} = 5 \qquad \text{Ymax} = 1$$
$$\text{Xscl} = 1 \qquad \text{Yscl} = 1$$

the resulting screen is

By using the Trace feature, we can now see that one of the intercepts is between 3.21 and 3.25. To approximate to the nearest hundredth, Zoom again or redefine the window to

$$\text{Xmin} = 3.2 \qquad \text{Ymin} = -0.1$$
$$\text{Xmax} = 3.3 \qquad \text{Ymax} = 0.1$$
$$\text{Xscl} = 1 \qquad \text{Yscl} = 1$$

If we use the Trace feature again, we see that, to the nearest hundredth, the x-intercept is 3.24. By repeating this process, we can approximate the other x-intercept to be -1.24.

To check, find $f(3.24)$ and $f(-1.24)$. Both of these values should be close to 0. (They will not be exactly 0 because we approximated these solutions.)

$$f(3.24) = 0.0176 \quad \text{and} \quad f(-1.24) = 0.0176$$

Solve each of these quadratic equations by graphing the related function and approximating the x-intercepts to the nearest thousandth.

1. $x^2 + 3x - 2 = 0$ **2.** $5x^2 - 7x + 1 = 0$

3. $2.3x^2 - 4.4x - 5.6 = 0$ **4.** $0.2x^2 + 6.2x + 2.1 = 0$

5. $0.09x^2 - 0.13x - 0.08 = 0$ **6.** $x^2 + 0.08x - 0.01 = 0$

 Vocabulary, Readiness & Video Check

Solve each equation for the variable. See Example 1.

1. $(x - 3)(x + 5) = 0$ **2.** $(y + 5)(y + 3) = 0$ **3.** $(z - 3)(z + 7) = 0$

4. $(c - 2)(c - 4) = 0$ **5.** $x(x - 9) = 0$ **6.** $w(w + 7) = 0$

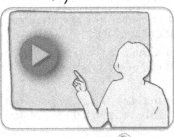

Martin-Gay Interactive Videos

See Video 5.8 🔘

Watch the section lecture video and answer the following questions.

OBJECTIVE 1 **7.** As shown in Examples 1–3, what two things have to be true in order to use the zero factor property?

OBJECTIVE 2 **8.** In ▥ Example 5, why aren't both solutions to the equation accepted?

OBJECTIVE 3 **9.** From ▥ Example 6, how can finding the x-intercepts of the graph of a quadratic equation in two variables lead to solving a quadratic equation by factoring?

5.8 **Exercise Set** MyMathLab® ▶

Solve each equation. See Example 1.

▶ **1.** $(x + 3)(3x - 4) = 0$

2. $(5x + 1)(x - 2) = 0$

3. $3(2x - 5)(4x + 3) = 0$

4. $8(3x - 4)(2x - 7) = 0$

Solve each equation. See Examples 2 through 5.

5. $x^2 + 11x + 24 = 0$ **6.** $y^2 - 10y + 24 = 0$

7. $12x^2 + 5x - 2 = 0$ **8.** $3y^2 - y - 14 = 0$

9. $z^2 + 9 = 10z$ **10.** $n^2 + n = 72$

▶ **11.** $x(5x + 2) = 3$ **12.** $n(2n - 3) = 2$

13. $x^2 - 6x = x(8 + x)$ **14.** $n(3 + n) = n^2 + 4n$

15. $\dfrac{z^2}{6} - \dfrac{z}{2} - 3 = 0$

16. $\dfrac{c^2}{20} - \dfrac{c}{4} + \dfrac{1}{5} = 0$

17. $\dfrac{x^2}{2} + \dfrac{x}{20} = \dfrac{1}{10}$

18. $\dfrac{y^2}{30} = \dfrac{y}{15} + \dfrac{1}{2}$

19. $\dfrac{4t^2}{5} = \dfrac{t}{5} + \dfrac{3}{10}$

20. $\dfrac{5x^2}{6} - \dfrac{7x}{2} + \dfrac{2}{3} = 0$

Solve each equation. See Examples 6 and 7.

21. $(x + 2)(x - 7)(3x - 8) = 0$

22. $(4x + 9)(x - 4)(x + 1) = 0$

23. $(x^2 - 1)(6x + 1) = 0$

24. $(x^2 - 25)(3x + 1) = 0$

25. $y^3 = 9y$

26. $n^3 = 16n$

▶ **27.** $x^3 - x = 2x^2 - 2$

28. $m^3 = m^2 + 12m$

MIXED PRACTICE

Solve each equation. See Examples 1 through 7.

29. $(2x + 7)(x - 10) = 0$

30. $(x + 4)(5x - 1) = 0$

31. $3x(x - 5) = 0$

32. $4x(2x + 3) = 0$

33. $x^2 - 2x - 15 = 0$

34. $x^2 + 6x - 7 = 0$

35. $12x^2 + 2x - 2 = 0$

36. $8x^2 + 13x + 5 = 0$

37. $w^2 - 5w = 36$

38. $x^2 + 32 = 12x$

39. $25x^2 - 40x + 16 = 0$

40. $9n^2 + 30n + 25 = 0$

41. $2r^3 + 6r^2 = 20r$

42. $-2t^3 = 108t - 30t^2$

43. $z(5z - 4)(z + 3) = 0$

44. $2r(r + 7)(5r - 4) = 0$

▶ **45.** $2z(z + 6) = 2z^2 + 12z - 8$

46. $3c^2 - 8c + 2 = c(3c - 8)$

47. $(x - 1)(x + 4) = 24$

48. $(2x - 1)(x + 2) = -3$

49. $\dfrac{x^2}{4} - \dfrac{5}{2}x + 6 = 0$

50. $\dfrac{x^2}{18} + \dfrac{x}{2} + 1 = 0$

51. $y^2 + \dfrac{1}{4} = -y$

52. $\dfrac{x^2}{10} + \dfrac{5}{2} = x$

53. $y^3 + 4y^2 = 9y + 36$

54. $x^3 + 5x^2 = x + 5$

55. $2x^3 = 50x$

56. $m^5 = 36m^3$

57. $x^2 + (x + 1)^2 = 61$

58. $y^2 + (y + 2)^2 = 34$

59. $m^2(3m - 2) = m$

60. $x^2(5x + 3) = 26x$

61. $3x^2 = -x$

62. $y^2 = -5y$

63. $x(x - 3) = x^2 + 5x + 7$

64. $z^2 - 4z + 10 = z(z - 5)$

65. $3(t - 8) + 2t = 7 + t$

66. $7c - 2(3c + 1) = 5(4 - 2c)$

67. $-3(x - 4) + x = 5(3 - x)$

68. $-4(a + 1) - 3a = -7(2a - 3)$

Solve. See Examples 8 and 9.

69. One number exceeds another by five, and their product is 66. Find the numbers.

70. If the sum of two numbers is 4 and their product is $\dfrac{15}{4}$, find the numbers.

△ **71.** An electrician needs to run a cable from the top of a 60-foot tower to a transmitter box located 45 feet away from the base of the tower. Find how long he should make the cable.

Tower Rewiring Plan

60 feet

transmitter box

45 feet

△ **72.** A stereo system installer needs to run speaker wire along the two diagonals of a rectangular room whose dimensions are 40 feet by 75 feet. Find how much speaker wire she needs.

75 ft

40 ft

73. If the cost, $C(x)$, for manufacturing x units of a certain product is given by $C(x) = x^2 - 15x + 50$, find the number of units manufactured at a cost of $9500.

△ **74.** Determine whether any three consecutive integers represent the lengths of the sides of a right triangle.

△ ▶ **75.** The shorter leg of a right triangle is 3 centimeters less than the other leg. Find the length of the two legs if the hypotenuse is 15 centimeters.

△ **76.** The longer leg of a right triangle is 4 feet longer than the other leg. Find the length of the two legs if the hypotenuse is 20 feet.

△ **77.** Marie Mulroney has a rectangular board 12 inches by 16 inches around which she wants to put a uniform border of shells. If she has enough shells for a border whose area is 128 square inches, determine the width of the border.

12 in.

16 in.

x

x

△ **78.** A gardener has a rose garden that measures 30 feet by 20 feet. He wants to put a uniform border of pine bark around the outside of the garden. Find how wide the border should be if he has enough pine bark to cover 336 square feet.

79. While hovering near the top of Ribbon Falls in Yosemite National Park at 1600 feet, a helicopter pilot accidentally drops his sunglasses. The height $h(t)$ of the sunglasses after t seconds is given by the polynomial function

$$h(t) = -16t^2 + 1600$$

When will the sunglasses hit the ground? (*Hint:* Let the height, $h(t)$, be 0 and solve for t.)

80. After t seconds, the height $h(t)$ of a model rocket launched from the ground into the air is given by the function

$$h(t) = -16t^2 + 80t$$

Find how long it takes the rocket to reach a height of 96 feet.

△ **81.** The floor of a shed has an area of 90 square feet. The floor is in the shape of a rectangle whose length is 3 feet less than twice the width. Find the length and the width of the floor of the shed.

△ **82.** A vegetable garden with an area of 200 square feet is to be fertilized. If the length of the garden is 1 foot less than three times the width, find the dimensions of the garden.

83. The function $W(x) = 0.5x^2$ gives the number of servings of wedding cake that can be obtained from a two-layer x-inch square wedding cake tier. What size square wedding cake tier is needed to serve 50 people? (*Source:* Based on data from the *Wilton 2000 Yearbook of Cake Decorating*)

84. Use the function in Exercise 83 to determine what size square wedding cake tier is needed to serve 200 people.

85. Suppose that a movie is being filmed in New York City. An action shot requires an object to be thrown upward with an initial velocity of 80 feet per second off the top of 1 Madison Square Plaza, a height of 576 feet. The height $h(t)$ in feet of the object after t seconds is given by the function

$$h(t) = -16t^2 + 80t + 576.$$

Determine how long before the object strikes the ground. (*Hint:* Let the height, $h(t)$, be 0 and solve for t.) (*Source: The World Almanac*)

576 ft

86. Suppose that an object is thrown upward with an initial velocity of 64 feet per second off the edge of a 960-foot cliff. The height $h(t)$ in feet of the object after t seconds is given by the function

$$h(t) = -16t^2 + 64t + 960$$

Determine how long before the object strikes the ground. (See the hint for Exercise 85 and note Exercise 100, Section 5.6.)

Match each polynomial function with its graph. See Example 10.

 87. $f(x) = (x - 2)(x + 5)$

88. $g(x) = (x + 1)(x - 6)$

89. $h(x) = x(x + 3)(x - 3)$

90. $F(x) = (x + 1)(x - 2)(x + 5)$

91. $G(x) = 2x^2 + 9x + 4$

92. $H(x) = 2x^2 - 7x - 4$

A.

B.

C.

D.

E.

F.

REVIEW AND PREVIEW

Write the x- and y-intercepts for each graph and determine whether the graph is the graph of a function. See Sections 3.1 and 3.2.

93.   **94.**

95.   **96.**

CONCEPT EXTENSIONS

Each exercise contains an error. Find and correct the error. See the Concept Check in the section.

97. $(x - 5)(x + 2) = 0$

$x - 5 = 0$ or $x + 2 = 0$

$x = -5$ or $x = -2$

98. $(4x - 5)(x + 7) = 0$

$4x - 5 = 0$ or $x + 7 = 0$

$x = \dfrac{4}{5}$ or $x = -7$

99. $y(y - 5) = -6$

$y = -6$ or $y - 5 = -5$

$y = -6$ or $y = 0$

100. $3x^2 - 19x = 14$

$-16x = 14$

$x = -\dfrac{14}{16}$

$x = -\dfrac{7}{8}$

Solve.

101. $(x^2 + x - 6)(3x^2 - 14x - 5) = 0$

102. $(x^2 - 9)(x^2 + 8x + 16) = 0$

With the constantly changing environment of technology, it is difficult to predict what will be the future ways to enjoy music. As of now, many Americans are relying on subscription services to stream their music digitally. It is complicated to calculate how many consumers belong to subscription services, but one forecast is $y = 0.7x^2 + 4.9x + 8$, where x is the number of years since 2010 and y is the number of music subscription consumers in millions. Use this equation for Exercises 103 and 104.

103. Let $y = 38.8$ and solve the resulting quadratic equation by factoring. (*Hint:* When factoring, first factor out a factor of 0.7 from all three terms of the trinomial.)

104. Write a sentence explain the meaning of the positive solution of Exercise 103.

105. Explain how solving $2(x - 3)(x - 1) = 0$ differs from solving $2x(x - 3)(x - 1) = 0$.

106. Explain why the zero factor property works for more than two numbers whose product is 0.

107. Is the following step correct? Why or why not?

$$x(x - 3) = 5$$
$$x = 5 \quad \text{or} \quad x - 3 = 5$$

108. Are the following steps correct? Why or why not?

$$x^2 + x = 6$$
$$x(x + 1) = 6$$
$$x = 6 \quad \text{or} \quad x + 1 = 6$$

Write a quadratic equation that has the given numbers as solutions.

109. 5, 3

110. 6, 7

111. −1, 2

112. 4, −3

113. Draw a function with intercepts $(-3, 0)$, $(5, 0)$, and $(0, 4)$.

114. Draw a function with intercepts $(-7, 0)$, $\left(-\frac{1}{2}, 0\right)$, $(4, 0)$, and $(0, -1)$.

Chapter 5 Vocabulary Check

Fill in each blank with one of the words or phrases listed below.

| quadratic equation | scientific notation | polynomial | exponents | 1 | monomial |
| binomial | trinomial | degree of a polynomial | degree of a term | 0 | factoring |

1. A(n) _____ is a finite sum of terms in which all variables are raised to nonnegative integer powers and no variables appear in any denominator.

2. _____ is the process of writing a polynomial as a product.

3. _____ are used to write repeated factors in a more compact form.

4. The _____ is the sum of the exponents on the variables contained in the term.

5. A(n) _____ is a polynomial with one term.

6. If a is not 0, $a^0 = $ _____.

7. A(n) _____ is a polynomial with three terms.

8. A polynomial equation of degree 2 is also called a(n) _____.

9. A positive number is written in _____ if it is written as the product of a number a, where $1 \le a < 10$, and a power of 10.

10. The _____ is the largest degree of all its terms.

11. A(n) _____ is a polynomial with two terms.

12. If a and b are real numbers and $a \cdot b = $ _____, then $a = 0$ or $b = 0$.

Chapter 5 Highlights

DEFINITIONS AND CONCEPTS	EXAMPLES

Section 5.1 Exponents and Scientific Notation

Product rule: $a^m \cdot a^n = a^{m+n}$

Zero exponent: $a^0 = 1, a \neq 0$

Quotient rule: $\dfrac{a^m}{a^n} = a^{m-n}, a \neq 0$

Negative exponent: $a^{-n} = \dfrac{1}{a^n}, a \neq 0$

A positive number is written in **scientific notation** if it is written as the product of a number a, where $1 \leq a < 10$, and an integer power of 10: $a \times 10^r$.

$$x^2 \cdot x^3 = x^5$$
$$7^0 = 1, (-10)^0 = 1$$
$$\frac{y^{10}}{y^4} = y^{10-4} = y^6$$
$$3^{-2} = \frac{1}{3^2} = \frac{1}{9}, \frac{x^{-5}}{x^{-7}} = x^{-5-(-7)} = x^2$$

Numbers Written in Scientific Notation
$$568{,}000 = 5.68 \times 10^5$$
$$0.0002117 = 2.117 \times 10^{-4}$$

Section 5.2 More Work with Exponents and Scientific Notation

Power rules:

$$(a^m)^n = a^{m \cdot n}$$
$$(ab)^m = a^m b^m$$
$$\left(\frac{a}{b}\right)^n = \frac{a^n}{b^n}, b \neq 0$$

$$(7^8)^2 = 7^{16}$$
$$(2y)^3 = 2^3 y^3 = 8y^3$$
$$\left(\frac{5x^{-3}}{x^2}\right)^{-2} = \frac{5^{-2} x^6}{x^{-4}}$$
$$= 5^{-2} \cdot x^{6-(-4)}$$
$$= \frac{x^{10}}{5^2}, \quad \text{or} \quad \frac{x^{10}}{25}$$

Section 5.3 Polynomials and Polynomial Functions

A **polynomial** is a finite sum of terms in which all variables have exponents raised to nonnegative integer powers and no variables appear in a denominator.

Polynomials
$$1.3x^2 \quad \text{(monomial)}$$
$$-\frac{1}{3}y + 5 \quad \text{(binomial)}$$
$$6z^2 - 5z + 7 \quad \text{(trinomial)}$$

A function P is a **polynomial function** if $P(x)$ is a polynomial.

For the polynomial function
$$P(x) = -x^2 + 6x - 12, \text{ find } P(-2)$$
$$P(-2) = -(-2)^2 + 6(-2) - 12 = -28.$$

To add polynomials, combine all like terms.

Add.
$$(3y^2 x - 2yx + 11) + (-5y^2 x - 7)$$
$$= -2y^2 x - 2yx + 4$$

To subtract polynomials, change the signs of the terms of the polynomial being subtracted, then add.

Subtract.
$$(-2z^3 - z + 1) - (3z^3 + z - 6)$$
$$= -2z^3 - z + 1 - 3z^3 - z + 6$$
$$= -5z^3 - 2z + 7$$

DEFINITIONS AND CONCEPTS	EXAMPLES

Section 5.4   Multiplying Polynomials

To multiply two polynomials, use the distributive property and multiply each term of one polynomial by each term of the other polynomial; then combine like terms.

Special Products

$$(a + b)^2 = a^2 + 2ab + b^2$$
$$(a - b)^2 = a^2 - 2ab + b^2$$
$$(a + b)(a - b) = a^2 - b^2$$

The FOIL method may be used when multiplying two binomials.

Multiply.

$$(x^2 - 2x)(3x^2 - 5x + 1)$$
$$= 3x^4 - 5x^3 + x^2 - 6x^3 + 10x^2 - 2x$$
$$= 3x^4 - 11x^3 + 11x^2 - 2x$$
$$(3m + 2n)^2 = 9m^2 + 12mn + 4n^2$$
$$(z^2 - 5)^2 = z^4 - 10z^2 + 25$$
$$(7y + 1)(7y - 1) = 49y^2 - 1$$

Multiply.

$$(x^2 + 5)(2x^2 - 9)$$

$$\quad\text{F}\qquad\text{O}\qquad\text{I}\qquad\text{L}$$
$$= x^2(2x^2) + x^2(-9) + 5(2x^2) + 5(-9)$$
$$= 2x^4 - 9x^2 + 10x^2 - 45$$
$$= 2x^4 + x^2 - 45$$

Section 5.5   The Greatest Common Factor and Factoring by Grouping

The greatest common factor (GCF) of the terms of a polynomial is the product of the GCF of the numerical coefficients and the GCF of the variable factors.

To factor a polynomial by grouping, group the terms so that each group has a common factor. Factor out these common factors. Then see if the new groups have a common factor.

Factor: $14xy^3 - 2xy^2 = 2 \cdot 7 \cdot x \cdot y^3 - 2 \cdot x \cdot y^2$

The GCF is $2 \cdot x \cdot y^2$, or $2xy^2$.

$$14xy^3 - 2xy^2 = 2xy^2(7y - 1)$$

Factor: $x^4y - 5x^3 + 2xy - 10$
$$x^4y - 5x^3 + 2xy - 10 = x^3(xy - 5) + 2(xy - 5)$$
$$= (xy - 5)(x^3 + 2)$$

Section 5.6   Factoring Trinomials

To Factor $ax^2 + bx + c$ by Trial and Check

Step 1. Write all pairs of factors of ax^2.

Step 2. Write all pairs of factors of c.

Step 3. Try combinations of these factors until the middle term bx is found.

To Factor $ax^2 + bx + c$ by Grouping

Find two numbers whose product is $a \cdot c$ and whose sum is b, write the term bx using the two numbers found, and then factor by grouping.

Factor: $28x^2 - 27x - 10$

Factors of $28x^2$: $28x$ and x, $2x$ and $14x$, $4x$ and $7x$

Factors of -10: -2 and 5, 2 and -5, -10 and 1, 10 and -1
$$28x^2 - 27x - 10 = (7x + 2)(4x - 5)$$

$$2x^2 - 3x - 5 = 2x^2 - 5x + 2x - 5$$
$$= x(2x - 5) + 1(2x - 5)$$
$$= (2x - 5)(x + 1)$$

Section 5.7   Factoring by Special Products

Perfect Square Trinomial
$$a^2 + 2ab + b^2 = (a + b)^2$$
$$a^2 - 2ab + b^2 = (a - b)^2$$

Difference of Two Squares
$$a^2 - b^2 = (a + b)(a - b)$$

Sum and Difference of Two Cubes
$$a^3 + b^3 = (a + b)(a^2 - ab + b^2)$$
$$a^3 - b^3 = (a - b)(a^2 + ab + b^2)$$

Factor.

$$25x^2 + 30x + 9 = (5x + 3)^2$$
$$49z^2 - 28z + 4 = (7z - 2)^2$$

$$36x^2 - y^2 = (6x + y)(6x - y)$$

$$8y^3 + 1 = (2y + 1)(4y^2 - 2y + 1)$$
$$27p^3 - 64q^3 = (3p - 4q)(9p^2 + 12pq + 16q^2)$$

(continued)

DEFINITIONS AND CONCEPTS	EXAMPLES

Section 5.7   Factoring by Special Products (continued)

To Factor a Polynomial

Step 1. Factor out the GCF.

Step 2. If the polynomial is a binomial, see if it is a difference of two squares or a sum or difference of two cubes. If it is a trinomial, see if it is a perfect square trinomial. If not, try factoring by methods of Section 5.6. If it is a polynomial with 4 or more terms, try factoring by grouping.

Step 3. See if any factors can be factored further.

Factor: $10x^4y + 5x^2y - 15y$

$$
\begin{aligned}
10x^4y + 5x^2y - 15y &= 5y(2x^4 + x^2 - 3) \\
&= 5y(2x^2 + 3)(x^2 - 1) \\
&= 5y(2x^2 + 3)(x + 1)(x - 1)
\end{aligned}
$$

Section 5.8   Solving Equations by Factoring and Problem Solving

To Solve Polynomial Equations by Factoring

Step 1. Write the equation so that one side is 0.

Step 2. Factor the polynomial completely.

Step 3. Set each factor equal to 0.

Step 4. Solve the resulting equations.

Step 5. Check each solution.

Solve.

$$
\begin{aligned}
2x^3 - 5x^2 &= 3x \\
2x^3 - 5x^2 - 3x &= 0 \\
x(2x + 1)(x - 3) &= 0
\end{aligned}
$$

$x = 0$ or $2x + 1 = 0$ or $x - 3 = 0$

$x = 0$ or $\quad x = -\dfrac{1}{2}$ or $\quad x = 3$

The solutions are 0, $-\dfrac{1}{2}$, and 3.

Chapter 5 Review

(5.1) *Evaluate.*

1. $(-2)^2$

2. $(-3)^4$

3. -2^2

4. -3^4

5. 8^0

6. -9^0

7. -4^{-2}

8. $(-4)^{-2}$

Simplify each expression. Write each answer with positive exponents only. Assume that variables in the exponents represent positive integers and that all other variables are not 0.

9. $-xy^2 \cdot y^3 \cdot xy^2z$

10. $(-4xy)(-3xy^2b)$

11. $a^{-14} \cdot a^5$

12. $\dfrac{a^{16}}{a^{17}}$

13. $\dfrac{x^{-7}}{x^4}$

14. $\dfrac{9a(a^{-3})}{18a^{15}}$

15. $\dfrac{y^{6p-3}}{y^{6p+2}}$

16. $(3x^{2a+b}y^{-3b})^2$

Write in scientific notation.

17. $36{,}890{,}000$

18. 0.000362

Write each number in standard notation, without exponents.

19. 1.678×10^{-6}

20. 4.1×10^5

(5.2) *Simplify. Use only positive exponents.*

21. $(8^5)^3$

22. $\left(\dfrac{a}{4}\right)^2$

23. $(3x)^3$

24. $(-4x)^{-2}$

25. $\left(\dfrac{6x}{5}\right)^2$

26. $(8^6)^{-3}$

27. $\left(\dfrac{4}{3}\right)^{-2}$

28. $(-2x^3)^{-3}$

29. $\left(\dfrac{8p^6}{4p^4}\right)^{-2}$

30. $(-3x^{-2}y^2)^3$

31. $\left(\dfrac{x^{-5}y^{-3}}{z^3}\right)^{-5}$

32. $\dfrac{4^{-1}x^3yz}{x^{-2}yx^4}$

33. $(5xyz)^{-4}(x^{-2})^{-3}$

34. $\dfrac{2(3yz)^{-3}}{y^{-3}}$

Simplify each expression.

35. $x^{4a}(3x^{5a})^3$

36. $\dfrac{4y^{3x-3}}{2y^{2x+4}}$

Use scientific notation to find the quotient. Express each quotient in scientific notation.

37. $\dfrac{(0.00012)(144{,}000)}{0.0003}$

38. $\dfrac{(-0.00017)(0.00039)}{3000}$

Simplify. Use only positive exponents.

39. $\dfrac{27x^{-5}y^5}{18x^{-6}y^2}\cdot\dfrac{x^4y^{-2}}{x^{-2}y^3}$

40. $\dfrac{3x^5}{y^{-4}}\cdot\dfrac{(3xy^{-3})^{-2}}{(z^{-3})^{-4}}$

(5.3) Find the degree of each polynomial.

41. $x^2y - 3xy^3z + 5x + 7y$ **42.** $3x + 2$

Simplify by combining like terms.

43. $4x + 8x - 6x^2 - 6x^2y$

44. $-8xy^3 + 4xy^3 - 3x^3y$

Add or subtract as indicated.

45. $(3x + 7y) + (4x^2 - 3x + 7) + (y - 1)$

46. $(4x^2 - 6xy + 9y^2) - (8x^2 - 6xy - y^2)$

47. $(3x^2 - 4b + 28) + (9x^2 - 30) - (4x^2 - 6b + 20)$

48. Add $(9xy + 4x^2 + 18)$ and $(7xy - 4x^3 - 9x)$.

49. Subtract $(3x - 5)$ from $2x$.

50. Subtract $(x - 7)$ from the sum of $(3x^2y - 7xy - 4)$ and $(9x^2y + x)$.

51. $\begin{array}{r} x^2 - 5x + 7 \\ -(x + 4) \\ \hline \end{array}$

52. $\begin{array}{r} x^3 \ \ \ + 2xy^2 - y \\ + (x - 4xy^2 - 7) \\ \hline \end{array}$

If $P(x) = 9x^2 - 7x + 8$, find the following.

53. $P(6)$ **54.** $P(0)$

55. $P(-2)$ **56.** $P(-3)$

If $P(x) = 2x - 1$ and $Q(x) = x^2 + 2x - 5$, find the following.

57. $P(x) + Q(x)$

58. $2 \cdot P(x) - Q(x)$

△ **59.** Find the perimeter of the rectangle.

$x^2y + 5$
cm

$2x^2y - 6x + 1$
cm

△ **60.** Find the perimeter of the triangle.

$(3x + 11)$ in. $(3x + 11)$ in.

$3x$ in.

(5.4) Multiply.

61. $-6x(4x^2 - 6x + 1)$

62. $-4ab^2(3ab^3 + 7ab + 1)$

63. $(x - 4)(2x + 9)$

64. $(-3xa + 4b)^2$

65. $(9x^2 + 4x + 1)(4x - 3)$

66. $(2x - 1)(x^2 + 2x - 5)$

67. $(5x - 9y)(3x + 9y)$

68. $\left(x - \dfrac{1}{3}\right)\left(x + \dfrac{2}{3}\right)$

69. $(x^2 + 9x + 1)^2$

70. $(m^2 + m - 2)^2$

Multiply, using special products.

71. $(3x - y)^2$

72. $(4x + 9)^2$

73. $(x + 3y)(x - 3y)$

74. $[4 + (3a - b)][4 - (3a - b)]$

△ **75.** Find the area of the rectangle.

$3y - 7z$
units

$3y + 7z$
units

△ **76.** Find the area of the square.

$(11y + 9)$
units

Multiply. Assume that all variable exponents represent positive integers.

77. $4a^b(3a^{b+2} - 7)$

78. $(3x^a - 4)(3x^a + 4)$

(5.5) Factor out the greatest common factor.

79. $16x^3 - 24x^2$

80. $36y - 24y^2$

81. $6ab^2 + 8ab - 4a^2b^2$

82. $14a^2b^2 - 21ab^2 + 7ab$

83. $6a(a + 3b) - 5(a + 3b)$

84. $4x(x - 2y) - 5(x - 2y)$

Factor by grouping.

85. $xy - 6y + 3x - 18$

86. $ab - 8b + 4a - 32$

87. $pq - 3p - 5q + 15$

88. $x^3 - x^2 - 2x + 2$

For Exercises 89 and 90, smaller squares are cut from larger rectangles. Write the area of each shaded region as a factored polynomial.

△ **89.**

△ **90.**

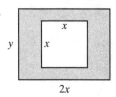

(5.6) *Completely factor each polynomial.*

91. $x^2 - 14x - 72$

92. $x^2 + 16x - 80$

93. $2x^2 - 18x + 28$

94. $3x^2 + 33x + 54$

95. $2x^3 - 7x^2 - 9x$

96. $3x^3 + 2x^2 - 16x$

97. $6x^2 + 17x + 10$

98. $15x^2 - 91x + 6$

99. $4x^2 + 2x - 12$

100. $9x^2 - 12x - 12$

101. $y^2(x + 6)^2 - 2y(x + 6)^2 - 3(x + 6)^2$

102. $(x + 5)^2 + 6(x + 5) + 8$

103. $x^4 - 6x^2 - 16$

104. $x^4 + 8x^2 - 20$

(5.7) *Factor each polynomial completely.*

105. $x^2 - 100$

106. $x^2 - 81$

107. $2x^2 - 32$

108. $6x^2 - 54$

109. $81 - x^4$

110. $16 - y^4$

111. $(y + 2)^2 - 25$

112. $(x - 3)^2 - 16$

113. $x^3 + 216$

114. $y^3 + 512$

115. $8 - 27y^3$

116. $1 - 64y^3$

117. $6x^4y + 48xy$

118. $2x^5 + 16x^2y^3$

119. $x^2 - 2x + 1 - y^2$

120. $x^2 - 6x + 9 - 4y^2$

121. $4x^2 + 12x + 9$

122. $16a^2 - 40ab + 25b^2$

△ **123.** The volume of the cylindrical shell is $(\pi R^2 h - \pi r^2 h)$ cubic units. Write this volume as a factored expression.

△ **124.** The surface area of the cylindrical shell (except for its top and bottom as drawn) is $(2\pi Rh + 2\pi rh)$ square units. Write this as a factored expression.

(5.8) *Solve each polynomial equation for the variable.*

125. $(3x - 1)(x + 7) = 0$

126. $3(x + 5)(8x - 3) = 0$

127. $5x(x - 4)(2x - 9) = 0$

128. $6(x + 3)(x - 4)(5x + 1) = 0$

129. $2x^2 = 12x$

130. $4x^3 - 36x = 0$

131. $(1 - x)(3x + 2) = -4x$

132. $2x(x - 12) = -40$

133. $3x^2 + 2x = 12 - 7x$

134. $2x^2 + 3x = 35$

135. $x^3 - 18x = 3x^2$

136. $19x^2 - 42x = -x^3$

137. $12x = 6x^3 + 6x^2$

138. $8x^3 + 10x^2 = 3x$

139. The sum of a number and twice its square is 105. Find the number.

△ **140.** The length of a rectangular piece of carpet is 5 meters less than twice its width. Find the dimensions of the carpet if its area is 33 square meters.

141. A scene from an adventure film calls for a stunt dummy to be dropped from above the second-story platform of the Eiffel Tower, a distance of 400 feet. Its height $h(t)$ at time t seconds is given by

$$h(t) = -16t^2 + 400$$

Determine when the stunt dummy will reach the ground.

400 ft

142. The Royal Gorge suspension bridge in Colorado is 1053 feet above the Arkansas River. Neglecting air resistance, the height of an object dropped off the bridge is given by the polynomial function $P(t) = -16t^2 + 1053$ after time t seconds. Find the height of the object when $t = 1$ second and when $t = 8$ seconds.

MIXED REVIEW

Perform the indicated operation.

143. $(x + 5)(3x^2 - 2x + 1)$

144. $(3x^2 + 4x - 1.2) - (5x^2 - x + 5.7)$

145. $(3x^2 + 4x - 1.2) + (5x^2 - x + 5.7)$

146. $\left(7ab - \dfrac{1}{2}\right)^2$

If $P(x) = -x^2 + x - 4$, find

147. $P(5)$

148. $P(-2)$

Factor each polynomial completely.

149. $12y^5 - 6y^4$

150. $x^2y + 4x^2 - 3y - 12$

151. $6x^2 - 34x - 12$

152. $y^2(4x + 3)^2 - 19y(4x + 3)^2 - 20(4x + 3)^2$

153. $4z^7 - 49z^5$

154. $5x^4 + 4x^2 - 9$

Solve each equation.

155. $8x^2 = 24x$ **156.** $x(x - 11) = 26$

1c

Chapter 5 Getting Ready for the Test

MATCHING *Match the expression with its simplified form. Letters may be used more than once or not at all.*

1. $x^a \cdot x^a$ **2.** $x^a + x^a$

3. $x^a \cdot x^b$ **4.** $x^a + x^b$

5. $(x^a)^b$ **6.** $\dfrac{x^a}{x^b}$

A. x^{ab}

B. x^{a^2}

C. x^{2a}

D. $2x^a$

E. x^{a-b}

F. x^{a+b}

G. this expression will not simplify

MULTIPLE CHOICE *Select the correct choice.*

7. Choose the polynomial that has degree 3.

A. $3x - 5$ **B.** $x^3y - 5x + 2$ **C.** $x^2y + 4y$ **D.** 3

8. If $P(x) = 5x^3 - 2x + 1$, find $P(-1)$

A. 4   **B.** -2 **C.** -6 **D.** 8

9. If $P(x) = 2x - 3$ and $Q(x) = 4x + 3$, find $P(x) - Q(x)$.

A. $6x$ **B.** $2x$ **C.** $-2x - 6$ **D.** $2x + 6$

10. Choose the expression that simplifies to 1.

A. $5x^0$ **B.** $-(5x)^0$ **C.** $(-5x)^0$ **D.** none of these

11. $7^{-2} =$

A. -14 **B.** -49 **C.** $\dfrac{1}{14}$ **D.** $\dfrac{1}{49}$

12. $(5x + 1)^2 =$

A. $25x^2 + 1$ **B.** $25x^2 + 10x + 1$ **C.** $25x^2 + 5x + 1$

13. Choose the greatest common factor of $25x^2y^3 - 10x^2y + 5x^2y^2$

    A. 5   **B.** $5x^2y^2$ **C.** $5x^2y$ **D.** $25x^2y^3$

MULTIPLE CHOICE *Identify each expression as*

    A. a factored expression or   **B.** not a factored expression

14. $(x - 2)(x^2 + 2x + 4)$

15. $x(y^2 + 16) + 5(y^2 + 16)$

16. $x^a \cdot x^a - 10 \cdot 10$

17. To solve $x(12x + 25) = 50$, which is an incorrect step?

    A. $x = 50$ or $12x + 25 = 50$ **B.** $12x^2 + 25x = 50$ **C.** $x(12x + 25) - 50 = 0$

Chapter 5 Test   MyMathLab° YouTube·

Simplify. Use positive exponents to write the answers.

1. $(-9x)^{-2}$

2. $-3xy^{-2}(4xy^2)z$

3. $\dfrac{6^{-1}a^2b^{-3}}{3^{-2}a^{-5}b^2}$

4. $\left(\dfrac{-xy^{-5}z}{xy^3}\right)^{-5}$

Write Exercises 5 and 6 in scientific notation.

5. 630,000,000

6. 0.01200

7. Write 5×10^{-6} without exponents.

8. Use scientific notation to find the quotient.

$$\frac{(0.0024)(0.00012)}{0.00032}$$

Perform the indicated operations.

9. $(4x^3y - 3x - 4) - (9x^3y + 8x + 5)$

10. $-3xy(4x + y)$

11. $(3x + 4)(4x - 7)$

12. $(5a - 2b)(5a + 2b)$

13. $(6m + n)^2$

14. $(2x - 1)(x^2 - 6x + 4)$

Factor each polynomial completely.

15. $16x^3y - 12x^2y^4$

16. $x^2 - 13x - 30$

17. $4y^2 + 20y + 25$

18. $6x^2 - 15x - 9$

19. $4x^2 - 25$

20. $x^3 + 64$

21. $3x^2y - 27y^3$

22. $6x^2 + 24$

23. $16y^3 - 2$

24. $x^2y - 9y - 3x^2 + 27$

Solve the equation for the variable.

25. $3n(7n - 20) = 96$

26. $(x + 2)(x - 2) = 5(x + 4)$

27. $2x^3 + 5x^2 = 8x + 20$

28. Write the area of the shaded region as a factored polynomial.

29. A pebble is hurled upward from the top of the Canada Trust Tower, which is 880 feet tall, with an initial velocity of 96 feet per second. Neglecting air resistance, the height $h(t)$ of the pebble after t seconds is given by the polynomial function

$$h(t) = -16t^2 + 96t + 880$$

    a. Find the height of the pebble when $t = 1$.

    b. Find the height of the pebble when $t = 5.1$.

    c. Factor the polynomial $-16t^2 + 96t + 880$.

    d. When will the pebble hit the ground?

Chapter 5 Cumulative Review

1. Find the roots.
   a. $\sqrt[3]{-27}$
   b. $\sqrt[5]{1}$
   c. $\sqrt[4]{16}$

2. Find the roots.
   a. $\sqrt[3]{64}$
   b. $\sqrt[4]{81}$
   c. $\sqrt[5]{32}$

3. Solve: $2(x - 3) = 5x - 9$

4. Solve: $0.3y + 2.4 = 0.1y + 4$

5. Karen Estes just received an inheritance of $10,000 and plans to place all the money in a savings account that pays 5% compounded quarterly to help her son go to college in 3 years. How much money will be in the account in 3 years?

6. A gallon of latex paint can cover 400 square feet. How many gallon containers of paint should be bought to paint two coats on each wall of a rectangular room whose dimensions are 14 feet by 18 feet? (Assume 8-foot ceilings.)

7. Solve and graph the solution set. Write the solution set in interval notation.
   a. $\frac{1}{4}x \le \frac{3}{8}$
   b. $-2.3x < 6.9$

8. Solve. Graph the solution set. Write the solution set in interval notation. $x + 2 \le \frac{1}{4}(x - 7)$

Solve.

9. $-1 \le \frac{2x}{3} + 5 \le 2$

10. $-\frac{1}{3} < \frac{3x + 1}{6} \le \frac{1}{3}$

11. $|y| = 0$

12. $8 + |4c| = 24$

13. $\left|2x - \frac{1}{10}\right| < -13$

14. Solve: $|5x - 1| + 9 > 5$

15. Graph the linear equation: $y = \frac{1}{3}x$

16. Graph the linear equation: $y = 3x$

17. Evaluate $f(2)$, $f(-6)$, and $f(0)$ for the function
$$f(x) = \begin{cases} 2x + 3 & \text{if } x \le 0 \\ -x - 1 & \text{if } x > 0 \end{cases}$$
Write your results in ordered pair form.

18. If $f(x) = 3x^2 + 2x + 3$, find $f(-3)$.

19. Graph: $x = 2$

20. Graph: $y - 5 = 0$

21. Find the slope of the line $y = 2$.

22. Find the slope of the line whose equation is $f(x) = -2x - 3$.

23. Find an equation of the horizontal line containing the point $(2, 3)$.

24. Find an equation of the vertical line containing the point $(-3, 2)$.

25. Graph $x + \frac{1}{2}y \ge -4$ or $y \le -2$.

26. Find the equation of the line containing the point $(-2, 3)$ and having a slope of 0.

27. Use the substitution method to solve the system.
$$\begin{cases} 2x + 4y = -6 \\ x = 2y - 5 \end{cases}$$

28. Use the substitution method to solve the system.
$$\begin{cases} 4x - 2y = 8 \\ y = 3x - 6 \end{cases}$$

29. Solve the system. $\begin{cases} 2x + 4y = 1 \\ 4x - 4z = -1 \\ y - 4z = -3 \end{cases}$

30. Solve the system. $\begin{cases} x + y - \frac{3}{2}z = \frac{1}{2} \\ -y - 2z = 14 \\ x - \frac{2}{3}y = -\frac{1}{3} \end{cases}$

31. A first number is 4 less than a second number. Four times the first number is 6 more than twice the second. Find the numbers.

32. One solution contains 20% acid and a second solution contains 60% acid. How many ounces of each solution should be mixed to have 50 ounces of a 30% acid solution?

33. Use matrices to solve the system. $\begin{cases} 2x - y = 3 \\ 4x - 2y = 5 \end{cases}$

34. Use matrices to solve the system. $\begin{cases} 4y = 8 \\ x + y = 7 \end{cases}$

35. The measure of the largest angle of a triangle is 80° more than the measure of the smallest angle, and the measure of the remaining angle is 10° more than the measure of the smallest angle. Find the measure of each angle.

36. Find an equation of the line with slope $\frac{1}{2}$ through the point $(0, 5)$. Write the equation using function notation.

37. Write each number in scientific notation.

   a. 730,000

   b. 0.00000104

38. Write each number in scientific notation.

   a. 8,250,000

   b. 0.0000346

39. Simplify each expression. Use positive exponents to write the answers.

   a. $(2x^0y^{-3})^{-2}$ **b.** $\left(\dfrac{x^{-5}}{x^{-2}}\right)^{-3}$

   c. $\left(\dfrac{2}{7}\right)^{-2}$ **d.** $\dfrac{5^{-2}x^{-3}y^{11}}{x^2y^{-5}}$

40. Simplify each expression. Use positive exponents to write the answers.

   a. $(4a^{-1}b^0)^{-3}$ **b.** $\left(\dfrac{a^{-6}}{a^{-8}}\right)^{-2}$

   c. $\left(\dfrac{2}{3}\right)^{-3}$ **d.** $\dfrac{3^{-2}a^{-2}b^{12}}{a^4b^{-5}}$

41. Find the degree of the polynomial $3xy + x^2y^2 - 5x^2 - 6.7$.

42. Subtract $(5x^2 + 3x)$ from $(3x^2 - 2x)$.

43. Multiply.

   a. $(2x^3)(5x^6)$

   b. $(7y^4z^4)(-xy^{11}z^5)$

44. Multiply.

   a. $(3y^6)(4y^2)$

   b. $(6a^3b^2)(-a^2bc^4)$

Factor.

45. $17x^3y^2 - 34x^4y^2$

46. $12x^3y - 3xy^3$

47. $x^2 + 10x + 16$

48. $5a^2 + 14a - 3$

Solve.

49. $2x^2 + 9x - 5 = 0$

50. $3x^2 - 10x - 8 = 0$

CHAPTER 6

Rational Expressions

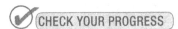

CHECK YOUR PROGRESS

Vocabulary Check

Chapter Highlights

Chapter Review

Getting Ready for the Test

Chapter Test

Cumulative Review

Polynomials are to algebra what integers are to arithmetic. We have added, subtracted, multiplied, and raised polynomials to powers, each operation yielding another polynomial, just as these operations on integers yield another integer. But when we divide one integer by another, the result may or may not be another integer. Likewise, when we divide one polynomial by another, we may or may not get a polynomial in return. The quotient $x \div (x + 1)$ is not a polynomial; it is a *rational expression* that can be written as $\dfrac{x}{x + 1}$.

In this chapter, we study these new algebraic forms known as rational expressions and the *rational functions* they generate.

Applications of the Doppler Effect

A Doppler echocardiogram measures the speed of blood flowing through the heart.

Bats use the Doppler effect to hunt for prey.

The Doppler effect on light waves helps determine the distance to another galaxy.

What is the Doppler effect?

To understand, we start with pitch. The pitch of a sound can be thought of as the location of a musical sound on a frequency-related scale, which we measure in hertz (named after a German physicist). Basically, the greater the frequency (in hertz), the higher the note sounds. See the bar graph below showing the frequencies of some notes.

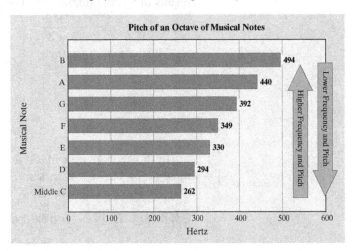

Now, what is the Doppler effect? A common example of the Doppler effect is the pitch of a siren on an ambulance or a fire engine. When the siren is coming towards us, we hear a higher pitch. After passing us, the siren is going away from us and we hear a lower pitch. We study this more in Section 6.6, Exercises 67 and 68.

6.1 Rational Functions and Multiplying and Dividing Rational Expressions

Recall that a *rational number*, or *fraction*, is a number that can be written as the quotient $\frac{p}{q}$ of two integers p and q as long as q is not 0. A **rational expression** is an expression that can be written as the quotient $\frac{P}{Q}$ of two polynomials P and Q as long as Q is not 0.

Examples of Rational Expressions

$$\frac{3x + 7}{2} \qquad \frac{5x^2 - 3}{x - 1} \qquad \frac{7x - 2}{2x^2 + 7x + 6}$$

Rational expressions are sometimes used to describe functions. For example, we call the function $f(x) = \frac{x^2 + 2}{x - 3}$ a **rational function** since $\frac{x^2 + 2}{x - 3}$ is a rational expression.

OBJECTIVE

1 Finding the Domain of a Rational Expression

As with fractions, a rational expression is **undefined** if the denominator is 0. If a variable in a rational expression is replaced with a number that makes the denominator 0, we say that the rational expression is **undefined** for this value of the variable. For example, the rational expression $\frac{x^2 + 2}{x - 3}$ is undefined when x is 3 because replacing x with 3 results in a denominator of 0. For this reason, we must exclude 3 from the domain of the function $f(x) = \frac{x^2 + 2}{x - 3}$.

The domain of f is then

$$\{x \mid x \text{ is a real number and } x \neq 3\}$$

"The set of all x such that x is a real number and x is not equal to 3."

In this section, we will use this set builder notation to write domains. Unless told otherwise, we assume that the domain of a function described by an equation is the set of all real numbers for which the equation is defined.

EXAMPLE 1   Find the domain of each rational function.

a. $f(x) = \dfrac{8x^3 + 7x^2 + 20}{2}$ **b.** $g(x) = \dfrac{5x^2 - 3}{x - 1}$ **c.** $f(x) = \dfrac{7x - 2}{x^2 - 2x - 15}$

Solution   The domain of each function will contain all real numbers except those values that make the denominator 0.

a. No matter what the value of x, the denominator of $f(x) = \dfrac{8x^3 + 7x^2 + 20}{2}$ is never 0, so the domain of f is $\{x \mid x \text{ is a real number}\}$.

b. To find the values of x that make the denominator of $g(x)$ equal to 0, we solve the equation "denominator = 0":

$$x - 1 = 0 \quad \text{or} \quad x = 1$$

The domain must exclude 1 since the rational expression is undefined when x is 1.

The domain of g is $\{x \mid x \text{ is a real number and } x \neq 1\}$.

c. We find the domain by setting the denominator equal to 0.

$$x^2 - 2x - 15 = 0 \quad \text{Set the denominator equal to 0 and solve.}$$
$$(x - 5)(x + 3) = 0$$

$$x - 5 = 0 \quad \text{or} \quad x + 3 = 0$$
$$x = 5 \quad \text{or} \quad x = -3$$

If x is replaced with 5 or with -3, the rational expression is undefined.

The domain of f is $\{x \mid x \text{ is a real number and } x \neq 5, x \neq -3\}$. ☐

PRACTICE
1   Find the domain of each rational function.

a. $f(x) = \dfrac{4x^5 - 3x^2 + 2}{-6}$ **b.** $g(x) = \dfrac{6x^2 + 1}{x + 3}$ **c.** $h(x) = \dfrac{8x - 3}{x^2 - 5x + 6}$ ∎

✔ **CONCEPT CHECK**

For which of these values (if any) is the rational expression $\dfrac{x - 3}{x^2 + 2}$ undefined?

a. 2   **b.** 3   **c.** −2   **d.** 0   **e.** None of these

---

OBJECTIVE
2 **Simplifying Rational Expressions**

Recall that a fraction is in lowest terms or simplest form if the numerator and denominator have no common factors other than 1 (or −1). For example, $\dfrac{3}{13}$ is in lowest terms since 3 and 13 have no common factors other than 1 (or −1).

To **simplify** a rational expression, or to write it in lowest terms, we use a method similar to simplifying a fraction.

Recall that to simplify a fraction, we essentially "remove factors of 1." Our ability to do this comes from these facts:

- If $c \neq 0$, then $\dfrac{c}{c} = 1$. For example, $\dfrac{7}{7} = 1$ and $\dfrac{-8.65}{-8.65} = 1$.

- $n \cdot 1 = n$. For example, $-5 \cdot 1 = -5$, $126.8 \cdot 1 = 126.8$, and $\dfrac{a}{b} \cdot 1 = \dfrac{a}{b}, b \neq 0$.

In other words, we have the following:

$$\frac{a \cdot c}{b \cdot c} = \frac{a}{b} \cdot \frac{c}{c} = \frac{a}{b}$$

$$\text{since } \frac{a}{b} \cdot 1 = \frac{a}{b}$$

Let's practice simplifying a fraction by simplifying $\dfrac{15}{65}$.

$$\frac{15}{65} = \frac{3 \cdot 5}{13 \cdot 5} = \frac{3}{13} \cdot \frac{5}{5} = \frac{3}{13} \cdot 1 = \frac{3}{13}$$

Let's use the same technique and simplify the rational expression $\dfrac{(x + 2)^2}{x^2 - 4}$.

$$\frac{(x + 2)^2}{x^2 - 4} = \frac{(x + 2)(x + 2)}{(x - 2)(x + 2)}$$
$$= \frac{(x + 2)}{(x - 2)} \cdot \frac{x + 2}{x + 2}$$
$$= \frac{x + 2}{x - 2} \cdot 1$$
$$= \frac{x + 2}{x - 2}$$

This means that the rational expression $\dfrac{(x+2)^2}{x^2-4}$ has the same value as the rational expression $\dfrac{x+2}{x-2}$ for all values of x except 2 and -2. (Remember that when x is 2, the denominators of both rational expressions are 0 and that when x is -2, the original rational expression has a denominator of 0.)

As we simplify rational expressions, we will assume that the simplified rational expression is equivalent to the original rational expression for all real numbers except those for which either denominator is 0.

Just as for numerical fractions, we can use a shortcut notation. Remember that as long as exact factors in both the numerator and denominator are divided out, we are "removing a factor of 1." We can use the following notation:

$$\dfrac{(x+2)^2}{x^2-4} = \dfrac{(x+2)\,(x+2)}{(x-2)\,(x+2)} \qquad \text{A factor of 1 is identified by the shading.}$$

$$= \dfrac{x+2}{x-2} \qquad \text{"Remove" the factor of 1.}$$

This "removing a factor of 1" is stated in the principle below:

Fundamental Principle of Rational Expressions

For any rational expression $\dfrac{P}{Q}$ and any polynomial R, where $R \neq 0$,

$$\dfrac{PR}{QR} = \dfrac{P}{Q} \cdot \dfrac{R}{R} = \dfrac{P}{Q} \cdot 1 = \dfrac{P}{Q}$$

or, simply,

$$\dfrac{PR}{QR} = \dfrac{P}{Q}$$

In general, the following steps may be used to simplify rational expressions or to write a rational expression in lowest terms.

Simplifying or Writing a Rational Expression in Lowest Terms

Step 1. Completely factor the numerator and denominator of the rational expression.

Step 2. Divide out factors common to the numerator and denominator. (This is the same as "removing a factor of 1.")

For now, we assume that variables in a rational expression do not represent values that make the denominator 0.

EXAMPLE 2 Simplify each rational expression.

a. $\dfrac{2x^2}{10x^3 - 2x^2}$
b. $\dfrac{9x^2 + 13x + 4}{8x^2 + x - 7}$

Solution

a. $\dfrac{2x^2}{10x^3 - 2x^2} = \dfrac{2x^2 \cdot 1}{2x^2\,(5x - 1)} = 1 \cdot \dfrac{1}{5x - 1} = \dfrac{1}{5x - 1}$

b. $\dfrac{9x^2 + 13x + 4}{8x^2 + x - 7} = \dfrac{(9x + 4)\,(x + 1)}{(8x - 7)\,(x + 1)}$ Factor the numerator and denominator.

$\qquad\qquad = \dfrac{9x + 4}{8x - 7} \cdot 1$ Since $\dfrac{x + 1}{x + 1} = 1$

$\qquad\qquad = \dfrac{9x + 4}{8x - 7}$ Simplest form   □

PRACTICE

2   Simplify each rational expression.

a. $\dfrac{5z^4}{10z^5 - 5z^4}$ **b.** $\dfrac{5x^2 + 13x + 6}{6x^2 + 7x - 10}$ ■

EXAMPLE 3   Simplify each rational expression.

a. $\dfrac{2 + x}{x + 2}$ **b.** $\dfrac{2 - x}{x - 2}$

Solution

a. $\dfrac{2 + x}{x + 2} = \dfrac{x + 2}{x + 2} = 1$ By the commutative property of addition, $2 + x = x + 2$.

b. $\dfrac{2 - x}{x - 2}$

The terms in the numerator of $\dfrac{2 - x}{x - 2}$ differ by sign from the terms in the denominator, so the polynomials are opposites of each other and the expression simplifies to -1. To see this, we factor out -1 from the numerator or the denominator. If -1 is factored from the numerator, then

$$\dfrac{2 - x}{x - 2} = \dfrac{-1(-2 + x)}{x - 2} = \dfrac{-1\,(x - 2)}{x - 2} = \dfrac{-1}{1} = -1$$

If -1 is factored from the denominator, the result is the same.

$$\dfrac{2 - x}{x - 2} = \dfrac{2 - x}{-1(-x + 2)} = \dfrac{2 - x}{-1\,(2 - x)} = \dfrac{1}{-1} = -1$$ □

> **Helpful Hint**
>
> When the numerator and the denominator of a rational expression are opposites of each other, the expression simplifies to -1.

PRACTICE

3   Simplify each rational expression.

a. $\dfrac{x + 3}{3 + x}$ **b.** $\dfrac{3 - x}{x - 3}$ ■

EXAMPLE 4   Simplify: $\dfrac{18 - 2x^2}{x^2 - 2x - 3}$

Solution $\dfrac{18 - 2x^2}{x^2 - 2x - 3} = \dfrac{2(9 - x^2)}{(x + 1)(x - 3)}$ Factor.

$\qquad\qquad = \dfrac{2(3 + x)(3 - x)}{(x + 1)(x - 3)}$ Factor completely.

$\qquad\qquad = \dfrac{2(3 + x) \cdot -1\,(x - 3)}{(x + 1)\,(x - 3)}$ Notice the opposites $3 - x$ and $x - 3$. Write $3 - x$ as $-1(x - 3)$ and simplify.

$\qquad\qquad = -\dfrac{2(3 + x)}{x + 1}$ □

PRACTICE

4   Simplify: $\dfrac{20 - 5x^2}{x^2 + x - 6}$ ■

> **Helpful Hint**
>
> Recall that for a fraction,
>
> $$\frac{a}{-b} = \frac{-a}{b} = -\frac{a}{b}$$
>
> For example
>
> $$\frac{-(x + 1)}{(x + 2)} = \frac{(x + 1)}{-(x + 2)} = -\frac{x + 1}{x + 2}$$

✔ **CONCEPT CHECK**

Which of the following expressions are equivalent to $\dfrac{x}{8 - x}$?

a. $\dfrac{-x}{x - 8}$ b. $\dfrac{-x}{8 - x}$ c. $\dfrac{x}{x - 8}$ d. $\dfrac{-x}{-8 + x}$

EXAMPLE 5   Simplify each rational expression.

a. $\dfrac{x^3 + 8}{2 + x}$ b. $\dfrac{2y^2 + 2}{y^3 - 5y^2 + y - 5}$

Solution

a. $\dfrac{x^3 + 8}{2 + x} = \dfrac{(x + 2)(x^2 - 2x + 4)}{x + 2}$ Factor the sum of the two cubes.

     $= x^2 - 2x + 4$ Divide out common factors.

b. $\dfrac{2y^2 + 2}{y^3 - 5y^2 + y - 5} = \dfrac{2(y^2 + 1)}{(y^3 - 5y^2) + (y - 5)}$ Factor the numerator.

     $= \dfrac{2(y^2 + 1)}{y^2(y - 5) + 1(y - 5)}$ Factor the denominator by grouping.

     $= \dfrac{2(y^2 + 1)}{(y - 5)(y^2 + 1)}$

     $= \dfrac{2}{y - 5}$ Divide out common factors. □

PRACTICE

5   Simplify each rational expression.

a. $\dfrac{x^3 + 64}{4 + x}$ b. $\dfrac{5z^2 + 10}{z^3 - 3z^2 + 2z - 6}$

✔ **CONCEPT CHECK**

Does $\dfrac{n}{n + 2}$ simplify to $\dfrac{1}{2}$? Why or why not?

OBJECTIVE

3   **Multiplying Rational Expressions**

Arithmetic operations on rational expressions are performed in the same way as they are on rational numbers.

> **Multiplying Rational Expressions**
>
> The rule for multiplying rational expressions is
>
> $$\frac{P}{Q} \cdot \frac{R}{S} = \frac{PR}{QS} \quad \text{as long as } Q \neq 0 \text{ and } S \neq 0.$$
>
> To multiply rational expressions, you may use these steps:
>
> **Step 1.** Completely factor each numerator and denominator.
>
> **Step 2.** Use the rule above and multiply the numerators and the denominators.
>
> **Step 3.** Simplify the product by dividing the numerator and denominator by their common factors.

When we multiply rational expressions, notice that we factor each numerator and denominator first. This helps when we apply the fundamental principle to write the product in simplest form.

EXAMPLE 6   Multiply.

a. $\dfrac{1 + 3n}{2n} \cdot \dfrac{2n - 4}{3n^2 - 2n - 1}$ **b.** $\dfrac{x^3 - 1}{-3x + 3} \cdot \dfrac{15x^2}{x^2 + x + 1}$

Solution

a. $\dfrac{1 + 3n}{2n} \cdot \dfrac{2n - 4}{3n^2 - 2n - 1} = \dfrac{1 + 3n}{2n} \cdot \dfrac{2(n - 2)}{(3n + 1)(n - 1)}$ Factor.

$= \dfrac{(1 + 3n) \cdot 2(n - 2)}{2n(3n + 1)(n - 1)}$ Multiply.

$= \dfrac{n - 2}{n(n - 1)}$ Divide out common factors.

b. $\dfrac{x^3 - 1}{-3x + 3} \cdot \dfrac{15x^2}{x^2 + x + 1} = \dfrac{(x - 1)(x^2 + x + 1)}{-3(x - 1)} \cdot \dfrac{3 \cdot 5x^2}{x^2 + x + 1}$ Factor.

$= \dfrac{(x - 1)(x^2 + x + 1) \cdot 3 \cdot 5x^2}{-1 \cdot 3(x - 1)(x^2 + x + 1)}$ Multiply.

$= \dfrac{5x^2}{-1} = -5x^2$ Simplest form   □

PRACTICE

6   Multiply.

a. $\dfrac{2 + 5n}{3n} \cdot \dfrac{6n + 3}{5n^2 - 3n - 2}$ **b.** $\dfrac{x^3 - 8}{-6x + 12} \cdot \dfrac{6x^2}{x^2 + 2x + 4}$

OBJECTIVE

4   Dividing Rational Expressions

Recall that two numbers are reciprocals of each other if their product is 1. Similarly, if $\dfrac{P}{Q}$ is a rational expression, then $\dfrac{Q}{P}$ is its **reciprocal**, since

$$\frac{P}{Q} \cdot \frac{Q}{P} = \frac{P \cdot Q}{Q \cdot P} = 1$$

The following are examples of expressions and their reciprocals.

Expression		Reciprocal
$\dfrac{3}{x}$	$\longrightarrow$	$\dfrac{x}{3}$
$\dfrac{2 + x^2}{4x - 3}$	$\longrightarrow$	$\dfrac{4x - 3}{2 + x^2}$
x^3	$\longrightarrow$	$\dfrac{1}{x^3}$
0	$\longrightarrow$	no reciprocal

Dividing Rational Expressions

The rule for dividing rational expressions is

$$\frac{P}{Q} \div \frac{R}{S} = \frac{P}{Q} \cdot \frac{S}{R} = \frac{PS}{QR} \quad \text{as long as } Q \neq 0, S \neq 0, \text{ and } R \neq 0.$$

To divide by a rational expression, use the rule above and multiply by its reciprocal. Then simplify if possible.

Notice that division of rational expressions is the same as for rational numbers.

EXAMPLE 7 Divide.

a. $\dfrac{8m^2}{3m^2 - 12} \div \dfrac{40}{2 - m}$

b. $\dfrac{18y^2 + 9y - 2}{24y^2 - 10y + 1} \div \dfrac{3y^2 + 17y + 10}{8y^2 + 18y - 5}$

Solution

a. $\dfrac{8m^2}{3m^2 - 12} \div \dfrac{40}{2 - m} = \dfrac{8m^2}{3m^2 - 12} \cdot \dfrac{2 - m}{40}$ Multiply by the reciprocal of the divisor.

$$= \frac{8m^2(2 - m)}{3(m + 2)(m - 2) \cdot 40}$$ Factor and multiply.

$$= \frac{8m^2 \cdot -1\,(m - 2)}{3(m + 2)\,(m - 2) \cdot 8 \cdot 5}$$ Write $(2 - m)$ as $-1(m - 2)$.

$$= -\frac{m^2}{15(m + 2)}$$ Simplify.

b. $\dfrac{18y^2 + 9y - 2}{24y^2 - 10y + 1} \div \dfrac{3y^2 + 17y + 10}{8y^2 + 18y - 5}$

$$= \frac{18y^2 + 9y - 2}{24y^2 - 10y + 1} \cdot \frac{8y^2 + 18y - 5}{3y^2 + 17y + 10}$$ Multiply by the reciprocal.

$$= \frac{(6y - 1)\,(3y + 2)}{(6y - 1)\,(4y - 1)} \cdot \frac{(4y - 1)\,(2y + 5)}{(3y + 2)\,(y + 5)}$$ Factor.

$$= \frac{2y + 5}{y + 5}$$ Simplest form □

PRACTICE

7 Divide.

a. $\dfrac{6y^3}{3y^2 - 27} \div \dfrac{42}{3 - y}$

b. $\dfrac{10x^2 + 23x - 5}{5x^2 - 51x + 10} \div \dfrac{2x^2 + 9x + 10}{7x^2 - 68x - 20}$

> **Helpful Hint**
>
> When dividing rational expressions, do not divide out common factors until the division problem is rewritten as a multiplication problem.

EXAMPLE 8   Perform each indicated operation.

$$\frac{x^2 - 25}{(x + 5)^2} \cdot \frac{3x + 15}{4x} \div \frac{x^2 - 3x - 10}{x}$$

Solution $\dfrac{x^2 - 25}{(x + 5)^2} \cdot \dfrac{3x + 15}{4x} \div \dfrac{x^2 - 3x - 10}{x}$

$$= \frac{x^2 - 25}{(x + 5)^2} \cdot \frac{3x + 15}{4x} \cdot \frac{x}{x^2 - 3x - 10} \qquad \text{To divide, multiply by the reciprocal}$$

$$= \frac{(x + 5)(x - 5)}{(x + 5)(x + 5)} \cdot \frac{3(x + 5)}{4x} \cdot \frac{x}{(x - 5)(x + 2)}$$

$$= \frac{3}{4(x + 2)}$$

PRACTICE
8   Perform each indicated operation.

$$\frac{x^2 - 16}{(x - 4)^2} \cdot \frac{5x - 20}{3x} \div \frac{x^2 + x - 12}{x}$$

OBJECTIVE
5   Using Rational Functions in Applications

Rational functions occur often in real-life situations.

EXAMPLE 9   **Cost for Pressing Compact Discs**

For the ICL Production Company, the rational function $C(x) = \dfrac{2.6x + 10,000}{x}$ describes the company's cost per disc for pressing x compact discs. Find the cost per disc for pressing:

    a. 100 compact discs

    b. 1000 compact discs

Solution

  a. $C(100) = \dfrac{2.6(100) + 10,000}{100} = \dfrac{10,260}{100} = 102.6$

  The cost per disc for pressing 100 compact discs is \$102.60.

  b. $C(1000) = \dfrac{2.6(1000) + 10,000}{1000} = \dfrac{12,600}{1000} = 12.6$

  The cost per disc for pressing 1000 compact discs is \$12.60. Notice that as more compact discs are produced, the cost per disc decreases.

PRACTICE
9   A company's cost per tee shirt for silk screening x tee shirts is given by the rational function $C(x) = \dfrac{3.2x + 400}{x}$. Find the cost per tee shirt for printing:

  a. 100 tee shirts   **b.** 1000 tee shirts

Graphing Calculator Explorations

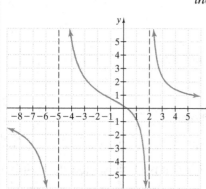

Since the rational expression $\dfrac{7x - 2}{(x - 2)(x + 5)}$ is not defined when $x = 2$ or when $x = -5$, we say that the domain of the rational function $f(x) = \dfrac{7x - 2}{(x - 2)(x + 5)}$ is all real numbers except 2 and -5. This domain can be written as $\{x \mid x$ is a real number and $x \neq 2, x \neq -5\}$. This means that the graph of $f(x)$ should not cross the vertical lines $x = 2$ and $x = -5$. The graph of $f(x)$ in *connected* mode is to the left. In connected mode, the graphing calculator tries to connect all dots of the graph so that the result is a smooth curve. This is what has happened in the graph. Notice that the graph appears to contain vertical lines at $x = 2$ and at $x = -5$. We know that this cannot happen because the function is not defined at $x = 2$ and at $x = -5$. We also know that this cannot happen because the graph of this function would not pass the vertical line test.

The graph of $f(x)$ in *dot* mode is to the left. In dot mode, the graphing calculator will not connect dots with a smooth curve. Notice that the vertical lines have disappeared, and we have a better picture of the graph. The graph, however, actually appears more like the hand-drawn graph below. By using a Table feature, a Calculate Value feature, or by tracing, we can see that the function is not defined at $x = 2$ and at $x = -5$.

Find the domain of each rational function. Then graph each rational function and use the graph to confirm the domain.

1. $f(x) = \dfrac{x + 1}{x^2 - 4}$

2. $g(x) = \dfrac{5x}{x^2 - 9}$

3. $h(x) = \dfrac{x^2}{2x^2 + 7x - 4}$

4. $f(x) = \dfrac{3x + 2}{4x^2 - 19x - 5}$

✓ Vocabulary, Readiness & Video Check

Use the choices below to fill in each blank. Some choices may not be used.

1	true	rational	simplified	$\dfrac{-a}{-b}$	$\dfrac{-a}{b}$	$\dfrac{a}{-b}$
-1	false	domain	0			

1. A _____ expression is an expression that can be written as the quotient $\dfrac{P}{Q}$ of two polynomials P and Q as long as $Q \neq 0$.

2. A rational expression is undefined if the denominator is _____.

3. The _____ of the rational function $f(x) = \dfrac{2}{x}$ is $\{x \mid x$ is a real number and $x \neq 0\}$.

4. A rational expression is _____ if the numerator and denominator have no common factors other than 1 or -1.

5. The expression $\dfrac{x^2 + 2}{2 + x^2}$ simplifies to _____.

6. The expression $\dfrac{y - z}{z - y}$ simplifies to _____.

7. For a rational expression, $-\dfrac{a}{b} =$ _____ $=$ _____ .

8. True or false: $\dfrac{a-6}{a+2} = \dfrac{-(a-6)}{-(a+2)} = \dfrac{-a+6}{-a-2}$. _____

Martin-Gay Interactive Videos

See Video 6.1

Watch the section lecture video and answer the following questions.

OBJECTIVE 1

9. From ▦ Examples 1 and 2, why can't the denominators of rational expressions be zero? How does this relate to the domain of a rational function?

OBJECTIVE 2

10. What conclusion does ▦ Example 4 lead us to?

OBJECTIVE 3

11. Does a person need to be comfortable with factoring polynomials in order to be successful with multiplying rational expressions? Explain, referencing ▦ Example 6 in your answer.

OBJECTIVE 4

12. Based on ▦ Example 7, complete the following statements. Division of rational expressions is similar to division of _____. Therefore, to divide rational expressions, it's the first rational expression times the _____ of the second rational expression.

OBJECTIVE 5

13. In ▦ Example 8d, we find the domain of the function. Do you think the domain should be restricted in any way given the context of this application? Explain.

6.1   Exercise Set   MyMathLab®

Find the domain of each rational function. See Example 1.

1. $f(x) = \dfrac{5x-7}{4}$

2. $g(x) = \dfrac{4-3x}{2}$

3. $s(t) = \dfrac{t^2+1}{2t}$

4. $v(t) = -\dfrac{5t+t^2}{3t}$

5. $f(x) = \dfrac{3x}{7-x}$

6. $f(x) = \dfrac{-4x}{-2+x}$

7. $f(x) = \dfrac{x}{3x-1}$

8. $g(x) = \dfrac{-2}{2x+5}$

9. $R(x) = \dfrac{3+2x}{x^3+x^2-2x}$

10. $h(x) = \dfrac{5-3x}{2x^2-14x+20}$

11. $C(x) = \dfrac{x+3}{x^2-4}$

12. $R(x) = \dfrac{5}{x^2-7x}$

Simplify each rational expression. See Examples 2 through 5.

13. $\dfrac{8x-16x^2}{8x}$

14. $\dfrac{3x-6x^2}{3x}$

15. $\dfrac{x^2-9}{3+x}$

16. $\dfrac{x^2-25}{5+x}$

17. $\dfrac{9y-18}{7y-14}$

18. $\dfrac{6y-18}{2y-6}$

19. $\dfrac{x^2+6x-40}{x+10}$

20. $\dfrac{x^2-8x+16}{x-4}$

21. $\dfrac{x-9}{9-x}$

22. $\dfrac{x-4}{4-x}$

23. $\dfrac{x^2-49}{7-x}$

24. $\dfrac{x^2-y^2}{y-x}$

25. $\dfrac{2x^2-7x-4}{x^2-5x+4}$

26. $\dfrac{3x^2-11x+10}{x^2-7x+10}$

27. $\dfrac{x^3-125}{2x-10}$

28. $\dfrac{4x+4}{x^3+1}$

29. $\dfrac{3x^2-5x-2}{6x^3+2x^2+3x+1}$

30. $\dfrac{2x^2-x-3}{2x^3-3x^2+2x-3}$

31. $\dfrac{9x^2-15x+25}{27x^3+125}$

32. $\dfrac{8x^3-27}{4x^2+6x+9}$

Multiply and simplify. See Example 6.

33. $\dfrac{2x-4}{15} \cdot \dfrac{6}{2-x}$

34. $\dfrac{10-2x}{7} \cdot \dfrac{14}{5x-25}$

35. $\dfrac{18a - 12a^2}{4a^2 + 4a + 1} \cdot \dfrac{4a^2 + 8a + 3}{4a^2 - 9}$

36. $\dfrac{a - 5b}{a^2 + ab} \cdot \dfrac{b^2 - a^2}{10b - 2a}$

▷ 37. $\dfrac{9x + 9}{4x + 8} \cdot \dfrac{2x + 4}{3x^2 - 3}$

38. $\dfrac{2x^2 - 2}{10x + 30} \cdot \dfrac{12x + 36}{3x - 3}$

39. $\dfrac{2x^3 - 16}{6x^2 + 6x - 36} \cdot \dfrac{9x + 18}{3x^2 + 6x + 12}$

40. $\dfrac{x^2 - 3x + 9}{5x^2 - 20x - 105} \cdot \dfrac{x^2 - 49}{x^3 + 27}$

41. $\dfrac{a^3 + a^2b + a + b}{5a^3 + 5a} \cdot \dfrac{6a^2}{2a^2 - 2b^2}$

42. $\dfrac{4a^2 - 8a}{ab - 2b + 3a - 6} \cdot \dfrac{8b + 24}{3a + 6}$

43. $\dfrac{x^2 - 6x - 16}{2x^2 - 128} \cdot \dfrac{x^2 + 16x + 64}{3x^2 + 30x + 48}$

44. $\dfrac{2x^2 + 12x - 32}{x^2 + 16x + 64} \cdot \dfrac{x^2 + 10x + 16}{x^2 - 3x - 10}$

Divide and simplify. See Example 7.

45. $\dfrac{2x}{5} \div \dfrac{6x + 12}{5x + 10}$

46. $\dfrac{7}{3x} \div \dfrac{14 - 7x}{18 - 9x}$

47. $\dfrac{a + b}{ab} \div \dfrac{a^2 - b^2}{4a^3b}$

48. $\dfrac{6a^2b^2}{a^2 - 4} \div \dfrac{3ab^2}{a - 2}$

49. $\dfrac{x^2 - 6x + 9}{x^2 - x - 6} \div \dfrac{x^2 - 9}{4}$

50. $\dfrac{x^2 - 4}{3x + 6} \div \dfrac{2x^2 - 8x + 8}{x^2 + 4x + 4}$

51. $\dfrac{x^2 - 6x - 16}{2x^2 - 128} \div \dfrac{x^2 + 10x + 16}{x^2 + 16x + 64}$

52. $\dfrac{a^2 - a - 6}{a^2 - 81} \div \dfrac{a^2 - 7a - 18}{4a + 36}$

▷ 53. $\dfrac{3x - x^2}{x^3 - 27} \div \dfrac{x}{x^2 + 3x + 9}$

54. $\dfrac{x^2 - 3x}{x^3 - 27} \div \dfrac{2x}{2x^2 + 6x + 18}$

55. $\dfrac{8b + 24}{3a + 6} \div \dfrac{ab - 2b + 3a - 6}{a^2 - 4a + 4}$

56. $\dfrac{2a^2 - 2b^2}{a^3 + a^2b + a + b} \div \dfrac{6a^2}{a^3 + a}$

MIXED PRACTICE

Perform each indicated operation. See Examples 2 through 8.

57. $\dfrac{x^2 - 9}{4} \cdot \dfrac{x^2 - x - 6}{x^2 - 6x + 9}$

58. $\dfrac{x^2 - 4}{9} \cdot \dfrac{x^2 - 6x + 9}{x^2 - 5x + 6}$

59. $\dfrac{2x^2 - 4x - 30}{5x^2 - 40x - 75} \div \dfrac{x^2 - 8x + 15}{x^2 - 6x + 9}$

60. $\dfrac{4a + 36}{a^2 - 7a - 18} \div \dfrac{a^2 - a - 6}{a^2 - 81}$

61. Simplify: $\dfrac{r^3 + s^3}{r + s}$

62. Simplify: $\dfrac{m^3 - n^3}{m - n}$

63. $\dfrac{4}{x} \div \dfrac{3xy}{x^2} \cdot \dfrac{6x^2}{x^4}$

64. $\dfrac{4}{x} \cdot \dfrac{3xy}{x^2} \div \dfrac{6x^2}{x^4}$

65. $\dfrac{3x^2 - 5x - 2}{y^2 + y - 2} \cdot \dfrac{y^2 + 4y - 5}{12x^2 + 7x + 1} \div \dfrac{5x^2 - 9x - 2}{8x^2 - 2x - 1}$

66. $\dfrac{x^2 + x - 2}{3y^2 - 5y - 2} \cdot \dfrac{12y^2 + y - 1}{x^2 + 4x - 5} \div \dfrac{8y^2 - 6y + 1}{5y^2 - 9y - 2}$

67. $\dfrac{5a^2 - 20}{3a^2 - 12a} \div \dfrac{a^3 + 2a^2}{2a^2 - 8a} \cdot \dfrac{9a^3 + 6a^2}{2a^2 - 4a}$

68. $\dfrac{5a^2 - 20}{3a^2 - 12a} \div \left(\dfrac{a^3 + 2a^2}{2a^2 - 8a} \cdot \dfrac{9a^3 + 6a^2}{2a^2 - 4a} \right)$

69. $\dfrac{5x^4 + 3x^2 - 2}{x - 1} \cdot \dfrac{x + 1}{x^4 - 1}$

70. $\dfrac{3x^4 - 10x^2 - 8}{x - 2} \cdot \dfrac{3x + 6}{15x^2 + 10}$

Find each function value. See Example 9.

71. If $f(x) = \dfrac{x + 8}{2x - 1}$, find $f(2), f(0)$, and $f(-1)$.

72. If $f(x) = \dfrac{x - 2}{-5 + x}$, find $f(-5), f(0)$, and $f(10)$.

73. If $g(x) = \dfrac{x^2 + 8}{x^3 - 25x}$, find $g(3), g(-2)$, and $g(1)$.

74. If $s(t) = \dfrac{t^3 + 1}{t^2 + 1}$, find $s(-1), s(1)$, and $s(2)$.

▷ 75. The total revenue from the sale of a popular book is approximated by the rational function $R(x) = \dfrac{1000x^2}{x^2 + 4}$, where x is the number of years since publication and $R(x)$ is the total revenue in millions of dollars.

   a. Find the total revenue at the end of the first year.

   b. Find the total revenue at the end of the second year.

   c. Find the revenue during the second year only.

   d. Find the domain of function R.

76. The function $f(x) = \dfrac{100{,}000x}{100 - x}$ models the cost in dollars for removing x percent of the pollutants from a bayou in which a nearby company dumped creosol.

   a. Find the cost of removing 20% of the pollutants from the bayou. [*Hint:* Find $f(20)$.]

   b. Find the cost of removing 60% of the pollutants and then 80% of the pollutants.

   c. Find $f(90)$, then $f(95)$, and then $f(99)$. What happens to the cost as x approaches 100%?

   d. Find the domain of function f.

REVIEW AND PREVIEW

Perform each indicated operation. See Section 1.3.

77. $\dfrac{4}{5} + \dfrac{3}{5}$

78. $\dfrac{4}{10} - \dfrac{7}{10}$

79. $\dfrac{5}{28} - \dfrac{2}{21}$

80. $\dfrac{5}{13} + \dfrac{2}{7}$

81. $\dfrac{3}{8} + \dfrac{1}{2} - \dfrac{3}{16}$

82. $\dfrac{2}{9} - \dfrac{1}{6} + \dfrac{2}{3}$

CONCEPT EXTENSIONS

Solve. For Exercises 83 and 84, see the second Concept Check in this section; for Exercises 85 and 86, see the third Concept Check.

83. Which of the expressions are equivalent to $\dfrac{x}{5-x}$?

a. $\dfrac{-x}{5-x}$

b. $\dfrac{-x}{-5+x}$

c. $\dfrac{x}{x-5}$

d. $\dfrac{-x}{x-5}$

84. Which of the expressions are equivalent to $\dfrac{-2+x}{x}$?

a. $\dfrac{2-x}{-x}$

b. $-\dfrac{2-x}{x}$

c. $\dfrac{x-2}{x}$

d. $\dfrac{x-2}{-x}$

85. Does $\dfrac{x}{x+5}$ simplify to $\dfrac{1}{5}$? Why or why not?

86. Does $\dfrac{x+7}{x}$ simplify to 7? Why or why not?

△ **87.** Find the area of the rectangle.

$\dfrac{5x}{x^2-4}$ m

$\dfrac{x+2}{x}$ m

△ **88.** Find the area of the triangle.

$\dfrac{4x}{10y^2}$ in.

$\dfrac{5y}{6x}$ in.

△ **89.** A parallelogram has an area of $\dfrac{x^2+x-2}{x^3}$ square feet and a height of $\dfrac{x^2}{x-1}$ feet. Express the length of its base as a rational expression in x. (*Hint:* Since $A = b \cdot h$, $b = \dfrac{A}{h}$ or $b = A \div h$.)

90. A lottery prize of $\dfrac{15x^3}{y^2}$ dollars is to be divided among $5x$ people. Express the amount of money each person is to receive as a rational expression in x and y.

91. In your own words, explain how to simplify a rational expression.

92. In your own words, explain the difference between multiplying rational expressions and dividing rational expressions.

93. Decide whether each rational expression equals 1, −1, or neither.

a. $\dfrac{x+5}{5+x}$

b. $\dfrac{x-5}{5-x}$

c. $\dfrac{x+5}{x-5}$

d. $\dfrac{-x-5}{x+5}$

e. $\dfrac{x-5}{-x+5}$

f. $\dfrac{-5+x}{x-5}$

94. Find the polynomial in the second numerator such that the following statement is true.

$$\dfrac{x^2-4}{x^2-7x+10} \cdot \dfrac{?}{2x^2+11x+14} = 1$$

95. In our definition of division for

$$\dfrac{P}{Q} \div \dfrac{R}{S}$$

we stated that $Q \neq 0$, $S \neq 0$, and $R \neq 0$. Explain why R cannot equal 0.

96. In your own words, explain how to find the domain of a rational function.

97. Graph a portion of the function $f(x) = \dfrac{20x}{100-x}$. To do so, complete the given table, plot the points, and then connect the plotted points with a smooth curve.

x	0	10	30	50	70	90	95	99
y or $f(x)$								

98. The domain of the function $f(x) = \dfrac{1}{x}$ is all real numbers except 0. This means that the graph of this function will be in two pieces: one piece corresponding to x values less than 0 and one piece corresponding to x values greater than 0. Graph the function by completing the following tables, separately plotting the points, and connecting each set of plotted points with a smooth curve.

x	$\dfrac{1}{4}$	$\dfrac{1}{2}$	1	2	4
y or $f(x)$					

x	−4	−2	−1	$-\dfrac{1}{2}$	$-\dfrac{1}{4}$
y or $f(x)$					

Simplify. Assume that no denominator is 0.

99. $\dfrac{p^x - 4}{4 - p^x}$

100. $\dfrac{3 + q^n}{q^n + 3}$

101. $\dfrac{x^n + 4}{x^{2n} - 16}$

102. $\dfrac{x^{2k} - 9}{3 + x^k}$

105. $\dfrac{y^{2n} + 9}{10y} \cdot \dfrac{y^n - 3}{y^{4n} - 81}$

106. $\dfrac{y^{4n} - 16}{y^{2n} + 4} \cdot \dfrac{6y}{y^n + 2}$

107. $\dfrac{y^{2n} - y^n - 2}{2y^n - 4} \div \dfrac{y^{2n} - 1}{1 + y^n}$

Perform the indicated operation. Write all answers in lowest terms.

103. $\dfrac{x^{2n} - 4}{7x} \cdot \dfrac{14x^3}{x^n - 2}$

104. $\dfrac{x^{2n} + 4x^n + 4}{4x - 3} \cdot \dfrac{8x^2 - 6x}{x^n + 2}$

108. $\dfrac{y^{2n} + 7y^n + 10}{10} \div \dfrac{y^{2n} + 4y^n + 4}{5y^n + 25}$

6.2 | Adding and Subtracting Rational Expressions ▶

OBJECTIVES

1 Add or Subtract Rational Expressions with a Common Denominator. ▶

2 Identify the Least Common Denominator (LCD) of Two or More Rational Expressions. ▶

3 Add or Subtract Rational Expressions with Unlike Denominators. ▶

OBJECTIVE

1 Adding or Subtracting Rational Expressions with a Common Denominator ▶

Rational expressions, like rational numbers, can be added or subtracted. We add or subtract rational expressions in the same way that we add or subtract rational numbers (fractions).

Adding or Subtracting Rational Expressions with a Common Denominator

If $\dfrac{P}{Q}$ and $\dfrac{R}{Q}$ are rational expressions, then

$$\frac{P}{Q} + \frac{R}{Q} = \frac{P + R}{Q} \quad \text{and} \quad \frac{P}{Q} - \frac{R}{Q} = \frac{P - R}{Q}$$

To add or subtract rational expressions with a common denominator, add or subtract the numerators and write the sum or difference over the common denominator.

EXAMPLE I   Add or subtract.

a. $\dfrac{x}{4} + \dfrac{5x}{4}$ **b.** $\dfrac{5}{7z^2} + \dfrac{x}{7z^2}$ **c.** $\dfrac{x^2}{x + 7} - \dfrac{49}{x + 7}$ **d.** $\dfrac{x}{3y^2} - \dfrac{x + 1}{3y^2}$

Solution   The rational expressions have common denominators, so add or subtract their numerators and place the sum or difference over their common denominator.

a. $\dfrac{x}{4} + \dfrac{5x}{4} = \dfrac{x + 5x}{4} = \dfrac{6x}{4} = \dfrac{3x}{2}$ \qquad Add the numerators and write the result over the common denominator.

b. $\dfrac{5}{7z^2} + \dfrac{x}{7z^2} = \dfrac{5 + x}{7z^2}$

c. $\dfrac{x^2}{x + 7} - \dfrac{49}{x + 7} = \dfrac{x^2 - 49}{x + 7}$ \qquad Subtract the numerators and write the result over the common denominator.

$\qquad\qquad = \dfrac{(x + 7)(x - 7)}{x + 7}$ \qquad Factor the numerator.

$\qquad\qquad = x - 7$ \qquad Simplify.

d. $\dfrac{x}{3y^2} - \dfrac{x + 1}{3y^2} = \dfrac{x - (x + 1)}{3y^2}$ \qquad Subtract the numerators.

$\qquad\qquad = \dfrac{x - x - 1}{3y^2}$ \qquad Use the distributive property.

$\qquad\qquad = -\dfrac{1}{3y^2}$ \qquad Simplify. □

> **Helpful Hint**
>
> **Very Important:** Be sure to insert parentheses here so that the entire numerator is subtracted.

1   Add or subtract.

a. $\dfrac{9}{11z^2} + \dfrac{x}{11z^2}$ **b.** $\dfrac{x}{8} + \dfrac{5x}{8}$ **c.** $\dfrac{x^2}{x+4} - \dfrac{16}{x+4}$ **d.** $\dfrac{z}{2a^2} - \dfrac{z+3}{2a^2}$

✔ **CONCEPT CHECK**

Find and correct the error.

$$\dfrac{3+2y}{y^2-1} - \dfrac{y+3}{y^2-1} = \dfrac{3+2y-y+3}{y^2-1}$$

$$= \dfrac{y+6}{y^2-1}$$

---

2   Identifying the Least Common Denominator (LCD) of Rational Expressions ▶

To add or subtract rational expressions with unlike denominators, first write the rational expressions as equivalent rational expressions with a common denominator.

The **least common denominator (LCD)** is usually the easiest common denominator to work with. The LCD of a list of rational expressions is a polynomial of least degree whose factors include the denominator factors in the list.

Use the following steps to find the LCD.

Finding the Least Common Denominator (LCD)

Step 1. Factor each denominator completely.

Step 2. The LCD is the product of all unique factors, each raised to a power equal to the greatest number of times that the factor appears in any factored denominator.

EXAMPLE 2   Find the LCD of the rational expressions in each list.

a. $\dfrac{2}{3x^5y^2}, \dfrac{3z}{5xy^3}$ **b.** $\dfrac{7}{z+1}, \dfrac{z}{z-1}$

c. $\dfrac{m-1}{m^2-25}, \dfrac{2m}{2m^2-9m-5}, \dfrac{7}{m^2-10m+25}$ **d.** $\dfrac{x}{x^2-4}, \dfrac{11}{6-3x}$

Solution

a. First we factor each denominator.

$$3x^5y^2 = 3 \cdot x^5 \cdot y^2$$
$$5xy^3 = 5 \cdot x \cdot y^3$$
$$\text{LCD} = 3 \cdot 5 \cdot x^5 \cdot y^3 = 15x^5y^3$$

> **Helpful Hint**
>
> The greatest power of x is 5, so we have a factor of x^5. The greatest power of y is 3, so we have a factor of y^3.

b. The denominators $z+1$ and $z-1$ do not factor further. Thus,

$$\text{LCD} = (z+1)(z-1)$$

c. We first factor each denominator.

$$m^2-25 = (m+5)(m-5)$$
$$2m^2-9m-5 = (2m+1)(m-5)$$
$$m^2-10m+25 = (m-5)(m-5)$$
$$\text{LCD} = (m+5)(2m+1)(m-5)^2$$

$$\dfrac{3+2y}{y^2-1} - \dfrac{y+3}{y^2-1}$$
$$= \dfrac{3+2y-y-3}{y^2-1} = \dfrac{y}{y^2-1}$$

d. Factor each denominator.

$$x^2 - 4 = (x + 2)(x - 2)$$
$$6 - 3x = 3(2 - x) = 3(-1)(x - 2)$$
$$\text{LCD} = 3(-1)(x + 2)(x - 2)$$
$$= -3(x + 2)(x - 2)$$

Helpful Hint

If opposite factors occur, do not use both in the LCD. Instead, factor -1 from one of the opposite factors so that the factors are then identical.

PRACTICE

2 Find the LCD of the rational expressions in each list.

a. $\dfrac{7}{6x^3y^5}, \dfrac{2}{9x^2y^4}$

b. $\dfrac{11}{x - 2}, \dfrac{x}{x + 3}$

c. $\dfrac{b + 2}{b^2 - 16}, \dfrac{8}{b^2 - 8b + 16}, \dfrac{5b}{2b^2 - 5b - 12}$

d. $\dfrac{y}{y^2 - 9}, \dfrac{3}{12 - 4y}$

OBJECTIVE

3 Adding or Subtracting Rational Expressions with Unlike Denominators

To add or subtract rational expressions with unlike denominators, we write each rational expression as an equivalent rational expression so that their denominators are alike.

Adding or Subtracting Rational Expressions with Unlike Denominators

Step 1. Find the LCD of the rational expressions.

Step 2. Write each rational expression as an equivalent rational expression whose denominator is the LCD found in Step 1.

Step 3. Add or subtract numerators and write the result over the common denominator.

Step 4. Simplify the resulting rational expression.

EXAMPLE 3 Perform the indicated operation.

a. $\dfrac{2}{x^2y} + \dfrac{5}{3x^3y}$

b. $\dfrac{3}{x + 2} + \dfrac{2x}{x - 2}$

c. $\dfrac{2x - 6}{x - 1} - \dfrac{4}{1 - x}$

Solution

a. The LCD is $3x^3y$. Write each fraction as an equivalent fraction with denominator $3x^3y$. To do this, we multiply both the numerator and denominator of each fraction by the factors needed to obtain the LCD as denominator.

The first fraction is multiplied by $\dfrac{3x}{3x}$ so that the new denominator is the LCD.

$$\dfrac{2}{x^2y} + \dfrac{5}{3x^3y} = \dfrac{2 \cdot 3x}{x^2y \cdot 3x} + \dfrac{5}{3x^3y} \qquad \text{The second expression already has a denominator of } 3x^3y.$$

$$= \dfrac{6x}{3x^3y} + \dfrac{5}{3x^3y}$$

$$= \dfrac{6x + 5}{3x^3y} \qquad \text{Add the numerators.}$$

b. The LCD is the product of the two denominators: $(x + 2)(x - 2)$.

$$\frac{3}{x + 2} + \frac{2x}{x - 2} = \frac{3 \cdot (x - 2)}{(x + 2) \cdot (x - 2)} + \frac{2x \cdot (x + 2)}{(x - 2) \cdot (x + 2)} \quad \text{Write equivalent rational expressions.}$$

$$= \frac{3x - 6}{(x + 2)(x - 2)} + \frac{2x^2 + 4x}{(x + 2)(x - 2)} \quad \text{Multiply in the numerators.}$$

$$= \frac{3x - 6 + 2x^2 + 4x}{(x + 2)(x - 2)} \quad \text{Add the numerators.}$$

$$= \frac{2x^2 + 7x - 6}{(x + 2)(x - 2)} \quad \text{Simplify the numerator.}$$

c. The LCD is either $x - 1$ or $1 - x$. To get a common denominator of $x - 1$, we factor -1 from the denominator of the second rational expression.

$$\frac{2x - 6}{x - 1} - \frac{4}{1 - x} = \frac{2x - 6}{x - 1} - \frac{4}{-1(x - 1)} \quad \text{Write } 1 - x \text{ as } -1(x - 1).$$

$$= \frac{2x - 6}{x - 1} - \frac{-1 \cdot 4}{x - 1} \quad \text{Write } \frac{4}{-1(x - 1)} \text{ as } \frac{-1 \cdot 4}{x - 1}$$

$$= \frac{2x - 6 - (-4)}{x - 1} \quad \text{Combine the numerators.}$$

$$= \frac{2x - 6 + 4}{x - 1} \quad \text{Simplify.}$$

$$= \frac{2x - 2}{x - 1}$$

$$= \frac{2(x - 1)}{x - 1} \quad \text{Factor.}$$

$$= 2 \quad \text{Simplest form} \qquad \square$$

PRACTICE

3   Perform the indicated operation.

a. $\dfrac{4}{p^3 q} + \dfrac{3}{5p^4 q}$ **b.** $\dfrac{4}{y + 3} + \dfrac{5y}{y - 3}$ **c.** $\dfrac{3z - 18}{z - 5} - \dfrac{3}{5 - z}$

EXAMPLE 4   Subtract: $\dfrac{5k}{k^2 - 4} - \dfrac{2}{k^2 + k - 2}$

Solution $\dfrac{5k}{k^2 - 4} - \dfrac{2}{k^2 + k - 2} = \dfrac{5k}{(k + 2)(k - 2)} - \dfrac{2}{(k + 2)(k - 1)}$ Factor each denominator to find the LCD.

The LCD is $(k + 2)(k - 2)(k - 1)$. We write equivalent rational expressions with the LCD as denominators.

$$\frac{5k}{(k + 2)(k - 2)} - \frac{2}{(k + 2)(k - 1)}$$

$$= \frac{5k \cdot (k - 1)}{(k + 2)(k - 2) \cdot (k - 1)} - \frac{2 \cdot (k - 2)}{(k + 2)(k - 1) \cdot (k - 2)} \quad \text{Write equivalent rational expressions.}$$

$$= \frac{5k^2 - 5k}{(k + 2)(k - 2)(k - 1)} - \frac{2k - 4}{(k + 2)(k - 2)(k - 1)} \quad \text{Multiply in the numerators.}$$

$$= \frac{5k^2 - 5k - 2k + 4}{(k + 2)(k - 2)(k - 1)} \quad \text{Subtract the numerators.}$$

$$= \frac{5k^2 - 7k + 4}{(k + 2)(k - 2)(k - 1)} \quad \text{Simplify.} \qquad \square$$

> | Helpful Hint |
> **Very Important:** Because we are subtracting, notice the sign change on 4.

PRACTICE

4   Subtract: $\dfrac{t}{t^2 - 25} - \dfrac{3}{t^2 - 3t - 10}$

EXAMPLE 5 Add: $\dfrac{2x-1}{2x^2-9x-5} + \dfrac{x+3}{6x^2-x-2}$

Solution

$\dfrac{2x-1}{2x^2-9x-5} + \dfrac{x+3}{6x^2-x-2} = \dfrac{2x-1}{(2x+1)(x-5)} + \dfrac{x+3}{(2x+1)(3x-2)}$ Factor the denominators.

The LCD is $(2x+1)(x-5)(3x-2)$.

$= \dfrac{(2x-1)\cdot(3x-2)}{(2x+1)(x-5)\cdot(3x-2)} + \dfrac{(x+3)\cdot(x-5)}{(2x+1)(3x-2)\cdot(x-5)}$

$= \dfrac{6x^2-7x+2}{(2x+1)(x-5)(3x-2)} + \dfrac{x^2-2x-15}{(2x+1)(x-5)(3x-2)}$ Multiply in the numerators.

$= \dfrac{6x^2-7x+2+x^2-2x-15}{(2x+1)(x-5)(3x-2)}$ Add the numerators.

$= \dfrac{7x^2-9x-13}{(2x+1)(x-5)(3x-2)}$ Simplify.   ☐

PRACTICE 5 Add: $\dfrac{2x+3}{3x^2-5x-2} + \dfrac{x-6}{6x^2-13x-5}$ ■

EXAMPLE 6 Perform each indicated operation.

$$\dfrac{7}{x-1} + \dfrac{10x}{x^2-1} - \dfrac{5}{x+1}$$

Solution $\dfrac{7}{x-1} + \dfrac{10x}{x^2-1} - \dfrac{5}{x+1} = \dfrac{7}{x-1} + \dfrac{10x}{(x-1)(x+1)} - \dfrac{5}{x+1}$ Factor the denominators.

The LCD is $(x-1)(x+1)$.

$= \dfrac{7\cdot(x+1)}{(x-1)\cdot(x+1)} + \dfrac{10x}{(x-1)(x+1)} - \dfrac{5\cdot(x-1)}{(x+1)\cdot(x-1)}$

$= \dfrac{7x+7}{(x-1)(x+1)} + \dfrac{10x}{(x-1)(x+1)} - \dfrac{5x-5}{(x+1)(x-1)}$ Multiply in the numerators.

$= \dfrac{7x+7+10x-5x+5}{(x-1)(x+1)}$ Add and subtract the numerators.

$= \dfrac{12x+12}{(x-1)(x+1)}$ Simplify.

$= \dfrac{12\,(x+1)}{(x-1)\,(x+1)}$ Factor the numerator.

$= \dfrac{12}{x-1}$ Divide out common factors.   ☐

PRACTICE 6 Perform each indicated operation.

$$\dfrac{2}{x-2} + \dfrac{3x}{x^2-x-2} - \dfrac{1}{x+1}$$
   ■

Graphing Calculator Explorations

A graphing calculator can be used to support the results of operations on rational expressions. For example, to verify the result of Example 3(b), graph

$$Y_1 = \frac{3}{x+2} + \frac{2x}{x-2} \quad \text{and} \quad Y_2 = \frac{2x^2 + 7x - 6}{(x+2)(x-2)}$$

on the same set of axes. The graphs should be the same. Use a Table feature or a Trace feature to see that this is true.

✔ Vocabulary, Readiness & Video Check

Name the operation(s) below that make each statement true.

    a. Addition   **b.** Subtraction   **c.** Multiplication   **d.** Division

1. The denominators must be the same before performing the operation. ____

2. To perform this operation, you multiply the first rational expression by the reciprocal of the second rational expression. ____

3. Numerator times numerator all over denominator times denominator. ____

4. These operations are commutative (order doesn't matter). ____

For the rational expressions $\dfrac{5}{y}$ and $\dfrac{7}{y}$, perform each operation mentally.

    5. Addition ____   **6.** Subtraction ____   **7.** Multiplication ____   **8.** Division ___

Martin-Gay Interactive Videos

See Video 6.2

Watch the section lecture video and answer the following questions.

OBJECTIVE 1

9. In ▦ Example 1, why are we told to be especially careful with subtraction when the second numerator has more than one term?

OBJECTIVE 2

10. In ▦ Example 2, $(a - b)$ appears as a factor three times within the two factored denominators. Why does the LCD only contain two factors of $(a - b)$?

OBJECTIVE 3

11. Based on ▦ Example 3, complete the following statements. To write an equivalent rational expression, you multiply the _____ of the expression by the exact same thing as the denominator. This is the same as multiplying the original rational expression by _____, which doesn't change the _____ of the original expression.

6.2 Exercise Set MyMathLab® ▶

Be careful when subtracting! For example, $\dfrac{8}{x+1} - \dfrac{x+5}{x+1} = \dfrac{8-(x+5)}{x+1} = \dfrac{3-x}{x+1}$ *or* $\dfrac{-x+3}{x+1}$.

Use the example above to help you perform each subtraction.

1. $\dfrac{5}{2x} - \dfrac{x+1}{2x} =$ _____

2. $\dfrac{9}{5x} - \dfrac{6-x}{5x} =$ _____

3. $\dfrac{y+11}{y-2} - \dfrac{y-5}{y-2} =$ _____

4. $\dfrac{z-1}{z+6} - \dfrac{z+4}{z+6} =$ _____

Add or subtract as indicated. Simplify each answer. See Example 1.

5. $\dfrac{2}{xz^2} - \dfrac{5}{xz^2}$

6. $\dfrac{4}{x^2y} - \dfrac{2}{x^2y}$

7. $\dfrac{2}{x-2} + \dfrac{x}{x-2}$

8. $\dfrac{x}{5-x} + \dfrac{7}{5-x}$

9. $\dfrac{x^2}{x+2} - \dfrac{4}{x+2}$

10. $\dfrac{x^2}{x+6} - \dfrac{36}{x+6}$

11. $\dfrac{2x-6}{x^2+x-6} + \dfrac{3-3x}{x^2+x-6}$

12. $\dfrac{5x+2}{x^2+2x-8} + \dfrac{2-4x}{x^2+2x-8}$

▶**13.** $\dfrac{x-5}{2x} - \dfrac{x+5}{2x}$

14. $\dfrac{x+4}{4x} - \dfrac{x-4}{4x}$

Find the LCD of the rational expressions in each list. See Example 2.

15. $\dfrac{2}{7}, \dfrac{3}{5x}$

16. $\dfrac{4}{5y}, \dfrac{3}{4y^2}$

17. $\dfrac{3}{x}, \dfrac{2}{x+1}$

18. $\dfrac{5}{2x}, \dfrac{7}{2+x}$

19. $\dfrac{12}{x+7}, \dfrac{8}{x-7}$

20. $\dfrac{1}{2x-1}, \dfrac{8}{2x+1}$

21. $\dfrac{5}{3x+6}, \dfrac{2x}{2x-4}$

22. $\dfrac{2}{3a+9}, \dfrac{5}{5a-15}$

▶ **23.** $\dfrac{2a}{a^2-b^2}, \dfrac{1}{a^2-2ab+b^2}$

24. $\dfrac{2a}{a^2+8a+16}, \dfrac{7a}{a^2+a-12}$

25. $\dfrac{x}{x^2-9}, \dfrac{5}{x}, \dfrac{7}{12-4x}$

26. $\dfrac{9}{x^2-25}, \dfrac{1}{50-10x}, \dfrac{6}{x}$

Add or subtract as indicated. Simplify each answer. See Examples 3(a) and 3(b).

▶ **27.** $\dfrac{4}{3x}+\dfrac{3}{2x}$

28. $\dfrac{10}{7x}+\dfrac{5}{2x}$

29. $\dfrac{5}{2y^2}-\dfrac{2}{7y}$

30. $\dfrac{4}{11x^4}-\dfrac{1}{4x^2}$

▶ **31.** $\dfrac{x-3}{x+4}-\dfrac{x+2}{x-4}$

32. $\dfrac{x-1}{x-5}-\dfrac{x+2}{x+5}$

33. $\dfrac{1}{x-5}-\dfrac{19-2x}{(x-5)(x+4)}$

34. $\dfrac{4x-2}{(x-5)(x+4)}-\dfrac{2}{x+4}$

Perform the indicated operation. If possible, simplify your answer. See Example 3(c).

35. $\dfrac{1}{a-b}+\dfrac{1}{b-a}$

36. $\dfrac{1}{a-3}-\dfrac{1}{3-a}$

37. $\dfrac{x+1}{1-x}+\dfrac{1}{x-1}$

38. $\dfrac{5}{1-x}-\dfrac{1}{x-1}$

39. $\dfrac{5}{x-2}+\dfrac{x+4}{2-x}$

40. $\dfrac{3}{5-x}+\dfrac{x+2}{x-5}$

Perform each indicated operation. If possible, simplify your answer. See Examples 4 through 6.

▶ **41.** $\dfrac{y+1}{y^2-6y+8}-\dfrac{3}{y^2-16}$

42. $\dfrac{x+2}{x^2-36}-\dfrac{x}{x^2+9x+18}$

43. $\dfrac{x+4}{3x^2+11x+6}+\dfrac{x}{2x^2+x-15}$

44. $\dfrac{x+3}{5x^2+12x+4}+\dfrac{6}{x^2-x-6}$

45. $\dfrac{7}{x^2-x-2}-\dfrac{x-1}{x^2+4x+3}$

46. $\dfrac{a}{a^2+10a+25}-\dfrac{4-a}{a^2+6a+5}$

47. $\dfrac{x}{x^2-8x+7}-\dfrac{x+2}{2x^2-9x-35}$

48. $\dfrac{x}{x^2-7x+6}-\dfrac{x+4}{3x^2-2x-1}$

49. $\dfrac{2}{a^2+2a+1}+\dfrac{3}{a^2-1}$

50. $\dfrac{9x+2}{3x^2-2x-8}+\dfrac{7}{3x^2+x-4}$

MIXED PRACTICE

Add or subtract as indicated. If possible, simplify your answer. See Examples 1 through 6.

51. $\dfrac{4}{3x^2y^3}+\dfrac{5}{3x^2y^3}$

52. $\dfrac{7}{2xy^4}+\dfrac{1}{2xy^4}$

53. $\dfrac{13x-5}{2x}-\dfrac{13x+5}{2x}$

54. $\dfrac{17x+4}{4x}-\dfrac{17x-4}{4x}$

55. $\dfrac{3}{2x+10}+\dfrac{8}{3x+15}$

56. $\dfrac{10}{3x-3}+\dfrac{1}{7x-7}$

57. $\dfrac{-2}{x^2-3x}-\dfrac{1}{x^3-3x^2}$

58. $\dfrac{-3}{2a+8}-\dfrac{8}{a^2+4a}$

59. $\dfrac{ab}{a^2-b^2}+\dfrac{b}{a+b}$

60. $\dfrac{x}{25-x^2}+\dfrac{2}{3x-15}$

61. $\dfrac{5}{x^2-4}-\dfrac{3}{x^2+4x+4}$

62. $\dfrac{3z}{z^2-9}-\dfrac{2}{3-z}$

63. $\dfrac{3x}{2x^2-11x+5}+\dfrac{7}{x^2-2x-15}$

64. $\dfrac{2x}{3x^2-13x+4}+\dfrac{5}{x^2-2x-8}$

65. $\dfrac{2}{x+1}-\dfrac{3x}{3x+3}+\dfrac{1}{2x+2}$

66. $\dfrac{5}{3x-6}-\dfrac{x}{x-2}+\dfrac{3+2x}{5x-10}$

67. $\dfrac{3}{x+3}+\dfrac{5}{x^2+6x+9}-\dfrac{x}{x^2-9}$

68. $\dfrac{x+2}{x^2-2x-3}+\dfrac{x}{x-3}-\dfrac{x}{x+1}$

69. $\dfrac{x}{x^2-9}+\dfrac{3}{x^2-6x+9}-\dfrac{1}{x+3}$

70. $\dfrac{3}{x^2 - 9} - \dfrac{x}{x^2 - 6x + 9} + \dfrac{1}{x + 3}$

71. $\left(\dfrac{1}{x} + \dfrac{2}{3}\right) - \left(\dfrac{1}{x} - \dfrac{2}{3}\right)$

72. $\left(\dfrac{1}{2} + \dfrac{2}{x}\right) - \left(\dfrac{1}{2} - \dfrac{1}{x}\right)$

MIXED PRACTICE (SECTIONS 6.1, 6.2)

Perform the indicated operation. If possible, simplify your answer.

73. $\left(\dfrac{2}{3} - \dfrac{1}{x}\right) \cdot \left(\dfrac{3}{x} + \dfrac{1}{2}\right)$

74. $\left(\dfrac{2}{3} - \dfrac{1}{x}\right) \div \left(\dfrac{3}{x} + \dfrac{1}{2}\right)$

75. $\left(\dfrac{2a}{3}\right)^2 \div \left(\dfrac{a^2}{a + 1} - \dfrac{1}{a + 1}\right)$

76. $\left(\dfrac{x + 2}{2x} - \dfrac{x - 2}{2x}\right) \cdot \left(\dfrac{5x}{4}\right)^2$

77. $\left(\dfrac{2x}{3}\right)^2 \div \left(\dfrac{x}{3}\right)^2$

78. $\left(\dfrac{2x}{3}\right)^2 \cdot \left(\dfrac{3}{x}\right)^2$

79. $\left(\dfrac{x}{x + 1} - \dfrac{x}{x - 1}\right) \div \dfrac{x}{2x + 2}$

80. $\dfrac{x}{2x + 2} \div \left(\dfrac{x}{x + 1} + \dfrac{x}{x - 1}\right)$

81. $\dfrac{4}{x} \cdot \left(\dfrac{2}{x + 2} - \dfrac{2}{x - 2}\right)$

82. $\dfrac{1}{x + 1} \cdot \left(\dfrac{5}{x} + \dfrac{2}{x - 3}\right)$

REVIEW AND PREVIEW

Use the distributive property to multiply the following. See Section 1.4.

83. $12\left(\dfrac{2}{3} + \dfrac{1}{6}\right)$

84. $14\left(\dfrac{1}{7} + \dfrac{3}{14}\right)$

85. $x^2\left(\dfrac{4}{x^2} + 1\right)$

86. $5y^2\left(\dfrac{1}{y^2} - \dfrac{1}{5}\right)$

Find each root. See Section 1.3.

87. $\sqrt{100}$

88. $\sqrt{25}$

89. $\sqrt[3]{8}$

90. $\sqrt[3]{27}$

91. $\sqrt[4]{81}$

92. $\sqrt[4]{16}$

Use the Pythagorean theorem to find the unknown length in each right triangle. See Section 5.8.

△**93.**

3 meters

4 meters

△**94.**

7 feet

24 feet

CONCEPT EXTENSIONS

Find and correct each error. See the Concept Check in this section.

95. $\dfrac{2x - 3}{x^2 + 1} - \dfrac{x - 6}{x^2 + 1} = \dfrac{2x - 3 - x - 6}{x^2 + 1}$

$= \dfrac{x - 9}{x^2 + 1}$

96. $\dfrac{7}{x + 7} - \dfrac{x + 3}{x + 7} = \dfrac{7 - x - 3}{(x + 7)^2}$

$= \dfrac{-x + 4}{(x + 7)^2}$

△**97.** Find the perimeter and the area of the square.

$\dfrac{x}{x + 5}$ ft

△**98.** Find the perimeter of the quadrilateral.

$\dfrac{3x}{x - 1}$ cm

$\dfrac{5}{x - 1}$ cm

$\dfrac{x^2 - 8}{x - 1}$ cm

$\dfrac{x^2 - 2x}{x - 1}$ cm

99. When is the LCD of two rational expressions equal to the product of their denominators? $\left(\textit{Hint: } \text{What is the LCD of } \dfrac{1}{x} \text{ and } \dfrac{7}{x + 5}?\right)$

100. When is the LCD of two rational expressions with different denominators equal to one of the denominators? $\left(\textit{Hint: } \text{What is the LCD of } \dfrac{3x}{x + 2} \text{ and } \dfrac{7x + 1}{(x + 2)^3}?\right)$

101. In your own words, explain how to add rational expressions with different denominators.

102. In your own words, explain how to multiply rational expressions.

103. In your own words, explain how to divide rational expressions.

104. In your own words, explain how to subtract rational expressions with different denominators.

*Perform each indicated operation. (**Hint:** First write each expression with positive exponents.)*

105. $x^{-1} + (2x)^{-1}$

106. $y^{-1} + (4y)^{-1}$

107. $4x^{-2} - 3x^{-1}$

108. $(4x)^{-2} - (3x)^{-1}$

Use a graphing calculator to support the results of each exercise.

109. Exercise 7

110. Exercise 8

6.3 Simplifying Complex Fractions

OBJECTIVES

1 Simplify Complex Fractions by Simplifying the Numerator and Denominator and Then Dividing.

2 Simplify Complex Fractions by Multiplying by a Common Denominator.

3 Simplify Expressions with Negative Exponents.

A rational expression whose numerator, denominator, or both contain one or more rational expressions is called a **complex rational expression** or a **complex fraction.**

Complex Fractions

$$\frac{\frac{1}{a}}{\frac{b}{2}} \qquad \frac{\frac{x}{2y^2}}{\frac{6x-2}{9y}} \qquad \frac{x+\frac{1}{y}}{y+1}$$

The parts of a complex fraction are

$$\left.\frac{x}{y+2}\right\} \leftarrow \text{Numerator of complex fraction}$$
$$\leftarrow \text{Main fraction bar}$$
$$\left.7+\frac{1}{y}\right\} \leftarrow \text{Denominator of complex fraction}$$

Our goal in this section is to simplify complex fractions. A complex fraction is simplified when it is in the form $\frac{P}{Q}$, where P and Q are polynomials that have no common factors. Two methods of simplifying complex fractions are introduced. The first method evolves from the definition of a fraction as a quotient.

OBJECTIVE

1 Simplifying Complex Fractions: Method 1

> **Simplifying a Complex Fraction: Method I**
>
> **Step 1.** Simplify the numerator and the denominator of the complex fraction so that each is a single fraction.
>
> **Step 2.** Perform the indicated division by multiplying the numerator of the complex fraction by the reciprocal of the denominator of the complex fraction.
>
> **Step 3.** Simplify if possible.

EXAMPLE I Simplify each complex fraction.

a. $\dfrac{\frac{2x}{27y^2}}{\frac{6x^2}{9}}$ **b.** $\dfrac{\frac{5x}{x+2}}{\frac{10}{x-2}}$ **c.** $\dfrac{\frac{x}{y^2}+\frac{1}{y}}{\frac{y}{x^2}+\frac{1}{x}}$

Solution

a. The numerator of the complex fraction is already a single fraction, and so is the denominator. Perform the indicated division by multiplying the numerator, $\frac{2x}{27y^2}$, by the reciprocal of the denominator, $\frac{6x^2}{9}$. Then simplify.

$$\frac{\frac{2x}{27y^2}}{\frac{6x^2}{9}} = \frac{2x}{27y^2} \div \frac{6x^2}{9}$$

$$= \frac{2x}{27y^2} \cdot \frac{9}{6x^2} \qquad \text{Multiply by the reciprocal of } \frac{6x^2}{9}.$$

$$= \frac{2x \cdot 9}{27y^2 \cdot 6x^2}$$

$$= \frac{1}{9xy^2}$$

Both the numerator and denominator are single fractions, so we perform the indicated division.

b. $\dfrac{\left\{\dfrac{5x}{x+2}\right.}{\left\{\dfrac{10}{x-2}\right.} = \dfrac{5x}{x+2} \div \dfrac{10}{x-2} = \dfrac{5x}{x+2} \cdot \dfrac{x-2}{10}$ Multiply by the reciprocal of $\dfrac{10}{x-2}$.

$= \dfrac{5x(x-2)}{2 \cdot 5(x+2)}$

$= \dfrac{x(x-2)}{2(x+2)}$ Simplify.

c. First simplify the numerator and the denominator of the complex fraction separately so that each is a single fraction. Then perform the indicated division.

$\dfrac{\dfrac{x}{y^2} + \dfrac{1}{y}}{\dfrac{y}{x^2} + \dfrac{1}{x}} = \dfrac{\dfrac{x}{y^2} + \dfrac{1 \cdot y}{y \cdot y}}{\dfrac{y}{x^2} + \dfrac{1 \cdot x}{x \cdot x}}$ Simplify the numerator. The LCD is y^2.

Simplify the denominator. The LCD is x^2.

$= \dfrac{\dfrac{x+y}{y^2}}{\dfrac{y+x}{x^2}}$ Add.

$= \dfrac{x+y}{y^2} \cdot \dfrac{x^2}{y+x}$ Multiply by the reciprocal of $\dfrac{y+x}{x^2}$.

$= \dfrac{x^2(x+y)}{y^2(y+x)}$

$= \dfrac{x^2}{y^2}$ Simplify.   □

PRACTICE
1   Simplify each complex fraction.

a. $\dfrac{\dfrac{5k}{36m}}{\dfrac{15k}{9}}$

b. $\dfrac{\dfrac{8x}{x-4}}{\dfrac{3}{x+4}}$

c. $\dfrac{\dfrac{5}{a} + \dfrac{b}{a^2}}{\dfrac{5a}{b^2} + \dfrac{1}{b}}$

✔ **CONCEPT CHECK**

Which of the following are equivalent to $\dfrac{\dfrac{5}{y}}{\dfrac{2}{z}}$?

a. $\dfrac{5}{y} \div \dfrac{2}{z}$

b. $\dfrac{5}{y} \cdot \dfrac{z}{2}$

c. $\dfrac{5}{y} \div \dfrac{z}{2}$

OBJECTIVE
2   Simplifying Complex Fractions: Method 2

Next we look at another method of simplifying complex fractions. With this method, we multiply the numerator and the denominator of the complex fraction by the LCD of all fractions in the complex fraction.

Answer to Concept Check:
a and b

> **Simplifying a Complex Fraction: Method 2**
>
> **Step 1.** Multiply the numerator and the denominator of the complex fraction by the LCD of the fractions in both the numerator and the denominator.
>
> **Step 2.** Simplify.

EXAMPLE 2 Simplify each complex fraction.

a. $\dfrac{\dfrac{5x}{x+2}}{\dfrac{10}{x-2}}$

b. $\dfrac{\dfrac{x}{y^2}+\dfrac{1}{y}}{\dfrac{y}{x^2}+\dfrac{1}{x}}$

Solution

a. Notice we are reworking Example 1(b) using method 2. The least common denominator of $\dfrac{5x}{x+2}$ and $\dfrac{10}{x-2}$ is $(x+2)(x-2)$. Multiply both the numerator, $\dfrac{5x}{x+2}$, and the denominator, $\dfrac{10}{x-2}$, by the LCD.

$$\dfrac{\dfrac{5x}{x+2}}{\dfrac{10}{x-2}} = \dfrac{\left(\dfrac{5x}{x+2}\right)\cdot(x+2)(x-2)}{\left(\dfrac{10}{x-2}\right)\cdot(x+2)(x-2)}$$ Multiply numerator and denominator by the LCD.

$$= \dfrac{5x\cdot(x-2)}{2\cdot5\cdot(x+2)}$$ Simplify.

$$= \dfrac{x(x-2)}{2(x+2)}$$ Simplify.

b. Here, we are reworking Example 1(c) using method 2. The least common denominator of $\dfrac{x}{y^2},\dfrac{1}{y},\dfrac{y}{x^2}$, and $\dfrac{1}{x}$ is x^2y^2.

$$\dfrac{\dfrac{x}{y^2}+\dfrac{1}{y}}{\dfrac{y}{x^2}+\dfrac{1}{x}} = \dfrac{\left(\dfrac{x}{y^2}+\dfrac{1}{y}\right)\cdot x^2y^2}{\left(\dfrac{y}{x^2}+\dfrac{1}{x}\right)\cdot x^2y^2}$$ Multiply the numerator and denominator by the LCD.

$$= \dfrac{\dfrac{x}{y^2}\cdot x^2y^2+\dfrac{1}{y}\cdot x^2y^2}{\dfrac{y}{x^2}\cdot x^2y^2+\dfrac{1}{x}\cdot x^2y^2}$$ Use the distributive property.

$$= \dfrac{x^3+x^2y}{y^3+xy^2}$$ Simplify.

$$= \dfrac{x^2(x+y)}{y^2(y+x)}$$ Factor.

$$= \dfrac{x^2}{y^2}$$ Simplify. □

PRACTICE

2 Use method 2 to simplify.

a. $\dfrac{\dfrac{8x}{x-4}}{\dfrac{3}{x+4}}$

b. $\dfrac{\dfrac{b}{a^2}+\dfrac{1}{a}}{\dfrac{a}{b^2}+\dfrac{1}{b}}$

OBJECTIVE

3 Simplifying Expressions with Negative Exponents

If an expression contains negative exponents, write the expression as an equivalent expression with positive exponents.

EXAMPLE 3 Simplify:

$$\frac{x^{-1} + 2xy^{-1}}{x^{-2} - x^{-2}y^{-1}}$$

Solution This fraction does not appear to be a complex fraction. If we write it by using only positive exponents, however, we see that it is a complex fraction.

$$\frac{x^{-1} + 2xy^{-1}}{x^{-2} - x^{-2}y^{-1}} = \frac{\dfrac{1}{x} + \dfrac{2x}{y}}{\dfrac{1}{x^2} - \dfrac{1}{x^2 y}}$$

The LCD of $\dfrac{1}{x}, \dfrac{2x}{y}, \dfrac{1}{x^2},$ and $\dfrac{1}{x^2 y}$ is $x^2 y$. Multiply both the numerator and denominator by $x^2 y$.

$$= \frac{\left(\dfrac{1}{x} + \dfrac{2x}{y}\right) \cdot x^2 y}{\left(\dfrac{1}{x^2} - \dfrac{1}{x^2 y}\right) \cdot x^2 y}$$

$$= \frac{\dfrac{1}{x} \cdot x^2 y + \dfrac{2x}{y} \cdot x^2 y}{\dfrac{1}{x^2} \cdot x^2 y - \dfrac{1}{x^2 y} \cdot x^2 y} \qquad \begin{array}{l}\text{Apply the}\\\text{distributive}\\\text{property.}\end{array}$$

$$= \frac{xy + 2x^3}{y - 1} \quad \text{or} \quad \frac{x(y + 2x^2)}{y - 1} \quad \text{Simplify.} \ \square$$

PRACTICE

3 Simplify: $\dfrac{3x^{-1} + x^{-2}y^{-1}}{y^{-2} + xy^{-1}}$

EXAMPLE 4 Simplify: $\dfrac{(2x)^{-1} + 1}{2x^{-1} - 1}$

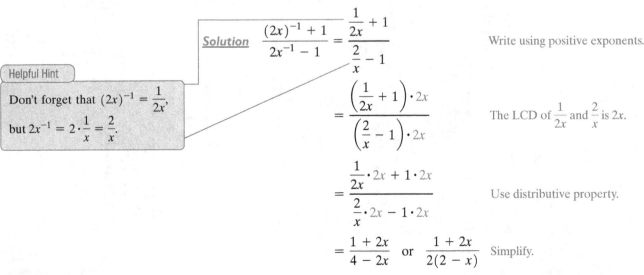

Solution $\dfrac{(2x)^{-1} + 1}{2x^{-1} - 1} = \dfrac{\dfrac{1}{2x} + 1}{\dfrac{2}{x} - 1}$ Write using positive exponents.

Helpful Hint

Don't forget that $(2x)^{-1} = \dfrac{1}{2x}$,

but $2x^{-1} = 2 \cdot \dfrac{1}{x} = \dfrac{2}{x}$.

$$= \frac{\left(\dfrac{1}{2x} + 1\right) \cdot 2x}{\left(\dfrac{2}{x} - 1\right) \cdot 2x} \qquad \text{The LCD of } \dfrac{1}{2x} \text{ and } \dfrac{2}{x} \text{ is } 2x.$$

$$= \frac{\dfrac{1}{2x} \cdot 2x + 1 \cdot 2x}{\dfrac{2}{x} \cdot 2x - 1 \cdot 2x} \qquad \text{Use distributive property.}$$

$$= \frac{1 + 2x}{4 - 2x} \quad \text{or} \quad \frac{1 + 2x}{2(2 - x)} \quad \text{Simplify.} \qquad \square$$

PRACTICE
4 Simplify: $\dfrac{(3x)^{-1} - 2}{5x^{-1} + 2}$

✓ Vocabulary, Readiness & Video Check

Complete the steps by writing the simplified complex fraction.

1. $\dfrac{\dfrac{7}{x}}{\dfrac{1}{x} + \dfrac{z}{x}} = \dfrac{x\left(\dfrac{7}{x}\right)}{x\left(\dfrac{1}{x}\right) + x\left(\dfrac{z}{x}\right)} = $ _____

2. $\dfrac{\dfrac{x}{4}}{\dfrac{x^2}{2} + \dfrac{1}{4}} = \dfrac{4\left(\dfrac{x}{4}\right)}{4\left(\dfrac{x^2}{2}\right) + 4\left(\dfrac{1}{4}\right)} = $ _____

Write with positive exponents.

3. $x^{-2} = $ _____

4. $y^{-3} = $ _____

5. $2x^{-1} = $ _____

6. $(2x)^{-1} = $ _____

7. $(9y)^{-1} = $ _____

8. $9y^{-2} = $ _____

Martin-Gay Interactive Videos

See Video 6.3 🌢

Watch the section lecture video and answer the following questions.

OBJECTIVE 1
9. From ▦ Example 2, before you can rewrite the complex fraction as division, describe how it must appear.

OBJECTIVE 2
10. How does finding an LCD in method 2, as in ▦ Example 3, differ from finding an LCD in method 1? In your answer, mention the purpose of the LCD in each method.

OBJECTIVE 3
11. Based on ▦ Example 4, what connection is there between negative exponents and complex fractions?

6.3 Exercise Set MyMathLab®

Simplify each complex fraction. See Examples 1 and 2.

1. $\dfrac{\dfrac{10}{3x}}{\dfrac{5}{6x}}$

2. $\dfrac{\dfrac{15}{2x}}{\dfrac{5}{6x}}$

9. $\dfrac{\dfrac{4x^2 - y^2}{xy}}{\dfrac{2}{y} - \dfrac{1}{x}}$

10. $\dfrac{\dfrac{x^2 - 9y^2}{xy}}{\dfrac{1}{y} - \dfrac{3}{x}}$

3. $\dfrac{1 + \dfrac{2}{5}}{2 + \dfrac{3}{5}}$

4. $\dfrac{2 + \dfrac{1}{7}}{3 - \dfrac{4}{7}}$

11. $\dfrac{\dfrac{x+1}{3}}{\dfrac{2x-1}{6}}$

12. $\dfrac{\dfrac{x+3}{12}}{\dfrac{4x-5}{15}}$

5. $\dfrac{\dfrac{4}{x-1}}{\dfrac{x}{x-1}}$

6. $\dfrac{\dfrac{x}{x+2}}{\dfrac{2}{x+2}}$

13. $\dfrac{\dfrac{2}{x} + \dfrac{3}{x^2}}{\dfrac{4}{x^2} - \dfrac{9}{x}}$

14. $\dfrac{\dfrac{2}{x^2} + \dfrac{1}{x}}{\dfrac{4}{x^2} - \dfrac{1}{x}}$

7. $\dfrac{1 - \dfrac{2}{x}}{x + \dfrac{4}{9x}}$

8. $\dfrac{5 - \dfrac{3}{x}}{x + \dfrac{2}{3x}}$

15. $\dfrac{\dfrac{1}{x} + \dfrac{2}{x^2}}{x + \dfrac{8}{x^2}}$

16. $\dfrac{\dfrac{1}{y} + \dfrac{3}{y^2}}{y + \dfrac{27}{y^2}}$

17. $\dfrac{\dfrac{4}{5-x}+\dfrac{5}{x-5}}{\dfrac{2}{x}+\dfrac{3}{x-5}}$

18. $\dfrac{\dfrac{3}{x-4}-\dfrac{2}{4-x}}{\dfrac{2}{x-4}-\dfrac{2}{x}}$

19. $\dfrac{\dfrac{x+2}{x}-\dfrac{2}{x-1}}{\dfrac{x+1}{x}+\dfrac{x+1}{x-1}}$

20. $\dfrac{\dfrac{5}{a+2}-\dfrac{1}{a-2}}{\dfrac{3}{2+a}+\dfrac{6}{2-a}}$

21. $\dfrac{\dfrac{2}{x}+3}{\dfrac{4}{x^2}-9}$

22. $\dfrac{2+\dfrac{1}{x}}{4x-\dfrac{1}{x}}$

23. $\dfrac{1-\dfrac{x}{y}}{\dfrac{x^2}{y^2}-1}$

24. $\dfrac{1-\dfrac{2}{x}}{x-\dfrac{4}{x}}$

25. $\dfrac{\dfrac{-2x}{x-y}}{\dfrac{y}{x^2}}$

26. $\dfrac{\dfrac{7y}{x^2+xy}}{\dfrac{y^2}{x^2}}$

27. $\dfrac{\dfrac{2}{x}+\dfrac{1}{x^2}}{\dfrac{y}{x^2}}$

28. $\dfrac{\dfrac{5}{x^2}-\dfrac{2}{x}}{\dfrac{1}{x}+2}$

29. $\dfrac{\dfrac{x}{9}-\dfrac{1}{x}}{1+\dfrac{3}{x}}$

30. $\dfrac{\dfrac{x}{4}-\dfrac{4}{x}}{1-\dfrac{4}{x}}$

31. $\dfrac{\dfrac{x-1}{x^2-4}}{1+\dfrac{1}{x-2}}$

32. $\dfrac{\dfrac{x+3}{x^2-9}}{1+\dfrac{1}{x-3}}$

33. $\dfrac{\dfrac{2}{x+5}+\dfrac{4}{x+3}}{\dfrac{3x+13}{x^2+8x+15}}$

34. $\dfrac{\dfrac{2}{x+2}+\dfrac{6}{x+7}}{\dfrac{4x+13}{x^2+9x+14}}$

Simplify. See Examples 3 and 4.

35. $\dfrac{x^{-1}}{x^{-2}+y^{-2}}$

36. $\dfrac{a^{-3}+b^{-1}}{a^{-2}}$

37. $\dfrac{2a^{-1}+3b^{-2}}{a^{-1}-b^{-1}}$

38. $\dfrac{x^{-1}+y^{-1}}{3x^{-2}+5y^{-2}}$

39. $\dfrac{1}{x-x^{-1}}$

40. $\dfrac{x^{-2}}{x+3x^{-1}}$

41. $\dfrac{a^{-1}+1}{a^{-1}-1}$

42. $\dfrac{a^{-1}-4}{4+a^{-1}}$

43. $\dfrac{3x^{-1}+(2y)^{-1}}{x^{-2}}$

44. $\dfrac{5x^{-2}-3y^{-1}}{x^{-1}+y^{-1}}$

45. $\dfrac{2a^{-1}+(2a)^{-1}}{a^{-1}+2a^{-2}}$

46. $\dfrac{a^{-1}+2a^{-2}}{2a^{-1}+(2a)^{-1}}$

47. $\dfrac{5x^{-1}+2y^{-1}}{x^{-2}y^{-2}}$

48. $\dfrac{x^{-2}y^{-2}}{5x^{-1}+2y^{-1}}$

49. $\dfrac{5x^{-1}-2y^{-1}}{25x^{-2}-4y^{-2}}$

50. $\dfrac{3x^{-1}+3y^{-1}}{4x^{-2}-9y^{-2}}$

REVIEW AND PREVIEW

Simplify. See Sections 5.1 and 5.2.

51. $\dfrac{3x^3y^2}{12x}$

52. $\dfrac{-36xb^3}{9xb^2}$

53. $\dfrac{144x^5y^5}{-16x^2y}$

54. $\dfrac{48x^3y^2}{-4xy}$

Solve the following. See Section 2.6.

55. $|x-5|=9$

56. $|2y+1|=1$

CONCEPT EXTENSIONS

Solve. For Exercises 57, 58, 61, and 62, see the Concept Check in this section.

57. Which of the following are equivalent to $\dfrac{\dfrac{x+1}{9}}{\dfrac{y-2}{5}}$?

   a. $\dfrac{x+1}{9}\div\dfrac{y-2}{5}$ b. $\dfrac{x+1}{9}\cdot\dfrac{y-2}{5}$ c. $\dfrac{x+1}{9}\cdot\dfrac{5}{y-2}$

58. Which of the following are equivalent to $\dfrac{\dfrac{a}{7}}{\dfrac{b}{13}}$?

   a. $\dfrac{a}{7}\cdot\dfrac{b}{13}$ b. $\dfrac{a}{7}\div\dfrac{b}{13}$ c. $\dfrac{a}{7}\div\dfrac{13}{b}$ d. $\dfrac{a}{7}\cdot\dfrac{13}{b}$

59. When the source of a sound is traveling toward a listener, the pitch that the listener hears due to the Doppler effect is given by the complex rational expression $\dfrac{a}{1-\dfrac{s}{770}}$, where a is the actual pitch of the sound and s is the speed of the sound source. Simplify this expression.

60. In baseball, the earned run average (ERA) statistic gives the average number of earned runs scored on a pitcher per game. It is computed with the following expression: $\dfrac{E}{\dfrac{I}{9}}$, where E is the number of earned runs scored on a pitcher and I is the total number of innings pitched by the pitcher. Simplify this expression.

61. Which of the following are equivalent to $\dfrac{\dfrac{1}{x}}{\dfrac{3}{y}}$?

a. $\dfrac{1}{x} \div \dfrac{3}{y}$ **b.** $\dfrac{1}{x} \cdot \dfrac{y}{3}$ **c.** $\dfrac{1}{x} \div \dfrac{y}{3}$

62. Which of the following are equivalent to $\dfrac{\dfrac{5}{2}}{a}$?

a. $\dfrac{5}{1} \div \dfrac{2}{a}$ **b.** $\dfrac{1}{5} \div \dfrac{2}{a}$ **c.** $\dfrac{5}{1} \cdot \dfrac{2}{a}$

63. In your own words, explain one method for simplifying a complex fraction.

64. Explain your favorite method for simplifying a complex fraction and why.

Simplify.

65. $\dfrac{1}{1 + (1 + x)^{-1}}$

66. $\dfrac{(x + 2)^{-1} + (x - 2)^{-1}}{(x^2 - 4)^{-1}}$

67. $\dfrac{x}{1 - \dfrac{1}{1 + \dfrac{1}{x}}}$

68. $\dfrac{x}{1 - \dfrac{1}{1 - \dfrac{1}{x}}}$

69. $\dfrac{\dfrac{2}{y^2} - \dfrac{5}{xy} - \dfrac{3}{x^2}}{\dfrac{2}{y^2} + \dfrac{7}{xy} + \dfrac{3}{x^2}}$

70. $\dfrac{\dfrac{2}{x^2} - \dfrac{1}{xy} - \dfrac{1}{y^2}}{\dfrac{1}{x^2} - \dfrac{3}{xy} + \dfrac{2}{y^2}}$

71. $\dfrac{3(a + 1)^{-1} + 4a^{-2}}{(a^3 + a^2)^{-1}}$

72. $\dfrac{9x^{-1} - 5(x - y)^{-1}}{4(x - y)^{-1}}$

*In the study of calculus, the difference quotient $\dfrac{f(a + h) - f(a)}{h}$ is often found and simplified. Find and simplify this quotient for each function $f(x)$ by following steps **a** through **d**.*

a. Find $(a + h)$.

b. Find $f(a)$.

c. Use steps **a** and **b** to find $\dfrac{f(a + h) - f(a)}{h}$.

d. Simplify the result of step **c**.

73. $f(x) = \dfrac{1}{x}$

74. $f(x) = \dfrac{5}{x}$

75. $f(x) = \dfrac{3}{x + 1}$

76. $f(x) = \dfrac{2}{x^2}$

6.4   Dividing Polynomials: Long Division and Synthetic Division

OBJECTIVES

1   Divide a Polynomial by a Monomial.

2   Divide by a Polynomial.

3   Use Synthetic Division to Divide a Polynomial by a Binomial.

4   Use the Remainder Theorem to Evaluate Polynomials.

OBJECTIVE

1   Dividing a Polynomial by a Monomial

Recall that a rational expression is a quotient of polynomials. An equivalent form of a rational expression can be obtained by performing the indicated division. For example, the rational expression

$$\frac{10x^3 - 5x^2 + 20x}{5x}$$

can be thought of as the polynomial $10x^3 - 5x^2 + 20x$ divided by the monomial $5x$. To perform this division of a polynomial by a monomial (which we do on the next page), recall the following addition fact for fractions with a common denominator.

$$\underbrace{\frac{a}{c} + \frac{b}{c} = \frac{a + b}{c}}$$

If a, b, and c are monomials, we might read this equation from right to left and gain insight into dividing a polynomial by a monomial.

> **Dividing a Polynomial by a Monomial**
>
> Divide each term in the polynomial by the monomial.
>
> $$\frac{a + b}{c} = \frac{a}{c} + \frac{b}{c}, \quad \text{where } c \neq 0$$

EXAMPLE 1   Divide: $10x^3 - 5x^2 + 20x$ by $5x$

Solution We divide each term of $10x^3 - 5x^2 + 20x$ by $5x$ and simplify.

$$\frac{10x^3 - 5x^2 + 20x}{5x} = \frac{10x^3}{5x} - \frac{5x^2}{5x} + \frac{20x}{5x} = 2x^2 - x + 4$$

Check: To check, see that (quotient) (divisor) = dividend, or

$$(2x^2 - x + 4)(5x) = 10x^3 - 5x^2 + 20x.$$ □

PRACTICE
1   Divide $18a^3 - 12a^2 + 30a$ by $6a$.   ■

EXAMPLE 2   Divide: $\dfrac{3x^5y^2 - 15x^3y - x^2y - 6x}{x^2y}$

Solution We divide each term in the numerator by x^2y.

$$\frac{3x^5y^2 - 15x^3y - x^2y - 6x}{x^2y} = \frac{3x^5y^2}{x^2y} - \frac{15x^3y}{x^2y} - \frac{x^2y}{x^2y} - \frac{6x}{x^2y}$$

$$= 3x^3y - 15x - 1 - \frac{6}{xy}$$ □

PRACTICE
2   Divide: $\dfrac{5a^3b^4 - 8a^2b^3 + ab^2 - 8b}{ab^2}$ ■

OBJECTIVE
2   **Dividing by a Polynomial** ▶

To divide a polynomial by a polynomial other than a monomial, we use **long division.** Polynomial long division is similar to long division of real numbers. We review long division of real numbers by dividing 7 into 296.

$$\begin{array}{r} 42 \\ 7\overline{)296} \\ -28 \\ \hline 16 \\ -14 \\ \hline 2 \end{array}$$

Divisor: $7\overline{)296}$
-28 $4(7) = 28$
16 Subtract and bring down the next digit in the dividend.
-14 $2(7) = 14$
2 Subtract. The remainder is 2.

The quotient is $42\dfrac{2 \text{ (remainder)}}{7 \text{ (divisor)}}$.

Check: To check, notice that

$$42(7) + 2 = 296, \text{ the dividend.}$$

This same division process can be applied to polynomials, as shown next.

EXAMPLE 3   Divide: $2x^2 - x - 10$ by $x + 2$

Solution $2x^2 - x - 10$ is the dividend, and $x + 2$ is the divisor.
Step 1.   Divide $2x^2$ by x.

$$x + 2\overline{)2x^2 - x - 10}$$ with quotient term $2x$ $\dfrac{2x^2}{x} = 2x$, so $2x$ is the first term of the quotient.

(Continued on next page)

Step 2. Multiply $2x(x + 2)$.

$$
\begin{array}{r}
2x \\
x + 2 \overline{)2x^2 - x - 10} \\
\underline{2x^2 + 4x}
\end{array}
$$

$2x(x + 2)$

Like terms are lined up vertically.

Step 3. Subtract $(2x^2 + 4x)$ from $(2x^2 - x - 10)$ by changing the signs of $(2x^2 + 4x)$ and adding.

$$
\begin{array}{r}
2x \\
x + 2 \overline{)\ 2x^2 - x - 10} \\
\underline{\cancel{+}2x^2 \cancel{+} 4x} \\
-5x
\end{array}
$$

Step 4. Bring down the next term, -10, and start the process over.

$$
\begin{array}{r}
2x \\
x + 2 \overline{)\ 2x^2 - x - 10} \\
\underline{\cancel{+}2x^2 \cancel{+} 4x} \ \ \downarrow \\
-5x - 10
\end{array}
$$

Step 5. Divide $-5x$ by x.

$$
\begin{array}{r}
2x - 5 \\
x + 2 \overline{)\ 2x^2 - x - 10} \\
\underline{\cancel{+}2x^2 \cancel{+} 4x} \\
-5x - 10
\end{array}
$$

$\dfrac{-5x}{x} = -5$, so -5 is the second term of the quotient.

Step 6. Multiply $-5(x + 2)$.

$$
\begin{array}{r}
2x - 5 \\
x + 2 \overline{)\ 2x^2 - x - 10} \\
\underline{\cancel{+}2x^2 \cancel{+} 4x} \\
-5x - 10 \\
-5x - 10
\end{array}
$$

Multiply $-5(x + 2)$. Like terms are lined up vertically.

Step 7. Subtract by changing signs of $-5x - 10$ and adding.

$$
\begin{array}{r}
2x - 5 \\
x + 2 \overline{)\ 2x^2 - x - 10} \\
\underline{\cancel{+}2x^2 \cancel{+} 4x} \\
-5x - 10 \\
\underline{\overset{+}{\cancel{+}}5x \overset{+}{\cancel{+}} 10} \\
0
\end{array}
$$

Subtract.

Remainder

Then $\dfrac{2x^2 - x - 10}{x + 2} = 2x - 5$. There is no remainder.

Check: Check this result by multiplying $2x - 5$ by $x + 2$. Their product is $(2x - 5)(x + 2) = 2x^2 - x - 10$, the dividend. ☐

PRACTICE

3 Divide $3x^2 + 7x - 6$ by $x + 3$.

EXAMPLE 4   Divide: $(6x^2 - 19x + 12) \div (3x - 5)$

Solution

$$
\begin{array}{r}
2x \\
3x - 5 \overline{)6x^2 - 19x + 12} \\
\underline{6x^2 - 10x} \\
-9x + 12
\end{array}
$$

Divide $\dfrac{6x^2}{3x} = 2x$.

Multiply $2x(3x - 5)$.

Subtract by adding the opposite.
Bring down the next term, $+12$.

$$
\begin{array}{r}
2x - 3 \\
3x - 5 \overline{)6x^2 - 19x + 12} \\
\underline{6x^2 - 10x} \\
-9x + 12 \\
\underline{-9x + 15} \\
-3
\end{array}
$$

Divide $\dfrac{-9x}{3x} = -3$.

Multiply $-3(3x - 5)$.
Subtract by adding the opposite.

Check: divisor $\cdot$ quotient $+$ remainder

$$(3x - 5) \quad \cdot \quad (2x - 3) \quad + \quad (-3) = 6x^2 - 19x + 15 - 3$$

$$= 6x^2 - 19x + 12 \quad \text{The dividend}$$

The division checks, so

$$\frac{6x^2 - 19x + 12}{3x - 5} = 2x - 3 + \frac{-3}{3x - 5}$$

$$\text{or} \quad 2x - 3 - \frac{3}{3x - 5}$$

> **Helpful Hint**
> This fraction is the remainder over the divisor.

PRACTICE
4   Divide: $(6x^2 - 7x + 8) \div (2x - 1)$

EXAMPLE 5   Divide: $(7x^3 + 16x^2 + 2x - 1) \div (x + 4)$

Solution

$$
\begin{array}{r}
7x^2 - 12x + 50 \\
x + 4 \overline{)7x^3 + 16x^2 + 2x - 1} \\
\underline{7x^3 + 28x^2} \\
-12x^2 + 2x \\
\underline{-12x^2 - 48x} \\
50x - 1 \\
\underline{50x + 200} \\
-201
\end{array}
$$

Divide $\dfrac{7x^3}{x} = 7x^2$.

$7x^2(x + 4)$

Subtract. Bring down $2x$.

$\dfrac{-12x^2}{x} = -12x$, a term of the quotient.

$-12x(x + 4)$ Subtract. Bring down -1.

$\dfrac{50x}{x} = 50$, a term of the quotient.

$50(x + 4)$ Subtract.

Thus, $\dfrac{7x^3 + 16x^2 + 2x - 1}{x + 4} = 7x^2 - 12x + 50 + \dfrac{-201}{x + 4}$ or

$$7x^2 - 12x + 50 - \frac{201}{x + 4}.$$

PRACTICE
5   Divide: $(5x^3 + 9x^2 - 10x + 30) \div (x + 3)$

EXAMPLE 6   Divide $3x^4 + 2x^3 - 8x + 6$ by $x^2 - 1$.

Solution Before dividing, we represent any "missing powers" by the product of 0 and the variable raised to the missing power. There is no x^2 term in the dividend, so we include $0x^2$ to represent the missing term. Also, there is no x term in the divisor, so we include $0x$ in the divisor.

$$
\begin{array}{r}
3x^2 + 2x + 3 \\
x^2 + 0x - 1{\overline{\smash{\big)}\,3x^4 + 2x^3 + 0x^2 - 8x + 6}} \\
\underline{3x^4 \mp 0x^3 \not\mp 3x^2} \\
2x^3 + 3x^2 - 8x \\
\underline{2x^3 \mp 0x^2 \not\mp 2x} \\
3x^2 - 6x + 6 \\
\underline{3x^2 \mp 0x \not\mp 3} \\
-6x + 9
\end{array}
$$

$\dfrac{3x^4}{x^2} = 3x^2$

$3x^2(x^2 + 0x - 1)$
Subtract. Bring down $-8x$.

$\dfrac{2x^3}{x^2} = 2x$, a term of the quotient.

$2x(x^2 + 0x - 1)$
Subtract. Bring down 6.

$\dfrac{3x^2}{x^2} = 3$, a term of the quotient.

$3(x^2 + 0x - 1)$
Subtract.

The division process is finished when the degree of the remainder polynomial is less than the degree of the divisor. Thus,

$$\frac{3x^4 + 2x^3 - 8x + 6}{x^2 - 1} = 3x^2 + 2x + 3 + \frac{-6x + 9}{x^2 - 1} \qquad \square$$

PRACTICE
6   Divide $2x^4 + 3x^3 - 5x + 2$ by $x^2 + 1$. ■

EXAMPLE 7   Divide $27x^3 + 8$ by $3x + 2$.

Solution We replace the missing terms in the dividend with $0x^2$ and $0x$.

$$
\begin{array}{r}
9x^2 - 6x + 4 \\
3x + 2{\overline{\smash{\big)}\,27x^3 + 0x^2 + 0x + 8}} \\
\underline{27x^3 \not\mp 18x^2} \\
-18x^2 + 0x \\
\underline{\mp 18x^2 \not\mp 12x} \\
12x + 8 \\
\underline{12x \not\mp 8} \\
0
\end{array}
$$

$9x^2(3x + 2)$
Subtract. Bring down $0x$.

$-6x(3x + 2)$
Subtract. Bring down 8.

$4(3x + 2)$

Thus, $\dfrac{27x^3 + 8}{3x + 2} = 9x^2 - 6x + 4.$ $\qquad \square$

PRACTICE
7   Divide $64x^3 - 125$ by $4x - 5$. ■

✔ **CONCEPT CHECK**

In a division problem, the divisor is $4x^3 - 5$. The division process can be stopped when which of these possible remainder polynomials is reached?

a. $2x^4 + x^2 - 3$ **b.** $x^3 - 5^2$ **c.** $4x^2 + 25$

OBJECTIVE

3   Using Synthetic Division to Divide a Polynomial by a Binomial ▶

When a polynomial is to be divided by a binomial of the form $x - c$, a shortcut process called **synthetic division** may be used. On the next page, on the left is an example of long division, and on the right, the same example showing the coefficients of the variables only.

$$
\begin{array}{r}
2x^2 + 5x + 2 \\
x - 3\overline{)2x^3 - x^2 - 13x + 1} \\
\underline{2x^3 - 6x^2} \\
5x^2 - 13x \\
\underline{5x^2 - 15x} \\
2x + 1 \\
\underline{2x - 6} \\
7
\end{array}
\qquad
\begin{array}{r}
2 \quad 5 \quad 2 \\
1 - 3\overline{)2 - 1 - 13 + 1} \\
\underline{2 - 6} \\
5 - 13 \\
\underline{5 - 15} \\
2 + 1 \\
\underline{2 - 6} \\
7
\end{array}
$$

Notice that as long as we keep coefficients of powers of x in the same column, we can perform division of polynomials by performing algebraic operations on the coefficients only. This shortcut process of dividing with coefficients only in a special format is called synthetic division. To find $(2x^3 - x^2 - 13x + 1) \div (x - 3)$ by synthetic division, follow the next example.

EXAMPLE 8   Use synthetic division to divide $2x^3 - x^2 - 13x + 1$ by $x - 3$.

Solution To use synthetic division, the divisor must be in the form $x - c$. Since we are dividing by $x - 3$, c is 3. Write down 3 and the coefficients of the dividend.

$$
\begin{array}{c|cccc}
c & & & & \\
3 & 2 & -1 & -13 & 1 \\
& \downarrow & & & \\
\hline
& 2 & & &
\end{array}
$$

Next, draw a line and bring down the first coefficient of the dividend.

$$
\begin{array}{c|cccc}
3 & 2 & -1 & -13 & 1 \\
& & 6 & & \\
\hline
& 2 & & &
\end{array}
$$

Multiply $3 \cdot 2$ and write down the product, 6.

$$
\begin{array}{c|cccc}
3 & 2 & -1 & -13 & 1 \\
& & 6 & & \\
\hline
& 2 & 5 & &
\end{array}
$$

Add $-1 + 6$. Write down the sum, 5.

$$
\begin{array}{c|cccc}
3 & 2 & -1 & -13 & 1 \\
& & 6 & 15 & \\
\hline
& 2 & 5 & 2 &
\end{array}
$$

$3 \cdot 5 = 15$
$-13 + 15 = 2$

$$
\begin{array}{c|cccc}
3 & 2 & -1 & -13 & 1 \\
& & 6 & 15 & 6 \\
\hline
& 2 & 5 & 2 & 7
\end{array}
$$

$3 \cdot 2 = 6$
$1 + 6 = 7$

The quotient is found in the bottom row. The numbers 2, 5, and 2 are the coefficients of the quotient polynomial, and the number 7 is the remainder. The degree of the quotient polynomial is one less than the degree of the dividend. In our example, the degree of the dividend is 3, so the degree of the quotient polynomial is 2. As we found when we performed the long division, the quotient is

$$2x^2 + 5x + 2, \quad \text{remainder } 7$$

or

$$2x^2 + 5x + 2 + \frac{7}{x - 3}$$

PRACTICE

8   Use synthetic division to divide $4x^3 - 3x^2 + 6x + 5$ by $x - 1$.

When using synthetic division, if there are missing powers of the variable, insert 0s as coefficients.

EXAMPLE 9 Use synthetic division to divide $x^4 - 2x^3 - 11x^2 + 34$ by $x + 2$.

Solution The divisor is $x + 2$, which in the form $x - c$ is $x - (-2)$. Thus, c is -2. There is no x-term in the dividend, so we insert a coefficient of 0. The dividend coefficients are $1, -2, -11, 0$, and 34.

$$
\begin{array}{r|rrrrr}
-2 & 1 & -2 & -11 & 0 & 34 \\
  &   & -2 & 8 & 6 & -12 \\
\hline
  & 1 & -4 & -3 & 6 & 22
\end{array}
$$

The dividend is a fourth-degree polynomial, so the quotient polynomial is a third-degree polynomial. The quotient is $x^3 - 4x^2 - 3x + 6$ with a remainder of 22. Thus,

$$\frac{x^4 - 2x^3 - 11x^2 + 34}{x + 2} = x^3 - 4x^2 - 3x + 6 + \frac{22}{x + 2}$$

PRACTICE

9 Use synthetic division to divide $x^4 + 3x^3 - 5x^2 + 12$ by $x + 3$.

✔ **CONCEPT CHECK**

Which division problems are candidates for the synthetic division process?

a. $(3x^2 + 5) \div (x + 4)$

b. $(x^3 - x^2 + 2) \div (3x^3 - 2)$

c. $(y^4 + y - 3) \div (x^2 + 1)$

d. $x^5 \div (x - 5)$

Helpful Hint

Before dividing by synthetic division, write the dividend in descending order of variable exponents. Any "missing powers" of the variable should be represented by 0 times the variable raised to the missing power.

EXAMPLE 10 If $P(x) = 2x^3 - 4x^2 + 5$,

a. Find $P(2)$ by substitution.

b. Use synthetic division to find the remainder when $P(x)$ is divided by $x - 2$.

Solution

a. $P(x) = 2x^3 - 4x^2 + 5$

$P(2) = 2(2)^3 - 4(2)^2 + 5$

$= 2(8) - 4(4) + 5 = 16 - 16 + 5 = 5$

Thus, $P(2) = 5$.

b. The coefficients of $P(x)$ are $2, -4, 0$, and 5. The number 0 is the coefficient of the missing power of x^1. The divisor is $x - 2$, so c is 2.

$$
\begin{array}{r|rrrr}
\overset{c}{\searrow} & & & & \\
2 & 2 & -4 & 0 & 5 \\
  &   & 4 & 0 & 0 \\
\hline
  & 2 & 0 & 0 & 5 \quad \text{remainder}
\end{array}
$$

The remainder when $P(x)$ is divided by $x - 2$ is 5.

PRACTICE
10   If $P(x) = x^3 - 5x - 2$,
   a. Find $P(2)$ by substitution.
   b. Use synthetic division to find the remainder when $P(x)$ is divided by $x - 2$. ∎

OBJECTIVE
4 Using the Remainder Theorem to Evaluate Polynomials ▶

Notice in the preceding example that $P(2) = 5$ and that the remainder when $P(x)$ is divided by $x - 2$ is 5. This is no accident. This illustrates the **remainder theorem.**

> **Remainder Theorem**
>
> If a polynomial $P(x)$ is divided by $x - c$, then the remainder is $P(c)$.

EXAMPLE 11   Use the remainder theorem and synthetic division to find $P(4)$ if
$$P(x) = 4x^6 - 25x^5 + 35x^4 + 17x^2$$

Solution To find $P(4)$ by the remainder theorem, we divide $P(x)$ by $x - 4$. The coefficients of $P(x)$ are $4, -25, 35, 0, 17, 0,$ and 0. Also, c is 4.

$$
\begin{array}{r|rrrrrrr}
c\searrow & & & & & & & \\
\underline{4|} & 4 & -25 & 35 & 0 & 17 & 0 & 0 \\
 & & 16 & -36 & -4 & -16 & 4 & 16 \\
\hline
 & 4 & -9 & -1 & -4 & 1 & 4 & 16 \quad \text{remainder}
\end{array}
$$

Thus, $P(4) = 16$, the remainder.   □

PRACTICE
11   Use the remainder theorem and synthetic division to find $P(3)$ if $P(x) = 2x^5 - 18x^4 + 90x^2 + 59x$. ∎

✓ **Vocabulary, Readiness & Video Check**

Martin-Gay Interactive Videos

See Video 6.4 ▶

Watch the section lecture video and answer the following questions.

OBJECTIVE 1
1. In the lecture before ▦ Example 1, dividing a polynomial by a monomial is compared to adding two fractions. What role does the monomial play in the fraction example?

OBJECTIVE 2
2. From ▦ Example 2, how do you know when to stop your long division?

OBJECTIVE 3
3. From ▦ Example 3, once you've completed the synthetic division, what does the bottom row of numbers mean? What is the degree of the quotient?

OBJECTIVE 4
4. From ▦ Example 4, given a polynomial function $P(x)$, under what circumstances might it be easier/faster to use the remainder theorem to find $P(c)$ rather than substituting the value c for x and then simplifying?

6.4 Exercise Set MyMathLab

Divide. See Examples 1 and 2.

1. $4a^2 + 8a$ by $2a$

2. $6x^4 - 3x^3$ by $3x^2$

3. $\dfrac{12a^5b^2 + 16a^4b}{4a^4b}$

4. $\dfrac{4x^3y + 12x^2y^2 - 4xy^3}{4xy}$

5. $\dfrac{4x^2y^2 + 6xy^2 - 4y^2}{2x^2y}$

6. $\dfrac{6x^5y + 75x^4y - 24x^3y^2}{3x^4y}$

Divide. See Examples 3 through 7.

7. $(x^2 + 3x + 2) \div (x + 2)$

8. $(y^2 + 7y + 10) \div (y + 5)$

9. $(2x^2 - 6x - 8) \div (x + 1)$

10. $(3x^2 + 19x + 20) \div (x + 5)$

11. $2x^2 + 3x - 2$ by $2x + 4$

12. $6x^2 - 17x - 3$ by $3x - 9$

13. $(4x^3 + 7x^2 + 8x + 20) \div (2x + 4)$

14. $(8x^3 + 18x^2 + 16x + 24) \div (4x + 8)$

15. $(2x^2 + 6x^3 - 18x - 6) \div (3x + 1)$

16. $(4x - 15x^2 + 10x^3 - 6) \div (2x - 3)$

17. $(3x^5 - x^3 + 4x^2 - 12x - 8) \div (x^2 - 2)$

18. $(2x^5 - 6x^4 + x^3 - 4x + 3) \div (x^2 - 3)$

19. $\left(2x^4 + \dfrac{1}{2}x^3 + x^2 + x\right) \div (x - 2)$

20. $\left(x^4 - \dfrac{2}{3}x^3 + x\right) \div (x - 3)$

Use synthetic division to divide. See Examples 8 and 9.

21. $\dfrac{x^2 + 3x - 40}{x - 5}$

22. $\dfrac{x^2 - 14x + 24}{x - 2}$

23. $\dfrac{x^2 + 5x - 6}{x + 6}$

24. $\dfrac{x^2 + 12x + 32}{x + 4}$

25. $\dfrac{x^3 - 7x^2 - 13x + 5}{x - 2}$

26. $\dfrac{x^3 + 6x^2 + 4x - 7}{x + 5}$

27. $\dfrac{4x^2 - 9}{x - 2}$

28. $\dfrac{3x^2 - 4}{x - 1}$

MIXED PRACTICE

Divide. See Examples 1–9.

29. $\dfrac{4x^7y^4 + 8xy^2 + 4xy^3}{4xy^3}$

30. $\dfrac{15x^3y - 5x^2y + 10xy^2}{5x^2y}$

31. $(10x^3 - 5x^2 - 12x + 1) \div (2x - 1)$

32. $(20x^3 - 8x^2 + 5x - 5) \div (5x - 2)$

33. $(2x^3 - 6x^2 - 4) \div (x - 4)$

34. $(3x^3 + 4x - 10) \div (x + 2)$

35. $\dfrac{2x^4 - 13x^3 + 16x^2 - 9x + 20}{x - 5}$

36. $\dfrac{3x^4 + 5x^3 - x^2 + x - 2}{x + 2}$

37. $\dfrac{7x^2 - 4x + 12 + 3x^3}{x + 1}$

38. $\dfrac{4x^3 + x^4 - x^2 - 16x - 4}{x - 2}$

39. $\dfrac{3x^3 + 2x^2 - 4x + 1}{x - \dfrac{1}{3}}$

40. $\dfrac{9y^3 + 9y^2 - y + 2}{y + \dfrac{2}{3}}$

41. $\dfrac{x^3 - 1}{x - 1}$

42. $\dfrac{y^3 - 8}{y - 2}$

43. $(25xy^2 + 75xyz + 125x^2yz) \div (-5x^2y)$

44. $(x^6y^6 - x^3y^3z + 7x^3y) \div (-7yz^2)$

45. $(9x^5 + 6x^4 - 6x^2 - 4x) \div (3x + 2)$

46. $(5x^4 - 5x^2 + 10x^3 - 10x) \div (5x + 10)$

For the given polynomial $P(x)$ and the given c, use the remainder theorem to find $P(c)$. See Examples 10 and 11.

47. $P(x) = x^3 + 3x^2 - 7x + 4; 1$

48. $P(x) = x^3 + 5x^2 - 4x - 6; 2$

49. $P(x) = 3x^3 - 7x^2 - 2x + 5; -3$

50. $P(x) = 4x^3 + 5x^2 - 6x - 4; -2$

51. $P(x) = 4x^4 + x^2 - 2; -1$

52. $P(x) = x^4 - 3x^2 - 2x + 5; -2$

53. $P(x) = 2x^4 - 3x^2 - 2; \dfrac{1}{3}$

54. $P(x) = 4x^4 - 2x^3 + x^2 - x - 4; \dfrac{1}{2}$

55. $P(x) = x^5 + x^4 - x^3 + 3; \dfrac{1}{2}$

56. $P(x) = x^5 - 2x^3 + 4x^2 - 5x + 6; \dfrac{2}{3}$

REVIEW AND PREVIEW

Solve each equation for x. See Sections 2.1 and 5.8.

57. $7x + 2 = x - 3$

58. $4 - 2x = 17 - 5x$

59. $x^2 = 4x - 4$

60. $5x^2 + 10x = 15$

61. $\dfrac{x}{3} - 5 = 13$

62. $\dfrac{2x}{9} + 1 = \dfrac{7}{9}$

Factor the following. See Sections 5.5 and 5.7.

63. $x^3 - 1$

64. $8y^3 + 1$

65. $125z^3 + 8$

66. $a^3 - 27$

67. $xy + 2x + 3y + 6$

68. $x^2 - x + xy - y$

69. $x^3 - 9x$

70. $2x^3 - 32x$

CONCEPT EXTENSIONS

Determine whether each division problem is a candidate for the synthetic division process. See the Concept Checks in this section.

71. $(5x^2 - 3x + 2) \div (x + 2)$

72. $(x^4 - 6) \div (x^3 + 3x - 1)$

73. $(x^7 - 2) \div (x^5 + 1)$

74. $(3x^2 + 7x - 1) \div \left(x - \dfrac{1}{3}\right)$

75. In a long division exercise, if the divisor is $9x^3 - 2x$, the division process can be stopped when the degree of the remainder is

  a. 1   **b.** 3   **c.** 9   **d.** 2

76. In a division exercise, if the divisor is $x - 3$, the division process can be stopped when the degree of the remainder is

  a. 1   **b.** 0   **c.** 2   **d.** 3

Solve.

△ **77.** A board of length $(3x^4 + 6x^2 - 18)$ meters is to be cut into three pieces of the same length. Find the length of each piece.

△ **78.** The perimeter of a regular hexagon is given to be $(12x^5 - 48x^3 + 3)$ miles. Find the length of each side.

△ **79.** If the area of the rectangle is $(15x^2 - 29x - 14)$ square inches, and its length is $(5x + 2)$ inches, find its width.

?

(5x + 2) in.

△ **80.** If the area of a parallelogram is $(2x^2 - 17x + 35)$ square centimeters and its base is $(2x - 7)$ centimeters, find its height.

(2x − 7) cm

△ **81.** If the area of a parallelogram is $(x^4 - 23x^2 + 9x - 5)$ square centimeters and its base is $(x + 5)$ centimeters, find its height.

Height

(x + 5) centimeters

△ **82.** If the volume of a box is $(x^4 + 6x^3 - 7x^2)$ cubic meters, its height is x^2 meters, and its length is $(x + 7)$ meters, find its width.

x^2 meters

(x + 7) meters

Width

Divide.

83. $\left(x^4 + \dfrac{2}{3}x^3 + x\right) \div (x - 1)$

84. $\left(2x^3 + \dfrac{9}{2}x^2 - 4x - 10\right) \div (x + 2)$

85. $\left(3x^4 - x - x^3 + \dfrac{1}{2}\right) \div (2x - 1)$

86. $\left(2x^4 + \dfrac{1}{2}x^3 - \dfrac{1}{4}x^2 + x\right) \div (2x + 1)$

87. $(5x^4 - 2x^2 + 10x^3 - 4x) \div (5x + 10)$

88. $(9x^5 + 6x^4 - 6x^2 - 4x) \div (3x + 2)$

For each given f(x) and g(x), find $\dfrac{f(x)}{g(x)}$. Also find any x-values that are not in the domain of $\dfrac{f(x)}{g(x)}$. (Note: Since g(x) is in the denominator, g(x) cannot be 0.)

89. $f(x) = 25x^2 - 5x + 30; g(x) = 5x$

90. $f(x) = 12x^4 - 9x^3 + 3x - 1; g(x) = 3x$

91. $f(x) = 7x^4 - 3x^2 + 2; g(x) = x - 2$

92. $f(x) = 2x^3 - 4x^2 + 1; g(x) = x + 3$

93. Try performing the following division without changing the order of the terms. Describe why this makes the process more complicated. Then perform the division again after putting the terms in the dividend in descending order of exponents.

$$\frac{4x^2 - 12x - 12 + 3x^3}{x - 2}$$

94. Explain how to check polynomial long division.

95. Explain an advantage of using the remainder theorem instead of direct substitution.

96. Explain an advantage of using synthetic division instead of long division.

We say that 2 is a factor of 8 because 2 divides 8 evenly, or with a remainder of 0. In the same manner, the polynomial $x - 2$ is a factor of the polynomial $x^3 - 14x^2 + 24x$ because the remainder is 0 when $x^3 - 14x^2 + 24x$ is divided by $x - 2$. Use this information for Exercises 97 and 98.

97. Use synthetic division to show that $x + 3$ is a factor of $x^3 + 3x^2 + 4x + 12$.

98. Use synthetic division to show that $x - 2$ is a factor of $x^3 - 2x^2 - 3x + 6$.

99. If a polynomial is divided by $x - 5$, the quotient is $2x^2 + 5x - 6$ and the remainder is 3. Find the original polynomial.

100. If a polynomial is divided by $x + 3$, the quotient is $x^2 - x + 10$ and the remainder is -2. Find the original polynomial.

101. eBay is the leading online auction house. eBay's annual net profit can be modeled by the polynomial function $P(x) = -0.08x^3 - 0.04x^2 + 1.06x + 1.9$, where $P(x)$ is net profit in billions of dollars and x is the number of years since 2010. eBay's annual revenues can be modeled by the function $R(x) = 2.2x + 9.38$, where $R(x)$ is revenue in billions of dollars and x is the number of years since 2010. (*Source:* eBay, Inc., annual reports 2010–2014)

a. Given that

$$\text{Net profit margin} = \frac{\text{net profit}}{\text{revenue}}$$

write a function, $m(x)$, that models eBay's net profit margin.

b. Use part **a** to predict eBay's profit margin in 2018. Round to the nearest hundredth.

102. Kraft Foods is a provider of many of the best-known food brands in our supermarkets. Among their well-known brands are Kraft, Oscar Mayer, Maxwell House, and Oreo. Kraft Foods' annual revenues since 2010 can be modeled by the polynomial function $R(x) = 0.11x^3 - 0.75x^2 + 1.36x + 17.83$, where $R(x)$ is revenue in billions of dollars and x is the number of years since 2010. Kraft Foods' net profit can be modeled by the function $P(x) = -0.21x^3 + 1.15x^2 - 1.37x + 1.97$, where $P(x)$ is the net profit in billions of dollars and x is the number of years since 2010. (*Source:* Based on data from Kraft Foods' annual reports)

a. Suppose that a market analyst has found the model $P(x)$ and another analyst at the same firm has found the model $R(x)$. The analysts have been asked by their manager to work together to find a model for Kraft Foods' net profit margin. The analysts know that a company's net profit margin is the ratio of its net profit to revenue. Describe how these two analysts could collaborate to find a function $m(x)$ that models Kraft Foods' net profit margin based on the work they have done independently.

b. Without actually finding $m(x)$, give a general description of what you would expect the answer to be.

103. From the remainder theorem, the polynomial $x - c$ is a factor of a polynomial function $P(x)$ if $P(c)$ is what value?

6.5 Solving Equations Containing Rational Expressions

OBJECTIVE

1 Solve Equations Containing Rational Expressions.

OBJECTIVE

1 Solving Equations Containing Rational Expressions

In this section, we solve equations containing rational expressions. Before beginning this section, make sure that you understand the difference between an *equation* and an *expression*. An **equation** contains an equal sign and an **expression** does not.

Equation	*Expression*
$\dfrac{x}{2} + \dfrac{x}{6} = \dfrac{2}{3}$	$\dfrac{x}{2} + \dfrac{x}{6}$

equal sign

Helpful Hint

The method described here is for equations only. It may *not* be used for performing operations on expressions.

Solving Equations Containing Rational Expressions

To solve *equations* containing rational expressions, first clear the equation of fractions by multiplying both sides of the equation by the LCD of all rational expressions. Then solve as usual.

✔ CONCEPT CHECK

True or false? Clearing fractions is valid when solving an equation and when simplifying rational expressions. Explain.

EXAMPLE 1 Solve: $\dfrac{4x}{5} + \dfrac{3}{2} = \dfrac{3x}{10}$

Solution The LCD of $\dfrac{4x}{5}, \dfrac{3}{2}$, and $\dfrac{3x}{10}$ is 10. We multiply both sides of the equation by 10.

$$\dfrac{4x}{5} + \dfrac{3}{2} = \dfrac{3x}{10}$$

$$10\left(\dfrac{4x}{5} + \dfrac{3}{2}\right) = 10\left(\dfrac{3x}{10}\right) \quad \text{Multiply both sides by the LCD.}$$

$$10 \cdot \dfrac{4x}{5} + 10 \cdot \dfrac{3}{2} = 10 \cdot \dfrac{3x}{10} \quad \text{Use the distributive property.}$$

$$8x + 15 = 3x \quad \text{Simplify.}$$

$$15 = -5x \quad \text{Subtract } 8x \text{ from both sides.}$$

$$-3 = x \quad \text{Solve.}$$

Verify this solution by replacing x with -3 in the original equation.

Check:

$$\dfrac{4x}{5} + \dfrac{3}{2} = \dfrac{3x}{10}$$

$$\dfrac{4(-3)}{5} + \dfrac{3}{2} \stackrel{?}{=} \dfrac{3(-3)}{10}$$

$$\dfrac{-12}{5} + \dfrac{3}{2} \stackrel{?}{=} \dfrac{-9}{10}$$

$$-\dfrac{24}{10} + \dfrac{15}{10} \stackrel{?}{=} -\dfrac{9}{10}$$

$$-\dfrac{9}{10} = -\dfrac{9}{10} \quad \text{True}$$

The solution is -3 or the solution set is $\{-3\}$. □

PRACTICE

1 Solve: $\dfrac{5x}{4} - \dfrac{3}{2} = \dfrac{7x}{8}$ ■

The important difference of the equations in this section is that the denominator of a rational expression may contain a variable. Recall that a rational expression is undefined for values of the variable that make the denominator 0. If a proposed solution makes any denominator 0, then it must be rejected as a solution of the original equation. Such proposed solutions are called **extraneous solutions.**

The following steps may be used to solve equations containing rational expressions.

Solving an Equation Containing Rational Expressions

Step 1. Multiply both sides of the equation by the LCD of all rational expressions in the equation.

Step 2. Simplify both sides.

Step 3. Determine whether the equation is linear, quadratic, or higher degree and solve accordingly.

Step 4. Check the solution in the original equation.

Answer to Concept Check:
false; answers may vary

EXAMPLE 2   Solve: $\dfrac{3}{x} - \dfrac{x + 21}{3x} = \dfrac{5}{3}$

Solution The LCD of the denominators x, $3x$, and 3 is $3x$. We multiply both sides by $3x$.

$$\frac{3}{x} - \frac{x + 21}{3x} = \frac{5}{3}$$

$$3x\left(\frac{3}{x} - \frac{x + 21}{3x}\right) = 3x\left(\frac{5}{3}\right) \quad \text{Multiply both sides by the LCD.}$$

$$3x \cdot \frac{3}{x} - 3x \cdot \frac{x + 21}{3x} = 3x \cdot \frac{5}{3} \quad \text{Use the distributive property.}$$

$$9 - (x + 21) = 5x \quad \text{Simplify.}$$

$$9 - x - 21 = 5x$$

$$-12 = 6x$$

$$-2 = x \quad \text{Solve.}$$

The proposed solution is -2.

Check: Check the proposed solution in the original equation.

$$\frac{3}{x} - \frac{x + 21}{3x} = \frac{5}{3}$$

$$\frac{3}{-2} - \frac{-2 + 21}{3(-2)} \overset{?}{=} \frac{5}{3}$$

$$-\frac{9}{6} + \frac{19}{6} \overset{?}{=} \frac{5}{3}$$

$$\frac{10}{6} \overset{?}{=} \frac{5}{3} \quad \text{True}$$

The solution is -2 or the solution set is $\{-2\}$.

PRACTICE
2   Solve: $\dfrac{6}{x} - \dfrac{x + 9}{5x} = \dfrac{2}{5}$

Let's talk more about multiplying both sides of an equation by the LCD of the rational expressions in the equation. In Example 3 that follows, the LCD is $x - 2$, so we will first multiply both sides of the equation by $x - 2$. Recall that the multiplication property for equations allows us to multiply both sides of an equation by any *nonzero* number. In other words, for Example 3 below, we may multiply both sides of the equation by $x - 2$ *as long as* $x - 2 \neq 0$ or as long as $x \neq 2$. Keep this in mind when solving these equations.

EXAMPLE 3   Solve: $\dfrac{x + 6}{x - 2} = \dfrac{2(x + 2)}{x - 2}$

Solution First we multiply both sides of the equation by the LCD, $x - 2$. (Remember, we can do this only if $x \neq 2$ so that we are not multiplying by 0.)

$$\frac{x + 6}{x - 2} = \frac{2(x + 2)}{x - 2}$$

$$(x - 2) \cdot \frac{x + 6}{x - 2} = (x - 2) \cdot \frac{2(x + 2)}{x - 2} \quad \text{Multiply both sides by } x - 2.$$

$$x + 6 = 2(x + 2) \quad \text{Simplify.}$$

$$x + 6 = 2x + 4 \quad \text{Use the distributive property.}$$

$$2 = x \quad \text{Solve.}$$

From above, we assumed that $x \neq 2$, so this equation has no solution. This will also be the case as we attempt to check this proposed solution.

Check: The proposed solution is 2. Notice that 2 makes a denominator 0 in the original equation. This can also be seen in a check. Check the proposed solution 2 in the original equation.

$$\frac{x+6}{x-2} = \frac{2(x+2)}{x-2}$$

$$\frac{2+6}{2-2} = \frac{2(2+2)}{2-2}$$

$$\frac{8}{0} = \frac{2(4)}{0}$$

The denominators are 0, so 2 is not a solution of the original equation. The solution is $\{\ \}$ or $\varnothing$.   □

PRACTICE
3   Solve: $\dfrac{x-5}{x+3} = \dfrac{2(x-1)}{x+3}$ ■

EXAMPLE 4   Solve: $\dfrac{2x}{2x-1} + \dfrac{1}{x} = \dfrac{1}{2x-1}$

Solution The LCD is $x(2x-1)$. Multiply both sides by $x(2x-1)$. By the distributive property, this is the same as multiplying each term by $x(2x-1)$.

$$x(2x-1)\cdot\frac{2x}{2x-1} + x(2x-1)\cdot\frac{1}{x} = x(2x-1)\cdot\frac{1}{2x-1}$$

$$x(2x) + (2x-1) = x \quad \text{Simplify}$$

$$2x^2 + 2x - 1 - x = 0$$

$$2x^2 + x - 1 = 0$$

$$(x+1)(2x-1) = 0$$

$$x+1 = 0 \quad \text{or} \quad 2x-1 = 0$$

$$x = -1 \text{ or} \qquad x = \frac{1}{2}$$

The number $\dfrac{1}{2}$ makes the denominator $2x-1$ equal 0, so it is not a solution. The solution is -1.   □

PRACTICE
4   Solve: $\dfrac{5x}{5x-1} + \dfrac{1}{x} = \dfrac{1}{5x-1}$ ■

EXAMPLE 5   Solve: $\dfrac{2x}{x-3} + \dfrac{6-2x}{x^2-9} = \dfrac{x}{x+3}$

Solution We factor the second denominator to find that the LCD is $(x+3)(x-3)$. We multiply both sides of the equation by $(x+3)(x-3)$. By the distributive property, this is the same as multiplying each term by $(x+3)(x-3)$.

$$\frac{2x}{x-3} + \frac{6-2x}{x^2-9} = \frac{x}{x+3}$$

$$(x+3)(x-3)\cdot\frac{2x}{x-3} + (x+3)(x-3)\cdot\frac{6-2x}{(x+3)(x-3)}$$

$$= (x+3)(x-3)\left(\frac{x}{x+3}\right)$$

$$2x(x+3) + (6-2x) = x(x-3) \quad \text{Simplify.}$$

$$2x^2 + 6x + 6 - 2x = x^2 - 3x \quad \text{Use the distributive property.}$$

(Continued on next page)

Next we solve this quadratic equation by the factoring method. To do so, we first write the equation so that one side is 0.

$$x^2 + 7x + 6 = 0$$
$$(x + 6)(x + 1) = 0 \quad \text{Factor.}$$
$$x = -6 \text{ or } x = -1 \quad \text{Set each factor equal to 0.}$$

Neither -6 nor -1 makes any denominator 0, so they are both solutions. The solutions are -6 and -1. □

PRACTICE 5   Solve: $\dfrac{2}{x - 2} - \dfrac{5 + 2x}{x^2 - 4} = \dfrac{x}{x + 2}$

EXAMPLE 6   Solve: $\dfrac{z}{2z^2 + 3z - 2} - \dfrac{1}{2z} = \dfrac{3}{z^2 + 2z}$

Solution   Factor the denominators to find that the LCD is $2z(z + 2)(2z - 1)$. Multiply both sides by the LCD. Remember, by using the distributive property, this is the same as multiplying each term by $2z(z + 2)(2z - 1)$.

$$\frac{z}{2z^2 + 3z - 2} - \frac{1}{2z} = \frac{3}{z^2 + 2z}$$

$$\frac{z}{(2z - 1)(z + 2)} - \frac{1}{2z} = \frac{3}{z(z + 2)}$$

$$2z(z + 2)(2z - 1) \cdot \frac{z}{(2z - 1)(z + 2)} - 2z(z + 2)(2z - 1) \cdot \frac{1}{2z}$$

$$= 2z(z + 2)(2z - 1) \cdot \frac{3}{z(z + 2)} \quad \begin{array}{l}\text{Apply the distributive}\\\text{property.}\end{array}$$

$$2z(z) - (z + 2)(2z - 1) = 3 \cdot 2(2z - 1) \quad \text{Simplify.}$$
$$2z^2 - (2z^2 + 3z - 2) = 12z - 6$$
$$2z^2 - 2z^2 - 3z + 2 = 12z - 6$$
$$-3z + 2 = 12z - 6$$
$$-15z = -8$$
$$z = \frac{8}{15} \quad \text{Solve.}$$

The proposed solution $\dfrac{8}{15}$ does not make any denominator 0; the solution is $\dfrac{8}{15}$. □

PRACTICE 6   Solve: $\dfrac{z}{2z^2 - z - 6} - \dfrac{1}{3z} = \dfrac{2}{z^2 - 2z}$

A graph can be helpful in visualizing solutions of equations. For example, to visualize the solution of the equation $\dfrac{3}{x} - \dfrac{x + 21}{3x} = \dfrac{5}{3}$ in Example 2, the graph of the related rational function $f(x) = \dfrac{3}{x} - \dfrac{x + 21}{3x}$ is shown. A solution of the equation is an x-value that corresponds to a y-value of $\dfrac{5}{3}$.

Notice that an x-value of -2 corresponds to a y-value of $\dfrac{5}{3}$. The solution of the equation is indeed -2 as shown in Example 2.

Vocabulary, Readiness & Video Check

Determine whether each is an equation or an expression. Do not solve or simplify.

1. $\dfrac{x}{2} = \dfrac{3x}{5} + \dfrac{x}{6}$

2. $\dfrac{3x}{5} + \dfrac{x}{6}$

3. $\dfrac{x}{x-1} + \dfrac{2x}{x+1}$

4. $\dfrac{x}{x-1} + \dfrac{2x}{x+1} = 5$

5. $\dfrac{y+7}{2} = \dfrac{y+1}{6} + \dfrac{1}{y}$

6. $\dfrac{y+1}{6} + \dfrac{1}{y}$

Choose the least common denominator (LCD) for the rational expressions in each equation. Do not solve.

7. $\dfrac{x}{7} - \dfrac{x}{2} = \dfrac{1}{2}$; LCD = _____

    a. 7   **b.** 2   **c.** 14   **d.** 28

8. $\dfrac{9}{x+1} + \dfrac{5}{(x+1)^2} = \dfrac{x}{x+1}$; LCD = _____

    a. $x+1$ **b.** $(x+1)^2$ **c.** $(x+1)^3$

9. $\dfrac{7}{x-4} = \dfrac{x}{x^2-16} + \dfrac{1}{x+4}$; LCD = _____

    a. $(x+4)(x-4)$ **b.** $x-4$ **c.** $x+4$ **d.** $(x^2-16)(x-4)(x+4)$

10. $3 = \dfrac{1}{x-5} - \dfrac{2}{x^2-5x}$; LCD = _____

    a. $x-5$ **b.** $3(x-5)$ **c.** $3x(x-5)$ **d.** $x(x-5)$

Martin-Gay Interactive Videos

See Video 6.5

Watch the section lecture video and answer the following questions.

OBJECTIVE 1

11. From ▦ Examples 2 and 3, why is it important to determine whether you have a linear or a quadratic equation before you finish solving the equation?

OBJECTIVE 1

12. From ▦ Examples 2 and 3, what extra check do you make for a proposed solution before you see that it satisfies the original equation?

6.5   Exercise Set   MyMathLab® ▶

Solve each equation. See Examples 1 and 2.

1. $\dfrac{x}{2} - \dfrac{x}{3} = 12$

2. $x = \dfrac{x}{2} - 4$

3. $\dfrac{x}{3} = \dfrac{1}{6} + \dfrac{x}{4}$

4. $\dfrac{x}{2} = \dfrac{21}{10} - \dfrac{x}{5}$

▶ 5. $\dfrac{2}{x} + \dfrac{1}{2} = \dfrac{5}{x}$

6. $\dfrac{5}{3x} + 1 = \dfrac{7}{6}$

7. $\dfrac{x^2+1}{x} = \dfrac{5}{x}$

8. $\dfrac{x^2-14}{2x} = -\dfrac{5}{2x}$

Solve each equation. See Examples 3 through 6.

9. $\dfrac{x+5}{x+3} = \dfrac{2}{x+3}$

10. $\dfrac{x-7}{x-1} = \dfrac{11}{x-1}$

11. $\dfrac{5}{x-2} - \dfrac{2}{x+4} = \dfrac{4}{x^2+2x-8}$

12. $\dfrac{1}{x-1} + \dfrac{1}{x+1} = \dfrac{2}{x^2-1}$

13. $\dfrac{1}{x-1} = \dfrac{2}{x+1}$

14. $\dfrac{6}{x+3} = \dfrac{4}{x-3}$

15. $\dfrac{x^2-23}{2x^2-5x-3} + \dfrac{2}{x-3} = \dfrac{-1}{2x+1}$

16. $\dfrac{4x^2-24x}{3x^2-x-2} + \dfrac{3}{3x+2} = \dfrac{-4}{x-1}$

17. $\dfrac{1}{x-4} - \dfrac{3x}{x^2-16} = \dfrac{2}{x+4}$

18. $\dfrac{3}{2x+3} - \dfrac{1}{2x-3} = \dfrac{4}{4x^2-9}$

19. $\dfrac{1}{x-4} = \dfrac{8}{x^2-16}$

20. $\dfrac{2}{x^2-4} = \dfrac{1}{2x-4}$

21. $\dfrac{1}{x-2} - \dfrac{2}{x^2-2x} = 1$

22. $\dfrac{12}{3x^2+12x} = 1 - \dfrac{1}{x+4}$

MIXED PRACTICE

Solve each equation. See Examples 1 through 6.

23. $\dfrac{5}{x} = \dfrac{20}{12}$

24. $\dfrac{2}{x} = \dfrac{10}{5}$

25. $1 - \dfrac{4}{a} = 5$

26. $7 + \dfrac{6}{a} = 5$

27. $\dfrac{x^2+5}{x} - 1 = \dfrac{5(x+1)}{x}$

28. $\dfrac{x^2+6}{x} + 5 = \dfrac{2(x+3)}{x}$

29. $\dfrac{1}{2x} - \dfrac{1}{x+1} = \dfrac{1}{3x^2+3x}$

30. $\dfrac{2}{x-5} + \dfrac{1}{2x} = \dfrac{5}{3x^2-15x}$

31. $\dfrac{1}{x} - \dfrac{x}{25} = 0$

32. $\dfrac{x}{4} + \dfrac{5}{x} = 3$

33. $5 - \dfrac{2}{2y-5} = \dfrac{3}{2y-5}$

34. $1 - \dfrac{5}{y+7} = \dfrac{4}{y+7}$

35. $\dfrac{x-1}{x+2} = \dfrac{2}{3}$

36. $\dfrac{6x+7}{2x+9} = \dfrac{5}{3}$

37. $\dfrac{x+3}{x+2} = \dfrac{1}{x+2}$

▶ **38.** $\dfrac{2x+1}{4-x} = \dfrac{9}{4-x}$

39. $\dfrac{1}{a-3} + \dfrac{2}{a+3} = \dfrac{1}{a^2-9}$

40. $\dfrac{12}{9-a^2} + \dfrac{3}{3+a} = \dfrac{2}{3-a}$

41. $\dfrac{64}{x^2-16} + 1 = \dfrac{2x}{x-4}$

42. $2 + \dfrac{3}{x} = \dfrac{2x}{x+3}$

43. $\dfrac{-15}{4y+1} + 4 = y$

44. $\dfrac{36}{x^2-9} + 1 = \dfrac{2x}{x+3}$

45. $\dfrac{28}{x^2-9} + \dfrac{2x}{x-3} + \dfrac{6}{x+3} = 0$

▶ **46.** $\dfrac{x^2-20}{x^2-7x+12} = \dfrac{3}{x-3} + \dfrac{5}{x-4}$

47. $\dfrac{x+2}{x^2+7x+10} = \dfrac{1}{3x+6} - \dfrac{1}{x+5}$

48. $\dfrac{3}{2x-5} + \dfrac{2}{2x+3} = 0$

REVIEW AND PREVIEW

TRANSLATING *Write each sentence as an equation and solve. See Section 2.2.*

49. Four more than 3 times a number is 19.

50. The sum of two consecutive integers is 147.

51. The length of a rectangle is 5 inches more than the width. Its perimeter is 50 inches. Find the length and width.

52. The sum of a number and its reciprocal is $\dfrac{5}{2}$.

The following graph is from a 2014 survey of state and federal prisons. Use this graph to answer Exercises 53 through 58. See Section 2.2.

State and Federal Prison Inmates

Source: Bureau of Justice Statistics, U.S. Department of Justice

53. What percent of state and federal prison inmates are age 45 to 54?

54. What percent of state and federal prison inmates are 50 years old or older?

55. What age category shows the highest percent of prison inmates?

56. What percent of state and federal prison inmates are 20 to 34 years old?

57. At the end of 2014, there were 1,574,742 inmates under the jurisdiction of state and federal correction authorities in the United States. Approximately how many 25- to 29-year-old inmates would you expect to have been held in the United States at the end of 2014? Round to the nearest whole. (*Source:* Bureau of Justice Statistics, U.S. Department of Justice)

58. Use the data from Exercise 57 to answer the following.

   a. Approximate the number of 35- to 39-year-old inmates you might expect to have been held in the United States at the end of 2014. Round to the nearest whole.

   b. Is your answer to part **a** greater than or less than your answer to Exercise 57? Is this reasonable? Why or why not?

CONCEPT EXTENSIONS

59. In your own words, explain the differences between equations and expressions.

60. In your own words, explain why it is necessary to check solutions to equations containing rational expressions.

61. The average cost of producing x game disks for a computer is given by the function $f(x) = 3.3 + \dfrac{5400}{x}$. Find the number of game disks that must be produced for the average cost to be $5.10.

62. The average cost of producing x electric pencil sharpeners is given by the function $f(x) = 20 + \dfrac{4000}{x}$. Find the number of electric pencil sharpeners that must be produced for the average cost to be $25.

Solve each equation. Begin by writing each equation with positive exponents only.

63. $x^{-2} - 19x^{-1} + 48 = 0$

64. $x^{-2} - 5x^{-1} - 36 = 0$

65. $p^{-2} + 4p^{-1} - 5 = 0$

66. $6p^{-2} - 5p^{-1} + 1 = 0$

Solve each equation. Round solutions to two decimal places.

67. $\dfrac{1.4}{x - 2.6} = \dfrac{-3.5}{x + 7.1}$

68. $\dfrac{-8.5}{x + 1.9} = \dfrac{5.7}{x - 3.6}$

69. $\dfrac{10.6}{y} - 14.7 = \dfrac{9.92}{3.2} + 7.6$

70. $\dfrac{12.2}{x} + 17.3 = \dfrac{9.6}{x} - 14.7$

Solve each equation by substitution.

(For example, to solve Exercise 71, first let $u = x - 1$. After substituting, we have $u^2 + 3u + 2 = 0$. Solve for u and then substitute back to solve for x.)

71. $(x - 1)^2 + 3(x - 1) + 2 = 0$

72. $(4 - x)^2 - 5(4 - x) + 6 = 0$

73. $\left(\dfrac{3}{x - 1}\right)^2 + 2\left(\dfrac{3}{x - 1}\right) + 1 = 0$

74. $\left(\dfrac{5}{2 + x}\right)^2 + \dfrac{5}{2 + x} - 20 = 0$

Use a graphing calculator to verify the solution of each given exercise.

75. Exercise 23

76. Exercise 24

77. Exercise 35

78. Exercise 36

| Integrated Review | ## Expressions and Equations Containing Rational Expressions

Sections 6.1–6.5

It is very important that you understand the difference between an expression and an equation containing rational expressions. An equation contains an equal sign; an expression does not.

Expression to be Simplified	**Equation to be Solved**
$\dfrac{x}{2} + \dfrac{x}{6}$	$\dfrac{x}{2} + \dfrac{x}{6} = \dfrac{2}{3}$

Expression to be Simplified

Write both rational expressions with the LCD, 6, as the denominator.

$$\dfrac{x}{2} + \dfrac{x}{6} = \dfrac{x \cdot 3}{2 \cdot 3} + \dfrac{x}{6}$$

$$= \dfrac{3x}{6} + \dfrac{x}{6}$$

$$= \dfrac{4x}{6} = \dfrac{2x}{3}$$

Equation to be Solved

Multiply both sides by the LCD, 6.

$$6\left(\dfrac{1}{2} + \dfrac{x}{6}\right) = 6\left(\dfrac{2}{3}\right)$$

$$3 + x = 4$$

$$x = 1$$

Check to see that the solution is 1.

> **Helpful Hint**
>
> Remember: Equations can be cleared of fractions; expressions cannot be.

Perform each indicated operation and simplify or solve the equation for the variable.

1. $\dfrac{x}{2} = \dfrac{1}{8} + \dfrac{x}{4}$

2. $\dfrac{x}{4} = \dfrac{3}{2} + \dfrac{x}{10}$

3. $\dfrac{1}{8} + \dfrac{x}{4}$

4. $\dfrac{3}{2} + \dfrac{x}{10}$

5. $\dfrac{4}{x + 2} - \dfrac{2}{x - 1}$

6. $\dfrac{5}{x - 2} - \dfrac{10}{x + 4}$

7. $\dfrac{4}{x + 2} = \dfrac{2}{x - 1}$

8. $\dfrac{5}{x - 2} = \dfrac{10}{x + 4}$

9. $\dfrac{2}{x^2 - 4} = \dfrac{1}{x + 2} - \dfrac{3}{x - 2}$

10. $\dfrac{3}{x^2 - 25} = \dfrac{1}{x + 5} + \dfrac{2}{x - 5}$

11. $\dfrac{5}{x^2 - 3x} + \dfrac{4}{2x - 6}$

12. $\dfrac{5}{x^2 - 3x} \div \dfrac{4}{2x - 6}$

13. $\dfrac{x - 1}{x + 1} + \dfrac{x + 7}{x - 1} = \dfrac{4}{x^2 - 1}$

14. $\left(1 - \dfrac{y}{x}\right) \div \left(1 - \dfrac{x}{y}\right)$

15. $\dfrac{a^2 - 9}{a - 6} \cdot \dfrac{a^2 - 5a - 6}{a^2 - a - 6}$

16. $\dfrac{2}{a - 6} + \dfrac{3a}{a^2 - 5a - 6} - \dfrac{a}{5a + 5}$

17. $\dfrac{2x + 3}{3x - 2} = \dfrac{4x + 1}{6x + 1}$

18. $\dfrac{5x - 3}{2x} = \dfrac{10x + 3}{4x + 1}$

19. $\dfrac{a}{9a^2 - 1} + \dfrac{2}{6a - 2}$

20. $\dfrac{3}{4a - 8} - \dfrac{a + 2}{a^2 - 2a}$

21. $-\dfrac{3}{x^2} - \dfrac{1}{x} + 2 = 0$

22. $\dfrac{x}{2x + 6} + \dfrac{5}{x^2 - 9}$

23. $\dfrac{x - 8}{x^2 - x - 2} + \dfrac{2}{x - 2}$

24. $\dfrac{x - 8}{x^2 - x - 2} + \dfrac{2}{x - 2} = \dfrac{3}{x + 1}$

25. $\dfrac{3}{a} - 5 = \dfrac{7}{a} - 1$

26. $\dfrac{7}{3z - 9} + \dfrac{5}{z}$

Use $\dfrac{x}{5} - \dfrac{x}{4} = \dfrac{1}{10}$ *and* $\dfrac{x}{5} - \dfrac{x}{4} + \dfrac{1}{10}$ *for Exercises 27 and 28.*

27. **a.** Which one above is an expression?
   b. Describe the first step to simplify this expression.
   c. Simplify the expression.

28. **a.** Which one above is an equation?
   b. Describe the first step to solve this equation.
   c. Solve the equation.

For each exercise, choose the correct statement. * *Each figure represents a real number, and no denominators are 0.*

29. **a.** $\dfrac{\triangle + \square}{\triangle} = \square$ **b.** $\dfrac{\triangle + \square}{\triangle} = 1 + \dfrac{\square}{\triangle}$ **c.** $\dfrac{\triangle + \square}{\triangle} = \dfrac{\square}{\triangle}$ **d.** $\dfrac{\triangle + \square}{\triangle} = 1 + \square$ **e.** $\dfrac{\triangle + \square}{\triangle - \square} = -1$

30. **a.** $\dfrac{\triangle}{\square} + \dfrac{\square}{\triangle} = \dfrac{\triangle + \square}{\square + \triangle} = 1$ **b.** $\dfrac{\triangle}{\square} + \dfrac{\square}{\triangle} = \dfrac{\triangle + \square}{\triangle \square}$ **c.** $\dfrac{\triangle}{\square} + \dfrac{\square}{\triangle} = \triangle \triangle + \square \square$

   d. $\dfrac{\triangle}{\square} + \dfrac{\square}{\triangle} = \dfrac{\triangle \triangle + \square \square}{\square \triangle}$ **e.** $\dfrac{\triangle}{\square} + \dfrac{\square}{\triangle} = \dfrac{\triangle \square}{\square \triangle} = 1$

31. **a.** $\dfrac{\triangle}{\square} \cdot \dfrac{\bigcirc}{\square} = \dfrac{\triangle \bigcirc}{\square}$ **b.** $\dfrac{\triangle}{\square} \cdot \dfrac{\bigcirc}{\square} = \triangle \bigcirc$ **c.** $\dfrac{\triangle}{\square} \cdot \dfrac{\bigcirc}{\square} = \dfrac{\triangle + \bigcirc}{\square + \square}$ **d.** $\dfrac{\triangle}{\square} \cdot \dfrac{\bigcirc}{\square} = \dfrac{\triangle \bigcirc}{\square \square}$

32. **a.** $\dfrac{\triangle}{\square} \div \dfrac{\bigcirc}{\triangle} = \dfrac{\triangle \triangle}{\square \bigcirc}$ **b.** $\dfrac{\triangle}{\square} \div \dfrac{\bigcirc}{\triangle} = \dfrac{\bigcirc \square}{\triangle \triangle}$ **c.** $\dfrac{\triangle}{\square} \div \dfrac{\bigcirc}{\triangle} = \dfrac{\bigcirc}{\square}$ **d.** $\dfrac{\triangle}{\square} \div \dfrac{\bigcirc}{\triangle} = \dfrac{\triangle + \triangle}{\square + \bigcirc}$

33. **a.** $\dfrac{\frac{\triangle + \square}{\bigcirc}}{\frac{\triangle}{\bigcirc}} = \square$ **b.** $\dfrac{\frac{\triangle + \square}{\bigcirc}}{\frac{\triangle}{\bigcirc}} = \dfrac{\triangle \triangle + \triangle \square}{\bigcirc \bigcirc}$ **c.** $\dfrac{\frac{\triangle + \square}{\bigcirc}}{\frac{\triangle}{\bigcirc}} = 1 + \square$ **d.** $\dfrac{\frac{\triangle + \square}{\bigcirc}}{\frac{\triangle}{\bigcirc}} = \dfrac{\triangle + \square}{\triangle}$

My thanks to Kelly Champagne for permission to use her Exercises for 29 through 33.

6.6 Rational Equations and Problem Solving

OBJECTIVE

1   Solving Equations with Rational Expressions for a Specified Variable

In Section 2.3, we solved equations for a specified variable. In this section, we continue practicing this skill by solving equations containing rational expressions for a specified variable. The steps given in Section 2.3 for solving equations for a specified variable are repeated here.

Solving Equations for a Specified Variable

Step 1. Clear the equation of fractions or rational expressions by multiplying each side of the equation by the least common denominator (LCD) of all denominators in the equation.

Step 2. Use the distributive property to remove grouping symbols such as parentheses.

Step 3. Combine like terms on each side of the equation.

Step 4. Use the addition property of equality to rewrite the equation as an equivalent equation with terms containing the specified variable on one side and all other terms on the other side.

Step 5. Use the distributive property and the multiplication property of equality to get the specified variable alone.

EXAMPLE 1   Solve for x: $\dfrac{1}{x} + \dfrac{1}{y} = \dfrac{1}{z}$

Solution   To clear this equation of fractions, we multiply both sides of the equation by xyz, the LCD of $\dfrac{1}{x}$, $\dfrac{1}{y}$, and $\dfrac{1}{z}$.

$$\frac{1}{x} + \frac{1}{y} = \frac{1}{z}$$

$$xyz\left(\frac{1}{x} + \frac{1}{y}\right) = xyz\left(\frac{1}{z}\right) \qquad \text{Multiply both sides by } xyz.$$

$$xyz\left(\frac{1}{x}\right) + xyz\left(\frac{1}{y}\right) = xyz\left(\frac{1}{z}\right) \qquad \text{Use the distributive property.}$$

$$yz + xz = xy \qquad \text{Simplify.}$$

Notice the two terms that contain the specified variable x.

Next, we subtract xz from both sides so that all terms containing the specified variable x are on one side of the equation and all other terms are on the other side.

$$yz = xy - xz$$

Now we use the distributive property to factor x from $xy - xz$ and then the multiplication property of equality to solve for x.

$$yz = x(y - z)$$

$$\frac{yz}{y - z} = x \quad \text{or} \quad x = \frac{yz}{y - z} \qquad \text{Divide both sides by } y - z. \qquad \square$$

PRACTICE

1   Solve for a: $\dfrac{1}{a} - \dfrac{1}{b} = \dfrac{1}{c}$

^{OBJECTIVE} Solving Number Problems Modeled by Rational Equations

~~Problem~~ solving sometimes involves modeling a described situation with an equation containing rational expressions. In Examples 2 through 5, we practice solving such problems and use the problem-solving steps first introduced in Section 2.2.

EXAMPLE 2 Finding an Unknown Number

If a certain number is subtracted from the numerator and added to the denominator of $\frac{9}{19}$, the new fraction is equivalent to $\frac{1}{3}$. Find the number.

Solution

1. UNDERSTAND the problem. Read and reread the problem and try guessing the solution. For example, if the unknown number is 3, we have

$$\frac{9-3}{19+3} = \frac{1}{3}$$

To see if this is a true statement, we simplify the fraction on the left side.

$$\frac{6}{22} = \frac{1}{3} \quad \text{or} \quad \frac{3}{11} = \frac{1}{3} \quad \text{False}$$

Since this is not a true statement, 3 is not the correct number. Remember that the purpose of this step is not to guess the correct solution but to gain an understanding of the problem posed.

We will let n = the number to be subtracted from the numerator and added to the denominator.

2. TRANSLATE the problem.

In words:	when the number is subtracted from the numerator and added to the denominator of the fraction $\frac{9}{19}$	this is equivalent to	$\frac{1}{3}$
	↓	↓	↓
Translate:	$\frac{9-n}{19+n}$	$=$	$\frac{1}{3}$

3. SOLVE the equation for n.

$$\frac{9-n}{19+n} = \frac{1}{3}$$

To solve for n, we begin by multiplying both sides by the LCD of $3(19 + n)$.

$$3(19 + n) \cdot \frac{9-n}{19+n} = 3(19 + n) \cdot \frac{1}{3} \quad \text{Multiply both sides by the LCD.}$$

$$3(9 - n) = 19 + n \quad \text{Simplify.}$$

$$27 - 3n = 19 + n$$

$$8 = 4n$$

$$2 = n \quad \text{Solve.}$$

4. INTERPRET the results.

Check: If we subtract 2 from the numerator and add 2 to the denominator of $\frac{9}{19}$, we have $\frac{9-2}{19+2} = \frac{7}{21} = \frac{1}{3}$, and the problem checks.

State: The unknown number is 2. ☐

PRACTICE
2 Find a number that when added to the numerator and subtracted from the denominator of $\frac{3}{11}$ results in a fraction equivalent to $\frac{5}{2}$. ■

OBJECTIVE

3   Solving Problems Modeled by Proportions

A **ratio** is the quotient of two numbers or two quantities. Since rational expressions are quotients of quantities, rational expressions are ratios also. A **proportion** is a mathematical statement that two ratios are equal.

Let's review two methods for solving a proportion such as $\dfrac{x-3}{10} = \dfrac{7}{15}$.

We can multiply both sides of the equation by the LCD, 30.

$$30 \cdot \frac{x-3}{10} = 30 \cdot \frac{7}{15}$$
$$3(x-3) = 2 \cdot 7$$
$$3x - 9 = 14$$
$$3x = 23$$
$$x = \frac{23}{3}$$

We can also solve a proportion by setting cross products equal. Here, we are using the fact that if $\dfrac{a}{b} = \dfrac{c}{d}$, then $ad = bc$.

$$\frac{x-3}{10} = \frac{7}{15}$$

$$15(x-3) = 10 \cdot 7 \qquad \text{Set cross products equal.}$$
$$15x - 45 = 70 \qquad \text{Use the distributive property.}$$
$$15x = 115$$
$$x = \frac{115}{15} \quad \text{or} \quad \frac{23}{3}$$

A ratio of two different quantities is called a **rate**. For example, $\dfrac{3 \text{ miles}}{2 \text{ hours}}$ or 1.5 miles/hour is a rate. The proportions we write to solve problems will sometimes include rates. When this happens, make sure that the rates contain units written in the same order.

EXAMPLE 3   Calculating Homes Heated by Electricity

In the United States, 7 out of every 20 homes built since 1990 are heated by electricity. At this rate, how many homes in a community of 36,000 homes built since 1990 would you predict are heated by electricity? (*Source:* U.S. Energy Information Administration, 2014)

Solution

1. UNDERSTAND. Read and reread the problem. Try to estimate a reasonable solution. For example, since 7 is less than $\dfrac{1}{2}$ of 20, we might reason that the solution would be less than $\dfrac{1}{2}$ of 36,000 or 18,000.

   Let's let x = number of homes in the community heated by electricity.

2. TRANSLATE.

   homes heated by electricity → $\dfrac{7}{20} = \dfrac{x}{36{,}000}$ ← homes heated by electricity
   total homes →   ← total homes

3. SOLVE. To solve this proportion, we can multiply both sides by the LCD, 36,000, or we can set cross products equal. We will set cross products equal.

$$\frac{7}{20} = \frac{x}{36{,}000}$$

$$20x = 7 \cdot 36{,}000$$
$$x = \frac{252{,}000}{20}$$
$$x = 12{,}600$$

(Continued on next page)

4. INTERPRET.

Check: To check, replace x with 12,600 in the proportion and see that a true statement results. Notice that our answer is reasonable since it is less than 18,000 as we stated in Step 1.

State: We predict that 12,600 homes in this community are heated by electricity. □

PRACTICE

3 In the United States, 2 out of 5 homes built since 1990 are heated with natural gas. At this rate, how many homes in a new community of 36,000 homes are heated by natural gas? (*Source:* U.S. Energy Information Administration, 2014) ■

OBJECTIVE

4 Solving Problems About Work

The following work example leads to an equation containing rational expressions.

EXAMPLE 4 Calculating Work Hours

Melissa Scarlatti can clean the house in 4 hours, whereas her husband, Zack, can do the same job in 5 hours. They have agreed to clean together so that they can finish in time to watch a movie on TV that starts in 2 hours. How long will it take them to clean the house together? Can they finish before the movie starts?

Solution

1. UNDERSTAND. Read and reread the problem. The key idea here is the relationship between the *time* (in hours) it takes to complete the job and the *part of the job* completed in 1 unit of time (1 hour). For example, if the *time* it takes Melissa to complete the job is 4 hours, the part of the job she can complete in 1 hour is $\frac{1}{4}$. Similarly, Zack can complete $\frac{1}{5}$ of the job in 1 hour. We will let $t =$ *the time* in hours it takes Melissa and Zack to clean the house together. Then $\frac{1}{t}$ represents the *part of the job* they complete in 1 hour. We summarize the given information in a chart.

	Hours to Complete the Job	*Part of Job Completed in 1 Hour*
MELISSA ALONE	4	$\frac{1}{4}$
ZACK ALONE	5	$\frac{1}{5}$
TOGETHER	t	$\frac{1}{t}$

2. TRANSLATE.

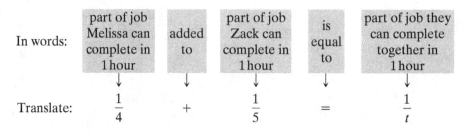

In words:

part of job Melissa can complete in 1 hour	added to	part of job Zack can complete in 1 hour	is equal to	part of job they can complete together in 1 hour

Translate: $\quad \frac{1}{4} \quad + \quad \frac{1}{5} \quad = \quad \frac{1}{t}$

3. SOLVE.

$$\frac{1}{4} + \frac{1}{5} = \frac{1}{t}$$

$$20t\left(\frac{1}{4} + \frac{1}{5}\right) = 20t\left(\frac{1}{t}\right) \qquad \text{Multiply both sides by the LCD, } 20t.$$

$$5t + 4t = 20$$

$$9t = 20$$

$$t = \frac{20}{9} \quad \text{or} \quad 2\frac{2}{9} \quad \text{Solve.}$$

4. INTERPRET.

Check: The proposed solution is $2\frac{2}{9}$. That is, Melissa and Zack would take $2\frac{2}{9}$ hours to clean the house together. This proposed solution is reasonable since $2\frac{2}{9}$ hours is more than half of Melissa's time and less than half of Zack's time. Check this solution in the originally stated problem.

State: Melissa and Zack can clean the house together in $2\frac{2}{9}$ hours. They cannot complete the job before the movie starts. □

PRACTICE
4 Elissa Juarez can clean the animal cages at the animal shelter where she volunteers in 3 hours. Bill Stiles can do the same job in 2 hours. How long would it take them to clean the cages if they work together? ◼

OBJECTIVE
5 Solving Problems About Distance, Rate, and Time ▶

Before we solve Example 5, let's review what we learned in Chapter 2 about the formula

$$d = r \cdot t, \quad \text{or} \quad \text{distance} = \text{rate} \cdot \text{time}$$

For example, if we travel at a rate or speed of 60 mph for a time of 3 hours, the distance we travel is

$$d = 60 \text{ mph} \cdot 3 \text{ hr}$$
$$= 180 \text{ mi}$$

The formula $d = r \cdot t$ is solved for distance, d. We can also solve this formula for rate r or for time t.

Solve $d = r \cdot t$ for r.

$$d = r \cdot t$$
$$\frac{d}{t} = \frac{r \cdot t}{t}$$
$$\frac{d}{t} = r$$

Solve $d = r \cdot t$ for t.

$$d = r \cdot t$$
$$\frac{d}{r} = \frac{r \cdot t}{r}$$
$$\frac{d}{r} = t$$

All three forms of the distance formula are useful, as we shall see.

EXAMPLE 5 Finding the Speed of a Current

Steve Deitmer takes $1\frac{1}{2}$ times as long to go 72 miles upstream in his boat as he does to return. If the boat cruises at 30 mph in still water, what is the speed of the current?

Solution

1. UNDERSTAND. Read and reread the problem. Guess a solution. Suppose that the current is 4 mph. The speed of the boat upstream is slowed down

(Continued on next page)

by the current: $30 - 4$, or 26 mph, and the speed of the boat downstream is speeded up by the current: $30 + 4$, or 34 mph. Next let's find out how long it takes to travel 72 miles upstream and 72 miles downstream. To do so, we use the formula $d = rt$, or $\dfrac{d}{r} = t$.

	Upstream		**Downstream**
	$\dfrac{d}{r} = t$		$\dfrac{d}{r} = t$
	$\dfrac{72}{26} = t$		$\dfrac{72}{34} = t$
	$2\dfrac{10}{13} = t$		$2\dfrac{2}{17} = t$

Since the time upstream $\left(2\dfrac{10}{13}\text{ hours}\right)$ is not $1\dfrac{1}{2}$ times the time downstream $\left(2\dfrac{2}{17}\text{ hours}\right)$, our guess is not correct. We do, however, have a better understanding of the problem.

We will let

$$x = \text{the speed of the current}$$
$$30 + x = \text{the speed of the boat downstream}$$
$$30 - x = \text{the speed of the boat upstream}$$

This information is summarized in the following chart, where we use the formula $\dfrac{d}{r} = t$.

	Distance	**Rate**	**Time** $\left(\dfrac{d}{r}\right)$
UPSTREAM	72	$30 - x$	$\dfrac{72}{30 - x}$
DOWNSTREAM	72	$30 + x$	$\dfrac{72}{30 + x}$

2. TRANSLATE. Since the time spent traveling upstream is $1\dfrac{1}{2}$ times the time spent traveling downstream, we have

In words: time upstream   is $1\dfrac{1}{2}$ times   time downstream

Translate: $\dfrac{72}{30 - x}$ $=$ $\dfrac{3}{2}$ $\cdot$ $\dfrac{72}{30 + x}$

3. SOLVE.

$$\dfrac{72}{30 - x} = \dfrac{3}{2} \cdot \dfrac{72}{30 + x}$$

First we multiply both sides by the LCD, $2(30 + x)(30 - x)$.

$$2(30 + x)(30 - x) \cdot \dfrac{72}{30 - x} = 2(30 + x)(30 - x)\left(\dfrac{3}{2} \cdot \dfrac{72}{30 + x}\right)$$

$$72 \cdot 2(30 + x) = 3 \cdot 72 \cdot (30 - x) \quad \text{Simplify.}$$

$$2(30 + x) = 3(30 - x) \quad \text{Divide both sides by 72.}$$

$$60 + 2x = 90 - 3x \quad \text{Use the distributive property.}$$

$$5x = 30$$

$$x = 6 \quad \text{Solve.}$$

4. INTERPRET.

Check: Check the proposed solution of 6 mph in the originally stated problem.

State: The current's speed is 6 mph.   □

PRACTICE
5   A tugboat takes $1\frac{2}{3}$ times as long to go 100 miles upstream along the Mississippi River as it does to return. If the speed of the current of the Mississippi River is 2 miles per hour, find the speed of the tugboat in still water.

✔ Vocabulary, Readiness & Video Check

Martin-Gay Interactive Videos

See Video 6.6 🔘

Watch the section lecture video and answer the following questions.

OBJECTIVE
1   **1.** In 🎬 Example 1, an equation is solved for a specified variable. What is done differently here to get the specified variable alone on one side of the equation than was done in the past?

OBJECTIVE
2   **2.** In general, if x represents a nonzero number, how do we represent its reciprocal?

OBJECTIVE
3   **3.** For 🎬 Example 3, how are units used to write a correct proportion?

OBJECTIVE
4   **4.** From 🎬 Example 4, how can you determine a somewhat reasonable answer to a work application before you even begin to solve it?

OBJECTIVE
5   **5.** For 🎬 Example 5, if the boat travels upstream at a rate of $x - y$, what is the boat's rate downstream? Use the letters x and y.

6.6 Exercise Set   MyMathLab® ▶

Solve each equation for the specified variable. See Example 1.

1. $F = \frac{9}{5}C + 32$ for C

△ **2.** $V = \frac{1}{3}\pi r^2 h$ for h

3. $Q = \frac{A - I}{L}$ for I

4. $P = 1 - \frac{C}{S}$ for S

▶ **5.** $\frac{1}{R} = \frac{1}{R_1} + \frac{1}{R_2}$ for R

6. $\frac{1}{R} = \frac{1}{R_1} + \frac{1}{R_2}$ for R_1

7. $S = \frac{n(a + L)}{2}$ for n

8. $S = \frac{n(a + L)}{2}$ for a

△ **9.** $A = \frac{h(a + b)}{2}$ for b

△ **10.** $A = \frac{h(a + b)}{2}$ for h

11. $\frac{P_1 V_1}{T_1} = \frac{P_2 V_2}{T_2}$ for T_2

12. $H = \frac{kA(T_1 - T_2)}{L}$ for T_2

13. $f = \frac{f_1 f_2}{f_1 + f_2}$ for f_2

14. $I = \frac{E}{R + r}$ for r

15. $\lambda = \frac{2L}{n}$ for L

16. $S = \frac{a_1 - a_n r}{1 - r}$ for a_1

17. $\frac{\theta}{\omega} = \frac{2L}{c}$ for c

18. $F = \frac{-GMm}{r^2}$ for M

Solve. For Exercises 19 and 20, the solutions have been started for you. See Example 2.

▶ **19.** The sum of a number and 5 times its reciprocal is 6. Find the number(s).

Start the solution:

1. UNDERSTAND the problem. Reread it as many times as needed. Let's let

$$x = \text{a number. Then}$$

$$\frac{1}{x} = \text{its reciprocal.}$$

2. TRANSLATE into an equation. (Fill in the blanks below.)

a number	plus	5	times	its reciprocal	is	6
↓	↓	↓	↓	↓	↓	↓
____	+	5	·	____	=	6

Finish with:

3. SOLVE and

4. INTERPRET

20. The quotient of a number and 9 times its reciprocal is 1. Find the number(s).

Start the solution:

1. UNDERSTAND the problem. Reread it as many times as needed. Let's let

$$x = \text{a number. Then}$$
$$\frac{1}{x} = \text{its reciprocal.}$$

2. TRANSLATE into an equation. (Fill in the blanks below.)

a number	divided by	9	times	its reciprocal	is	1
↓	↓	↓	↓	↓	↓	↓
____	÷	9	·	____	=	1

Finish with:

3. SOLVE and

4. INTERPRET

21. If a number is added to the numerator of $\frac{12}{41}$ and twice the number is added to the denominator of $\frac{12}{41}$, the resulting fraction is equivalent to $\frac{1}{3}$. Find the number.

22. If a number is subtracted from the numerator of $\frac{13}{8}$ and added to the denominator of $\frac{13}{8}$, the resulting fraction is equivalent to $\frac{2}{5}$. Find the number.

Solve. See Example 3.

▶ **23.** An Arabian camel can drink 15 gallons of water in 10 minutes. At this rate, how much water can the camel drink in 3 minutes? (*Source:* Grolier, Inc.)

24. An Arabian camel can travel 20 miles in 8 hours, carrying a 300-pound load on its back. At this rate, how far can the camel travel in 10 hours? (*Source:* Grolier, Inc.)

25. In 2014, 16.3 out of every 100 active duty army personnel were women. If there were 535,370 total army personnel on active duty, estimate the number of women. Round to the nearest whole. (*Source:* goarmy.com)

26. In 2014, 4 out of every 5 active duty air force officers were men. If there were 61,283 active duty air force officers, esti-

mate the number of male officers. Round to the nearest whole. (*Source:* Air Force Personnel Center)

Solve. See Example 4.

27. An experienced roofer can roof a house in 26 hours. A beginning roofer needs 39 hours to complete the same job. Find how long it takes for the two to do the job together.

28. Alan Cantrell can word process a research paper in 6 hours. With Steve Isaac's help, the paper can be processed in 4 hours. Find how long it takes Steve to word process the paper alone.

▶ **29.** Three postal workers can sort a stack of mail in 20 minutes, 30 minutes, and 60 minutes, respectively. Find how long it takes them to sort the mail if all three work together.

30. A new printing press can print newspapers twice as fast as the old one can. The old one can print the afternoon edition in 4 hours. Find how long it takes to print the afternoon edition if both printers are operating.

Solve. See Example 5.

31. Mattie Evans drove 150 miles in the same amount of time that it took a turbopropeller plane to travel 600 miles. The speed of the plane was 150 mph faster than the speed of the car. Find the speed of the plane.

32. An F-100 plane and a Toyota truck leave the same town at sunrise and head for a town 450 miles away. The speed of the plane is three times the speed of the truck, and the plane arrives 6 hours ahead of the truck. Find the speed of the truck.

▶ **33.** The speed of Lazy River's current is 5 mph. If a boat travels 20 miles downstream in the same time that it takes to travel 10 miles upstream, find the speed of the boat in still water.

34. The speed of a boat in still water is 24 mph. If the boat travels 54 miles upstream in the same time that it takes to travel 90 miles downstream, find the speed of the current.

MIXED PRACTICE

Solve.

35. The sum of the reciprocals of two consecutive integers is $-\frac{15}{56}$. Find the two integers.

36. The sum of the reciprocals of two consecutive odd integers is $\frac{20}{99}$. Find the two integers.

37. One hose can fill a goldfish pond in 45 minutes, and two hoses can fill the same pond in 20 minutes. Find how long it takes the second hose alone to fill the pond.

38. If Sarah Clark can do a job in 5 hours and Dick Belli and Sarah working together can do the same job in 2 hours, find how long it takes Dick to do the job alone.

39. Two trains going in opposite directions leave at the same time. One train travels 15 mph faster than the other. In 6 hours, the trains are 630 miles apart. Find the speed of each.

40. The average speed of the winner Meb Keflezighi during the 2014 Boston marathon was 1.46 kilometers per hour faster than the first female to cross the finish line, Rita Jeptoo. If Keflezighi ran 29.52 kilometers in the time that Jeptoo ran 27.33 kilometers, find the speed of Jeptoo, rounded to the nearest tenth.

41. A giant tortoise can travel 0.17 miles in 1 hour. At this rate, how long would it take the tortoise to travel 1 mile? Round to the nearest tenth of an hour. (*Source: The World Almanac*)

42. A black mamba snake can travel 88 feet in 3 seconds. At this rate, how long does it take to travel 300 feet (the length of a football field)? Round to the nearest tenth of a second. (*Source: The World Almanac*)

43. A local dairy has three machines to fill half-gallon milk cartons. The machines can fill the daily quota in 5 hours, 6 hours, and 7.5 hours, respectively. Find how long it takes to fill the daily quota if all three machines are running.

44. The inlet pipe of an oil tank can fill the tank in 1 hour, 30 minutes. The outlet pipe can empty the tank in 1 hour. Find how long it takes to empty a full tank if both pipes are open.

45. A plane flies 465 miles with the wind and 345 miles against the wind in the same length of time. If the speed of the wind is 20 mph, find the speed of the plane in still air.

46. Two rockets are launched. The first travels at 9000 mph. Fifteen minutes later, the second is launched at 10,000 mph. Find the distance at which both rockets are an equal distance from Earth.

47. Two joggers, one averaging 8 mph and one averaging 6 mph, start from a designated initial point. The slower jogger arrives at the end of the run a half-hour after the other jogger. Find the distance of the run.

48. A semi truck travels 300 miles through the flatland in the same amount of time that it travels 180 miles through the Great Smoky Mountains. The rate of the truck is 20 miles per hour slower in the mountains than in the flatland. Find both the flatland rate and mountain rate.

49. The denominator of a fraction is 1 more than the numerator. If both the numerator and the denominator are decreased by 3, the resulting fraction is equivalent to $\frac{4}{5}$. Find the fraction.

50. The numerator of a fraction is 4 less than the denominator. If both the numerator and the denominator are increased by 2, the resulting fraction is equivalent to $\frac{2}{3}$. Find the fraction.

51. In 2 minutes, a conveyor belt can move 300 pounds of recyclable aluminum from the delivery truck to a storage area. A smaller belt can move the same quantity of cans the same distance in 6 minutes. If both belts are used, find how long it takes to move the cans to the storage area.

52. Gary Marcus and Tony Alva work at Lombardo's Pipe and Concrete. Mr. Lombardo is preparing an estimate for a customer. He knows that Gary can lay a slab of concrete in 6 hours. Tony can lay the same size slab in 4 hours. If both work on the job and the cost of labor is $45.00 per hour, determine what the labor estimate should be.

53. The world record for the largest white bass caught is held by Ronald Sprouse of Virginia. The bass weighed 6 pounds 13 ounces. If Ronald rows to his favorite fishing spot 9 miles downstream in the same amount of time that he rows 3 miles upstream and if the current is 6 mph, find how long it takes him to cover the 12 miles.

54. An amateur cyclist training for a road race rode the first 20-mile portion of his workout at a constant rate. For the 16-mile cooldown portion of his workout, he reduced his speed by 2 miles per hour. Each portion of the workout took equal time. Find the cyclist's rate during the first portion and his rate during the cooldown portion.

55. Smith Engineering is in the process of reviewing the salaries of their surveyors. During this review, the company found that an experienced surveyor can survey a roadbed in 4 hours. An apprentice surveyor needs 5 hours to survey the same stretch of road. If the two work together, find how long it takes them to complete the job.

56. Mr. Dodson can paint his house by himself in four days. His son will need an additional two days to complete the job if he works by himself. If they work together, find how long it takes to paint the house.

57. An experienced bricklayer can construct a small wall in 3 hours. An apprentice can complete the job in 6 hours. Find how long it takes if they work together.

58. Scanner A can scan a document in 3 hours. Scanner B takes 5 hours to do the same job. If both scanners are used, how long will it take for the document to be scanned?

59. In 2014, 12 out of the 20 top-grossing movies were rated PG-13. At this rate, how many movies in a year with 692 releases would you predict to be rated PG-13? Round to the nearest whole number. (*Source:* Motion Picture Association of America)

60. In 2014, 3 out of 10 U.S./Canadian citizens had viewed a 3-D movie. At this rate, how many citizens in a town of 46,000 had viewed a 3-D movie? (*Source:* Movie Theater Owners Association)

REVIEW AND PREVIEW

Solve each equation for x. See Section 2.1.

61. $\dfrac{x}{5} = \dfrac{x+2}{3}$

62. $\dfrac{x}{4} = \dfrac{x+3}{6}$

63. $\dfrac{x-3}{2} = \dfrac{x-5}{6}$

64. $\dfrac{x-6}{4} = \dfrac{x-2}{5}$

CONCEPT EXTENSIONS

Calculating body mass index (BMI) is a way to gauge whether a person should lose weight. Doctors recommend that body mass index values fall between 19 and 25. The formula for body mass index B is $B = \dfrac{703w}{h^2}$, where w is weight in pounds and h is height in inches. Use this formula to answer Exercises 65 and 66.

65. A patient is 5 ft 8 in. tall. What should his or her weight be to have a body mass index of 25? Round to the nearest whole pound.

66. A doctor recorded a body mass index of 47 on a patient's chart. Later, a nurse notices that the doctor recorded the patient's weight as 240 pounds but neglected to record the patient's height. Explain how the nurse can use the information from the chart to find the patient's height. Then find the height.

In physics, when the source of a sound is traveling toward an observer, the relationship between the actual pitch a of the sound and the pitch h that the observer hears due to the Doppler effect is described by the formula $h = \dfrac{a}{1 - \dfrac{s}{770}}$, *where s is the speed of the sound source in miles per hour. Use this formula to answer Exercises 67 and 68.*

67. An emergency vehicle has a single-tone siren with the pitch of the musical note E. As it approaches an observer standing by the road, the vehicle is traveling 50 mph. Is the pitch that the observer hears due to the Doppler effect lower or higher than the actual pitch? To which musical note is the pitch that the observer hears closest?

Pitch of an Octave of Musical Notes in Hertz (Hz)	
Note	*Pitch*
Middle C	261.63
D	293.66
E	329.63
F	349.23
G	392.00
A	440.00
B	493.88

Note: Greater numbers indicate higher pitches (acoustically).
(*Source:* American Standards Association)

68. Suppose an emergency van has a single-tone siren with the pitch of the musical note G. If the van is traveling at 80 mph approaching a standing observer, name the pitch the observer hears (rounded to the nearest tenth) and the musical note closest to that pitch.

In electronics, the relationship among the resistances R_1 and R_2 (in ohms) of two resistors wired in a parallel circuit and their combined resistance R is described by the formula $\dfrac{1}{R} = \dfrac{1}{R_1} + \dfrac{1}{R_2}$. *Use this formula to solve Exercises 69 through 71.*

69. If the combined resistance is 2 ohms and one of the two resistances is 3 ohms, find the other resistance.

70. Find the combined resistance of two resistors of 12 ohms each when they are wired in a parallel circuit.

71. The relationship among resistance of two resistors wired in a parallel circuit and their combined resistance may be extended to three resistors of resistances R_1, R_2, and R_3. Write an equation you believe may describe the relationship and use it to find the combined resistance if R_1 is 5, R_2 is 6, and R_3 is 2.

72. For the formula $\dfrac{1}{x} = \dfrac{1}{y} + \dfrac{1}{z} - \dfrac{1}{w}$, find x if $y = 2$, $z = 7$, and $w = 6$.

6.7 Variation and Problem Solving

OBJECTIVES

1 Solve Problems Involving Direct Variation.

2 Solve Problems Involving Inverse Variation.

3 Solve Problems Involving Joint Variation.

4 Solve Problems Involving Combined Variation.

OBJECTIVE

1 Solving Problems Involving Direct Variation

A very familiar example of direct variation is the relationship of the circumference C of a circle to its radius r. The formula $C = 2\pi r$ expresses that the circumference is always 2π times the radius. In other words, C is always a constant multiple (2π) of r. Because it is, we say that **C varies directly as r,** that **C varies directly with r,** or that **C is directly proportional to r.**

$C = 2\pi r$
constant

Direct Variation

y varies directly as x, or **y is directly proportional to x**, if there is a nonzero constant k such that

$$y = kx$$

The number k is called the **constant of variation** or the **constant of proportionality.**

In the above definition, the relationship described between x and y is a linear one. In other words, the graph of $y = kx$ is a line. The slope of the line is k, and the line passes through the origin.

For example, the graph of the direct variation equation $C = 2\pi r$ is shown. The horizontal axis represents the radius r, and the vertical axis is the circumference C. From the graph, we can read that when the radius is 6 units, the circumference is approximately 38 units. Also, when the circumference is 45 units, the radius is between 7 and 8 units. Notice that as the radius increases, the circumference increases.

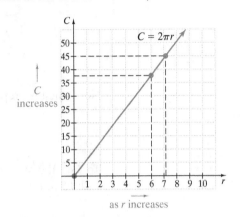

EXAMPLE 1   Suppose that y varies directly as x. If y is 5 when x is 30, find the constant of variation and the direct variation equation.

<u>Solution</u> Since y varies directly as x, we write $y = kx$. If $y = 5$ when $x = 30$, we have that

$$y = kx$$
$$5 = k(30) \quad \text{Replace } y \text{ with 5 and } x \text{ with 30.}$$
$$\frac{1}{6} = k \quad \text{Solve for } k.$$

The constant of variation is $\frac{1}{6}$.

After finding the constant of variation k, the direct variation equation can be written as $y = \frac{1}{6}x$. ☐

PRACTICE

1   Suppose that y varies directly as x. If y is 20 when x is 15, find the constant of variation and the direct variation equation.

EXAMPLE 2   **Using Direct Variation and Hooke's Law**

Hooke's law states that the distance a spring stretches is directly proportional to the weight attached to the spring. If a 40-pound weight attached to the spring stretches the spring 5 inches, find the distance that a 65-pound weight attached to the spring stretches the spring.

(Continued on next page)

Solution

1. UNDERSTAND. Read and reread the problem. Notice that we are given that the distance a spring stretches is **directly proportional** to the weight attached. We let

d = the distance stretched and

w = the weight attached.

The constant of variation is represented by k.

65 lb

2. TRANSLATE. Because d is directly proportional to w, we write

$$d = kw$$

3. SOLVE. When a weight of 40 pounds is attached, the spring stretches 5 inches. That is, when $w = 40$, $d = 5$.

$$d = kw$$
$$5 = k(40) \quad \text{Replace } d \text{ with 5 and } w \text{ with 40.}$$
$$\frac{1}{8} = k \quad \text{Solve for } k.$$

Now when we replace k with $\frac{1}{8}$ in the equation $d = kw$, we have

$$d = \frac{1}{8}w$$

To find the stretch when a weight of 65 pounds is attached, we replace w with 65 to find d.

$$d = \frac{1}{8}(65)$$
$$= \frac{65}{8} = 8\frac{1}{8} \quad \text{or} \quad 8.125$$

4. INTERPRET.

Check: Check the proposed solution of 8.125 inches in the original problem.

State: The spring stetches 8.125 inches when a 65-pound weight is attached. □

PRACTICE
2 Use Hooke's law as stated in Example 2. If a 36-pound weight attached to a spring stretches the spring 9 inches, find the distance that a 75-pound weight attached to the spring stretches the spring. ■

OBJECTIVE
2 Solving Problems Involving Inverse Variation

When y is proportional to the **reciprocal** of another variable x, we say that **y varies inversely as x,** or that **y is inversely proportional to x.** An example of the inverse variation relationship is the relationship between the pressure that a gas exerts and the volume of its container. As the volume of a container decreases, the pressure of the gas it contains increases.

Inverse Variation

y varies inversely as x, or **y is inversely proportional to x,** if there is a nonzero constant k such that

$$y = \frac{k}{x}$$

The number k is called the **constant of variation** or the **constant of proportionality.**